HARVEST OF DEATH

Harvest
of
Death

CHEMICAL WARFARE
IN VIETNAM AND CAMBODIA

J. B. NEILANDS

GORDON H. ORIANS

E. W. PFEIFFER

ALJE VENNEMA

ARTHUR H. WESTING

With a Foreword by Gunnar Myrdal

 THE FREE PRESS, New York

Collier-Macmillan Limited, London

COPYRIGHT © 1972 BY THE FREE PRESS
A DIVISION OF THE MACMILLAN COMPANY

Printed in the United States of America

The Free Press
A DIVISION OF THE MACMILLAN COMPANY
866 Third Avenue, New York, New York 10022

Collier-Macmillan Canada Ltd., Toronto, Ontario

Library of Congress Catalog Number: 72–143521

                printing number
    1   2   3   4   5   6   7   8   9   10

Contents

Foreword   xi

Preface   xiii

A Note about the Authors   xv

Part I   Antipersonnel Gases

Chapter **1   Gas Warfare in Vietnam in Perspective**

J. B. NEILANDS   3

PRELUDE TO CHEMICAL AGGRESSION   3
  Personal Engagement   3
  Historical Résumé   5
  Geneva Protocol   5
  Chemical Weapons between the World Wars   6
  Erosion of Restraints   7
  The Chemical Arsenal   8
VIETNAM PROVING GROUND   11
  Biological Agents?   11
  Napalm and White Phosphorus   14
  Nerve Gas?   17
  Agent BZ   18

Agents CN, DM, CS   18
    Terminology   18
    The Agents   19
    Packages and Payloads   25
    Responsibility   28
    First Use   29
    Reaction   31
    The Lull   32
    Evolution   33
    Results   42
    Credible Calculations   46
    Retaliation?   47
    Sources   47
TOXICOLOGY OF RIOT CONTROL AGENTS   51
    Inside the Living Cell   51
    Agent CN   53
    Agent DM   55
    Agent CS   55
CHEMICAL WEAPONS AT HOME   57
    Vietnam Fallout   57
    Berkeley People's Park   58
    Londonderry   63
    Civil Liberties and Public Health   64
LEGAL STATUS   67
    Grotius to Russell   67
    Geneva Protocol Revisited   72
    Cry and Die   78
PROGRAM FOR THE FUTURE   82
    The Problem Defined   82
    The Remedy   85
        Public Pressure   85
        Scientific Catalysis   87
        Congressional Action   90
SUMMARY   91
ACKNOWLEDGEMENT   92

Chapter **2** **Medical Aspects of Antipersonnel Gases**
                               ALJE VENNEMA   102
WHO ARE THE PATIENTS, AND WHERE DO THEY LIVE?   104
PHYSIOLOGY   107
THE GAS VICTIMS   107
NGUYEN NAM AND NGUYEN THI LUONG   109

Part II   Herbicides

Chapter **3**   **The Military Uses of Herbicides in Vietnam**
E. W. Pfeiffer and Gordon H. Orians   117
A HISTORY OF THE USE OF HERBICIDES   121
THE USE OF HERBICIDES IN VIETNAM   124
THE INVOLVEMENT OF THE AAAS IN THE HERBICIDE
  PROBLEM   131
THE ECOLOGY OF VIETNAM   144
THE ECOLOGICAL EFFECTS OF THE MILITARY USE OF
  HERBICIDES IN VIETNAM   150
  Direct Effects on Vegetation   150
  Effects on Rubber Production   156
  Crop Destruction Program   159
  Effects of Herbicides on Animals   162
DOES THE USE OF HERBICIDES IN VIETNAM
  CONSTITUTE CHEMICAL WARFARE?   174

Chapter **4**   **Herbicidal Damage to Cambodia**
Arthur H. Westing   177
UNFOLDING OF THE EVENT   178
OBJECTIVES OF THE TRIP   181
WHAT SEEMS TO HAVE OCCURRED   182
THE DAMAGED REGION   187
DAMAGE TO RUBBER TREES   188
DAMAGE TO FOOD CROPS AND OTHER VEGETATION   194
DAMAGE TO LIVESTOCK AND OTHER ANIMALS   196
EFFECT ON HUMAN HEALTH   197
EFFECT ON ECONOMIC WELFARE   199
CONCLUSION   200
ACKNOWLEDGEMENTS   201

Part III   Appendixes

I   **The Geneva Protocol of June 17, 1925, and a List
of the 98 Signatory States**   209

II   **Chemical Properties of CN, DM, and CS**   212

III   **Excerpts from** *Department of the Army Training Circular
3–16,* **April 9, 1969**   216

IV   Excerpts from Dean Rusk Press Conference of
      March 24, 1965   259

V   Editorial from *Chemical and Engineering News,*
      August 16, 1965   262

VI   Richard M. Nixon Policy Statement of November
      25, 1969, on Chemical and Biological Warfare   264

VII   United Nations General Assembly Resolution of
      December 16, 1969   266

VIII Excerpt from The Gellner and Wu Report of May
      17, 1970, on the Use of Tear Gas in War   268

IX   Message from Richard M. Nixon and William P.
      Rogers to the U.S. Senate, August 19, 1970, on
      the Geneva Protocol   271

X   Herbicides in Vietnam: AAAS Study Finds Wide-
      spread Devastation   274

XI   Resolution on Chemical Defoliants Adopted by
      the Council of the AAAS at Its 1970 Annual
      Meeting in Chicago   285

Glossary: Abbreviations, Definitions, Scientific Names,
      and Terminology   286

Bibliography   294

Index   297

To the people of Indochina with whom we have worked, we dedicate this book. Their tolerance, understanding, and courage under the awesome conditions of modern war are an inspiration to us all.

Foreword

Decades ago, by the accidents of life and work, I came to know and love America. Eventually—inexorably—I became deeply identified with its aspirations and ideals. In recent years I have been severely critical of specific policies of the United States government that I have seen as a betrayal of those ideals. I have felt happy that my views have been shared, and *in amplissima forma* expressed, by competent and devoted American citizens. Their activity is what, in spite of everything that has happened, upholds my high hopes about the United States' future as a great democracy that will come to be a force for the realization of humane values, for peace, and for progress in the world.

Just as are all those in the United States who share my critical views of what has been permitted to occur in this period, I am most definitely a friend of America. In my opinion, one of the most unfortunate effects of the policies I criticize has been the worldwide "hate America" campaign that is fed on the common disgust felt in the whole world about what the United States government has committed abroad and, specifically, in Indochina. Even more generally, the air is increasingly filled by hatred that portends nothing wholesome for mankind. We all need to try to emulate Mohandas Gandhi's dictum that our hatred should be directed against the wrong-doing, whereas we should love the wrong-doer. This is an exalted maxim, but in the deep demoralization of our world today we must try to mold our strivings in that direction.

I need to make this frank personal declaration to explain why I have been willing to write this foreword and to explain what I mean by writing it. Given my views about what America has been, is, and should come to be, it is not enough to me that the United States get out of Indochina, however important and urgent this may be, on the motivation that the war cannot be won, implying also that it was a mistake from the beginning to get into it. To that point perhaps a majority of Americans have already arrived. The largest possible number of Americans have also to go through an intellectual and moral catharsis and recognize that the war has been immoral, cruel, and illegal. Otherwise, the United States will not regain the confidence and trust of good people everywhere in the world. This is a particularly important matter for a nation that wants to exert leadership and that because of its size and might is foredoomed to try to do this. Nobody is so in need of goodwill as the leader.

More importantly, and primarily, the American nation needs to go through such a catharsis in order to be at peace with itself. Living on and simply forgetting the Vietnam war is not possible, except that the nation accept a serious break in its history and flagrantly give up its cherished aspirations and ideals. This is what the authors of this book imply when they refer to "our collective conscience."

In this light, those Americans who conservatively are attached to those aspirations and ideals, as I am also, must be happy when five distinguished scientists take it upon themselves to establish the facts in regard to chemical warfare in Indochina. They are rendering the same immensely important service to their country and the world as have the equally distinguished jurists who have scrutinized the Indochina war from the viewpoint of the American Constitution, the Charter of the United Nations, other international treaties, and the general doctrines of international law—what in old time was called *jus gentium*. These men are mightily contributing to upholding the respect for, and trust in, the United States as an open democratic society that can go wrong but that will be able to return to the humane tradition of its glorious history.

The authors end their preface with a paraphrase of a quotation from Abraham Lincoln which reads, more fully: "To sin by silence when they should protest makes cowards of men." It is my firm conviction that the academic community in the United States will not commit that sin. And when they speak up, this will in the somewhat longer run not be without decisive importance. For it is to the fundamental decency of the American nation that they appeal.

> GUNNAR MYRDAL
> The Stockholm University's Institute
> for International Economic Studies

Preface

Following establishment of the Scientists' Committee on Chemical and Biological Warfare at the 1968 convention of the American Association for the Advancement of Science in Dallas, the executive body of the committee made plans to publish a definitive account of United States policy and practice in chemical and biological warfare, with special emphasis on the use of herbicides in Vietnam. Suddenly, in the spring of 1969, the United States defoliated a large tract in eastern Cambodia. Shortly thereafter, the massive escalation in use of CS gas in the war became generally known. These events brought chemical warfare in Indochina to the forefront of our collective conscience. The emergency nature of the situation seemed to us to require a rapid response from the scientific community. It was concluded that action could be accelerated and simplified by working independently rather than through a larger committee. Accordingly, we undertook, as an *ad hoc* group of scientists, to report our eyewitness and personal knowledge of the military uses of chemical agents in the Indochina war. The Free Press immediately came forth with an agreement to publish our report.

All of us have spent some time in the Indochinese theatre, and we bring to the problem a certain level of private commitment. We have, nevertheless, attempted to achieve the same level of objectivity in these reports as we have in any other work we have performed in the scientific or medical spheres.

The engines of war are derived from basic discoveries in science. There may be legitimate uses for herbicides in agriculture and for tear gases in civil law enforcement. However, we concur with the sentiment expressed by the United Nations that, on December 16, 1969, voted eighty to three to place these agents under the prohibitions contained in the 1925 Geneva Protocol on Chemical and Biological Warfare. Thus, it would seem incumbent upon American scientists and their professional societies to inform the public of the facts and consequences of the chemical warfare program in Indochina.

Then it will be the responsibility of the Congress to legislate remedial measures and, to the extent that it is possible, compensate for the damage. The Congress must determine whether the American people wish their government and its allies to continue to use such technology for military purposes.

We trust that publication of this volume will be one of a series of efforts by American scientists and their organizations to increase public understanding of the problems posed by modern military technology. Only by doing this can we of the American scientific community escape the charge: "Guilty of the crime of silence."

J. B. NEILANDS, Berkeley, California
GORDON H. ORIANS, Seattle, Washington
E. W. PFEIFFER, Missoula, Montana
ALJE VENNEMA, Burlington, Ontario
ARTHUR H. WESTING, Putney, Vermont

A Note about the Authors

J. B. NEILANDS is Professor of Biochemistry at the University of California, Berkeley. After receiving his Ph.D. from the University of Wisconsin in 1949, he spent two years as a National Research Council Fellow at the Nobel Medical Institute in Stockholm and a year on a Guggenheim Foundation Fellowship at the Universities of Vienna, London, and Copenhagen. Professor Neilands has published more than a hundred papers from his research on iron metabolism in microorganisms and related subjects and is coauthor (with P. K. Stumpf) of the textbook *Outlines of Enzyme Chemistry* (New York: Wiley). Professor Neilands visited North Vietnam during March, 1967.

GORDON H. ORIANS is Professor of Zoology at the University of Washington, Seattle. He received his Ph.D. from the University of California, Berkeley, in 1960. His research on the ecology of vertebrate social systems and the structure of temperate and tropical bird communities has taken him throughout the Americas and to Europe and has resulted in a series of outstanding professional publications. Professor Orians visited South Vietnam during March and April of 1969.

E. W. PFEIFFER is Professor of Zoology at the University of Montana, Missoula. He received his Ph.D. from the University of California, Berkeley, in 1954. Although Professor Pfeiffer is well known among his fellow vertebrate zoologists for his studies of reproduction and kidney function, he is more generally known within the larger scientific community as one of its earliest and most outspoken critics of United States defoliation programs in Indochina. Professor Pfeiffer visited South Vietnam in March, 1969, and August, 1971, Cambodia during December and January of 1969–70, and Laos and North Vietnam during June, 1970.

ALJE VENNEMA is presently studying tuberculosis and chest diseases at the Welsh National School of Medicine. He received his M.D. from McGill University, Montreal, in 1962, and a M.P.H. from Tulane University, New Orleans, in 1969. Doctor Vennema served at the Provincial Hospital in Quang Ngai, South Vietnam from 1964 through 1968, first as Team Captain of a CARE-MEDICO Volunteer Medical Team, then as a Technical Advisor to the Government of South Vietnam under the Canadian Colombo Plan, and finally as Director of Canadian Medical Assistance to South Vietnam. In 1965 he was awarded the Order of Merit by the government of South Vietnam. In 1966 he was awarded the Canadian government's highest civilian distinction, the Medal of Service, and was given a Distinguished Graduate Award by McGill University. In 1968 he was awarded the Order of Distinguished Service to the Vietnamese People by the government of South Vietnam.

ARTHUR H. WESTING is Professor of Botany and Chairman of the Science Division of Windham College in Putney, Vermont. He received his Ph.D. from Yale in 1959 and has done postdoctoral work at Harvard. He worked for the United States Forest Service and taught at Purdue University before joining Windham College. He has written several dozen technical publications, primarily in the area of tree growth and development. Professor Westing examined the herbicidal damage in Cambodia in December, 1969, and made a similar inspection tour of South Vietnam during August of 1970 and 1971.

PART I

Antipersonnel Gases

Chapter 1

Gas Warfare in Vietnam in Perspective

J. B. NEILANDS

Prelude to Chemical Aggression

PERSONAL ENGAGEMENT

Vietnam, a small country in southeast Asia, has attained a historical significance out of all proportion to the size and population of the nation. Much has been written about the political implications of the challenge to, and defeat of, American imperialism in Vietnam. As a biochemist, I have few qualifications for commenting on such geopolitical matters. I enjoy science, and for an avocation I prefer to putter in my garden. But the character and mechanisms of the war in Indochina have been too troubling to the conscience for "business as usual."

It was early in 1965 when a student on Sproul Plaza on the Berkeley campus first handed me a leaflet describing the situation in Vietnam. Later that spring I attended the Teach-In and absorbed some additional facts from Norman Thomas, I. F. Stone, Benjamin Spock, Phil Ochs, and others. In the summer of that year I began a sabbatical leave in Stockholm and one of my first acts, in cooperation with Sara Lidman and Åsa Hallström, was to establish a Swedish Vietnam Day Committee. Since then I have travelled over 50,000 miles and spent out of my own pocket more than five thousand dollars in developing my knowledge of the Vietnam "problem."

The most important of these trips was one to the Democratic Republic

References to this chapter are on pages 93–101.

3

of Vietnam in March, 1967, as a member of the Third Investigating Commission of the International War Crimes Tribunal, better known as the Bertrand Russell Tribunal. This was during a period of active bombardment of the country, and movement outside of Hanoi was difficult. Nonetheless, our limited excursions into the field and our discussions with officials at all levels of the government, which included President Ho Chi Minh, enabled us to conclude that here was a willful attack on civilians and their institutions with bombs designed specifically for the purpose. "Psychosocial warfare," in the jargon of the Pentagon, required the use of special weapons and these were all laid out in stupefying array by the Weapons Committee in Hanoi. The collection included conventional projectiles, rockets and bombs of all weights and types, fragmentation bombs of diverse sorts, napalm, white phosphorus, canisters of antipersonnel gas, and various other relics from the battlefields of Vietnam, North and South. My attention was drawn to the steel pellet bombs because I had just seen evidence, reported in detail elsewhere (1), of the terrible wounds inflicted on the people of Viet Tri with this diabolical device. Here was one of the more sophisticated weapons in the vast United States arsenal of death, the technology of which rests on principles of physics, chemistry, and engineering. Obviously, this was perversion of science on a grand scale.

As a consequence of my encounter with the steel pellet bomb, I decided to become a student of an aspect of the Vietnam war that could be readily understood by the American scientific community, *viz.,* chemical warfare. All the major American media, even *The New York Times,* which should have assumed the responsibility for revealing to the American public the true character of the war, resisted for years the notion that criminal policies were afoot in Vietnam (2). A scientist who is also a peace activist has an opportunity, within limits, to bypass this "paper and airwave curtain" by working through the professional science societies.

The reader should be forewarned that this chapter is not an impartial discourse on the merits or demerits of gas warfare in Vietnam. Nevertheless, to be committed is not to lose objectivity entirely. We build the case by reporting what we have seen with our own eyes, by documenting the statements of our leaders, and by citing our sources.

Apologists for the use of poison in Vietnam say, "War is horrible, so why single out any specific weapon for condemnation?" Unfortunately, this remark does not take into account the theory and history of arms limitation. This is a sphere of human endeavor to which our own country has in times past contributed in no small measure. Seen in this perspective, the chemical war in Vietnam is more than a tragedy of our generation. It may have institutionalized and legitimized the use of weapons that will kill very large numbers of people in any wars of the future.

HISTORICAL RÉSUMÉ

Application of chemical agents in the context of armed conflict is as old as organized warfare. Examples frequently cited are the use of poisoned arrows and various kinds of irritant, toxic, or hypnotic smokes (3). However, the modern history of chemical warfare dates to World War I and is credited with a million casualties and over 100,000 deaths throughout the four years of that engagement. The Germans are usually designated as the perpetrators, but in fact a few French soldiers used rifle-launched tear gas grenades as early as August, 1914 (4). Chemical escalation followed rapidly, and before the war ended chlorine, phosgene, and mustard gas had been deployed on an enormous scale. Clearly, the lesson of World War I was that the most toxic chemical that could be economically produced and efficiently delivered would be used once the taboo against chemicals had been eliminated by means of an initial attack with any substance, even a tear gas.

GENEVA PROTOCOL

The experience of World War I inspired, at least in military circles, some confidence in this new means of mass killing, and as a consequence many countries set up research and development centers in chemical and biological warfare (CBW). A second consequence, fortunately, was the conclusion that this form of warfare must be circumscribed by international agreement. Prior to World War I certain hesitant steps had already been taken to legally prohibit chemical warfare. The Hague Gas Declaration of 1889 sought to bar the use of projectiles ". . . the sole object of which is the diffusion of asphyxiating or deleterious gases" (5).

The United States, for a variety of reasons, did not agree to this convention or to a provision in the 1919 Versailles (German Peace) Treaty, which outlawed ". . . the use of asphyxiating, poisonous, or other gases and of all analogous liquids, materials or devices."

However, we can take pride in the fact that the American government eventually seized the initiative in mobilizing world opinion against the scourge of CBW. Secretary of State Charles Evans Hughes proposed that the Washington Arms Conference of 1922 should adopt a prohibition in war of the use of the chemical agents that would have been denied to Germany under the terms of the Versailles Treaty. In fact, he put forth exactly the same phraseology used three years earlier. The treaty was duly signed, approved by the Senate without dissent, and ratified by President Harding on June 9, 1923; however, it never came into effect because the French, although supporting the substance of the agreement, objected to a provision dealing with submarines. Nonetheless, the language of the Versailles and Washington treaties persisted and reappeared a few years later in the Geneva Protocol of 1925

(Appendix I). This treaty, the prime international instrument prohibiting CBW, was signed initially by forty-nine states and came into effect in 1928. Emerging states have tended to ratify the Protocol *pro forma,* so that by 1969 the total number of signatories had risen to eighty-four. The United States is the only major industrialized power that has not yet subscribed to the treaty. In a later section we shall examine the effect of the Geneva Protocol on United States policy on CBW over the years.

Because the 1922 Washington Treaty had been adopted without a single negative vote in the Senate, Secretary of State Frank B. Kellog assumed that the Geneva Protocol would experience no difficulties in the Congress. But veterans' groups, the chemical industry, and the American Chemical Society, the latter a spokesman for the military-chemical corporate complex, mounted a clamor of opposition. As a result, the Protocol was sent back to committee where it remained until Arthur H. Vandenberg took over chairmanship of the Senate Foreign Relations Committee. Then, in a message to the Senate, which was released to the Press on April 8, 1947, President Truman asked that the Protocol and certain other "obsolete" treaties be returned to the White House (6). There it remained until President Richard M. Nixon announced with a flourish on November 25, 1969, that the Senate would again be asked for consent to ratification. The president's timing is of interest in that, although the whole official posture toward CBW had been under review for several months, the announcement followed by one day the establishment of a panel headed by Lieutenant General William R. Peers to investigate the "nature and scope" of alleged massacres of civilians in Vietnam (7).

CHEMICAL WEAPONS BETWEEN THE WORLD WARS

Respect for the Geneva Protocol has been such that there is not a single agreed-upon fracture of its prohibition of biological agents and, prior to Vietnam, the instances of use of chemical weapons were few in number. Rumors of use, or actual use, may well have accompanied to some slight extent every case of armed hostilities in the past few decades. However, only two major violations are generally recognized, *viz.,* the use of mustard and other gases during the Italian campaign in Ethiopia and the use of similar agents by the Japanese on the mainland of China. In 1936 Emperor Haile Selassie told the Assembly of the League of Nations:

. . . the Italian command followed the procedure which it is now my duty to denounce to the world. Special sprayers were installed on aircraft so that they would vaporize over vast areas of territory a fine, death-dealing rain. (8)

The Emperor's commander-in-chief of the southern battlefront commented:

I am not a savage . . . anyone who will employ such a substance is a savage. I know nothing of gas, because I have not the savage learning. (9)

The Italian experiments proved the feasibility of spraying mustard gas on an enemy largely devoid of all defenses, including antiaircraft fire, and it is not surprising that in 1937 to 1945 Japan is believed to have made extensive use of chemicals in bombs, shells, and candles during her invasion of China. In fact, the Japanese technique of using harassing gases in conjunction with conventional firepower can be viewed as a fairly direct precursor of the corresponding use of these agents in Vietnam.

EROSION OF RESTRAINTS

Several authors have noted the lack of utterances from the White House against chemical and biological weapons that began in the period following the death of President Roosevelt on April 12, 1945 (10). President Truman had never been prominently identified as opposed to such weapons and, moreover, after the defeat of Germany it was perhaps considered more acceptable to contemplate the use of various types of chemicals against the "Japs." Such use did not occur, however, because the forces aligned against the initiation of chemical warfare were still in a dominant position. On the other hand, a breakthrough to a new policy may have been imminent at this time. In his 1946 Report to the Secretary of War, George R. Merck stated: "Only the rapid ending of the war prevented field trials in an active theater of synthetic agents which would, without injury to human or animal life, affect the growing crops and make them useless." (11)

The 1950s witnessed an intense nuclear arms race between East and West in which each side in turn escalated the megatonnage of terror. The nuclear stalemate, the need for weapons better suited for fighting counter-insurgency and limited wars, the sudden availability of new incapacitating chemicals ("war without death") all contributed to a climate favorable to CBW (12). President Eisenhower, however, remained skeptical. In response to a press conference query on possible changes in our "no first use" policy he said, "No official suggestion has been made to me, and so far as my own instinct is concerned, it is not to start such a thing first" (13). Although John F. Kennedy maintained a discreet silence about CBW, total spending for research and procurement in these weapons tripled during his brief tenure in office and reached an estimated $300 million annually by fiscal 1964 (14). The actual expenditures for CBW may well have been double these sums since the budget for just one installation, Edgewood Arsenal, has been running between $200 and $300 million. The significant feature of the Kennedy years is the relative escalation in spending for CBW. Philip E. Hartman, professor of biology at Johns Hopkins University, researched this point and published his results by means of a letter in *The New York Times*. His data show the sharp escalation in financial commitment to CBW that began about 1960 and that propelled spending for this purpose into a far steeper rate of growth than the Department of Defense budget or the GNP (see Figure 1).

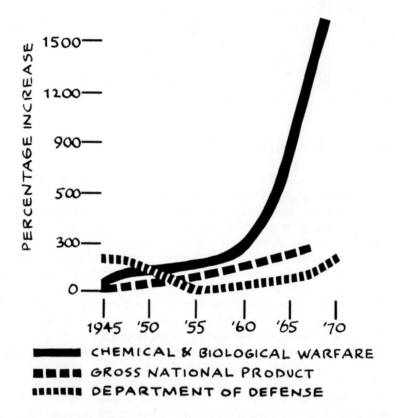

Figure 1–1. Relative increase in spending for chemical and biological warfare in the period 1945–1970. Adapted from Philip E. Hartman, *New York Times,* November 9, 1969.

Representative Robert W. Kastenmeier of Wisconsin noted the rising CBW budget and the aggressive statements of proponents of this means of warfare. In 1959 he introduced a resolution to reaffirm the "no first use" edict established by President Roosevelt; it was not approved. Chemical weapons continued to be developed and stockpiled at a runaway pace so that when the Vietnam war arrived an impressive choice of poisons was available to field commanders.

THE CHEMICAL ARSENAL

The balance of terror in CBW weaponry was severely dislocated by the discovery of the nerve gases, and following World War II many nations hastened to manufacture these and a variety of less toxic chemicals. By the middle 1960s the United States had settled on seven so-called standardized chemical warfare agents having a spectrum of toxicities and useful applications as munitions.

The usual means of comparing the potency of chemical agents is the expression

$$mg\text{-}min/m^3$$

which means the weight in milligrams of chemical vapor per cubic meter multiplied by exposure time in minutes that will result in 50 per cent kill in animal or human populations. Assuming a breathing rate of 15 liters per minute as typical of mild activity in the human subject, the mortal dose in milligrams can readily be estimated from this formula.

The first of the United States' seven standardized chemicals is agent GB, or isopropyl methylphosphonofluoridate, the trivial name of which is sarin. This nerve gas was first made in a 1,000-pound batch in Germany during World War II. The German expertise in this line of chemicals developed from their earlier research on insecticides. GB is a colorless, odorless, fairly volatile liquid that is very soluble in water. It is intended to enter the body by inhalation, and the lethal airborne exposure is about 100 mg-min/m^3. GB is not very persistent; splashed on the ground it will quickly evaporate away except in a very cold climate, where it may remain for up to two days.

$$
\begin{array}{c}
O \\
\parallel \\
H_3C-P \\
H_3C \diagdown \qquad \diagup \diagdown F \\
H-C-O \\
H_3C \diagup
\end{array}
$$

Agent GB

The chemical formula of agent VX is a secret, but a Roumanian publication (15) refers to it as ethyl S-dimethylaminoethyl methylphosphonothiolate (13). This fast-acting nerve gas was developed in England at the end of the 1950s. It is a colorless liquid that is both less volatile and less soluble in water

$$
\begin{array}{c}
O \\
\parallel \\
H_3C-P \qquad\qquad\qquad CH_3 \\
\diagup \diagdown \qquad\qquad\qquad + \diagup \\
H_5C_2O \qquad S-CH_2-CH_2-N \\
\qquad\qquad\qquad\qquad\qquad | \diagdown CH_3 \\
\qquad\qquad\qquad\qquad\qquad H
\end{array}
$$

Agent VX?

than GB. It is also distinguished from GB by its increased potency and stability in the environment. It will persist for several days to several weeks at normal temperatures. The lethal concentration–exposure time is 10 mg-min/m^3. VX will penetrate the skin; the lethal dose by the percutaneous route is about 6 mg/min. VX, or a closely related substance, was responsible for the death of 6,000 sheep at Dugway Proving Ground, Utah, in March, 1968.

The third agent is BZ, the precise chemical formulation of which, like VX, is a secret. The WHO (16) report speculates that it belongs to the family of psychochemicals known as benzilates, and the Union of Concerned Scientists has published the structure shown below (17). Such compounds, *i.e.*, phenyl glycolate esters of 3-quinuclidinol, although generally not lethal, produce

Agent BZ?

profound mental disturbances at a dose of 0.1 to 0.2 mg. The symptoms may appear a half hour after exposure and may persist for some days. Consequently, this agent is classified as "incapacitating." BZ has proven highly unpredictable in its effects and is not regarded as a satisfactory chemical warfare agent, although it has been loaded into munitions and aerial delivery systems.

The fourth substance is code-named HD and is a vesicant or blistering agent, commonly called mustard gas. This agent was heavily employed in World War I and was stockpiled in World War II. A large family of related mustard gases have been prepared, of which the one shown here, bis (2-chloro-ethyl) sulfide, is the classic example. This is a relatively nonvolatile, water-

Mustard Gas

insoluble, oily liquid with a faintly agreeable odor. It has a durability under normal climatic conditions of several days. Although classed as lethal and still a very important war gas, mustard gas is perhaps better designated as an incapacitating agent since, relative to nerve gas, the concentration required to kill is relatively high. A properly fitted mask will protect against GB and BZ; but in the cases of HD and VX, all parts of the body must be covered.

The three remaining United States standard chemicals are the "riot control agents," CN, DM, and CS, all of which have been implicated in the Vietnam war. The properties and characteristics of these agents will be described in detail in a subsequent section of this report.

The full range of "standardized" chemical horrors has been listed here in order to illustrate the growth potential for an activity such as CBW. Once the lid of this Pandora's box has been lifted, the way is open for steady progression through the entire spectrum of substances. Even if there is not an immediate reciprocal escalation—which seems to be the case in Vietnam—any use of chemicals in war tends to stimulate interest by military establishments everywhere, thus magnifying the problems of control and disarmament. And since biological weapons have been historically bound up with the chemicals in the annals of international law, this means that the search for infectious agents will also be perpetuated. The modern techniques of bacterial genetics can enable the selection of a mutant organism that is at once biochemically equipped both to resist the common antibiotics and defeat the normal immunity response in the infected human subject. The development of this "doomsday bug" could be the ultimate dividend of our investment in chemical warfare in Vietnam (18).

Vietnam Proving Ground

BIOLOGICAL AGENTS?

Although no charges have ever been made of a deliberate introduction of biological weapons in Vietnam, the enormous destruction accompanying a quarter century of continuous warfare has resulted in a general breakdown in public health facilities and a florid growth of indigenous infections and ailments (19). So far as the source of this destruction is concerned, the vast bulk of it must be charged to the Americans. Thus, statistics on bomb tonnage compiled by the Department of Defense and published in May, 1970, by Clergy and Laymen Concerned About Vietnam show that the United States has delivered 9,279,295 tons since 1965 while the combined delivery of the National Liberation Front (NLF)/Democratic Republic of Vietnam (DRV) came to only 17,500 tons (20). In one year, 1968, it was estimated that 2.6 million bomb craters were produced. These provide ideal breeding grounds for mosquitoes.

A medical anthropologist who investigated the plague problem in South Vietnam is reported to have said, "I would submit that the kind of conventional war that has been raging . . . is, intentionally or not, a kind of covert biological warfare" (21).

Bubonic plague is endemic in Vietnam, having been introduced at the Saigon waterfront at the turn of the century by means of infected rats from Hong Kong and Canton (22). The disease spread rapidly but receded to insignificant levels in the next several decades. As the war escalated, so also did the incidence of the plague (see Table 1-1). Epidemics occur when the causal organism, *Pasteurella pestis,* is communicated by wild rats to highly susceptible domestic rats. On the death of the latter, fleas *(Xenopsylla cheopis)* carry the microorganism to man (23). As the data in Table 1-1 show, the plague is a very serious problem in South Vietnam. A survey by the World Health Organization in 1968 found the disease in almost half the provinces, but the same report concluded that plague had been eliminated in the North (24). This undoubtedly reflects the decreased ability of dislocated populations to resist the disease—a stable community is able to adapt ecologically to plague. In spite of the bombing of the DRV, there has not been the mass movement of people in that zone such as that which has occurred in the South.

Since the plague bacillus is one of the favorite organisms of the CBW research laboratories, the question arises if the United States has wilfully contributed to the statistics listed in Table 1-1. In 1968 a letter written on Office of Naval Research stationery to Indian newspapers gave assurances that the handling of biological warfare agents by United States forces in Viet-

TABLE 1–1

Bubonic Plague in South Vietnam

Year	Estimated Number of Cases	Fatalities	Source
1954–62	40 average	—	*New York Times,* December 3, 1967
1961	8	—	*Ibid.,* April 14, 1968
1963	120	17	*Medical Tribune,* July 8, 1968
1965	4000–6000	—	*San Francisco Chronicle,* March 29, 1967
1966	4453	—	*New York Times,* December 3, 1967
1966	2404 suspected	119	*Medical Tribune,* February 15, 1968
	351 confirmed	26	*Ibid.*
1967	5500	350	*New York Times,* April 14, 1968
1968 (first half)	3000	—	*Medical Tribune,* July 8, 1968

Additional references: *New York Times,* February 28 and July 2, 1968; *San Francisco Chronicle,* March 23 and November 15, 1967, March 27 and April 3, 1968; *Berkeley Gazette,* March 29, 1967; *Manchester Guardian,* September 26, 1966; *Science,* February 23, 1968.

nam posed no threat of an epidemic throughout southeast Asia (25). The *Bombay Free Press* exclaimed: "Holy Ghost! Couldn't the Free World be defended some other way!" The United States embassy in New Delhi denounced the letter as a hoax, and in the following year the Department of Defense, in answer to a query from the Scientists' Committee on Chemical and Biological Warfare, stated that biological agents were not then stored abroad ". . . nor had they ever been" (26).

There is little prospect that the plague situation will improve. The disease is confined almost exclusively to the civilian population because the American soldiers, unlike the natives, are protected by a regular immunization program. In the opinion of one expert:

The possibility of plague eradication from this area of the world is remote. The socio-economic condition of the people, the maldistribution of qualified doctors, as well as the unstable conditions created by the current conflict, are not conducive to the intensive program that would be necessary to eliminate plague. (27)

A sharp rise in malaria infection in the United States has been attributed to a Vietnamese parasite that has shown up as a delayed infection in returning American servicemen (28). Similarly, melioidosis has appeared in veterans who became infected with *Pseudomonas pseudomallei* during their tour of duty in Vietnam (29). The late syndicated columnist Drew Pearson once commented upon the "exotic" diseases imported from Vietnam (30), but they do not seem to have reached serious proportions in the United States.

Other health problems of major importance in South Vietnam are tuberculosis, malaria, leprosy, dysentery, gastroenteritis, typhoid fever, parasitic infections, childhood pneumonia, and venereal disease (31).

In late September and early October, 1969, Canadian news media reported a mysterious epidemic in Hanoi; a résumé appeared in the Canadian issue of *Time* magazine of October 10. The disease was identified as a hemorrhagic dengue-like fever transmitted by the *Aedes aegypti* mosquito. *Time* set the deaths at 1,000, with 95 per cent of the victims in the age group two to fifteen, and attributed the outbreak to severe summer floods that had polluted local water supplies and furnished breeding grounds for *A. aegypti*. Swedish sources with direct links to the DRV confirmed that an epidemic of dengue fever had indeed killed "many children" in Hanoi and that the disease was rampant in the South (32). These sources declined comment on the suspicion that the fever might have been induced by United States military forces; in any case, epidemics of dengue fever have been reported in years past from Manila, Bangkok and Singapore (33). Dengue and related viral diseases are the subject of a recent monograph by Susumu Hotta (34).

The use of sharpened spears smeared with human excrement (punji sticks) has been cited as an illustration of biological warfare, but this appears to be purely a defensive weapon employed by the native Vietnamese and as such it is not a routine weapon employed by the organized military resistance (35).

Figure 1–2. J. B. Neilands taking testimony for the Russell War Crimes Tribunal in North Vietnam during March, 1967. Photo courtesy of War Crimes Commission, Hanoi.

NAPALM AND WHITE PHOSPHORUS

Should napalm and white phosphorus be considered chemical weapons? *Encyclopaedia Britannica* defines napalm as a "sticky syrup used in chemical warfare"; white phosphorus is listed in the *Chemical Reference Handbook, Army Field Manual 3-8,* dated January, 1967. However, both napalm and white phosphorus are properly classified as incendiary weapons in spite of the fact that each may have a chemical mechanism as the basis for its action. Possibly they should be regarded as banned under treaties relating to weapons causing unnecessary suffering (36). In any event, the very extensive use of napalm and white phosphorus in the war in Vietnam requires that some consideration be given to them in any review of chemical munitions.

Napalm is the invention of chemistry professor Louis Fieser of Harvard University. In his own words: "On February 14 (1942) we reported . . . development of two lines of gels that could be prepared by stirring with gasoline at room temperature. To one, made from aluminum *na*phthenate and aluminum *palm*itate, I gave the name napalm" (37). Subsequently it was found that the product described as "aluminum palmitate" was a crude mixture of aluminum salts of the fatty acids of coconut oil, which was comprised of

48 per cent lauric acid and only 8.2 per cent palmitic acid. However, the name "napalm" has persisted and is applied to all formulations of jellied gasoline, including the new, refined products with superior qualities of adhesion. One such brand, developed by Dow Chemical Company and designated "Napalm B," contains 50 per cent polystyrene and 25 per cent each of benzene and gasoline (38). In 1966 the consumption of polystyrene for napalm was estimated to run about 300 million pounds annually or 18 per cent of total production capacity. At $14\frac{1}{2}$¢ per pound for polystyrene, the cost of the plastic alone in the 1966 requisition of napalm would amount to $43 million. The heavy demand for polystyrene required for napalm production boosted the price of the commodity and precipitated a shortage of some domestic items such as laboratory dishes (39).

Napalm was used heavily in the Korean war, with a total drop estimated at 32,215 tons, but even before that it was employed in the Pacific theater in the waning years of World War II. The fact that it was not used in Europe has prompted the speculation that it would not be thrown by the white race against their own kind. However, in early 1967 President René Barrientos of Bolivia announced that napalm would be among the weapons he would choose for the antiguerrilla campaign (40). Later, an American official in La Paz is reported to have said, ". . . we are certainly not going to supply the means for Bolivian Army hotheads to start bombing and napalming villages . . ." (41). Israel is using napalm in attacks on Jordan and Egypt (42). In spite of the politically sensitive status of the weapon, Dow Chemical Company has explained, "We feel we've made a moral decision in continuing the production of napalm" (43). Thus, napalm seems to have become institutionalized in the arsenals of modern armies.

In March, 1968, the Defense Department estimated total napalm usage by Air Force operations in Vietnam at an excess of 100,000 tons. The breakdown by year was given as: 1963, 2181 tons; 1964, 1777; 1965, 17,659; 1966, 54,670. These figures are exclusive of the napalm contained in Navy bombs and in Army flamethrowers. Spending for napalm procurement per month in the first half of 1967 stood at almost $3 million (44).

The indiscriminate use of napalm by American forces in Indochina has been recorded from time to time in the western press. A report in the *Washington Post* in 1965 said American pilots were "given a square mile on a map and told to hit every hamlet within the area" with napalm bombs (45). A reporter for the *San Francisco Chronicle* gave a vivid description of his experience as a passenger in a Phantom 11F4 flown from a carrier:

We flattened out over the target . . . and I had a glimpse of three thatched huts burning along the edge of some water. Then I closed my eyes and could not open them again until we were several thousand feet up. Below, the trees and huts were blotted out by a cloud of nauseous black smoke. . . . On the second run I managed to hold my eyes open. As we pulled out through the smoke, I saw the second napalm bomb a couple of seconds after it had burst. A ball of brilliant flame was rolling out across more than

200 feet, swelling like a giant orange cauliflower. . . . I asked the commander about the target. . . . "Well, we don't rightly know for sure," he said. "You can't rightly see much at those speeds. . . . But most times you can reckon that whatever moves in the Delta is V.C." (46)

Similarly, Frank Harvey in his authoritative book, *Air War—Vietnam,* confirmed that napalm had been used when the targets were mere hamlets, huts, and hootches. (47)

There has been a dispute about the number of napalm victims seeking medical attention in the South. Dr. Howard A. Rusk, a medical consultant to *The New York Times* and a member of the staff at the New York University College of Medicine, toured twenty civilian hospitals in the area between the Gulf of Siam and the seventeenth parallel. His survey, conducted in March, 1967, turned up not a single napalm burn and only two burns that could be attributed to phosphorus shells. Rusk estimated that only 15 per cent of admissions were for war casualties, the remainder being for disease and accidents. He thought that most of the burns were caused by inexperience in handling pilfered gasoline (48). On the other hand, Rusk's conclusions were challenged on the grounds that he visited only certain of the wards in only 20 per cent of the civilian hospitals in South Vietnam and that he had relied too much on statistics given out by the government of South Vietnam (49). Another interpretation is that a great many napalm victims never make it to a hospital of any kind, although Robert Guillain, writing in *Le Monde,* claims to have seen several in a clinic in central South Vietnam (50).

Phosphorus bombs and shells began to come into heavy use in Vietnam in early 1967. Phosphorus has found many uses as an incendiary weapon, including that of the ignition substance for napalm bombs. In a civil defense manual by Fairhurst there occurs the comment: "One thing to remember about these phosphorus bombs is to be sure that the solid particles that are in the air do not touch your skin. They cause terrible burns" (51).

A French physician, Dr. Abraham Behar, visited North Vietnam in January, 1967. Later he described some of the phosphorus burns he had seen:

Phosphorus has the particularity that inside the wound or burn, it burns slowly. On occasion this slow combustion lasts up to 15 days. At night can be seen the greenish light produced by the material that continues burning the flesh and bones. Besides this, accompanied by the wounds and the profound burns, the victims suffer a severe intoxication produced by the augmentation by three or more times the quantity of inorganic phosphorus in the body. (52)

That white phosphorus is used as an antipersonnel weapon was confirmed in a press report in 1969: "We killed them one by one with grenades, direct hits with Willie Peter—white phosphorus artillery shells—or with napalm." This is a statement attributed to a major serving as a commander in the Special Forces' Fifth Mobile Strike Force (53).

A substantial amount of medical information on both napalm and phosphorous burns was compiled by both the Bertrand Russell and the Tokyo war crimes tribunals on Vietnam (54). Napalm burns, according to these reports, may produce keloid scars that are difficult to treat and that may develop tumorous growths. Napalm may also kill by means of the carbon monoxide generated during incomplete combustion of the carbonaceous fuel; hence, some of the casualties can be ascribed to asphyxiation. Dr. John Takman has collected a substantial body of information on napalm in a volume titled *Napalm, An International Symposium* (55). This useful work has appeared in Swedish, Norwegian, German, and Spanish (Havana and Barcelona) editions but not in English.

George Wald, writing in the *New York Review of Books,* has called for a criminal indictment against the manufacturers of napalm. After recounting how the weapon has been used in Vietnam, Wald concludes: "If there is such a thing as individual or corporate responsibility for participating in a 'crime against humanity,' one could hardly find a better instance of it than this" (56).

Similarly, the North Vietnamese have frequently denounced the use of both napalm and white phosphorus: "Since the beginning of 1967, the U.S. imperialists have been making systematic use of phosphorus bombs and shells which are of many types . . ." (57). "The team (Sixth Investigating Commission of the Bertrand Russell War Crimes Tribunal) . . . saw victims of napalm, phosphorus . . .—arms forbidden by mankind . . ." (58); " . . . it (napalm) has also been extensively employed against North Vietnam . . ." (59).

NERVE GAS?

In May, 1970, press accounts appeared on the storage of agent GB in Vietnam (60). This was the first public disclosure of the possible presence of a lethal chemical in Vietnam, although the same agent has been held at United States bases in Okinawa and West Germany. Larry Rottman of Watertown, Massachusetts, is reported to have stated at a news conference of the Citizens' Commission of Inquiry on U.S. War Crimes in Vietnam that he had seen GB stored at an air base at Bien Hoa while he was on duty there in 1967 and 1968 as an assistant information officer for the 25th Infantry Division. He said he had never seen the gas used but had heard reports of its use.

On August 8, 1970, Tom Marlowe of Dispatch News Service International filed a story from Saigon titled: "US Uses Nerve Gas in Cambodia." His account appears to have been printed *in toto* in a large Swedish daily newspaper (61). According to this account, agent VX was used against a North Vietnamese troop concentration inside Cambodia in 1969 in an operation, designated "Redcap," which was part of an experimental project known as "Waterfall." The source claimed that "Redcap" was unknown even to General Creighton Abrams until the murder of a Vietnamese national, believed to be a double agent, in an incident involving the Green Berets. Although it was stated that two fifty-kilogram containers of VX were dispersed over the target area, no information was reported on the effects of the attack.

Representative R. D. McCarthy states that in July, 1969, *Newsweek* magazine reported the finding, by Green Berets, of a cache of "nerve gas" in Vietnam. He immediately consulted the editor, Osborne Elliot, who checked with the correspondent in Vietnam, Kevin Buckley. The material turned out to be "tear gas" (62), also described as "tear gas in new bottles" (63). This event was considered noteworthy because, had the substance been nerve gas and had it been used, it would have amounted to a replay of the World War I experience where instant escalation was the rule of gas warfare.

AGENT BZ

Pierre D'Arcourt wrote in *L'Express* of an attack in Vietnam in which the hallucinogenic agent BZ was delivered by hand grenades (64). The incident was said to have taken place in Bong-san in March, 1966, and was charged to the 1st Cavalry (Airmobile) Division. However, Hersh points out that the Army manuals do not list grenades as being filled with BZ, and United States officials in both Washington and Saigon have denied any use of BZ in Vietnam. We must conclude that if this particular incapacitating agent has been deployed in Vietnam, it has been on only a small, experimental scale.

AGENTS CN, DM, CS

Terminology

The three "standardized" riot control munitions of the United States Army are code-named CN, DM, and CS. Although CN and DM are being phased out in favor of CS (65), consideration of all three agents is germane to any discussion of the chemical war in Vietnam.

There is some confusion about the proper terminology for agents such as CN, DM, and CS. They are variously known as "antipersonnel," "non-lethal," "tear gas," "lachrymators," "incapacitating," "harassing," or "irritant." "Antipersonnel" makes no distinction between "lethal" and "non-lethal," a separation which, in any case, is of dubious validity so far as Vietnam is concerned. DM has a barely detectable odor and is better designated as a "vomiting gas" than a "tear gas." The United Nations classifies both psychochemicals and tear gas as "incapacitating," but since "incapacitating" is most commonly applied to the hallucinogens, this leaves either "harassing" or "irritant" as what perhaps should now be agreed upon as the correct technical terminology for the group CN, DM, and CS. The designation "riot control agents" is easily recognized as a public relations gambit by the military and a part of their untiring effort to relate their weapons to the American domestic scene. To call these three gases riot control agents is a concession I am not prepared to accept. The important point to remember is that all three agents may be lethal, depending on the dose and exposure time.

The Agents

CN is the "classical" tear gas used by police departments around the world for over half a century. It was first compounded in the last century; the chemical name is chloroacetophenone or 2–chloroacetophenone. It is practically insoluble in water but dissolves readily in organic solvents such as alcohol or ether. It is resistant to heat and moisture and when pure consists of colorless crystals (66). Its handling is facilitated by the fact that the molten form is stable and may be poured into munitions casings. It is efficiently dispersed by distillation into the air by heat generated in a combustion mixture. At a low concentration the gas has a faint odor of apple blossoms. Further details of the properties of CN are given in Appendix II.

$$\text{Benzene ring}-\overset{\displaystyle O}{\overset{\|}{C}}-CH_2Cl$$

Agent CN

The military potential of CN was suggested by police experience with related lachrymators, the substance ethylbromacetate having been used by the Paris police department in 1912 (67). It has been stated that tear gas munitions were stocked but not used by the French Army in World War I (68); other accounts say the French used rifle-launched lachrymators in August, 1914, prior to the German attack with chlorine gas (69).

Although CN itself does not appear to have been used in World War I, the substance was the subject of intensive research in the United States in the post-war period (70). Its potency, ease of synthesis, and low cost all figured in its development as an offensive chemical. Edgewood Arsenal put up a manufacturing plant, and the agent was promoted by the Chemical Warfare Service and furnished to the Philadelphia police department for experimental evaluation (71). Massive quantities were stockpiled by the major belligerent powers during World War II. Meanwhile, between the wars, police use of CN accelerated, and various grenades and projectiles loaded with the compound became standard equipment (72). The methods used for dissemination included simple volatilization of liquids and release of vapor through combustion. In World War II research showed that CN prepared as a fine powder, with particle sizes equivalent to those of talc, gave a more potent and persistent product than either the combustion or liquid vaporization techniques of dissemination. Liquid CN has been largely discontinued, and the agent is now commonly packaged in both combustion (*i.e.,* burning) and bursting types of munitions.

According to Prentiss (73), CN is active at a concentration of 0.3 mg/m^3 —lethal on exposure for ten minutes to an airborne density of 850 mg/m^3. It has been responsible for the deaths of several civilians through improper use in the hands of police. Interestingly, Prentiss in 1937 noted the irritant properties of CN but dismissed the effects on skin as "entirely harmless." We now know that this assessment was far too optimistic (see p. 53).

The United States *Army Field Manual* had this to say about CN:

This agent quickly irritates the upper respiratory passages and eyes, causing an intense flow of tears from unmasked personnel within seconds of exposure. As a secondary effect, in high concentrations CN is irritating to the skin and can cause a burning, itching sensation, especially on moist parts of the body. Some individuals experience nausea following exposure. CN is dispersed as a thermally or explosively generated aerosol or as a solution in chloroform (CNC). (74)

CN is the active ingredient of Chemical Mace[R] or Mace[R], a weapon acquired by many police systems in 1965.[1] It is currently estimated that 4,000 police departments stock squirt cans of this agent, although local jurisdictions have prohibited its use in some communities. The agent, which is delivered as a liquid stream, has no special military significance; however, it will be discussed further in connection with the adoption of chemical agents by civil authorities. CN as an aerosol, or at higher dosages, may cause more damage to the eyes and skin than either DM or CS (see p. 53).

A colloquy between Representative Clement Zablocki and Admiral William E. Lemos before a congressional hearing in 1969 revealed the official military reasons for supplanting CN by CS:

Z: As far as the use of CN and CS is concerned, you make quite a point at the beginning of your statement that CS is less likely to cause harm to those exposed to it than the other agent that has been classed as a riot-control agent, namely, CN.
L: Yes, sir.
Z: Yet in summary you say that CN, because of its relative ineffectiveness, is now seldom used. Would you explain to the committee where CS is more effective and in what ways? If the difference is not too great and you say there is nothing to be alarmed about the use of CS, then what is the reference to the ineffectiveness of CN?
L: It is the relative ineffectiveness. CS is better than CN.
Z: In what respects?
L: It is quicker acting.
Z: Longer lasting?
L: No, sir. It is not longer lasting. It is quicker acting, and *statistically* it has proved to be less toxic than CN. [Emphasis added]

This exchange did not illuminate the fact that pound for pound CS goes farther than CN. It did show, however, that resort to statistics is required to distinguish the toxic properties of the two gases. And because the airborne concentration of CS required to kill half of a population of laboratory animals is somewhat greater than that of CN, the former agent is "safe." This is a

---

[1] Trademark registered to the General Ordnance Equipment Corporation, PO Box 11211, Freeport Road, Pittsburgh, Pennsylvania 15238

little like saying that because it is safer to drive at ninety rather than 100 miles per hour, it is "safe" to drive at the former speed.

Agent DM is diphenylaminochlorarsine, commonly called "adamsite" or "vomiting gas." It contains about 27 per cent arsenic. It is regarded as the most dangerous of the three riot control agents herein described, and in fact the Army cautions: "This material contains arsenic; therefore, it should not be used in confined spaces" (75). Although DM is a powerful

Cl
|
As
N
|
H

Agent DM

emetic, the effect of the gas is not apparent until several minutes after exposure, and for this reason it is usually packaged in combination with CN. According to Applegate, it is not considered a basic riot control agent, but it can be secured on special order by civil law enforcement departments (76). Prentiss notes that, when mixed with CN, DM has proved very effective in suppressing riots and civil disturbances of a "more serious character" (77).

DM was developed by the American chemist Roger Adams during World War I as an improvement on diphenylchlorarsine, the latter having been introduced by the Germans (78). On recrystallization from benzene-glacial acetic acid, DM is a yellow solid with essentially no odor. It is an irritant at a concentration of a fraction of a milligram per cubic meter and is believed to be lethal at 1500 mg/m^3 for 10 minutes exposure. The lack of reliable data on toxicity, according to the Edgewood Arsenal, can be ascribed to a reluctance to perform such research ". . . because the need for the information did not justify the possible hazard to volunteers involved in the test" (79). The same report states, without elaboration, that death occurred in one of twenty-two men exposed to DM while asleep in an Army barracks. The victim was exposed from five to thirty minutes, according to different estimates, while he was trapped in a confined space (80).

The agent DM is cheaply and conveniently prepared by mixing diphenyl-amine with arsenic trichloride. The product used in chemical munitions is grossly impure and contains a variety of contaminants. Further details on the chemistry and properties of DM may be found in Appendix II.

The section of the *Army Field Manual 3-10* on DM states:

This agent causes violent sneezing, nausea, and vomiting. DM1 is micropulverized DM. The physiological reaction to DM is sufficiently severe to incapacitate personnel for several hours after exposure. Since DM requires several minutes to produce maximum effects, it may be combined with CN munitions to produce effects more rapidly. CN–DM munitions are particularly useful against violent rioters. DM alone is not approved for use in riot control dispersers in any operation where deaths are not acceptable. Excessive, and possibly lethal, or completely incapacitating dosages can be developed from its use. However, it may be used in military or paramilitary operations, in counterinsurgency operations, or in limited or general war where control of target personnel by the incapacitating effects is desired and where possible deaths are acceptable. (81)

According to the authoritative *Merck Index,* Volume 8, page 804, 1968, DM causes ". . . profuse watery nasal discharge; severe pain in nose and chest; sneezing, coughing, nausea, vomiting, depression, weakness. Sensory disturbances may occur."

The most common riot control agent in both police and military arsenals is now CS. It has several advantages over both CN and DM, of which the most important is its extreme potency; hence, CS is sometimes called "super tear gas." CS was first prepared in 1928 by two American chemists, Ben Corson and Roger Stoughton. The code initials were taken from the first letters of the names of the discoverers (82). The proper chemical name is ortho-chloro-benzalmalononitrile or ortho-chlorobenzylidenemalononitrile. The original paper noted the irritant properties of the new product: ". . . the face smarts, especially if damp. The smarting is intensified by washing" (83).

However, it remained for the British CBW laboratory at Porton Down, the Chemical Defence Experimental Establishment, to develop CS as a riot control agent. The objective was to find a substance that would be both more potent and without the side effects associated with CN. CS was selected in 1957 to 1958 after some ninety-one possible replacements for CN had been evaluated. The British Government, in patenting the production process made this claim for the product: "A concentration of between one part in ten million and one part in a million is enough to drive all but the most determined persons out of it within a few seconds" (84).

About thirty nations, including Sweden, are believed to stock CS as a riot control agent.

Agent CS

Pure CS is a crystalline, almost colorless solid with a distinctive, peppery odor (see Appendix II). It dissolves easily in alcohol, ether, and other organic solvents and is very sparingly soluble in water. A solution concentration of about 10^{-5} M can be achieved. It is rapidly hydrolyzed to ortho-chlorobenzaldehyde and malononitrile, especially in alkaline media. The half-life of CS in water solution at neutral pH is believed to be about ten minutes.

The *Army Field Manual* says of CS:

This agent irritates the eyes, nose, and throat. CS is the most effective of the riot control agents, even in extremely low concentrations. Its effects on the eyes and respiratory system continue for five or ten minutes after exposure to fresh air. During that time most personnel are incapable of effective action. CS that is inhaled before masking or that is trapped in the mask while it is being put on gives the impression that the mask is leaking. This impression, coupled with such effects as chest tightness, nausea, and a burning sensation of the eyes, may cause poorly trained troops to remove their masks, thereby exposing themselves to additional concentrations of CS or of any other agent used in conjunction with CS. (85)

A British description of CS is that it causes ". . . streaming from the eyes and nose, spasm of the eyelids, marked salivation and retching or sometimes vomiting, burning of the mouth and throat, and a gripping pain in the chest of such intensity that breathing becomes restricted to shallow gasps" (86).

CS is a lachrymator and sternutator at levels as low as 0.05 mg/m^3. The mortal concentration is not known with precision, but fairly detailed studies have been conducted with laboratory animals. From these data it is possible to estimate that CS is approximately as lethal as other combat gases. For example, it may be compared with cyanide through the following calculations. Prentiss (87) lists 200 mg/m^3 as the lethal concentration of cyanide for a ten-minute exposure. If we assume a breathing rate of fifteen liters per minute, which is typical of mild activity, the individual would inhale $((10 \times 15)/1000) \times 200$ or 30 milligrams in the ten-minute time. Since the molecular weight of hydrogen cyanide is 27, the lethal dose is hence just over a millimole of the substance. At one time the Army computed 25,000 mg-min/m^3 as the lethal concentration of CS, but subsequent tests with slightly larger laboratory animals suggested that this figure should be enlarged. The revision does not appear to be based on sound scientific data, and the more conservative value of 25,000 mg-min/m^3 should be retained. Calculations identical to those just performed for cyanide would give 375 milligrams as the lethal weight of CS for the human. Since the molecular weight of CS is 188.5, this is about 2 millimoles. Thus, CS can be seen to be approximately as potent as cyanide as a lethal chemical agent.

The Edgewood Arsenal states that "no deaths have been attributed to CS" (88)[2]. However, Russell Stetler, in a letter to a British newspaper, describes the death of a two-year-old child in Belfast under circumstances possibly involving CS (89). There is no doubt that CS must be regarded as a moderately

---

[2] See the chapter in this book by Alje Vennema on gas poisoning fatalities in Vietnam.

toxic compound, as the experiments by Punte *et al.* (90) first demonstrated. Guinea pigs are especially sensitive, and monkeys expire at an inhalation dose close to the 25,000 mg-min/m^3 formerly established for man. Moore has pointed out that the proposal to raise the value to about 60,000 mg-min/m^3 for man seems to be without a rational experimental foundation (91). In view of the spectrum in lethal dose response observed in different animal species, caution would require that the lower value be adopted.

In the summer of 1966 the Army conducted tests of the effects of thermally generated CS aerosol on human skin. The work was reported in 1967 (92). Human volunteers were obtained without "coercion or enticement" and were exposed to high concentrations of CS for periods of up to one hour under conditions simulating a tropical climate. Second degree burns were noted in four of the eight subjects, the blue-eyed blonds being more susceptible than the non-Caucasians. The resulting vesication was observed to incapacitate the individual up to ten days. Also, at higher concentrations erythema, bullae, nausea, vomiting, and diarrhea were observed (93).

An additional factor that must be considered is the effect of an agent such as CS on children, the aged, and most especially, on people with lung and respiratory ailments. After the massive use of CS in Northern Ireland in August, 1969, a local physician wrote:

... (1) In view of the fact that CS gas was released on an entire section of the community, has the effect of the gas on unhealthy lung tissue been investigated? (2) In view of the fact that CS gas is based on chlorobenzene, have animal experiments shown any evidence of possible liver and kidney damage? (3) Is there experimental work available to demonstrate the possible toxicological effects of the hundreds of empty gas canisters left lying on the streets of the Bogside, with particular reference to possible effects on children? ... I should imagine that five or six canisters fired into a tightly packed crowd would result in rapid dispersal. However, the gas was used in the Bogside area to support a containing action. Petrol bombs were fired from behind the barricades, and CS gas was fired into the barricade area almost continuously from 11:50 PM on August 12 until approximately 4 PM on 14 August. The Royal Ulster Constabulary admit to firing approximately 1,000 cartridges and 14 CS handgrenades during this time. An important feature was the atmospheric conditions prevailing at the time. These were warm, muggy and humid. A gentle breeze carried the CS aerosol away from the barricade area and into the densely built-up area of the Bogside. As a result, many families were exposed to a varying but constantly irritating atmospheric concentration of CS for a period of up to 48 hours. (94)

CS is dispersed as an aerosol or dust. The earliest methods of dissemination were by means of thermal volatilization; this gives an aerosol consisting of solid particles one or two microns in diameter. In this form CS displays a classic lachrymatory action. Improvements in the technology of handling the compound have resulted in the development of a micropulverized form suitable for packaging in bulk disseminators and bursting-type munitions. The powdered CS is designated CS1 and is much more durable than the aerosol form of the agent. As a further refinement, CS1 is coated with silicone to extend its field persistence up to several weeks; the weatherproofed variety is called CS2. In the field it may be stirred up by the weather or by the movement of vehicles or people.

Because the finely divided particles of CS aerosol or CS1 dust can penetrate to the alveoli of the lungs, McCarthy believes that it should be classed as a "lung gas" rather than a tear gas. A lung irritant typically causes pulmonary edema, a flooding of the lungs with water, with the result that the victim suffocates from lack of oxygen (95).

Decontamination of CS is achieved with mildly alkaline solutions. For the skin (not eyes) Weigand recommends a recipe containing 6 per cent sodium bicarbonate, 3 per cent sodium carbonate, and 1 per cent benzalkonium chloride (Zephiran chloride) in water (96). A simpler recipe for washing the skin is 0.25 per cent sodium bisulfite (97). McWhorter suggests a combination of bisulfite and the Weigand solution (98). CS will be most irritating in a humid climate and on a moist skin surface.

Packages and Payloads

In April, 1969, the Army published a new, eighty-five-page edition of *Training Circular 3-16* titled: "Employment of Riot Control Agents, Flame, Smoke, Anti-Plant Agents, and Personnel Detectors in Counter Guerrilla Operations." Portions of this manual have been reproduced in Appendix III. In the United States there was minor press comment about this manual when it appeared, *i.e.,* it was cited in some press accounts of Meselson's July, 1969, disclosure of the huge stockpiles of CS gas requisitioned for Vietnam (99). However, although the manual is not classified, it has received miniscule distribution among even those scientists who are most actively engaged in the struggle against CBW. The circular was reprinted and distributed in Sweden during the Fifth Stockholm Conference on Vietnam, March 28 to March 30, 1970 (100). It is the best single source for specifications of the multifarious types of riot control agents and equipment for chemical warfare employed in Vietnam. Many of these weapons can be found to have their civilian counterparts (101).

Training Circular 3-16 begins with a statement of scope which, as may be seen by reference to Appendix III, makes the point: "The general guidance offered in this training circular is oriented towards the environment and combat conditions in Southeast Asia." Because weather and terrain are important considerations in the use of combat chemicals, these features of southeast Asia, including Cambodia, are treated in Chapter 1 of the circular. Elsewhere the document makes this significant observation: "The information in this training circular is also applicable to internal defense and/or internal development operations."

Chapter 2 of the circular deals with both standard and recently developed riot control agents, equipment, and munitions. Typical information contained in this section are details on the construction of a standard M7 series CS grenade fitted with an eight- to twelve-second delay fuse. Such a grenade may be dropped from an altitude of about 1,500 feet or it may be launched from a rifle. A variety of cartridges are described, some of which contain up to 4.4 kilos (9.7 pounds) of CS/pyrotechnic mixture. The larger shells are fired with howitzers and have a range of up to fifteen kilometers (nine miles).

The M106 disperser described in the circular is a military version of an agricultural blower. It is capable of dispersing either bulk CS1 or CS/smoke from burning-type grenades, and it may be employed to blow the chemicals either into the open air or into a confined space such as a tunnel, cave, or bunker.

Training Circular 3-16 also describes various canister clusters, aircraft and helicopter dispensers, and bombs packed with CS. For example, the CBU-30/A dispenser contains 1,280 grenades and is capable of blanketing an area $67,100 \text{ m}^2$. The CH-47 Chinook helicopter can be outfitted with racks to hold thirty 55-gallon drums of CS1 or CS2. Since each drum contains eight 10-pound plastic bags filled with the agent, the total weight of the cargo in this arrangement is 2,400 pounds.

Table 1-2 gives specifications for some of the chemical-filled grenades listed in a 1967 edition of the *Chemical Reference Handbook FM 3-8*. Since *Training Circular 3-16* states that CS grenade XM54 is merely a standard M7 series equipped with a delay fuse, and since the combined weight of CS (112 grams) and pyrotechnic mixture (185 grams) totals 297 grams or about two-thirds pound, the filling weights recorded in Table 1-2 refer to the agent-combustion mixture. Hence, we can estimate that the usual amount of CS in a burning-type grenade will be about one-fourth pound. Applegate quotes the common burning-type M7A3 grenade as containing 4.5 ounces or 128 grams of CS (102). This type of grenade is subject to "throwback"; it presents a fire hazard from the pyrotechnic mix, and it generates the gas in a molten form which condenses to a liquid aerosol that is not stable for much more than minutes. The M25A2 is a bursting-type grenade about three inches in diameter. It is made by cementing together two plastic hemispheres. Although the charge in this munition is only about 2 ounces (55 grams), the particular agent used, CS1, is much more persistent. These so-called "baseball" grenades present a hazard from flying plastic, and they can be dangerous if exploded in the hand. Such grenades, according to Applegate, may explode spontaneously if dropped on a hard surface (103).

The Vietnamese have apparently not published any detailed compilation of the types of chemical munitions deployed by United States forces and their allies, but it is not difficult to find general statements:

Chemical weapons are now an official method of warfare used by the American troops, satellite troops and puppet troops. All types of forces—air, naval, motorized troops, paratroopers, marine corps, and infantry are now armed with material which makes it possible for them to use poisonous gas. Also, the task force commando units, the police in the countryside, and the militia are armed with the same type of materiel for chemical warfare. The poison weapons that the U.S. troops and satellite troops

TABLE 1–2

Characteristics of Chemical-Filled Grenades[a]

| Munition | Agent | Weight (lb) | | Remarks |
		Filling	Filled munition	
Hand grenade CN1, ABC–M25A1	CN1	0.22	0.47	Bursting type grenade with radius 5 m, 1.5–3 sec delay fuse.
Hand grenade CN1, ABC–M25A2	CN1	0.22	0.50	Special type bursting munition.
Hand grenade CS1, M25A2	CS1	0.22	0.50	′′
Hand grenade DM1, ABC–M25A2	DM1	0.14	0.50	′′
Hand grenade CN–DM, M6	CN–DM	0.64	1.06	Burning type; 2 sec delay fuse.
Hand grenade M6A1, CN–DM	CN–DM	0.59	1.25	Burning type; CN–DM mix.
Hand grenade, CN, M7	CN	0.64	1.06	Burning type; 1–2 sec delay fuse.
Hand grenade, CN, M7A1	CN	0.79	1.16	Burning type; 2 sec delay fuse.
Hand grenade, CS, M7A1	CS	0.59	0.96	Special purpose burning type.
Hand grenade, CS, M7A2	CS	0.59	1.00	′′
Hand grenade, CS, M7A3	CS	0.59	1.00	′′

[a]U.S. Army Field Manual FM 3–8, Table (75).

use are hand grenades, mortar shells, navy artillery projectiles, the Air Force's bombs and rockets, as well as gas pump (dispensers) machines fixed to a helicopter or carried on the back of a specially trained soldier. . . . (104)

If this report is authentic, it would seem that most if not all of the munitions systems described in *Training Circular 3-16* are in actual combat operation in Vietnam.

Gas warfare in Vietnam has been an experimental operation in which CN and DM have been sidetracked in favor of CS, various methods of dispersal have been tested, and different formulations of the chosen agent, *i.e.,* CS1 and CS2, have been tried.

Obviously, "riot control" is not a particularly accurate description for an agent delivered by a howitzer with a range of ten miles.

Responsibility

The special status of chemical and biological weapons is recognized by the fact that they, like nuclear weapons, require presidential authorization prior to deployment (105). *Army Field Manual 3-10* states:

The decision to employ lethal or incapacitating chemical or biological agents is a matter of national policy. When the decision is made, United States Army, Navy, Air Force and Marine Corps commanders will receive through command channels the authority to use such agents and specific guidance in their use.

The *Manual* also notes that ". . . the United States is not a party to any treaty, now in force, that prohibits or restricts the use in warfare of toxic or non-toxic gases . . . or of bacteriological warfare" (106).

It is, of course, possible to debate the classification of riot control agents as "incapacitating," although they are so designated by the United Nations (107). The inclusion of the reference in the *Field Manual* to nontoxic gases would imply that they require the same authorization prior to use. In spite of these regulations it was alleged that President Lyndon B. Johnson was not consulted on the first use of gas in Vietnam. His press secretary, George Reedy, disassociated the president from the incident and placed full responsibility on the field commander in Saigon, General William C. Westmoreland (108). Representative Richard D. McCarthy saw the failure to secure prior presidential approval as a further blow to the American image. He said, "Use of gas by the Armed Services in Vietnam, never cleared at the top levels of government or outside the Pentagon, reduced the credibility of U.S. statesmen and diplomats" (109).

Later, President Johnson stated he was never told about the initiation of gas warfare in Vietnam. He went on to remark, "I just wish there was concern with our soldiers who are dying as they are with somebody's eyes who watered a little bit [sic]" (110). It was intimated in Washington that for many years the authority to use tear-gas-type munitions had been delegated to area commanders. A spokesman at the State Department offered the opinion that there had been no reason to consult with other governments on the use of gas in Vietnam (111).

At the CBW hearings held by Representative Clement Zablocki in late 1969, Representative Robert W. Kastenmeier threw some light on the responsibility for the first use of gas in Vietnam:

May I submit for the record, an exchange of correspondence I had with the Secretary of the Army in 1965 relating to this, some of the background material we have? It was my understanding that at the time the use as such had not been cleared at the White House or the very highest levels, the State Department or Pentagon, but was considered at some point at a low level and put into instructions to area commanders. And I was dismayed that the person responding to this in March, 1965, was the Secretary of State, after the fact and supporting the area commanders. I thought it was really gratuitous for the Secretary of State, in a sense, to involve himself approvingly, and after the fact. This did give approval at a high level. And, as I say, I think thereafter established it as national policy, although I do have some correspondence, I think, touching on this point that I could make available. (112)

To this Representative Zablocki responded:

It would be most helpful if your correspondence would shed some light on this particular situation. Apparently gas was approved at a low level for a limited use and then was escalated and used beyond the purpose agreed upon. There was, indeed, no formal Government policy accepted by tacit approval or by formal decree that it could be used for the purpose of flushing out and killing. (113)

Kastenmeier's correspondence was never made part of the record, and so one is left with the impression that the decision to turn to gas was initiated at the Pentagon and subsequently defended at the highest levels of government.

Later in these hearings, when the official spokesman for the Pentagon took the stand, it was revealed that official permission had been sought in late 1965, about a year after the riot control agents first appeared in Vietnam. Admiral William E. Lemos, speaking for the Department of Defense, told the Zablocki committee:

The Department of Defense with the concurrence of the Department of State obtained Presidential approval in November, 1965, for the use of CS and CN in Vietnam. COMUSMACV[3] delegated to his subordinate commanders authority to use these agents in military operations against the enemy. These commanders were authorized to further delegate this authority to the extent deemed suitable for insuring both timely employment and proper control. (114)

First Use

The publication, *In The Name of America,* has collected a substantial number of press reports on the use of riot control agents in Vietnam. Another valuable source is *Against the Crime of Silence,* the proceedings of the

---

[3] Commander of the United States Military Assistance Command, Vietnam.

Bertrand Russell War Crimes Tribunal. These two sources (115) plus the issues of *The New York Times* for March 24 and 25, 1965, help to document in point of time the initiation of gas warfare in Vietnam.

In early 1965 press reports from both Washington and Saigon confirmed that the United States was giving South Vietnamese forces "types of tear gas" for combat use. These reports, datelined March 22, did not identify the precise nature of the agents, but there was emphasis on the agents' nauseating and cathartic effects and on the fact that they were to be used to separate the enemy from civilians, *i.e.,* the "intermingled situation" (116).

Agents CS and CN apparently were used to disperse a Buddhist riot in Saigon in November, 1964 (117), but the incidents that were to trigger a world-wide reaction came shortly thereafter. The South Vietnamese Army employed CN, CS, and DM on December 23, 25, and 28 in Xu Yen, Tay Ninh and Phu Yen provinces (118). On March 22, 1965, an Associated Press reporter, Horst Faas, learned of the planned use of DM in a mission near Saigon (119). A dispatch by Faas brought the gas question to the surface and prompted the statements issued the following day from the White House, the Pentagon, and the State Department (120).

The March 24 and 25, 1965, editions of *The New York Times* made a complete analysis of this new dimension to the war. It was noted that the gases had been furnished to the South Vietnamese Government in 1962 without special restrictions or authorization requirements on their use. Secretary McNamara said DM, CS, and CN were the agents involved, and he outlined the properties and effects of each. He also said the gases had been used only two or three times, the last being on January 27, 1965, in Phu Yen province. On March 23, 1965, United States officers in Saigon had acknowledged that gas had been employed since the previous December. Resort to gas was said to have been inspired by an incident in which Viet Cong guerrillas drove civilians ahead of them during an attack (121). There was a good deal of interest in the fact that agent DM was being employed, in view of the potentially lethal nature of this gas. It was said to have a "peppery" odor and must have been confused in this respect with CS.

All these initial uses were alleged to be in situations where guerrillas were intermixed with civilians, and the objective was said to be "to save lives." According to the United States assessment, the experience was negative. In two cases, no enemy could be found; in another, the wind was wrong. James Reston commented: "The main effect was merely to nauseate a lot of people all over the world with the thought that gas could be used merely on the authority of the South Vietnamese soldiers concerned" (122).

President Johnson's comments have already been noted. At the time of the incident his press secretary, George Reedy, said the materials used were "standard-type riot control" agents. Secretary Rusk took the unusual step of stopping in at a press briefing in the State Department. His remarks on this occasion are of special interest and will be analyzed in a later section.

Most of the reports from the National Liberation Front and the Democratic Republic of Vietnam confirm that gas came into the war in late 1964 or earlier. For example, "In the years 1963–64 the U.S. aggressors many times fired shells or dropped bombs containing gases on a certain number of villages in the Ben Tre, Co Cong, Can Tho, Ca Mau, Phu Yen and Quang Nam provinces" (123). Dr. Abraham Behar, a French physician familiar with the development of chemical warfare in Vietnam, reported that the spraying of "toxic" gas into shelters at Vinh Quang hamlet in Binh Dinh province on September 5, 1963, resulted in the poisoning of twenty-five and the death of thirty-five, of whom twenty-eight were children and twenty-six women (124). In a report issued in 1970 the NLF dated the use of gas to 1964: ". . . they, as from 1964, began generally to use poisonous gases" (125).

Reaction

The disclosure of the military use of gas in Vietnam ignited an international uproar. *The New York Times* March 24, 1965 edition summarized world-wide comment and made special reference to the debate in the House of Commons (126). Prime Minister Harold Wilson refused to commit himself on the question of tear gas but said later that he had not been advised that the materials were to be used. When asked by Sir Alec Douglas Home, leader of the Conservatives, to confirm that the "gas" was merely "tear gas" of the type used in civil disturbances, Mr. Wilson was reported to have asserted that it was not of a type that would violate international agreements. A delegation of fourteen Labour Party members, led by Eric Heffer of Liverpool, lodged a protest at the American Embassy (127). The British Foreign Secretary, Michael Stewart, was in the United States at the time. In a speech at the National Press Club he said he had expressed grave concern to Secretary of State Dean Rusk and added, "I am, in fact, asking your Government . . . to display a decent respect for the opinions of mankind" (128).

The international comment was overwhelmingly negative and ranged from charges of criminality and barbarity from Peking and Hanoi to very serious misgivings in the Western press. At the United Nations, delegates of all shades of political opinion were disturbed although they did not speak in public. A typical remark was said to be, "It sounds bad, and if it does not kill them, what is the purpose of using it?" The Soviet Union took up the issue at the United Nations and sent a sharp note of protest to the United States embassy in Moscow (129).

In its editorial on the subject *The New York Times* found the move counter-productive from the point of view of the moral stature of the United States: "People—ordinary people everywhere—have a strong psychological revulsion, if not horror, at the idea of any kind of poisonous gas. . . . This is something that no Asian, Communist or not, will forget. . . . Gas is a wretched means to achieve the most valid ends" (130).

Arthur Krock concurred, saying, "The diplomatic liability to the Administration that would come with the exposure that it was initiating chemical warfare in Vietnam should have been obvious in advance" (131).

On March 23, 1965, five House Republicans had sent a letter to President Johnson to protest the use of gas. The Republicans, John Lindsay, New York, Charles Mathias, Jr., Maryland, Frank Horton, New York, F. Bradford Morse, Massachusetts, and Stanley Tupper, Maine, concluded that gas would only stiffen the enemy resistance and tarnish the image of America in Asia (132).

The intensity and virulence of the opposition seems to have been unanticipated by the Administration. At a news conference described as "hastily arranged" Secretary Rusk denigrated criticism of what he too called "riot control agents." He said these did not violate the "Geneva Convention of 1925" (Geneva Protocol?). An excerpt of Rusk's statement, as it appeared in *The New York Times,* is reproduced in Appendix IV. As may be seen, Rusk drew a distinction between "military gases" and "riot control agents," although United States *Army Field Manuals* make no such separation. The Secretary did not rule out the possibility that the gases would be used again. However, he implied that such use, if it did occur, would be circumscribed: "We do not expect that gas will be used in ordinary military operations. . . . The anticipation is, of course, that these weapons will be used only in those situations involving riot control or situations analogous to riot control."

Although agent CS may cause nausea at higher concentrations, the frequent reference to "nausea gas" in the first reports of gas use in Vietnam suggests that DM or CN–DM munitions may have been employed at that time.

Secretary of Defense Robert McNamara explained the use of gas to a closed meeting of the Senate Foreign Relations Committee. Afterward, Senator J. W. Fulbright, chairman of the committee, told reporters that gas was ". . . the most humane way to deal with the disorder" (133).

Thus, while high officials in the American government saw the use of gas as a humanitarian aid to military operations, the armed forces on the scene had another view: "What the hell, by pumping gas down there we can knock out groundfire, so that lets us get closer on the ground and from the air to kill all the more of the enemy. If women and children are down there at the time, it will be no better for them than it is now" (134).

The Lull
Some weeks after the initial furor, President Johnson came to the defense of the various governmental departments that had earlier justified the initiation of gas warfare. He told a press conference that the agents were products which could be obtained ". . . by any individual from open stocks in this country just like you order something out of a Sears and Roebuck catalogue" (135). And Secretary Rusk minimized the problem of international criticism, saying that he saw hopeful signs that some of the critics were having "second thoughts" (136). In spite of this "hard line" on gas, however, it is a fact that these agents disappeared from the Vietnam war for over half a year. *The New York Times* speculated that field commanders had been given instructions to suspend the use of all types of gas (137).

Meanwhile, a skillful public relations campaign was mounted to assure public acceptance of riot control agents. The American Chemical Society, faithful to its historic opposition to the Geneva Protocol, ran an editorial on August 16, 1965, that advocated "Chemical Agents for Guerrilla Warfare" (see Appendix V).

Suddenly, in September, 1965, gas reappeared in Vietnam in an incident widely assumed to have been a trial balloon (138). Early that month Saigon reported an operation at Qui Nhon in which forty-seven canisters of tear gas had been used to flush a mixed group of civilians and enemy out of tunnels. The reports stated that fifty suspects were separated from 400 civilians (139). Both Peking and Hanoi claimed a number of casualties resulted in this operation; Hanoi set the figure at thirty-five deaths (140). It was explained immediately that the field commander in charge, Lt. Colonel L. N. Utter, had used gas without authorization and that he would be subject to disciplinary proceedings (141). On September 25, General Westmoreland stated that no action would be taken against Utter (142); it is believed that three days earlier the general had asked the Pentagon for permission to renew the use of tear gas (143). The consensus seemed to be that Westmoreland had never been officially stripped of his power to employ gas but had been merely cautioned against exercise of the authority during the sensitive period following the public clamor in the month of March.

That the Utter incident was indeed a public relations ploy seems amply confirmed from Hersh's careful research of the circumstances surrounding the incident (144). He reports an editorial in the *Washington Daily News* of October 11, 1965 as stating:

Little if any public protest is being voiced over renewed use of tear gas and other non-lethal gases by U. S. troops in Vietnam. There is a lesson to be learned from the contrast between this quiet acceptance and the loud outcry which arose last March. . . . At that time, public opinion here and abroad was totally unprepared.

Evolution

On October 6, 1965, preparatory to a joint American-Australian sweep through an area near Saigon, gas was furnished to the 173rd Airborne Brigade (145). The commander of the operation, Brigadier General Ellis Williamson, is said to have emphasized beforehand to reporters that "tear gas" might be used, thus giving the impression at this stage that DM, the classical "nausea gas," had been discarded in favor of CN or CS (146). The de-emphasis of nausea gas my have been on orders from the White House (147). Troops engaged in the October 8 sweep were said to be seen carrying baseball-sized grenades stamped with the letters CN and CS (148).

Table 1-3 shows procurement costs for riot control munitions for the period 1963 to 1969. These data illustrate the very sharp rise in expenditures for chemicals following 1965, the year gas came back to the Vietnam war on a large scale.

TABLE 1–3

U.S. Armed Services Procurement Costs for Riot Control Agents[a]

Fiscal year	Expenditure ($ million)
1963	2.4
1964	2.9
1965	1.1
1966	16.8
1967	17.3
1968	16.3
1969	80.5

[a] From General Accounting Office, U.S. Comptroller General.

After the autumn of 1965 numerous press accounts began to appear on the generalized use of gas in different aspects of the war, although initially the agents seem to have been confined to tunnel operations. However, as early as January, 1966, the 173rd Airborne Brigade sprayed tear gas from helicopters in a sweep through the northern part of the Mekong Delta (149). Again on February 21, 1966, helicopters dropped hundreds of grenades on a patch of jungle northeast of Saigon prior to a B-52 raid (150). The Department of Defense explained that the new tactic was designed to flush the enemy out of bunkers since previous experience had indicated that in aerial bombardment northing short of a direct hit was effective in putting the enemy out of action. Thus, it was explained, the function of the gas was designed to flush the enemy to the surface where he could be assaulted with fragmentation bombs.

Other news items in the months to follow confirmed the growing reliance on gas:

It was a long, bloody mile we walked today. At times it was an inferno. Riot gas drifted through the trees, burning where it touched a man's sweating skin. The wounded writhed on the ground, looking grotesque in their black gas masks. . . . Helicopters carrying gas came in to assist. They plastered the Viet Cong bunkers with scores of tear gas grenades. (151)

Before the bombers struck the area, 12 miles southeast of Bongson, hundreds of tear gas grenades were dropped from helicopters. The first soldiers to enter the zone wore gas masks. Similar tactics were used in the area yesterday, apparently to flush the Viet Cong from fortified positions so that the bombs could have maximum effects. (152)

As far as gas is concerned, experts are again adamant that the gas used is non-poisonous. . . . They say the gas used is chlorobenzalmalononitrile. . . . Gas is used for two purposes in Vietnam, first to flush out the Viet Cong and civilians hiding in bunkers, and second to fill tunnel systems and make them inaccessible to the Viet Cong. Recently, American and Australian forces have been discovering tunnel systems too complex and long to be destroyed by high explosives. Thus they have been pumping them full of gas. (153)

Additional press comment reinforced the conclusion that 1966 was the year in which riot control agents, CS in particular, came into routine field use in Vietnam. A brief chronology of some of the reports follows:

May 10, 1966, *New York Times* (datelined Washington, DC)—7,200 pounds of tear gas powder, identified as CS1, was dropped by aircraft in an area northwest of Saigon.

May 11, 1966, *New York Times* (datelined Saigon)—Apparently this is the same operation reported on the previous day; the aircraft were specified as helicopters, and the agent was said to have been dispersed from eighty-pound drums.

July 14, 1966, *Christian Science Monitor*—This is a report of an operation by the "Big Red One" at Quan Loi in which powdered gas was dropped "in big barrels from helicopters."

October, 1966, *Argosy*—The writer of the article, who was exposed to CS gas pouring out of a tunnel-clearing operation, complained of extreme pain and blisters.

November 22, 1966, *World Journal Tribune*—Tunnel rats seeded the floors of enemy shelters with gas crystals.

January 22, 1967, *Los Angeles Times*—This article describes the pumping of nausea gas (not further identified) by means of a blower into a tunnel complex in the Ho Bo woods twenty-five miles northwest of Saigon.

August 18, 1967, *Asahi Evening News*—Marine helicopters were said to have dumped thousands of gallons of tear-nausea gas on suspected enemy positions.

Vietnamese sources repeatedly have complained about United States use of gas and "toxic chemicals." Thus, the *Vietnam Courier* reported the attack in the Ho Bo woods (see above) and said that shortly thereafter, on January 24, 1967, gas was sprayed into a cave in northern Binh Dinh (154). The following citations are derived from the *Black Paper* (155):

In the years 1963–64, the U.S. aggressors many times fired shells or dropped bombs containing gases on a certain number of villages in the Ben Tre, Go Cong, Can Tho, Ca Mau, Phu Yen and Quang Nam provinces. To retrieve the repeated reverses of the puppet army commanded by them, and to cope with the mounting anti-U.S. tide in the South Vietnamese cities, the U.S. aggressors, since the end of 1964, have been intensifying the use of combat gases, along with the spraying of noxious chemicals on an ever larger scale.

In early 1965, during three days, January 25, 26, and 27, U.S. aircraft made intensi-fied sprayings of noxious chemicals on Phu Lac hamlet, Phu Yen province, and dropped explosives and napalm bombs, causing heavy losses to the local population. Poisonous

Figure 1–3. A drum used for the dispersal of CS-1. Photographed by the National Liberation Front in South Vietnam. Photo courtesy of Weapons Committee, Hanoi.

gases alone killed eighty people, and hundreds of others were seriously affected, most of whom were old people, women and children.

The crimes of the U.S. imperialists have aroused great indignation among the public opinion of the world. On March 22, 1965, the U.S. military spokesman in Saigon admitted that gases had been used for weeks, and on many occasions (AP, March 22, 1965). Later on U.S. Defense Secretary McNamara had to convene a press conference, in which he showed a colored catalogue from the chemical factories of the Federal Laboratories, which sell various kinds of riot gases (*Newsweek,* April 5, 1965). McNamara told a lie when asserting that gases used in Vietnam were only tear gases, which were not lethal. But he could convince nobody. The following day Secretary of State Dean Rusk denied that the U.S. had started chemical warfare in South Vietnam, and added that poisonous gases would not be used in normal actions *(Newsweek).*

The deceitful denials of the war criminals cannot dupe anybody, but only aggravate their crimes.

When raiding Vinh Quang hamlet, Tuy Phuoc district, Binh Dinh province on September 5, 1965, a U.S. marine corps commanded by Lieutenant Colonel Leon Utter emptied 48 toxic gas canisters into the people's houses and shelters, killing 35 people on the spot and seriously poisoning 19 others. Among the victims were 28 children, 26 women, including 18 old women. A family of seven was tragically killed or blinded by toxic gas.

On September 8, 1965, only three days after the Vinh Quang raid, U.S. soldiers threw toxic grenades into the people's shelters in Ba Long An, Quang Ngai province, killing 78 civilians at the same time. In the October 6, 1965, raid in the southeast of Ben Cat, Dau Mot province, U.S. para-brigade 173 and a number of Australian units were equipped with gas masks. According to AFP on October 8, 1965, they got "permission" to use the types of gas from Westmoreland himself. Since then toxic gas has been considered as a "basic weapon" of U.S. troops in South Vietnam, and the use of toxic gas in attacks has been openly intensified.

In the January 2, 1966, raid on the Bau Trai area. Cho Lon province, the U.S. aggressors used infantry guns to pump toxic chemicals in the form of gas or powder at 285 km per hour.

On January 10, 1966, while raiding Kim Tai hamlet, Binh Dinh province, the U.S. aggressors, indulging in mass murder, committed an extremely savage crime. They herded 42 villagers into shelters and killed them by toxic gas. It was also in January, 1966, that more than 100,000 U.S., Australian, New Zealand and puppet soldiers in their raid in Nhu N Duc, Duc Hiep and Phu My Hung villages, Chu Chi district, Gia Dinh province, pumped toxic gas into the people's shelters, killing more than 100 people and seriously wounding hundreds of others. In this raid they used aircraft to extensively spray CNS gas mixed with toxic chemicals and lobbed gas grenades into hamlets. Reuters reported on January 12:

> An Australian corporal, Robert Bowtell, 24, born in Sydney, was killed by poisonous gas on January 11, 1966, though he had put on a gas mask while he was using gas against the population in an area north-west of Saigon. Two other soldiers, who came to his rescue, were also hurt and fell unconscious, while six others were also affected and sent to hospital.

On February 1, 1968, in the Ky Anh area, Tam Ky district, Quang Nam province, the U. S. aggressors fumigated 141 civilian shelters with toxic gas, killing many people, among them 74 children. On February 3 and 4, 1966, helicopters dropped 800 gas grenades on the Bang Son area, Binh Dinh province. In March, 1966, they again exploded 3,000 more in this area, killing and wounding many people.

Early in April, 1966, in west Pieime. Gia Rai province, the U.S. troops carried out the so-called "combined toxic gas, aircraft, and artillery action."

UPI boasted on April 12, 1966, that 1st Airmobile Cavalry Division troopers dropped rings of CS toxic gas grenades on the Chu Pong area. Between April 23 and May 9 U. S. aircraft dropped fifteen tons of gas-producing powder on some areas of the Tay Ninh province. The powder is of an ivory color, very fine and as hot as chili. The affected people got burning and tearing of the eyes, itches, blistered skin and mucous membrane, dyspnoea, nausea, and paralysis. Cattle and poultry were killed in great numbers. Toxic powder fell on the Nga Cay and Lo Go river sections, killing more than 300 kg of fish, among which were fish weighing over 5 kg.

Even in Saigon city the U.S. aggressors and their lackeys did not stop at using a toxic gas to suppress the people's demonstrations at the end of May, 1966.

Saigon Mayor, Colonel Vu Van Cua, himself cynically warned:

Our army has 4 new types of weapons at its disposal. There are 4 kinds of gas grenades. Apart from tear gas we have colored gas effective within 3 days in spite of hard rubbings and washings, gas inducing diarrhoea within 24 hours and nausea gas.

The first session of a special committee of the Stockholm Conference in Vietnam, named the International Commission for Investigation of U.S. War Crimes in Vietnam, was held in Stockholm on October 22–25, 1970. At that time a delegation from the DRV submitted a report that was current through September, 1970, and that claimed that chemical warfare activities have been stepped up under the Nixon administration.

Many times lethal gases have been used against civilians. During sweeps in Ba Leong An and Son My (Quang Ngai province) in January and February, 1969 the raiders sprayed gases in 15 places. At Son My they flushed an underground with gas, killing 12 aged persons and children.

On February 12, 1969, in a raid on Binh Nam village, Quang Nam province, US troops forced 10 people from 64 to 77 years of age and a woman with child into an underground and cut them all down with tear gas.

On July 18 and 20, 1969, US aircraft sprayed toxic agents and US artillery fired more than 100 gas shells on Ba Den area, Tay Ninh province, intoxicating thousands of civilians, many fatally, including 30 children who died instantly.

On January 31, 1970, US planes on 3 occasions dropped 100 gas bombs and CS barrels on Ky Phuoc and Ky An villages, Tam Ky district, Quang Nam province. The gas shrouded all the 5 hamlets of these 2 villages, and spread to hamlets of other villages, affecting 250 people. Several days later, gas still emanated from those barrels and bomb shells.

Obviously, there is a substantial parallel between these reports and those appearing in the Western media over the same time span. The Vietnamese data corroborate the fact that a six- or seven-month lull took place in the middle of 1965. The same conclusion is reached after perusal of the section on gas warfare in the proceedings of the Bertrand Russell War Crimes Tribunal (156). Unfortunately, the NLF and DRV literature often speaks of "toxic" and "noxious" chemicals in a context that could mean either herbicides, riot control agents, or both of these substances.

In 1968 there was a dearth of media information on riot control agents in Vietnam. It was, however, a period in which books began to appear on the general topic of CBW. Possibly these two facts are related in some way (157). Perhaps chemical warfare in Vietnam wasn't "news" any more. Perhaps managing editors of the press and other media decided to "cool it." At any rate: On February 25, 1968, the *London Observer* published an account of the British role in the development of CS (158). The article pointed out that some types of CS weapons are covered by British patent 967660 issued November, 1960. At the London conference on CBW on February 22 and 23, 1968, it was alleged that Britain, in licensing the production of CS weapons in the United States, was collaborating with the Americans in making available weapons of dubious legality (159).

CS continued in heavy use in Vietnam throughout 1968 as new methods were devised to take advantage of this versatile military weapon. As an example: "The officer generally acknowledged as having perfected the cordon and pile-on is Colonel Henry Emerson . . . he often pounded the area with tear gas in an effort to drive the enemy into the open . . . In one operation his men killed 130 of the enemy" (160).

The year 1969 saw renewed press interest in the use of CS gas in the war. The *Montreal Star* gave details of the method of fouling bunkers with CS crystals, a practice of some years' duration in South Vietnam. In this particular operation Australian engineers seeded the agent in a Viet Cong divisional headquarters eighteen miles north of Nui Dat, South Vietnam. The agent was said to come sealed in airtight, eight-pound bags. A detonator was placed under each bag and all were blown up simultaneously. The CS crystals were thereby embedded in the walls of the tunnel which, according to the report, would be uninhabitable for a period estimated as three months (161).

In July, 1969, Matthew S. Meselson, a professor of biology at Harvard University and a consultant to the United States Arms Control and Disarmament Agency, issued a press release concerning the escalation in use of CS in Vietnam (162). Meselson's figures, which were derived from sources in the Pentagon, show that sixteen times as much of the agents was purchased in 1969 as in 1964 (Table 1-4). He charged that, if dispersed by helicopter, all forms of CS gas bought for Vietnam could cover 80,000 square miles or an area some 14,000 square miles greater than the total area of South Vietnam.

All pretense that CS was being employed for humanitarian purposes appears to have been shattered by a report made public in September 1969 (163). According to this account, the American command in Saigon had told the Pentagon some six months previously that tear gas had rarely saved civilian lives and, furthermore, it was doubted that the gas could serve that purpose. Civilians, it was pointed out, generally stayed away from fighting areas; the use of gas could, in fact, drive them into the open and make them vulnerable to conventional fire and air attacks. The Pentagon was at this time advised that the largest amount of CS was being used against enemy camps, bunkers, and caves, and that it had rarely been employed to save civilian lives or property.

Army Magazine was enthusiastic about the merits of CS in Vietnam. In its October, 1969, issue it reported:

Another comparatively recent ordnance trend is the growing tactical use of tear-producing CS gas and the proliferation of associated weapons and munitions. CS

TABLE 1–4

U.S. Armed Services Procurement of CS[a]
(in thousands of pounds)

Fiscal year	CS (in weapons)	CS1 (bulk)	CS2 (bulk)	Annual total
1964	233	142	0	375
1965	93	182	0	275
1966	458	1,217	0	1,675
1967	509	770	0	1,279
1968[b]	869	3,504	931	5,304
1969[b]	2,334	192	3,884	6,410
Total	4,496	6,007	4,815	

Grand total, all forms, 1964–1969 = 15,318

[a] Hearings, Part 6, Department of Defense Appropriations, 1970.

[b] Programmed figures: a slightly different set of figures was published by McCarthy (63) and Meselson (162), *i.e.,* 13,760,000 pounds of all forms of CS acquired for fiscal 1964 to fiscal 1969 (see the *Congressional Record,* June 12, 1969, H4775). It is not clear if these quantities represent the total for southeast Asia or if additional amounts are used by services other than the Army, other agencies, and the Republic of South Vietnam.

has proved particularly effective in Vietnam in flushing the enemy out of bunkers preceding high explosive fire or infantry assaults. It has also been useful in perimeter defense.

At the end of 1969, *The New York Times* ran a special report from Saigon titled: "U. S. Now Uses Tear Gas as a Routine War Weapon." The account featured direct reports from a prepared statement distributed by American authorities in Vietnam. It stated:

There is continuing effort to use the most effective tactics and weapons in every combat situation in Vietnam to hold U.S. and Republic of Vietnam armed forces casualties to the absolute minimum.

This effort can include the use of riot control agents, either tear gas or CS. These agents have been used in the Republic of Vietnam to drive enemy personnel from caves, tunnels and fortified positions. It has also been used on occasions when the enemy has infiltrated into population centers, built up areas, and is suspected of holding innocent civilian hostages.

Enemy troops who are driven from their bunkers or fortified positions and who do not surrender and who continue to fight are engaged as any dangerous armed enemy would be. Since the effects of the riot control agents last only a few minutes it is not uncommon for the enemy to resume shooting at our soldiers.

In short, the riot control agents are employed when they will help save the lives of non-combatants and soldiers of the free world military forces. The use of riot control agents also permits rendering the enemy ineffective and subject to capture without taking his life when the situation permits. (164)

Although in theory the people flushed out by the use of CS are supposed to be captured, American soldiers have only a split second to determine if the people intend to surrender or fight. Thus, the report continued, ". . . the Americans may shoot rather than take chances." A spokesman at headquarters said that gas was usually introduced into tunnels by means of hand grenades, which were available to all units at the lowest level and which could be used without special permission. In continuing its general survey of the use of gas, *The Times* also noted the helicopter dusting operations that were designed to make the enemy vulnerable to air or ground attacks. The case of Lieut. Col. L. N. Utter (see p. 33) was reviewed, and it was stated that he had been charged with the "unauthorized" use of forty-eight canisters of CN gas.

In his testimony before the Subcommittee on National Security Policy and Scientific Developments of the House Committee on Foreign Affairs in December, 1969, Rear Admiral William E. Lemos, a spokesman for the Pentagon, gave the specific situations in which gas was used. He cited six main uses: (1) attacks against occupied positions, (2) defense of positions, (3) tunnel clearing, (4) breaking contact with the enemy, (5) defense against ambush, and (6) rescuing downed airmen. In summary Lemos stated:

Perhaps the most valid indication of the effectiveness of CS in combat operations is that U.S. personnel continue to carry CS grenades to the field in lieu of some of their normal high explosive ammunition, and ground commanders often call for CS rather than high explosives. Riot control agents are a valuable aid in accomplishing our mission and in protecting our forces. (165)

In contrast to the expectation of Secretary of State Dean Rusk in 1965, not only were the agents not used in riot control but COMUSMACV directed that the agents not be employed by U.S. elements in situations involving civil disturbances, riots, or demonstrations as these were judged to be the province of the government of South Vietnam. Admiral Lemos and his subordinates were unwilling to accept the designation of any form of CS as a "lung gas." Under close questioning by Representative Donald Fraser, Lemos acknowledged that ". . . riot control agents have no prohibition on their use in such situations as we are facing in Vietnam." As for agent DM he said the chemical had not been used by the United States in Vietnam and that steps were being taken to remove it from the riot control inventory. In spite of this denial there are two reasons why the use of DM in South Vietnam should receive closer scrutiny. First, in the hearings just described, the amount of riot control agents sent overseas was classified. In the second place, the experience of Dr. Alje Vennema in Vietnam suggests that his civilian patients had been attacked with DM or some other nausea gas (see Chapter 2).

The massive procurement of CS in the early fall of 1965 did not entirely escape attention in Washington. On October 7, 1965, the Directorate for News Services of the Department of Defense was asked the following pointed questions in regard to a $1.02 million contract for CS1 awarded to Fisher Chemical:

1. Does the contract signify an increase in buying for CS1 in FY66?
2. What was the buy in FY64?
3. What percentage of projected FY66 supply of CS1 does this contract represent?
4. The Gamma Chemical Co., a subsidiary of Fisher, has been awarded this work. Has Gamma been awarded previous contracts?
5. What usable tactical form does CS1 take? Grenades, smoke pots, pressurized tanks?
6. How many grenades would this contract make, considering that there are 256,720 lbs of CS1 in the order?
7. Who capsulates it?
8. Can you tell me how much CS1 is presently on hand?
9. Does the increase in buy represented in this contract signify possible increased humanitarian use in Vietnam to separate hostages from suspected VC?

The answer to questions 1, 2, and 9 came the next day:

1. Yes.
2. $607,112.
9. The Department of Defense does not comment on tactics.

The remaining questions had been answered by previous query response:

3. This is contractual information pre-release, which is not permitted.
4. Yes.
5. M-25 grenades, M-5 & M-3 dispensers (pots).
6. There is about 1/4 lb of CS1 per M-25 grenade.
7. Dispensers are filled by troops in the field. Grenades are filled by the contractor or under separate contract.
8. Classified.

Results

In the absence of any systematic survey of gas casualties in Vietnam, the number of fatalities can only be surmised. M. Francis Kahn, M.D., a French physician who toured the liberated zones of South Vietnam in early 1968, estimated the number of deaths at several hundred and those affected at many thousands (166). Prior to December, 1967, according to Kahn, the NLF claimed to have established a minimum of thirty authenticated fatalities owing to gas poisoning.

The first case of death by gas asphyxiation in Vietnam that became widely known in the Western world was that of the Australian Corporal Robert Bowtell (see p. 37). He died in an accident in a tunnel-clearing operation in Hau Nghia province in January, 1966. He and the other men in his party were wearing gas masks; nonetheless, they were overcome by what was probably a combination of tear gas and carbon monoxide (167). The agent responsible is believed to have been CN delivered by means of burning-type grenades (168), although one report states positively that CS was involved (169). The case was fully reported in the Australian press, and carbon monoxide was stated as contributing to the cause of death (170). *Training Circular 3-16* draws attention to the fact that carbon monoxide can be expected as a by-product of the burning-type grenades, and it cautions that the usual protective mask will not filter out this gas.

An article in the October 11, 1967, issue of the *Saigon Post* titled "U.S. Tear Gas Saves Lives of Viet Innocents" drew a wry comment from a Christian Service worker who had witnessed the effects of tear gas on civilians:

About three and one-half months ago, I was involved in an attempt to be of assistance to some six thousand new refugees that had been created in Quang Ngai Province by a forced evacuation of an area under Viet Cong control. . . . I took two of them, a ten-year old boy and a twelve-year old girl, by far the most seriously ill, and drove the eight miles back to Quang Ngai. Emergency measures proved fatal for the boy; he was in the morgue the next morning when I went to the hospital; he died from an overdose of tear gas. . . . The victims reported that about twenty women and children did not even make it out of the cave. (171)

From Vietnamese sources come numerous reports of fatalities arising from the American use of gas from grenades, helicopters, pumps, mortars, bombs, projectiles, and rockets. The Committee for the Denunciation of War Crimes Committed by the U. S. Imperialists and Their Lackeys in South Vietnam made available to the 1968 London Conference on CBW the Committee's fairly detailed records of gas poisonings for the period January, 1965 through July, 1966. The following reports are from a document issued in February, 1970:

Poisonous gases [are] used by the Americans in South Vietnam under the heading "tear gases."

As from 1964, the Americans have mainly used the following poisonous gases:
—CS, CS1, and CS2 (the active part consisting of "ortho-chlorobenzalmalononitrile," the latter two being spread in powder form)
—CN (chloroacetophenone)
—DM (adamsite or diphenylaminochloroarsine)
—ethylbromacetate
—poisonous gases affecting the central nervous system.

In order to mass exterminate the South Vietnamese population the Americans indiscriminately use the poisonous gases (in very densely populated areas and, to a still greater extent) in combination with other weapons. During the Nixon Government the Americans have even more intensified the use of poisonous gases. According to the *Montreal Star* (24 July, 1969) the USA's fighting forces so far during 1969 have bought 16 times more of chemical means of warfare than during 1964. . . .

1. During 1969, the Americans have continued to use poison gases to a still larger extent than earlier. When the gases are dropped, in highly concentrated form and on one and the same occasion covering very large areas then the "tear gases" no longer have a strongly irritant effect—they become lethal gases for man.

In January 1969 American aircraft dropped large quantities of CS gas and "herbicides" over the fields of, amongst others, locations in the provinces of Binh Dinh, Ninh Khe, Hoai An, Hoai Nhon, An Lao, Vinh Thanh, An Nhon, Tuy Phuoc, Phu My and Phu Cat.

From the 10th to 30th September 1969, American aircraft have time after time spread poisonous chemicals and dropped thousands of gas grenades (containing CS) over the communities of Ninh Than and Hiep Ninh in the region of Tay Ninh, which is the Caodai-sect's holy place. The area that was chosen for this chemical attack has a circumference of about 15 square kilometers. At the same time these communities were bombarded with more than 500 artillery grenades, filled with gas. More than one thousand Caodai-sect believers were poisoned. Thirteen children died. . . .

2. Tear gases which are used in very low concentration have a very strong irritating effect on the eyes and air passages. When they are used in a stronger concentration as in an underground shelter against people without protective masks, they are often fatal.

DM, CN and CS are all very strong irritants even at very weak concentrations. They are deadly at stronger concentrations if persons exposed to their effects cannot quickly escape. Adamsite (DM) has been shown to be a lethal gas at a concentration of 3 mg/liter of air with an exposure time in the air of 10 minutes. *USA troops in South Vietnam throw poison gas in powder form (usually with gas grenades) into those shelters which the people have hidden in—by this killing many of them.*

During a "mopping up" operation, which the U.S. troops and puppet troops took part in on the peninsula of Ba Long An (in Quang Ngai province) from the 13th January to the 3rd February they used gas grenades, smoke screen apparatus and gas pumps to drive the poisonous gases into the shelters and underground tunnels.

In the district of Thang Binh (province of Quang Nam) the US troops undertook a "mopping up" operation on 12th February 1969 against the village of Binh Nam and forced ten persons, 64–77 years old and a pregnant woman, down into a shelter and killed them there by throwing gas in powder form into the shelter.

Chemical weapons are now an official method of warfare used by the American troops and puppet troops. All types of forces—air, naval, motorized troops, paratroopers, marine corps, and infantry—are now armed with material which makes it possible for them to use poison gas. Also, the task forces, commando units, the police in the countryside and the militia are armed with the same type of material for chemical warfare. The poison weapons that the U.S. troops and satellite troops use are handgrenades, mortar shells, navy artillery projectiles, the air force's bombs and rockets as well as gas pump (dispensers) machines fixed to a helicopter or carried on the back of a specially trained soldier. The U.S. air force for its part is armed with several newly constructed devices, bombs and spraying apparatus which have the ability of spreading poisonous chemicals and poisonous gases on a very large scale. (172)

The reference to ethylbromacetate has never been confirmed elsewhere. This was the first combat gas used in World War I. It was deployed by the

French by means of rifle-launched grenades in August, 1914. Ethylbrom-acetate is a lachrymator at concentrations as low as 0.003 mg/ml; since a level of 2.3 mg/ml is fatal on ten minutes exposure, it is over twice as toxic as chlorine (173).

American officials have maintained that there have been no *verified* instances of fatalities due to use of CS either at home or in Vietnam. The Edgewood Arsenal report on the toxicology of CS states flatly: "No deaths have been attributed to CS" (174).

A careful analysis of all the available information and evidence from Vietnam leads to this conclusion: It is not known if CS is introduced in tunnels and shelters with the objective of asphyxiating the inhabitants; but if it should have that effect, there is no great concern expressed by the Army. Thus, *Training Circular 3-16* makes no provision for safe exit of civilians from tunnels gassed with CS, and indeed, the thrust of the presentation is in the opposite direction. The *Circular* recommends that vents be blocked up to prevent escape of the gas.

When the agents are used in conjunction with conventional firepower, the purpose is to kill as many of the enemy as possible. At the House CBW hearings in December, 1969, Representative Donald Fraser tried to extract from the Pentagon witness, Rear Admiral William E. Lemos, some specific information on the manner of use of CS in Vietnam. The dialogue went this way:

Mr. Fraser. I would like to get the record straight on this. You have read these reports that riot control agents have been used to flush the enemy out and the B-52's have come along as a follow-on.

Admiral Lemos. I have not read of follow-on B-52's.

Mr. Fraser. Then maybe my impression or information is wrong. I would like to get the record straight. The impression has been given to this subcommittee—I do not remember where it came from—that from time to time these riot control agents are used in effect to increase the casualties on the other side. . . .

Admiral Lemos. I cannot possibly testify that I know of all uses. There are uses delegated to commanders at battalion level. It is just not possible to answer your question in a definitive way. (175)

Thus did CS gas achieve the status of a routine combat weapon with a diversity of applications in Vietnam. As explained by *Training Circular 3-16:* "The uses for these munitions and the techniques for employing them are limited only by the imagination of the user." (See Appendix III.) The circumstances would seem to require an international investigation on the spot in South Vietnam to determine as exactly as possible how many civilians have been killed by gas. The information contained in Chapter 2 in this volume by Alje Vennema, M.D. is the single best documented evidence to date that the "tear gases" have been responsible for a number of civilian deaths. When I met Dr. Vennema in London on November 16, 1969, I attempted to find out if he could identify the particular agents used on his patients.

When handed a canister of CS, he said that it had an odor very reminiscent of that of one of the agents associated with the Vietnamese gas victims.

Credible Calculations

As pointed out by Meselson (176), the amount of all forms of CS gas sent to Vietnam in the past five years—some 13,700,000 pounds (6.25 million kilograms[4])—is sufficient to cover all of South Vietnam with a fairly heavy dose of the agent. Taking the land area of South Vietnam at 166,000 square kilometers and assuming that the 6,250,000 million milligrams of agent were spread uniformly, the resultant density would be 37.6 mg/m^2. This is sufficient to form a layer two meters high over the ground in which the concentration would be about 19 mg/m^3. If one accepts as the lethal exposure figure 25,000 mg-min/m^3, a mortal dose would be acquired by breathing the air for some twenty-one hours. Stated another way, if the total quantity of CS sent to Vietnam were dispersed in a single application over the entire land mass of the country to a height of just above six feet, every single person would receive a lethal dose on breathing the contaminated air for less than a day. This calculation is unrealistic, of course, because the CS has been disseminated over a period of years and even the most durable form, CS2, lasts only a few weeks. On the other hand, the Army study shows that 20 mg/m^3 of CS is sufficient to cause incapacitation in about thirty seconds. This means that people exposed to even low doses of CS can be immobilized and fall prey to conventional arms fire.

Although these computations may to some extent amount only to idle speculation, they do nonetheless illustrate the staggering amounts of CS unleashed in the Vietnam war.

Similar but more realistic calculations can be applied to the use of CS in tunnels and other confined spaces. Suppose one M7 type canister, which contains 115 grams of CS gas, is thrown into a small tunnel 1 m^2 × 10 m. This will give an aerosol concentration of 11,500 mg/m^3, *i.e.,* a period of just over two minutes would result in death of half of the individuals exposed. Such burning-type grenades can be expected to volatilize about 80 per cent of the charge of CS; they will also produce smoke, generate carbon monoxide (itself a deadly respiratory poison), and cause oxygen depletion in the atmosphere. In this situation a mask will not afford a great deal of protection. *Training Circular 3-16* recommends that canisters be thrown into the tunnels at intervals of "2 to 4 minutes." For larger tunnels, say 2m^2 × 100 m, a ten-pound bag of CS1 fed through the hopper of the M106 Mity Mite disperser would give almost exactly the half-kill concentration for one minute's exposure. The M106 can deliver ten pounds of CS1 or CS2 every three or four minutes.

---

[4] The programmed total shown in Table 1-4 is slightly larger than this figure.

Retaliation?

A question that arises from time to time is, "Do the Viet Cong use these agents?"

Although the DRV troops carry Chinese masks and the NLF is said to be equipped with improvised masks in the form of plastic bags, it seems not to be the general policy of these groups to employ gas. This may be the consequence of a political decision and/or the lack of a technical capability of integrating such materials with their other weapons systems. However, there have been sporadic claims that gas has been used by the other side. Thus:

The United States military authorities say enemy troops have occasionally fired mortar shells filled with a CS type gas at American troops. They have also thrown back captured United States gas grenades. (177)

The undocumented assertion by Brown that "Viet Cong/North Vietnamese Army" forces have employed riot control agents has sometimes been cited as evidence that gas is used by both parties (178). Similarly, the Federation of American Scientists stated, without citing a source for their information: ". . . they are using CS against us" (179).

In summary, the routine use by the DRV/NLF is unverified at the present time. In any case there is no disagreement that the chemicals were introduced in 1964, first used by the South Vietnamese forces, and subsequently adopted as a general field weapon by the Americans and Australians. Hence, there is unanimity of opinion that the "first use" must be charged to the latter group and not to the DRV/NLF. It is noteworthy, in this connection, that the Geneva Protocol has generally been interpreted as banning only the initiation of chemical/biological warfare. Thus, most nations have concluded, perhaps incorrectly, that both the manufacture and stockpiling of CBW weapons, as well as the right to "retaliation in kind," were not outlawed by that instrument.

Sources

Table 1-5 lists suppliers of CS munitions and gas-delivery equipment. This must be regarded as an incomplete and minimal compilation because chemical procurement can readily be disguised as "ordnance items." Also, I have not recorded items identified only as "chemicals" but have restricted the selection to CS alone. It should also be noted that contracts of less than $1 million have not been entered in the Defense Industry Bulletin (DIB).

Applegate lists the following suppliers of tear gas munitions: AA1 Corporation, Cockeysville, Maryland, Federal Laboratories, Saltsburg, Pennsylvania, Penguin Industries, Parkesburg, Pennsylvania, Lake Erie Chemical Co., Rock Creek, Ohio, Brunswick Corp., Chicago, Illinois, and Northrop Carolina, Asheville, North Carolina (180).

Fisher, Northrop Carolina, Thiokol, and Federal are also on Hersh's list (181). Federal Laboratories is thought to be the largest supplier of tear gas products in the world (182). Another company believed to be involved

TABLE 1-5

Suppliers of CS Agent, Munitions, and Equipment [a]

Company	Item	Amount	Documentation
Anchor Precision Products, Hackensack, N.J.	M5 dispenser	$211,575	DAAA15–67–C–0408 (GCD) [b]
Buffalo Turbine Agricultural Equipment, Gowanda, N.Y.	M106 dispenser (Mity Mite)	$122,379	DAAA15–67–C–0254 (GCD)
Federal Labs., Inc., Saltsburg, Pa.	M7A3 CS grenade	$531,472	DAAA15–67–0228 (GCD)
	ditto	$1,140,221	DAAA15–69–C–0177 (CBD) [c]
	CS1	$604,800	DAAA15–69–C–0153 (CBD)
Fisher Chemical Co., Englewood Cliffs, N.J.	CS1	$824,019	DAAA15–67–C–0622 (GCD)
	CS	$360,691	DAAA15–67–C–0246 (GCD)
		$87,472	DAAA15–69–C–0555 (CBD)
Liquidonics, Inc., Wesbury, N.J.	Components, M3 dispenser	$136,250	DAAA15–67–C–0513 (GCD)
Northrop Carolina, Inc., Asheville, N.C.	M25A2 CS1 grenade	$2,440,971	DAAA15–67–C–0250 (GCD)
	CS1	$45,389	DAAA15–69–C–0456 (GCD)
Thiokol Chemical Corp., Denville, N.J.	CS1	$38,340	DAAA15–69–C–0150 (CBD)

TABLE 1-5 (continued)

Issue, DIB	Contract date	Company	Item	Amount
1(10), 27, 1965	30-9-65	Fisher Chemical Co., New York, N.Y.	CS1	$1,021,746
3(1), 42, 1967	13-12-66	Northrop Carolina, Inc., Asheville, N.C.	Riot hand grenades	$2,440,971
3(7), 32, 1967	29-6-67	Thiokol Chemical Corp., Brunswick, Ga.	Tear gas (probably a form of CS)	$1,002,000
4(2), 50, 1968	18-12-67	Northrop Carolina, Inc., Asheville, N.C.	CS1	$1,191,000
4(5), 42, 1968	22-3-68	Northrop Carolina, Inc., Asheville, N.C.	CS1	$4,440,800
4(7), 36, 1968	2-5-68	Northrop Carolina, Inc., Swannanoa, N.C.	CS1	$2,214,300
4(8), 40, 1968	20-6-68	Thiokol Chemical Corp., Woodbine, Ga.	CS2	$1,190,016
4(8), 40, 1968	20-6-68	Brunswick Corp., Sugar Grove, Va.	CS2 35 mm cartridges	$1,521,450
4(12), 37, 1968	29-10-68	Thiokol Chemical Corp., Woodbine, Ga.	CS2	$1,868,035
			CS1	$8,437,673
5(3), 49, 1969	24-1-69	Brunswick Corp., Sugar Grove, Va.	CS-filled launchers	$3,529,680
5(3), 49, 1969	24-1-69	Atlantic Research Corp., West Hanover, Mass.	CS-filled launchers	$3,032,778
5(5), 50, 1969	13-3-69	Thiokol Chemical Corp., Woodbine, Ga.	CS2-filled munitions	$1,757,538
5(8), 32, 1969	11-6-69	Thiokol Chemical Corp., Woodbine, Ga.	CS cartridges	$1,898,190

a NARMIC (National Action/Research on the Military Industrial Complex), 160 North 15th Street, Philadelphia, Pa., and *Defense Industry Bulletin* (DIB).

b GCD *(Government Contracts Directory),* Government Data Publications, Inc. 1969.

c CBD *(Commerce Business Daily),* U.S. Department of Commerce.

in the production of riot control material for United States military forces is the General Tire and Rubber Co.

If American industry has difficulty in measuring the Army's chemical needs, its problems are greatly simplified by certain private agencies. Here we can cite the role of the National Security Industrial Association (NSIA). According to its own literature it is a "non-profit, non-political, non-lobbying" organization of over 400 American companies that deal with the Department of Defense, military departments, and other branches of the government. It was conceived in 1944 by the late James Forrestal as a means of perpetuating in peacetime ". . . the mutual respect and cooperation traditionally developed between industry and the Government in time of war." Its stated objective is to provide a means of direct communication between the maker and the user of defense materials. NSIA maintains that Industry (spelled with a capital "I") and government must always be "partners in preparedness" and that every company can make a significant contribution to the effort to protect the United States and its people. NSIA offers to supply further information from its office at 1030 15th Street NW, Washington, D.C. 20005.

The intimate association of the United States military establishment and the weapons industry can be illustrated by reference to a joint conference of the Army Munitions Command and NSIA held in Pasadena, California, on February 14 to 15, 1968. The meeting was billed as a secret advanced planning "briefing," but the printed program was designated as unclassified. I have a copy of that program and herewith recount some of the items of special interest.

The conference was held at the U. S. Army Southwest Procurement Agency, 125 South Grand Avenue, Pasadena. Participants were required to have what was described as "properly processed security clearance." The program states the Army's motivation for the parley:

As one of the largest buyers of defense materials, the U.S. Army Munitions Command welcomes the opportunity to tell about its organizations, needs and methods of operation in an effort to improve the interchange of information between industry and the Command. It is believed that this information in regards to the Munition Command's mission means greater opportunities for industry participation which will result in more effective accomplishment of the national munitions job. It will be mutually advantageous for industry to participate as a bidder or subcontractor in the various munitions programs. You are invited to examine the Munitions Command industrial orientation material and to seriously consider the possibility of doing business with the Command.

The specific aims of this particular conference were:

. . . to keep industry informed on the long range research and development plans for munitions and related items. It is intended to present problems requiring solutions together with technological forecasts and assessments of the state of the technology. The conference is designed specifically for industry executives who are advanced systems planners, directors of research and technology, senior engineers and individuals concerned with the formulation of corporate long range objectives. Individual briefings should provide the basis for future direct dialogue between industry and the government in the field of munitions and related items.

At the Pasadena session the Chemicals and Biologicals were discussed under separate assemblies presided over by Dr. Charles A. Reynolds of Edgewood Arsenal and Colonel P. G. Olenchuk of Fort Detrick, respectively. All speakers were from either Edgewood or Detrick, and the titles of the individual papers, although vague, convey an impression of the subject matter presented. For example, in the Biological section Dr. C. F. Minarik of Fort Detrick spoke about "Improved Defoliants/Herbicides."

The enormous impact of defense spending in local communities can be appreciated by perusal of documents such as *Federal Outlays,* a publication of the Office of Economic Opportunity. Inspection of the edition for California shows that even in a city such as Berkeley, normally not considered a bastion of "Middle America," the Department of Defense spent $15.5 million in fiscal 1969, most of it for prime contracts. Berkeley is a city of only 100,000 inhabitants, and the annual budget is of the order of $20 million (183).

Toxicology of Riot Control Agents

INSIDE THE LIVING CELL

The requirements for an effective riot control agent are, first, that a very small amount must produce a reaction and, second, that there be an enormous discrepancy between the level required to irritate and the level resulting in death. This is the so-called "safety factor," and it cannot be denied that for CS this factor is very large indeed. Thus, if we accept 20 mg-min/m^3 as the incapacitating dose—a figure that is probably twice as large as the actual— and divide this into the estimated lethal inhalation dose of 25,000 mg-min/m^3, we obtain a safety factor of 1,250. The number might easily be double this because CS may reach incapacitation levels at 10 mg-min/m^3. Naturally, in the choice of a riot control agent, these biomedical considerations must be tempered with practical matters such as the ease of preparation and low cost.

Unfortunately, a large safety factor may give an unwarranted implication that short- or long-term toxic reactions cannot be obtained. Proponents of chemical warfare and enterprising chiefs of police have been guilty of gross oversimplification in dismissing the possible toxic effects resulting from exposure to agents such as CN, DM, and CS. On the basis of incomplete studies suggesting that CS is less toxic than CN, CS seems to have been adopted under the assumption that its use presents no hazard whatsoever. It is the purpose of this section to outline some of the recent information that has come to bear on this problem and that debunks the myth that the riot control agents pose no threat to human health. It should be noted that policemen and soldiers who employ the agents and who are hence continually exposed to them may be numerically the most common victims. Furthermore, because firemen are called upon increasingly to control blazes in a riot situation where CS/CN may have been deployed, they too must be regarded as exposed to the occupational hazard of breathing the riot control agents. It has also frequently happened that tear gas weapons have exploded in the hands of individuals, leading to prolonged and sometimes permanent anesthesia of portions of the hands and fingers (184).

Dr. Sumner Kalman, Professor of Pharmacology at Stanford University, is a vigorous advocate of better regulation of riot control agents. He convened a symposium on the pharmacology of these substances at the national meeting of the Federated American Societies for Experimental Biology on April 16, 1970, in Atlantic City. This symposium, which has been published (185), served to bring together the rather diffuse and fragmentary knowledge of the cellular chemistry of the main riot control materials, CN and CS.

Most of the lachrymators and the common blistering agents are alkylating agents, *i.e.,* they tend to attach themselves to atoms such as oxygen, nitrogen, and sulfur. All three of these atoms occur in proteins, and oxygen and nitrogen are found in nucleic acids—both DNA and RNA. Once proteins (enzymes) or nucleic acids become alkylated, they are generally unable to function normally; the ultimate result may vary from a mild irritation to cancer. Thus, alkylating agents have been implicated as the causative agents in carcinogenesis, mutagenesis, and teratogenesis. CS is an effective alkylating agent because the two strongly electron-withdrawing nitrile (CN) groups, reinforced by the chlorobenzene ring, place a positive charge on the bridge carbon atom. The result is a hyperactive bridge carbon that can be attacked directly with nucleophiles such as water or thiol groups. Mustard gas, which was the main war gas stockpiled (but not used) in World War II, is a potent alkylating agent, and in fact this property is used as a color test for the presence of the substance. A significantly increased incidence of cancer in the respiratory tract (mainly the lungs) has been reported in workers who manufactured this munition in World War II (186).

Consequently, as stressed by the consultants to the World Health Organization (187), those chemicals used in war should be evaluated for their possible delayed reaction in human subjects. So far as the riot control agents are concerned, a safety analysis must involve more than a simple measurement of the airborne concentration necessary to kill half of a population of laboratory animals. Such an analysis will involve testing the substances for their capacity to promote cellular and genetic abnormalities.

Information on the cellular toxicity of CS is difficult to find in the scientific literature. I review here the work of Cucinell (188) and the unpublished papers of McWhorter, Moore, and Rhodes. Copies of the latter papers are on file in my office at the Department of Biochemistry, University of California, Berkeley 94720. More data are available on CN, thanks to the work of Penneys and his colleagues (189), but the medical community is still in urgent need for comprehensive information on the long-term effects to be expected from tear gas.

AGENT CN

Although agent CN is being displaced by the faster acting, more irritant, and less toxic CS, it is nonetheless still used to some extent and is of special interest domestically in that it is the active ingredient of Chemical Mace[R]. This product contains 0.9 per cent chloroacetophenone (CN) dissolved in an inert vehicle of halogenated hydrocarbons said to consist of 1,1,2-trichloro-1,2,2-trifluoroethane, 70 to 80 per cent; 1,1,1-trichloroethane, about 5 per cent; kerosene-like hydrocarbons, about 4 per cent (190). Actual analysis for chloroacetophenone indicates that the product run may contain up to 1.2 per cent chloroacetophenone.

Most injuries from Mace[R] can be expected to occur in the eyes. This is because the agent is delivered as a liquid stream and is often fired at close range. The primary effects of Mace[R] on the eyes is lachrymation and photophobia. A substantial literature on serious eye injuries due to Mace[R] exists. It may cause permanent corneal scars (191) and in two cases has, in fact, resulted in total monocular blindness (192). Cases such as these would not normally be expected to occur in the Vietnam war.

In 1969 Penneys *et al.* (193), writing in the prestigious *New England Journal of Medicine,* described several cases of contact dermatitis ascribed to Chemical Mace[R]. Two of the four cases were of the allergic contact variety, and the other two represented inadvertently acquired sensitization to chloroacetophenone. Case No. 1 was a twenty-seven-year-old male who had been admitted to hospital with a subsiding "erythrematous, crusted eruption" on the left side of the face and eye. The dermatitis appeared about three hours after he had been sprayed with Chemical Mace[R] in an incident that took place four days prior to admission. Three weeks before the second exposure, he had been sprayed with the same agent but had not developed a reaction at that time. Case No. 2 was a thirty-year-old policeman who had been exposed to Chemical Mace[R] in the course of his work, the last exposure resulting in an acute "vesicular dermatitis" on the forearm. The two remaining cases, one male and one female, had been exposed under occlusive patch for twenty-four hours. Both displayed a scaly, pruritic eruption at the site of application two weeks following exposure. These cases had been accidentally sensitized during the initial handling of Case No. 1.

All four cases showed positive patch tests to chloroacetophenone at a concentration 1/100 of that found in Chemical Mace[R]. Cases 1 and 3 responded similarly to Chemical Mace[R] diluted 1/100 in acetone but gave no reaction to the Mace vehicle [subsequently identified as 1,1,1-trichloroethane, 1,1,1-trichloro-2,2,2-trifluoroethane, petroleum ethers (194); this is essentially similar to the vehicle described elsewhere (195)]. The fact that five out of eight subjects tested could be shown to have developed contact sensitivity suggested to Penneys *et al* that a high percentage of people will show a sensitization to Chemical Mace[R]. Since a one-second spray from a squirt can of Mace will deliver a maximum of about 25 milligrams of CN, most of which will not reach the target, and since two of the four cases reported resulted from exposure during the evaluation of a Mace[R] victim, the authors conclude that chloroacetophenone is a potent sensitizing agent. In this study, removal of the agent after one minute with soap and water eliminated the reaction; however, a delay in removal beyond one minute resulted in development of a dermatitis that typically occurred forty-eight hours after the exposure.

In a second report Penneys (196) emphasized that those persons whose occupations result in frequent exposures should bear in mind the propensity of chloroacetophenone to sensitize the human subject. The particular contact dermatitis that develops may result in itching, erythema, edema, vesiculation and, in the worst cases, purpura and necrosis. Furthermore, substances chemically related to the initial allergen may also cause reaction in cases of allergic contact dermatitis.

Other reports on CN maintain that it can cause loss of nerve function and lead to inflammation and necrosis of skeletal muscles in situations involving close discharge of gas guns (197). In such cases it may be difficult to evaluate effects due to CN *per se* and those resulting from mechanical injury caused by the cartridge or pen (198). CN has also been implicated as a carcinogenic "promoter" or "co-carcinogen." The tumors observed were benign papillomas of the skin. In these experiments a 1 per cent solution of CN was painted on the skin of mice that had been pre-treated with the known carcinogen 9,10-dimethyl-1,2-benzanthracene (199).

Edgewood Arsenal's report on the toxicology of CN states that deaths associated with inhalation of either this agent or DM reveal as the most important signs rales, rhonchi, dyspnea, chest pains, and shortness of breath. The pathological lesions were listed as edema, congestion, hemorrhage of lungs, pseudomembrane formation, and pneumonia. All the signs and lesions can be related to damage to the air passages and lungs (200).

Penneys' results indicate that decontamination of the skin can be achieved by prompt washing with soap and water (201). In a letter written in 1968 to state and local health officers, Surgeon General William H. Stewart recommended flushing the exposed areas of the body with water as treatment for Mace[R] victims (202). In the event of severe exposure ". . . gentle but copious flushing of the conjunctiva, fluorescein examination, and anti-inflammatory drops may be beneficial," wrote Stewart. He warned against application of salves, creams, or ointments that would tend to concentrate Mace at the site of irritation.

AGENT DM

The toxicology of DM will not be discussed here because it is an agent, if we can believe official proclamations, that is being eliminated from military stores. The onset of symptoms from exposure to DM will appear more slowly and will be more persistent than in the case of either CN or CS. According to Edgewood Arsenal:

DM may have a persistent action not shared by CN or CS. However, the doses required for this action and the safety factor between the systemically effective doses and the lethal doses have not been established. (203)

AGENT CS

Animals dying after exposure to CS show increased counts of goblet cells in the respiratory tract and conjunctiva, necrosis in the respiratory and gastrointestinal tract, pulmonary edema, and hemorrhage in the adrenals. Death results from impaired oxygen transfer to the blood stream as a result of edema, hemorrhage, and obstruction of the air passages in the lungs (204).

In the case of a substance such as CS, attention must be directed to the breakdown products that will be derived from it in the human body. Cleavage or hydrolysis into malononitrile and ortho-chlorobenzaldehyde is a reaction that is 50 per cent complete in about ten minutes. The malononitrile is believed to suffer degradation to cyanide and thiocyanate whereas the remainder of the molecule is combined with glycine and excreted as ortho-chlorohippuric acid (205). Malononitrile is itself highly toxic. The mortal dose for a 150-pound person is estimated to be about a gram or less (206). An item in the December 11, 1967 issue of *Chemical and Engineering News* (p. 64) states:

. . . malononitrile is one of the most toxic chemicals involved in chemical process operations. A 50% solution applied to the skin of rabbits . . . is lethal after 30 minutes.

If CS penetrates to nerve tissue, there is a possibility that it can be attacked by the active nucleophilic oxygen atom at the serine residue of acetylcholine esterase. This enzyme is required to catalyze the hydrolysis of the acetylcholine formed in the nerve transmission process; it is the enzyme that is poisoned by nerve gas. Interestingly, the clinical symptoms of CS poisoning parallel those for intoxication with nerve gas—bronchoconstriction, lachrymation, salivation, difficulty in breathing, and convulsions (207).

Experiments conducted at the Biochemistry Department of the University of California in 1970 indicated CS killed the test bacterium *Salmonella typhimurium,* but there was no evidence for mutagenesis. The experiments were repeated with bacteriophage, which is more permeable to organic molecules than bacteria. Using the mutagenic analysis of Benzer (208) with Phage T4r11, no evidence for strong mutagenic effects could be detected by Gregory Rhodes.

In contrast with these (thus far) negative results of the reaction of CS with nucleic acid, the combination of the reagent with thiol groups is a certainty (209). Glutathione, cysteine, and dihydrolipoic acid will all react rapidly with CS. Some years ago I found that lactic dehydrogenase, an enzyme required for energy metabolism, contains essential thiol groups (210). Cucinell (211) showed that both CN and CS poisoned the enzyme; addition of excess glutathione partially relieved the inhibition caused by CS but not that caused by CN. Mackworth (212) tested a series of lachrymators (but not CS, however) on several enzymes and found that their thiol groups reacted better than did simple thiols such as cysteine. Thus, there is sufficient evidence to show that the riot control agents, and specifically CS, combine with proteins *in vivo*. The antigenicity and toxicity of these derived proteins is a matter of some interest, but nothing is yet known in this area.

The claim of the Johnson administration that the riot control agents in use in Vietnam are readily available from commercial sources is negated by my own experience. I have been unable to obtain samples of CS from any source, including the campus police department at the University of California at Berkeley. Although the pure chemicals CN, CS, and DM can be obtained from laboratory supply houses, the point here is to analyze the commercial riot control preparations. Such formulations are usually of technical grade and may be no more than 80 or 90 per cent pure.

Similarly, Secretary Robert Finch of the Department of Health Education and Welfare took four and one half months to reply to the following letter from the Scientists' Committee on Chemical and Biological Warfare:

The Scientists' Committee on Chemical and Biological Warfare is seeking information on toxic effects of the agent CS (*o*-chlorobenzalmalononitrile). This riot control agent is used commonly by police departments in the United States and we assume, therefore, that such accounts would be on record in your office.

We are aware of a United States Army report which attributes second degree burns as a result of exposure to thermally generated CS aerosols, but we have no information on the internal effects of CS. Also, we are most anxious to acquire knowledge of the long term toxicity of CS, and its metabolic products, in the human organism. (213)

The response, dated September 8, 1970, acknowledged that:

We are not aware of studies that have exposed animals to these chemicals for long terms (sizeable fractions of a lifetime) at either low or high levels. (214)

The lack of concern by the Department of Health Education and Welfare notwithstanding, there is now abundant presumptive evidence for the indictment of CS as a hazardous material that should be regarded and handled as a drug rather than a weapon. We know that industrial exposure to CS produces dermatitis in workers engaged in the processing of the agent. Thus Weigand remarked:

... a single exposure resulting in significant inflammation is sufficient to sensitize in some cases, and very slight exposures thereafter can elicit the eczematous reaction ... apparently the most hazardous agent processing activities are powder-pressing for grenades, micropulverization and operation of drying ovens. (215)

Reference to Table 1-5, which gives production sites, will show where the American victims of chronic exposure to CS might be expected to be.

Chemical Weapons at Home

VIETNAM FALLOUT

Since the spring of 1967, chemical weapons have made their appearance with increasing frequency in domestic riots, campus demonstrations, and civil disturbances, and the agent used has, as in Vietnam, narrowed to CS. The promotion of chemicals for these uses seems to have been a policy developed during the Johnson administration, and, as we shall see, it has been used to bolster the chemical warfare program in Vietnam. There is, for example, abundant evidence that the Pentagon took the initiative in explaining the benefits of riot control agents to civil law enforcement officials. As George Bunn noted:

Things like tear gas, the CS that is being used in Vietnam, have a tendency to find their way into domestic use. The Army sees to it that police departments are aware of these refinements. In Madison the police were given tear gas of a somewhat refined kind by the Army at no extra cost. (216)

In August, 1968, the United States Attorney General is believed to have circulated a letter to all major law enforcement agencies in which he recommended nonlethal chemical agents as the safest, most effective, and most humane means of mob control. It was noted also that the chemicals would reduce injury, minimize the chance of death, and prevent property loss (217). The history and some legal problems associated with the escalating use of the riot control agents in domestic life have been reviewed elsewhere in detail (218), so it is necessary here to report only two outstanding incidents where gas was misused, one in Berkeley, California, and one in Londonderry, Northern Ireland.

BERKELEY PEOPLE'S PARK

The police and National Guard riots that took place in Berkeley in May, 1969, have been rightly called a stampede of violence and brutality (219). They illustrated the extent to which chemicals could be used to effect political control by force and violence. They demonstrated that law enforcement officials are prepared to shoot and kill white demonstrators, and they were thus a precursor by one year of the murder of four white students at Kent State University in Ohio. Such executions have long been familiar to the black community and they are now the particular experience of the Black Panther Party.

The methods devised for application of tear gas in Vietnam—the canister, the portable blower, and the helicopter—were all used in Berkeley. Thus, the People's Park incident was a graphic demonstration of "Vietnam come home" or, as Martin Luther King once said, "The bombs that fall in Vietnam explode at home."

The Regents of the University of California in the middle 1950s had used (in part) funds derived from student sources to acquire a block of property on the south side of the campus. Their purpose was to demolish the old brown-shingle dwellings and erect a high-rise student dormitory. Shortly after the Regents purchased the property, the private owners began to move out, and the large houses were converted to student flats and rooms. Soon the area was designated as "high crime" by the Berkeley city administration, the city fathers defining "crime" in this case as cohabitation and marijuana smoking. The university was asked to accelerate the schedule for construction of the dormitory. The area was cleared of dwellings in 1968, but because of budget limitations the lot lay fallow over the entire winter. It was used as an unofficial parking lot and, lacking a surface, it soon became a mud hole.

In April, 1969, the underground press in Berkeley announced that a "people's park" would be built on the site. It was to be "a place to sleep and think in the sun" and "a cultural, political freak-out and rap center for the western world." Within a few weeks a very impressive park was created entirely by donations and volunteer labor. The governor of the state, Ronald Reagan, viewed this as usurpation of private property.

Before daybreak on May 15, "Bloody Thursday," a posse of about 300 police ousted a small group of vigilers from People's Park. A work crew hired by the university threw up an eight-foot wire fence around the perimeter of the property. The plants and the sod, which had been purchased by street collection, began to wither in the hot, California sun. A rally was held at noon that day on the steps of Sproul Plaza and 3,000 students set off in a peaceful march toward the Park. En route a confrontation developed with the police who brought gas, birdshot, buckshot, and bullets into the fray. James Rector was killed with a blast of "double O" buckshot through the heart and another bystander was blinded by bird shot.

GRENADE, HAND, RIOT, CS
DOT SPECIAL PERMIT
3240 APPLIES

FED. SPEC. PPP·B·621b
J. H. DUNNING CORP.
DARIEN, CONN.
FOR OVERSEAS USE
MAXIMUM WT. OF CONTENTS 60 LBS.
TYPE 1 LOAD

Figure 1—4. Boards from a crate of tear gas made for use in Vietnam but used domestically. Berkeley Campus, May 20, 1969. Photo by James Yudelson.

The campus and surrounding community were occupied for the next several weeks by 2,000 National Guardsmen and by local police, highway patrol officers, and police from adjacent cities. The campus was kept under constant surveillance by a helicopter. Gas was used to disperse even small crowds, and on May 20 an Army helicopter sprayed tear gas down through the center of the campus. Canisters of tear gas were thrown into classrooms and into the men's gym. Since the authorities seemed reluctant to use gas in the business district, student leaders led a protest march into downtown Berkeley. The result of this new tactic was that 482 people were arrested and transported to the Alameda County Prison Farm at Santa Rita, where they were required to lie face down on the pavement for five hours. The brutal treatment of the prisoners was the subject of an investigation, and in the end some reprimands were dispensed. As an excuse for the behavior of the guards, one official offered the opinion that many of his men were Vietnam veterans and they tended to regard demonstrators as "Viet Cong." Cecil Poole, a black United States District Attorney in San Francisco, attempted to indict some of the police officers. He was denied a judgeship and was eased out of office by the Nixon administration.

I have been informed by B. R. Baker, Chief of Police in Berkeley, that ". . . no specific report has been prepared covering the use of tear gas" in

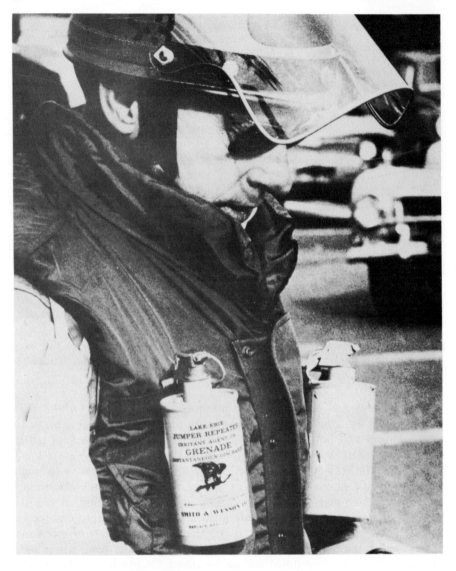

Figure 1–5. The tear-gas grenade is an increasingly popular weapon in the modern law-enforcement officer's armamentarium. Berkeley Campus, May 20, 1969. Photo by James Yudelson.

the People's Park incident (220). He did confirm that the gas was mainly CS and some CN, but cautioned that "several agencies" were involved in the episode. One newspaper report stated that a can of "U.S. No. 6 Blister Gas" had been found on the campus, but this has not been verified (221).

Figure 1–6. The rifle-launched grenade is superior to the hand-thrown canister because it can be carefully aimed, it travels a great distance, and it strikes its target with considerable force. Berkeley Campus, May 20, 1969. Photo by James Yudelson.

The Instant News Service brought out a special issue titled "Chemical Warfare in Berkeley" and charged therein that five different types of riot control agents had been deployed in Berkeley in the preceding five months. These were stated to be CS, CN, "nausea gas," blister gas, and Mace[R]. Apart from this single report, there is no additional evidence that DM or any type of mustard gas has been employed in Berkeley at any time in the recent past.

The U-19 Army helicopter used on May 20, 1969, is believed to have dispersed a fifty-pound charge of CS1, plus some smoke added for psychological effects (222). The Army series M7 burning-type canisters of CS and a civilian analogue supplied by the Lake Erie Chemical Company were used in very large numbers. The exploding-type hand grenades were also used.

Chief Baker reported that two types of portable dispensers, one of which was auto-mounted, were employed. The hand-carried "pepper-fog machine" was used for dissemination of bulk quantities of CS. The General Ordnance Equipment Pepper-Fog[R] tear gas–smoke generator can be operated for ten

Figure 1–7. An Army helicopter, operated by the National Guard, sprays CS-1 over the Berkeley Campus of the University of California on May 20, 1969 Photo by James Yudelson.

minutes with one loading and is the device used for laying down a barrage of agent over a wide area. The gas is vaporized in this machine as a liquid aerosol. An advertisement for the apparatus in the October, 1969, issue of *Police Chief* claims that it:

... Leaves virtually no residual contamination, because chemical agents are so thoroughly vaporized. ... The weapon-like appearance and low, threatening roar of the pepper-fog tear-smoke generator alone have great psychological impact.

The hasty decision to apply CS by means of an airborne attack seems to have been a case of overkill on the part of authorities. The Grand Jury report on the People's Park incident singled out the helicopter for special condemnation and recommended that this means of dissemination not be employed in highly populated areas. Apart from this cursory report by a Grand Jury, the People's Park incident was never followed by a special investigation such as that carried out by the Himsworth Committee, which was appointed by the British Government to examine the hazards associated with the massive use of gas in the Bogside, Northern Ireland. This is to be regretted because there were many rumors of illness in babies, attacks which affected school yards, and the like, which should have been probed by some officially appointed body. In this situation the police and military authorities arrogated to themselves the right and the responsibility for the use of potentially dangerous chemical substances.

LONDONDERRY

From August 12 to 14, 1969, in a continuous period of about thirty-six hours, the Royal Ulster Constabulary of Northern Ireland discharged some 1,019 cartridges and fourteen grenades in an attempt to control civil disturbances in Londonderry. People living in the area were exposed to a heavy concentration of CS throughout this entire period (223). Gas was again used in Ulster in early April, 1970, and subsequently in the summer of that year (224). Consequently, the area has achieved the status of a kind of testing ground for CS.

As a result of the first incident, a governmental committee was appointed under the leadership of a former secretary of the Medical Research Council, Sir Harold Himsworth, to look into all aspects of the affair. The report of the committee was scheduled to be submitted by the end of 1970 (225). In the meantime, the massive use of CS in Ulster has touched off a lively debate, especially in scientific circles, and has likely had international repercussions so far as the relation of tear gas to the Geneva Protocol is concerned.

Pending the appearance of the Himsworth report, a substantial amount of information on the use of CS in Ulster is available from the work of Stetler and the Roses (226). Scientific journals such as *Nature* and *Science* have also reported on the case (227), and a book has been written on the subject (228).

The preliminary findings appear to be that CS may cause gastrointestinal upsets in infants (229) and may magnify the breathing difficulties of people suffering from asthma or bronchitis. The aged and the infirm may be similarly specially afflicted. In other words, those segments of the population least likely to be engaged in rioting were the principal victims. Most of the information thus far published on the Ulster case has been gathered by the British Society for Social Responsibility in Science, which sent a team of investigators to Londonderry, and which later, on November 15, 1969, held a conference on CS in London (230). The general patterns of use in Ulster and Berkeley have much in common, *i.e.*, CS was employed indiscriminately and in massive overdose.

The British government's preoccupation with civil control in Ulster has not been without influence on Britain's stance toward the relation of tear gases to the Geneva Protocol. Hugh Dalton, an Under Secretary in the Foreign Office, had ruled in 1930 that "tear gases" were forbidden under the terms of the Protocol (231). However, in the December, 1969, consideration of the issue at the United Nations, Britain abstained from voting (232). Finally, on February 3, 1970, the British barriers collapsed completely. On that day the Foreign Secretary, Michael Stewart, advised the House of Commons by means of a written statement that

... modern technology has developed CS smoke which, unlike the tear gas available in 1930, is considered to be not significantly harmful to man in other than wholly exceptional circumstances.... We regard CS and other such gases accordingly as being outside the scope of the Geneva Protocol. CS is in fact less toxic than the screening smokes which the 1930 statement specifically excluded. (233)

The reversal of British policy was considered remarkable in view of the fact that it came prior to the official, scientific opinion of the Himsworth committee, which was still sitting. The decision was doubtless politically motivated in view of the circumstances facing the British in Ulster, which in some respects are not unlike those facing the Americans in Vietnam.

CIVIL LIBERTIES AND PUBLIC HEALTH

Because chemicals are widely employed for the control of insects and weeds, it is perhaps not surprising that chemicals should also be called upon to alleviate the pain and discomfort of political dissent. This seems to be the developing trend, as exemplified by the Berkeley and Ulster cases just described. That the civil liberties of the people have been abridged cannot be denied; that the people may have also been exposed unnecessarily to noxious environmental contaminants is not yet so well recognized.

In 1968, prior to the political emergency in Ulster, CS munitions were stated to be used ". . . only to deal with armed criminals or violently insane persons in buildings from which they cannot be dislodged without danger of loss of life, or as a means of self-defense in a desperate situation, and that in no circumstances should they be used to assist in control of disturbances" (234).

In the United States the absence of effective controls on the use of riot agents is deplorable. Levine and Stahl (235), in their study of eye injury caused by tear gas weapons, made the point that outside of New York, Illinois, and California, few regulations govern the sale of such items and devices.

Their review of thirteen cases on file in the Armed Forces Institute of Pathology revealed that fourteen enucleations (eyeball removal) had been performed as a result of tear gas injury. Pathological symptoms may develop years after the incident. One enucleation was performed fifteen years after an initial accident which, like most of the cases, involved the direct discharge of a tear gas gun in the face. The authors conclude: ". . . the public and legal authorities regard exposure to tear gas only in terms of its transient effects . . ." and ". . . because of its indiscriminate and widespread distribution among civilians, it is likely that injuries of the eye from tear gas weapons will be more frequently encountered in the future. . . ."

In an article on lachrymators written in 1935, two chemists at Vanderbilt University summed up the prevailing attitude toward tear gas:

The chemical agents introduced during the World War proved very effective, as shown by the reports of the War Departments of the countries involved and the increased number of gas shells fired during the latter part of the war. Despite these facts, there is still an unholy fear of such agents on the part of the average citizen, owing to the mass of war propaganda against the use of gas and the lack of accurate information concerning same. Men fear the unknown; it is easier for them to maintain morale in the face of bullets, naked bayonets, and the sword's edge than in the presence of invisible gas; likewise a mob has less fear of the fire hose, night clubs, and bullets than of gas. There is always the uncertainty in their minds as to the effects of the gas, and more especially if there be a little smoke mixed with it, for they know not what may be behind it. The only real danger of serious injury from using non-toxic tear gas is from the possibility that members of the crowd may be trampled upon in attempts to escape. (236)

In its September, 1969, issue the *Newsletter* of the Society for Social Responsibility in Science noted that Mace[R] could be ordered through the mails from the KHR Corporation of Del Mar, Delaware and that the chemical is stocked by more than 3,000 local and state law enforcement agencies (237). Although CS is usually either thermally generated as a liquid aerosol or disseminated as a dust by an explosive charge, one product, Paralyzer[R], contains the agent in a spray can. The composition is 1 to 2 per cent CS, 7 per cent dichloromethane, 19 per cent mineral oil, and 73 per cent propellant 11 (a Freon) (238).

The chemical weapons made available to police do not require approval under the Federal Hazardous Substances Labeling Act, although tear gas pencils may be covered by the Act (239). Such materials are not under the jurisdiction of the Food and Drug Administration, and a spokesman for that agency explained the reason for this was that the riot control agents were designed to have ". . . a deleterious effect . . . not shown to be 'safe and efficacious'" (240). As demonstrators lose their fear of CS, more potent and noxious preparations will be called into play, and the existing situation will be exacerbated. Applegate is quoted as saying: "American manufacturing and inventive genius is developing many other devices and weapons that will aid law enforcement personnel to make it . . . collectively and individually . . . uncomfortable and unprofitable to riot" (241). At the same time, however, the police are almost totally unprepared to handle safely those chemical weapons that are already a part of their chemical arsenals. A survey by the International Association of Chiefs of Police disclosed that although about 80 per cent of all law enforcement agencies in the United States stock chemical spray cans, only a third of the departments furnish written instructions on the use of the weapons; and in most cases such directions deal only with the mechanical details of operation (242).

No fatalities have yet been ascribed to police use of CS, but a credible calculation can be performed to illustrate the potential risk from discharge of a single grenade in a room nine feet by twelve feet by fifteen feet. This is $2.73 \times 3.64 \times 4.54$ or 45.2 m^3. Since one M7 type grenade contains 115,000 milligrams CS, the airborne density will be $115,000/45.2$ or about 2500 mg/m^3. Using the estimated lethal formula for CS as $25,000\text{-min/m}^3$, a ten-minute exposure at 2500 mg/m^3 would furnish a mortal dose. If the nebulization of the CS were only 80 per cent efficient, the exposure time would have to be extended to about twelve minutes; on the other hand, the smoke and O_2 depletion would augment the toxicity and lethal potential of the CS.

Clearly, Federal legislation is in order to set reasonable safeguards and to fix responsibility for compliance with standards that will not victimize policemen, soldiers of the National Guard, and citizens—all of whom may be forced to come into contact with hazardous riot control agents. Such legislation may be difficult to obtain in view of the Pentagon's vested interest in promoting the chemicals. A spokesman for the Department of Defense was alleged to have said: ". . . by using gas in civil situations we accomplish two purposes: controlling crowds and also educating people on gas. . . . We . . . control the public outcry against chemicals that has hindered its usage in wartime" (243).

One desires an ultimate return to a democracy that could function without resort to chemicals and other prostheses. Chemicals in the hands of police can turn into weapons of sadistic suppression. We have seen time after time that they have been improperly and even indolently used. Unlike a billy club, chemicals are impersonal and indiscriminate, and they thus tend to victimize the general public. I have never heard of their being used to save lives; in fact, the hazard to life has generally been that a "peace officer" will shoot someone. Also, the riot control agents have dubious use in preserving property but instead may contaminate it for weeks. They tend to infuriate crowds and may be counterproductive so far as preservation of property is concerned. Cynical politicians can stimulate riots by deployment of tear gas, call in the forces of repression, and then bask in the approval of a public that was never informed of the issues of the confrontation in the first place.

Legal Status

GROTIUS TO RUSSELL

George Bunn, formerly General Counsel to the Arms Control and Disarmament Agency, has prepared a detailed history of official United States attitude toward poison gas and germ warfare. The reader is referred to Bunns' papers for background information on the decision to employ chemicals in Vietnam (244).

The legal basis for American political and military intervention in Vietnam has been argued elsewhere pro and con (245). The political aspects are intimately linked to the types of weapons used because elusive enemies, whether at home or abroad, are best attacked by agents that will assault the whole population.

There is a monumental confusion in the United States on the question of prohibited weapons, it being generally assumed that "Might is Right." Thus, since the United States is backed up by the technology to "zap those commie gooks and slants," it seems taken for granted that we have also a moral and legal right to do so. Such an attitude displays a regrettable ignorance of the laws and customs of war. The concept that belligerents should not have unlimited means of destruction, even in full-scale war between nations, dates to the sixteenth and seventeenth centuries and is explicitly stated in the writings of Grotius, a father of international law (246). A Red Cross convention in 1864 established rules for treatment of the sick and wounded. Four years later, in 1868, a conference was convened at the initiative of the Tsar of Russia. This parley resulted in the Declaration of St. Petersburg, a call to ban types of bullets causing unnecessary suffering. At the turn of the century the Hague Conventions codified in some detail the laws of war (247). Of special interest is Convention IV, Annex, October 18, 1907, to which the United States is a party. Article 23 of the Convention states that it is "especially forbidden" to employ "poison or poisoned weapons" or to employ arms, projectiles, or "material calculated to cause unnecessary suffering." An earlier Hague Convention, in 1899, had sought to ban the use of projectiles the sole objective of which was the diffusion of asphyxiating or deleterious gases (248). The United States was the only one of the twenty-eight participants to fail to agree to the prohibition. As it turned out, the treaty had little impact on the introduction of chemicals in World War I because the French did not regard tear gas as "asphyxiating or deleterious," and the Germans, in retaliating with chlorine, released the gas from cylinders and thus circumvented the restriction on projectiles. Later, use of gas-filled munitions was defended on the basis that such shells and projectiles also disseminated bomb fragments. Thus, the 1899 Hague Convention was proven to be too vague for practical inhibition and restraint of chemical warfare.

At the end of World War I the peace treaty with Germany executed at

Versailles in 1919 provided that: "The use of asphyxiating, poisonous, or other gases and of all analogous liquids, materials or devices being prohibited, their manufacture and importation are strictly forbidden in Germany." This treaty, although again not signed by the United States, is considered to be an important precursor of the Geneva Protocol. At a 1922 meeting in Washington on sea warfare and the use of noxious gases, the restriction outlined in the Versailles Treaty was once more proposed, but this time the ban would apply to all civilized nations. The Washington Arms Conference adopted the phraseology:

The use in war of asphyxiating, poisonous or other gases, and all analogous liquids, materials or devices, having been justly condemned by the general opinion of the civilized world and a prohibition of such use having been declared in treaties to which a majority of the civilized Powers are parties, the Signatory Powers . . . agree to be bound thereby and invite all other civilized nations to adhere thereto.

The Washington Treaty received unanimous consent in the United States Senate, but it was not put into effect because of a French objection relating to submarines.

The language of the Geneva (Gas) Protocol of 1925 borrowed heavily from that of the Washington Conference. (See Appendix I.) At the suggestion of Poland, a prohibition was added on bacteriological weapons. Ironically, the Geneva Protocol was promoted vigorously by the United States. It was embraced generally by the world community of nations but was never ratified by the United States. The concerted opposition of veterans' groups, the chemical industry, and the American Chemical Society was brought to bear on the Senate with the result that ratification has been delayed to this day (249). After 1925 the sentiment to de-legalize war remained strong, and in August, 1928, the Paris or Kellogg-Briand Pact was adopted. This instrument outlawed resort to war as a legitimate means of settling international disputes: "The High Contracting Parties solemnly declare in the names of the respective peoples that they condemn recourse to war for the solution of international controversies and renounce it as an instrument of national policy in their relations with one another." The Kellogg-Briand Pact was duly ratified by the United States and bears the signature of President Herbert Hoover. The pact figured prominently in the prosecution of the Axis powers at Nuremberg and was a forerunner of the provision in the Charter of the United Nations that calls on all members to ". . . refrain in their international relations from the threat or use of force against the territorial integrity or political independence of any state or in any other manner inconsistent with the purpose of the United Nations."

At the end of the 1920s there was a consensus that nothing further could be achieved by means of international legislation to stigmatize and prohibit use of certain weapons of war or even the use of war itself. However, the activities of the Axis powers in World War II were considered so monstrous as to require reevaluation of the laws of war existing at that time. A prime contribution of the Nuremberg Judgment was the establishment of individual responsibility for illegal acts committed in wartime. Although a complete discussion of the Nuremberg Tribunal is outside the scope of this review, it is pertinent to note that it referred to ". . . murder, ill treatment or deportation . . . of civilian populations." As pointed out by Chesneaux, the International War Tribunal for the Far East, better known as the Tokyo Tribunal, has direct relevance to Vietnam (250). The military activities are in each case sited in the same geographical area and in the same social milieu. Furthermore, the Tokyo Tribunal was almost exclusively the creature of the United States government and as such it provides valuable insights into American theories of war crimes. Annex D of the indictment listed fourteen crimes against humanity, of which item nine dealt with "Use of Poisonous Products Against the Civilian Population." Interestingly, the conviction of General Yamashita by the Tokyo Tribunal was upheld by the United States Supreme Court. Tomoyuki Yamashita had been held responsible for war crimes committed by soldiers under his command although it was shown at his trial that he had no knowledge of the atrocities (251).

After World War II the only significant legal document on crimes against humanity was the Genocide Convention, which has been adopted by the General Assembly of the United Nations. The following are the articles that apply to Vietnam:

Article I
    The contracting parties confirm that genocide, whether committed in time of peace or in time of war, is a crime under international law which they undertake to prevent and punish.

Article II
    In the present convention, genocide means any of the following acts committed with intent to destroy, in whole or in part, a national ethnical, racial or religious group, as such:
    (a) Killing members of the group
    (b) Causing serious bodily or mental harm to members of the group
    (c) Deliberately inflicting on the group conditions of life calculated to bring about its physical destruction in whole or in part
    (d) Imposing measures intended to prevent birth within the group

Article III
    [enumerates the punishable acts]

Article IV
    Persons committing genocide or any of the other acts enumerated in Article III shall be punished, whether they are constitutionally responsible rulers, public officials or private individuals.

This statute has been invoked by the Black Panther Party in a petition for an international investigation of the treatment of minorities within the United States (252).

In reiterating its opposition to ratification of the Genocide Convention, the American Bar Association gave the opinion that the agreement would enable other nations to place the United States before an "alien" court on charges arising from the military activities in Vietnam and racial discrimination at home. As in the case of the Geneva Protocol, the United Nations Convention on Genocide was proposed and promoted by the United States. It has acquired the support of seventy-five nations, including all the major powers with the exception of the United States (253).

To what extent are citizens and soldiers of the United States bound by these agreements?

The United States Constitution in Article VI, CI. 2 declares:

This Constitution, and the Laws of the United States which shall be made in persuance thereof; and all treaties made, or which shall be made, under the authority of the United States, shall be the supreme law of the land; and the judges in every state shall be bound thereby, anything in the constitution or laws of any state to the contrary notwithstanding.

International law has been held to be part of the body of United States law, and Federal courts have ruled that it must be similarly administered. The Department of the Army, in its *Field Manual 27-10,* dated July 18, 1956 (reprinted in 1963) and titled "The Law of Land Warfare," has recognized the responsibilities of military personnel:

Any person, whether a member of the Armed Forces or a civilian, who commits an act which constitutes a crime under international law is responsible therefor and liable to punishment. Such offenses in connection with war comprise: (a) Crimes against peace, (b) Crimes against humanity, and (c) War crimes.

Alarmed by what he had read of the character and mechanisms of United States military operations in Vietnam, the illustrious British philosopher and mathematician, Bertrand Russell, set aside plans for retirement and in 1966 issued a call for the establishment of an International War Crimes Tribunal to be composed of private citizens. The full account of the creation, aims, and objectives of the Russell Tribunal can be found in the proceedings of its Stockholm and Copenhagen sessions held in 1967 (254).

The Russell Tribunal has been badly misrepresented in the West. It was universally referred to in quotation marks, labeled "so-called," and, in the most generous presentation, said to have "no official status." So deeply implanted was the idea of extra-constitutionality associated with the Tribunal that the appellation "so-called" even appeared in Russell's obituary in *Science* magazine (255). The Russell Tribunal, however, presented the first organized body of information on technical aspects of the war, such as herbicides, gas, steel pellet bombs, napalm, and the like, and it is hence related to the present discussion. Complaints against the Tribunal were directed both at its findings and especially against its "illegitimacy" and "one-sidedness."

In defense of the Tribunal, which was organized in large measure by his enterprising young American associate, Ralph Schoenman, Russell pointed out that the group was chosen on the basis of intellectual integrity and that it represented, in effect, the conscience of humanity.

A consistent theme in the press comments on the Tribunal were the personal assaults on Russell. Here is a random selection to illustrate the point:

The Tragedy of Bertrand Russell . . . the intellectual captive of a mysterious young American who wants to put LBJ on trial for murder. (256)

Read Look's eyebrow lifter about Bertrand Russell, another alleged man of peace, and see how big men become puppets. (257)

. . . an old man in a hurry, who has left judgement, his reputation and his usefulness behind. (258)

If a medieval Moorish king died on the eve of battle, retainers would dress his stiffened corpse, bind it astride a warhorse and lead it against the enemy to encourage the troops. . . . now we find the relic of Bertrand Russell, this century's most distinguished philosopher, led into battle as a totem from the extreme left. (259)

These vicious attacks, the last cited from the pen of a columnist for the nation's most prestigious newspaper, tell us more about the ability of American media to misinform the public than about the infractions of international law committed in Vietnam. The charges made at the Stockholm session of Russell's Tribunal were confirmed through the passage of time; why the facts were not revealed earlier has also become apparent. For example, the burden of the Stockholm session was that civilians and civilian institutions in the DRV were being bombed with weapons designed specifically for the purpose. It was not until late 1968, a year and a half after the Tribunal session, that a major story appeared in the American press on the actual nature of the targets (260). The background of the story is worth recounting here because it shows dramatically the time gap the media allowed before bringing the facts to the public.

Japan's star reporter, Minoru Omori, had visited the DRV in the fall of 1965. He described on the front pages of *Mainichi* the bombing of a leper colony and the destruction of churches, temples, and houses. The American Embassy in Tokyo called the charges "utterly false," and pressure from the State Department caused Omori to be dismissed from his job. The Japanese press, which had just been praised by the American Ambassador for its integrity, was suddenly castigated for "bias," "non-professionalism," "poor quality," and "emotional" and "slanted" reporting. However, a news report in 1968 cited an interview with the United States information "czar" who was in Saigon at the time of Omori's visit in the North. As he chain-smoked cigarettes, he confessed that the United States had been less than truthful with reporters, and he expressed the wish that ". . . we in Saigon had made it clearer than our air strikes in North Vietnam were not antiseptic" (261).

The Russell Tribunal had an eventual impact in the United States in that it established a climate for consideration of war crimes in Vietnam, now officially recognized by the appointment of an investigating commission under General Peers. Unfortunately, this may be only a device to contain the crimes to "isolated incidents" and to hold knowledge of them to a low level. The thrust of the Russell Tribunal has always been that the crimes have been on a scale that elevates them to the status of policy. In a legal memorandum published in the January, 1970 issue of *Trans-Action*, Professor Richard A. Falk of Princeton University has proposed that responsibility for United States action in Vietnam should not be limited to the individual servicemen involved.

On the constructive side, we see as successors to Russell's Tribunal the Stockholm Conference on Vietnam, organized by Bertil Svahnstrom, which held its fifth session in Stockholm on March 28 to 30, 1970. This most recent conference resulted in the formation of an international commission of inquiry on United States war crimes. Among the members of the commission are Dorothy Crowfoot Hodgkin, Gunnar Myrdal, Krishna Menon, and Pastor Martin Niemöller. In the United States two similar commissions have been created. One is the National Committee for a Citizen's Commission of Inquiry on U.S. War Crimes in Vietnam; it has offices at 156 Fifth Avenue, Room 1005, New York, New York 10010. The other is the Education-Action Conference on U.S. Crimes of War in Vietnam, 475 Riverside Drive, New York, New York 10027. In a detailed article in the *California Law Review*, D'Amato *et al.* conclude that "in service" personnel, and possibly draft resisters, raising a "Nuremberg defense" have standing for legal action and that they raise questions that are both "ripe and justiciable" (262). The authors surveyed all aspects of the war and drew heavily on the findings of the Russell Tribunal.

In view of the dismal record of respect for international law compiled by nations in general and by the United States in particular in Vietnam, what practical restraints can be expected from agreements such as the Geneva Protocol?

GENEVA PROTOCOL REVISITED

In spite of the failure of two major industrialized powers, Japan and the United States, to ratify the Geneva Protocol, the treaty has been remarkably successful in limiting the use of chemical and biological weapons.[5] With one exception (Korea), nations are agreed that biological agents have never been deployed in warfare (the United Nations has stated that there have been no verified uses) (263). Prior to Vietnam, chemicals were used only by the Italians in 1935 to 1936 in Ethiopia, and possibly by the Japanese in

---

[5] Japan became a party to the Protocol on May 21, 1970.

China and the United Arab Republic in Yemen. As McCarthy has written, the Geneva Protocol has been a vivid example of "humanity by agreement: arms limitations that work. . . ." (264).

The Protocol was fully respected by the belligerents throughout World War II, and all requests by the military for chemical munitions were similarly rejected during the Korean engagement (265). This nonuse was not for lack of stockpiles or for want of the technical ability to engage in this type of warfare. The explanation must therefore be found in the general taboo on chemicals engendered by the Protocol.[6] The first attribute of the Protocol is its broad and general prohibitions. As Schelling has stated: ". . . there is a simplicity to 'no gas' that makes it uniquely a focus for agreement when each side can only conjecture at what alternative rules the other side would propose" (266).

In a classical treatise on international law cited by D'Amato et al. it has been pointed out that "the dangers of recognizing any categories of permitted gases and thus sanctioning the manufacture of the necessary equipment for using them are obvious and great, so that, it is submitted, the society of States has adopted the right policy in endeavouring to extirpate this mode of warfare in toto" (267). It is a fact that the principles embodied in the Protocol have found near unanimous acceptance in the world community of nations. All members of the Warsaw Pact and all members of NATO, save the United States, are signatories. Emerging nations have subscribed as a matter of course so that ninety-eight nations currently have agreed, with certain reservations, to its terms. (See Appendix I.)

As an international legal document the Protocol has evidently long since achieved the status of a customary law binding on signatory and nonsignatory nations alike. Even the United States, although not a member, has often pledged respect for the principles of the Protocol. Indeed, the first statement of support to the Senate in 1926 came in a letter from General John J. Pershing to Senator Borah of the Foreign Relations Committee:

I cannot think it possible that our country should fail to ratify the Protocol which includes this or a similar provision. Scientific research may discover gas so deadly that it will produce instant death. To sanction the use of gas in any form would be to open the way for the use of the most deadly gases and the possible poisoning of whole populations of non-combatant men, women and children. The contemplation of such a result is shocking to the senses. It is unthinkable that civilization should deliberately decide upon such a course. (269)

President Franklin Roosevelt in 1937 declared: "It has been and is the policy of this Government to do everything in its power to outlaw the use of chemicals in warfare. . . . I am doing everything in my power to discourage the use of gases and other chemicals in any war between nations." Again

---

[6] An additional factor in this particular instance may have been Hitler's ignorance of the Allies' stockpiles. His uncertainty is said to have led him ultimately to reject a plan, discussed with his top military leaders in 1943, to attack Britain with agent GB (268).

in 1943 Roosevelt said: "I state categorically that we shall under no circumstances resort to the use of such weapons unless they are first used by our enemies."

After World War II Admiral Chester Nimitz spoke about tough decisions, such as the question of using poison gas at Iwo Jima. He recalled: "I decided the United States should not be the first to violate the Geneva Convention."

On December 5, 1966, the United Nations General Assembly, by a vote of ninety states, including the United States, invited ". . . all states to strictly conform to the principles and objectives" of the Protocol.

Finally, that the United States has accepted the Protocol as part of the body of international law in the customary sense was acknowledged in a letter dated December 22, 1967, from Assistant Secretary of State William B. Macomber, Jr. to Representative Benjamin Rosenthal of New York: "We consider that the basic rule set forth in this document (the Geneva Protocol) has been so widely accepted over a long period of time that it is now considered to form a part of *customary* international law" [emphasis added] (270).

Representative Robert Kastenmeier in 1959 had noted the sharply rising budget for CBW and the aggressive attitude toward use of chemical agents in the military, and by means of a resolution he sought to reaffirm the principles enunciated by Roosevelt. His resolution did not seek to prevent either stockpiling the weapons or their use for "retaliation in kind" but merely asked for reiteration of the no-first-use policy. The State Department opposed the resolution and later, in directing attention to the fact that it had not been adopted, the Department said: "The President thus remains free to determine American policy on the use of such weapons in any future war" (271).

In the 1950s the military succeeded in conveying the impression that no weapons were denied to them. The 1956 issue of *Army Field Manual 27-10* contains these passages:

The United States is not a party to any treaty now in force that prohibits or restricts the use in warfare of toxic or non-toxic gases, of smoke or incendiary materials or of bacteriological warfare. A treaty signed at Washington 6 February 1922 on behalf of the United States, the British Empire, France, Italy and Japan contains a provision forever prohibiting the use in war of asphyxiating, poisonous, or other gases and all analogous liquids, materials or devices, but that treaty was expressly conditioned to become effective only upon ratification of all the signatory powers, and not having been ratified by all the signatories has never become effective.

The Geneva Protocol for the prevention of the use in war of asphyxiating, poisonous or other gases and bacteriological methods of warfare signed on 17 June, 1925 on behalf of the United States and many other powers has been ratified or adhered to by and is now effective between a considerable number of states. However, the United States Senate has refrained from giving its advice and consent to the ratification of the Protocol by the United States and it is accordingly *not binding on this country* [emphasis added].

These statements by the military must be viewed as an aberration of our democratic form of government because the civilian agencies, to which the military is subordinate, have clearly accepted the fact that the United States is indeed bound by the Geneva Protocol by means of the mechanism of customary international law. So far as Vietnam is concerned, this fact has never been contested by the State Department or the White House, and it is worth noting that Secretary Rusk said of the chemical agents being used: "We are not talking about gas that is prohibited by the Geneva Convention of 1925" (272).

Quoting a State Department source, an item in *U.S. News and World Report* held: "The Geneva Protocol of 1925, prohibiting the use of 'asphyxiating, poisonous or other gases,' was never ratified by the U.S. Senate. So the United States is not bound by it. But the State Department does not consider the use of riot-control gas in Vietnam as a violation of this agreement anyway" (273).

Thus, the only dispute is about the particular agents covered by the Protocol, the United States maintaining stoutly that the tear gas and herbicides used in Vietnam do not constitute a fracture of the law. We shall return to this point in a moment.

In 1968 United Nations Secretary General U Thant drew attention to the threat of chemical and biological warfare and offered his opinion that ". . . the international community was not sufficiently conscious of the danger inherent in this new type of weapon of mass murder." Subsequently the secretary general appointed a panel of fourteen consultant experts to review the problem; their report was transmitted on June 30, 1969. U Thant took the occasion to remark:

I also feel it incumbent upon me, in the hope that further action will be taken to deal with the threat posed by the existence of these weapons, to urge that the Members of the United Nations undertake the following measures in the interests of enhancing the security of the peoples of the world:

1. To renew the appeal of all States to accede to the Geneva Protocol of 1925;
2. To make a clear affirmation that the prohibition contained in the Geneva Protocol applies to the use in war of all chemical, bacteriological and biological agents (including tear gas and other harassing agents) which now exist or which may be developed in the future;
3. To call upon all countries to reach agreement to halt the development, production and stockpiling of all chemical and bacteriological (biological) agents for purposes of war and to achieve their effective elimination from the arsenal of weapons. (274)

Meanwhile, the Nixon Administration had two weeks earlier announced a sweeping review of the United States chemical and biological warfare program. The announcement came in a letter from Gerard C. Smith, director of the Arms Control and Disarmament Agency, to Representative Richard D. McCarthy. Smith stated that the review would be conducted by appropriate agencies, as well as by the State and Defense Departments, and that when completed the study would be submitted to the National Security Council. The question of possible ratification of the Geneva Protocol was specifically mentioned as one of the items to be considered.

Earlier in 1969 Representative R. D. McCarthy, a Democrat from Buffalo, New York, had seen a National Broadcasting Company *First Tuesday* television documentary about CBW. The program stimulated him to submit a series of questions to the Defense Department dealing with policy and budget matters (275). Unsatisfied by the answers, McCarthy went on to become the leading congressional critic of CBW, including within his sphere of competence the use of tear gas and herbicides in Vietnam. By the fall of 1969 he had secured almost 100 representatives as co-sponsors of a bill requiring the president to resubmit the Geneva Protocol to the Senate. The Subcommittee on National Security Policy and Scientific Developments of the House Committee on Foreign Affairs met on November 20, 1969, to consider this and identical resolutions sponsored, or co-sponsored by a total of 108 members of the Congress. The hearings ran through November and December of 1969 and compiled 513 pages of testimony; this constitutes the most comprehensive analysis of CBW ever undertaken by the Congress (276).

On November 24, 1969, seven months after the Pentagon had been advised by private letter of a massacre at My Lai in South Vietnam, Army Secretary Resor and General Westmoreland announced the appointment of Lt. General William R. Peers to lead a panel to examine the "nature and scope" of the incident (277). The next day, November 25, President Nixon made a major policy proclamation on CBW (278). Observers have suggested that General Peer's findings were already known and, consequently, that the White House was in search of a news item to "brighten the image." Be that as it may, there is evidence that the news conference was hastily arranged.

The full text of President Nixon's statement appears in Appendix VI. In essence the president:

1. Reaffirmed the no-first-use policy for lethal chemicals.
2. Extended this policy to incapacitating (psycho) chemicals.
3. Scrapped production and stockpiling of biological agents.
4. Moved to send the Geneva Protocol to the Senate for ratification.

It is significant that the president did not himself mention tear gas or herbicides; however, the White House made it clear that such agents would continue to be used in Vietnam and were not to be regarded as prohibited under the terms of the Protocol.

World reaction to Nixon's new CBW policy, especially in the capitals of western Europe, was favorable, as was opinion in the Congress. In the Senate, Mike Mansfield, majority leader, said the measure would be approved before the end of the year; the chairman of the key Senate Foreign Relations Committee, J. W. Fulbright, also predicted swift approval. These evaluations were made without consideration of the tear gas-herbicide issue and the exemption of these agents. Representative McCarthy had learned of Nixon's announcement while flying home from a CBW meeting called by the Women's International League for Peace and Freedom in London. At that meeting McCarthy had said: "I believe the U.S. should not attempt to exclude tear gas from the coverage of the Protocol" (279).

Nixon's statement contained a second significant omission—the toxins. These are the poisonous products of living organisms, and they are pound for pound the most deadly agents known to man. The chemistry and biology of these substances has been studied in detail (280); suffice it to say here that the best known of them, botulinal toxin, may be produced by the culture of a relatively common bacterium, *Clostridium botulinum,* and that as little as one microgram will kill a human. Stated in another way, there are 5,000,000 lethal doses in a quantity of botuninal toxin equivalent to the weight of an American five-cent piece. Toxins have been classed as biological agents by both United States Army manuals of CBW and by the British proposals to the United Nations for renunciation of biological warfare. Toxins should properly be regarded as chemical substances, however, and in fact they were so classified by the United Nations report (281). However, even if they could be produced synthetically without use of the living bacterial cell, it must be acknowledged that some toxins are unlike ordinary poisons in that they are responsible for the disease symptoms that appear in the affected host.

The omission of toxins from the president's declaration touched off a vigorous debate and drew opposition from the scientific community. John T. Edsall, professor of biochemistry at Harvard University, wrote a letter to President Nixon in which he pointed out the serious consequences that would result from neglecting toxins (282). To produce the toxins current technology requires the culture of large vats of bacteria and, because this could be done in secret, the possibility exists for clandestine production of infectious biological agents. It was intimated that Nixon's November 25 proclamation on CBW would be known around the world as a "Big Lie" and that the credibility of the president and the government would be jeopardized if toxins were not included in the ban (283). A story in *The New York Times* claiming a disagreement between the Defense and State Departments on toxins was denied by government officials (284). Subsequently the *Times* reported that Nixon was weighing the options on toxins (285) and on February 15, 1970, the announcement came from Key Biscayne that such substances would no longer be stockpiled (286).

Although toxins have apparently not been deployed in Indochina, the story of their elimination has been recounted here because it lends credence to the theory that Nixon's declaration of the previous November 25 had been arranged in haste. Toxins were not originally included, a White House official said, because of a "slip-up" (287) and the matter just "fell between the cracks" (288).

By far the greatest criticism of the new CBW policy statement, however, centered on the omission of tear gas and herbicides—chemical weapons in use in the Vietnam war. There is evidence that support for this interpretation of the Protocol was sought across the Atlantic. The *London Observer* wrote:

The British Government . . . is . . . trying to sit on the fence. While not using these weapons in war it is trying to avoid having to commit itself to a resolution at the United Nations or in Geneva which would formally include their prohibition under the Geneva Protocol. (289)

CRY AND DIE

Although the language of the Geneva Protocol would seem to be straightforward and readily intelligible, there has nonetheless arisen a curious argument about the status of tear gas and herbicides. We have already noted that in the United States erosion of respect for the Geneva Protocol became apparent following the death of President Roosevelt. During the Truman, Eisenhower, and Kennedy years there were few opportunities for policy proclamations on CBW or the Geneva Protocol; nevertheless, the preparation of reports continued apace. The present position of the United States, as articulated at the United Nations in 1966, is that the Protocol was framed:

. . . to meet the horrors of poison gas warfare in the First World War and was intended to reduce suffering by prohibiting the use of poisonous gases such as mustard gas and phosgene. It does not apply to all gases. It would be unreasonable to contend that any rule of international law prohibits the use in combat against an enemy, for humanitarian purposes, of agents that Governments around the world commonly use to control riots by their own people. (290)

Thus, the United States contention is that the Protocol does not cover all gases and specifically does not those used by domestic law enforcement agencies. However, both points in this argument have dubious validity.

So far as the types of prohibited gases is concerned, it is instructive to quote from a letter by Philip Noel–Baker, who served in the Secretariat of the League of Nations and who won the Nobel Peace Prize in 1959. The letter appeared in the *London Times:*

He [President Nixon] says he will ratify the Geneva CBW Protocol of 1925, but will reserve the right to use "non-lethal" CS gas, defoliants and herbicides.

This would be no ratification of the Protocol. I was in Geneva while it was being drafted in 1925; everyone agreed that every kind of CB weapon must be abolished, and that the Protocol did that. . . .

I helped to draft the British Government Memorandum which Lord [Robert] Cecil laid before the League Preparatory Disarmament Commission on November 18, 1930. This reasserted that the Protocol forbade all chemical weapons, including tear gas. Only Mr. Hugh Gibson of the United States made objection. Throughout the Disarmament Conference of 1932–33 the Memorandum's view was accepted, and a little later, a new United States delegate, Mr. Hugh R. Wilson, endorsed the Memorandum and the Conference view. President Nixon's proposal is indubitably inconsistent with the Protocol.

It is a very grave inconsistency. CS has not been "non-lethal" in Vietnam. Used in 6 inch shells, it has driven the NLF soldiers from their trenches and bunkers into the open, where artillery and machine guns can kill them. It has been perhaps the most lethal of all weapons, and it is an offensive weapon: it breaks down defense. (291)

The Protocol does not mention that "lethal" gases are banned, and by application of similar semantic legerdemain, the United States could claim that nerve gas is not prohibited. Similarly, the mustard gases, which are neither asphyxiating nor poisonous but which were well known in 1925, were not specifically designated in the text; but they are nonetheless acknowledged to be forbidden. Goldblatt (292) has pointed out that a subcommittee of the League of Nations Temporary Mixed Commission, composed of experts, classified CBW agents as (1) irritant (lachrymatory, sneeze-producing, blistering), (2) suffocating or asphyxiating, (3) toxic. Because categories (2) and (3) were mentioned in the text, the phrase "other gases" could only signify the irritant chemicals. The French text—equally authentic—uses instead of "other gases" the phrase "ou similaires." This has been taken to imply restriction of the types of banned gases to asphyxiating or poisonous. However, both the British and French declared in 1930 that "the use of lachrymatory gases is covered by the prohibition" (293). Hence, Goldblatt concludes: "A mere conjecture made in 1930, which the United States itself has substantially discarded, took the shape of an ad hoc argument 36 years later when the U.S. representative at the 21st U.N. General Assembly spoke about the actual use of tear gas in Vietnam" (294). McCarthy reached the same conclusion following his comprehensive research on the history of the United States' stance toward tear gas as a war chemical (295).

As regards the assertion that it would be unreasonable to ban in warfare chemical agents that are used by police departments, it is only necessary to point out that even countries such as Sweden, a leader in CBW legislation on the world scene, use CS as a riot control agent. Here again the United States appears to be in a unique position in claiming that the Geneva Protocol imposes an inhibition on domestic uses of non-lethal chemicals. No other nation has so interpreted the Protocol and used that interpretation as an excuse not to ratify the Protocol and to extend coverage of the instrument to tear gas. The argument of the Johnson administration was prepared to accomodate the situation in Vietnam and, regrettably, it has been perpetuated by the Nixon administration. Thus, in a letter to Jay Orear, professor of of physics at Cornell University, Nixon's science adviser, Lee A. DuBridge, said:

As you know, the only antipersonnel chemical in use in Vietnam is the riot control agent CS which is used on U.S. citizens within this country and equally on citizens in many countries throughout the world by their governments. Its usage in South Vietnam, even every instance of its use, has the complete approval of the Government of South Vietnam and has not been discontinued. (296)

The matter of the relation of tear gas and herbicides vis-à-vis the Protocol seems to have been finally resolved by a resolution moved at the United Nations in December, 1969. The inspiration for the resolution is believed to have come from U Thant's earlier call for extension of the Protocol to all chemical agents. The resolution is referred to as the "Swedish resolution," and its text is found in Appendix VII.

The United States argued against the resolution on the grounds that the United Nations was not the proper forum for debate on interpretations of treaties. However, the resolution was adopted by a vote of eighty to three. The representative of Cambodia later informed the Secretariat that had he been present he would have voted in favor, thus making the tally eighty-one to three. The three negative votes were cast by the United States, Australia, and Portugal. There were thirty-six abstentions, most of which were cast by NATO countries and Britain, France, Canada, and Japan. The vote has been analyzed and rationalized in some detail but, in essence, it represents a convincing expression in the international community for a comprehensive interpretation of the chemicals prohibited by the Geneva Protocol (297). The resounding defeat of the United States before the United Nations was a major factor in stalling the Protocol in the White House. Thus, there was a gap of almost nine months after President Nixon announced with fanfare the resubmission of the Protocol before the treaty could be readied and sent to the Foreign Relations Committee. The delay, according to an article in *Science,* was the result of interagency wrangling between the State and Defense Departments, the former hoping for a "low profile" on herbicides and tear gas until after the Vietnam engagement and the latter holding out for a formal reservation on both types of agents (298).

On May 17, 1970, Representative Clement Zablocki of the Subcommittee on National Security Policy and Scientific Developments of the House Committee on Foreign Affairs released a report on the CBW hearings held during the previous year (299). Appended to the report was a survey by the Foreign Affairs Division, Legislative Reference Service, Library of Congress, of the use of tear gas in war. (See Appendix VIII.) A major conclusion of the review was that Nixon's new CBW policy was ". . . an attempt to reap the political advantages of the adoption of a new policy which includes ratification of the Geneva Protocol and at the same time retain for the United States a category of weapons which it considers to be militarily advantageous." Zablocki recommended that the president send the Protocol to the Senate forthwith; he called for speedy approval by that body and proposed that subsequent to ratification, talks could be held on the question of tear gas and herbicides. How the Senate will react to this suggestion remains to be seen. Senator J. W. Fulbright is known to favor a broad range of prohibitions under the Protocol.

On August 19, 1970, the same date that the scrap Liberty freighter *Le Baron Russell Briggs* was sunk with its controversial cargo of GB and VX off the Florida coast, President Nixon finally sent the Geneva Protocol to the Senate (300). The text of Nixon's message and an attached report by Secretary of State William P. Rogers are contained in Appendix IX. As expected, the submission included an incidental, almost apologetic, reference to tear gas and herbicides. The president did not ask the Senate to vote on the status of these agents under the Protocol but merely, by means of Roger's report, noted that it was the United States' "understanding" that riot control agents and herbicides are not part of the treaty. *The New York Times* commented editorially:

President Nixon deserves two cheers at most for finally sending to the Senate his request for approval of the Geneva Protocol of 1925.... It is bad enough that nine months of intramural wrangling followed the original announcement of the Administration's intention at the United Nations last November.... It is unfortunate that he has been persuaded to cling to a reservation that will downgrade his decision around the world and that may even put ratification of the Protocol in jeopardy. (301)

The options available to the Senate are several. It could fail to give consent, or the measure could remain in the Foreign Relations Committee as happened before—both seem unlikely possibilities. Or it could accept Mr. Nixon's exemptions on tear gas and herbicides, or exempt one of these agents. Or it could accept both exemptions and call for negotiations on the scope of the agents to be banned, which is the Zablocki position. Finally, the Senate could require that herbicides and tear gas be regarded as proscribed weapons under the Protocol.

The administration and the Pentagon apparently will try to slip the Protocol through the Senate with the lure that tear gas and herbicides can be discussed later among the signatory nations. Dr. Ivan Bennett, a long-time expert consultant to various agencies on CBW (302), has criticized Secretary General U Thant's call for a ban on all chemicals under the Protocol:

Laudable as the Secretary General's motives may have been, I regard this recommendation as unfortunate, in a political sense, at this time. This country is using the tear gas, CS, in Vietnam. To be sure, it was originally introduced with the assurances (which I believe were genuine) that it would be used for humane purposes, to avoid civilian casualties, etc. It is now used in huge quantities and is believed by field commanders to be an important addition to their weaponry.... At a time when our Administration is trying to find a way out of Vietnam and trying, among other things, to hold American casualties to an absolute minimum, any move that might be interpreted as taking an effective weapon away from our forces in Vietnam would surely carry domestic political risks.... There is no longer any pretext, incidentally, that CS is used primarily for "humane" purposes. It is an adjunct to conventional weapons and makes it possible to inflict more casualties on the enemy while holding down our own losses. (303)

Representative Donald Fraser is apparently of the same view: "... I would not like to see that issue (Vietnam) become the obstacle to ratification" (304).

Representative Robert Kastenmeier believes herbicides and tear gas should be included: "In ratifying the Geneva Protocol, the Senate has the opportunity of breaking with a dubious tradition of relying on the advice of the military on essentially political matters, and I urge it to do so" (305). Representative John Dellenback would defer review of the Protocol while chemicals are in use in Vietnam, but his solution to the problem would be "... to end chemical warfare in Vietnam, not to wait until the war is over to resubmit the Protocol" (306).

Hans Swyter, former staff member in the Department of Defense, saw the problem this way:

The use of CS and the defoliants in Vietnam constitute chemical warfare, in spite of the euphemisms to the contrary. That use is breaking down the barriers to chemical and biological warfare. That use could create more domestic and international embarrassment, as the Senate considers the Protocol. Our use of CS and the defoliants draws attention to our potential hypocrisy and to ambiguities in the Protocol. Exceptions, violations, and ambiguities all weaken the Protocol. To make our ratification genuinely meaningful, we ought to stop using the two chemicals. We ought to agree to a uniform interpretation. (307)

Thus, the Nixon administration has offered an emasculated· version of the Protocol made attractive by the total ban on biological weapons even if used in retaliation. It is hoping that the desire to banish the germs and toxins will be sufficiently strong to cause the Senate to overlook the absence of controls on tear gas and herbicides. Biological weapons are not regarded by the Pentagon as reliable and, in any case, the United States has unilaterally ended their production and stockpiling. The Senate has a unique and rare opportunity to bring the United States' policy on CBW into line with that of virtually every other nation in the world. If the opportunity is relinquished, it may not soon occur again.[7]

A Program for the Future

THE PROBLEM DEFINED

We have seen how CS gas has been promoted to the status of a routine combat tool during the years of the Vietnam war or, to quote Rear Admiral William E. Lemos, how it has come to be "... used as necessary in Vietnam in combat operations" (308). The CS experience illustrates dramatically the folly of entrusting any type of chemical weapon to the military. Just as the introduction of tear gas by the French in World War I led immediately to the adoption of the most deadly agents that could be deployed, so also the

---

[7] In March, 1971, the Senate Foreign Relations Committee held hearings on the question of ratification of the Geneva Protocol, but failed to report out the treaty pending clarification of the status of tear gas and herbicides. See *The New York Times* March 6, 17, 19, 23 and (editorial) 26, 1971.

hesitant approval of riot control agents by civilian branches of government in the early stages of American intervention in Vietnam has brought us to the point where essentially every weapon system in use in Indochina has a CS capability.

We have seen also that the new policy allowing use of tear gas was made by the military, advertised in their manuals, and then forced upon the government as a *fait accompli*. In this way the Pentagon took advantage of a cooperative chief executive and a compliant Congress to make policy on weapons that could be instrumental in determining the survival of the human race. The acceptance of tear gas represents a reversal of a half century of American leadership in the control and eradication of CBW. On only one previous occasion, in 1930, did the United States question the extension of the Geneva Protocol to tear gas. Thereafter this question was not only discarded, but within a few years American representatives were proposing that inventories be made of domestic stocks of riot control gases as a means of verification of compliance with the Protocol. Doubts about tear gas were again laid to rest at the United Nations in December, 1969, at the time of the near-unanimous decision to ban these agents as weapons of war.

The revived attempt to exempt tear gas and herbicides is a contingency precipitated by the Vietnam war and is the culmination of years of promotion of chemicals by the Pentagon and by their colleagues in the chemical industry. Tear gas was not used, so far as we know, in the Korean war; there the Pentagon was inhibited by forced cooperation with the armies of other nations. Suddenly, in Vietnam, gas has been accepted because that war is almost exclusively an American operation.

It is not possible to overestimate the seriousness of the Vietnam infraction of the Protocol when it is viewed in the context of the future of arms limitation. Suppose, for example, that Castro's Cuba should decide that biological weapons would fit into any plans they might have for the terrorization of neighboring states. If we accept herbicides and tear gas, other states could equally well accept those CBW weapons that happen to harmonize with their political requirements. Such is the destructive potential of modern weapons technology that there is little prospect for the survival of civilization unless nations can be induced to respect the rule of international law. In a world shrunken and burdened by a heavy encrustation of armaments, Americans have no more important task than that of requiring their own government to live up to international norms of law and order. By using chemical weapons in Indochina in flagrant violation both of international law and the general opinion of the civilized world, the United States has undermined all progress in what should be the first priority in international affairs—the eradication of insane weapons. And by breaking the taboo on chemicals, we stimulate the proliferation of all kinds of armaments, including the prime agents of indiscriminate destruction—the thermonuclear devices.

On March 25, 1968, I wrote to Representative L. Mendel Rivers, Chairman of the House Armed Services Committee, requesting a statement of policy on the use of tactical nuclear weapons in Vietnam. Specifically, I wished to know if such use could be considered a violation of international law. Mr. Rivers in turn referred the question to the State Department, and on April 30 he sent me a copy of the response he had obtained from William B. Macomber, Jr., Assistant Secretary of State for Congressional Relations. At question was the jurisdiction of a United Nations General Assembly resolution, No. 1653(XVI) of November 24, 1961, which declared:

(d) Any State using nuclear and thermonuclear weapons is to be considered as violating the Charter of the United Nations, as acting contrary to the laws of humanity and as committing a crime against mankind and civilization.

Although the resolution has been adopted by a vote of fifty-five for, twenty against, and twenty-six abstentions, Mr. Macomber explained that, "The United States does not consider the use of nuclear weapons regardless of the circumstances in which they are used as a violation of international law" (309). He cited the split vote as a main reason for the failure of the United States to acknowledge the nuclear restriction.

Mr. Rivers, in a plea for resumption of bombing made before a House subcommittee in 1970, said:

Now let us consider as a first step the resumption of the bombing, and if this doesn't work, let us consider something else. Let these people see something of value begin to disappear from the face of the earth up there. All the military needs is the order. They can wheel and sway and swing high in the sunlit silence, and hovering there, as the poet says, they can push those craft through those footless halls of air, and nobody can stop them. All they need are the orders. (310)

There is enough thermonuclear capacity in the arsenals of the United States and the USSR to melt down all the steel and concrete of our cities and render the world uninhabitable from lingering radiation. This could be the result of the kind of confrontation Representative Rivers seems to suggest. With such destructive power in the hands of nations, a layer of chemical weapons contributes nothing to national security. Indeed, the only collective security will be found in general and complete disarmament. Thus, to the extent that it has sanctified chemicals and delayed ratification of the Geneva Protocol, the Vietnam war has had a retrograde influence on arms limitation.

The escalating use of CS in Vietnam has had its parallel at home. Here we find the same substance used to strip citizens of their civil liberties and deprive them of their constitutional rights of assembly. At the same time people are exposed to an environmental contaminant the ultimate toxicity of which has never been ascertained. This is not to say that riot control agents have no legitimate role to play in civil disturbances or in police work. If a sniper is holed up in a building, it would seem to be the humanitarian approach to attempt to evict him with riot control agents rather than perform his execution with high-powered rifles. This evaluation is made notwithstanding the knowledge that most of the deaths associated with riot control agents in the United States have arisen from improper use of the riot control materials in the hands of police.

THE REMEDY

As our first order of business we should seek to eliminate the use of all "riot control agents" in the Indochina war. If this could be achieved, the Geneva Protocol would doubtless be approved *pro forma* in the Senate; it could then be ratified by the president without reservations or crippling amendments. This would restore the credibility of the United States government in the eyes of the world, and at home it would demonstrate that the civil authority is higher than that of the military.

Second, we should require that the so-called defensive research on biological weapons be opened up for public inspection. We should insist that the vast biological facilities at Fort Detrick and elsewhere be converted to research laboratories dealing with environmental and public health problems (311). Could there be a more fitting gesture than to rededicate Fort Detrick, as a congressman has suggested (312), as the Rachel Carson Center for investigation of hazardous substances in the environment?

Finally, in the civilian sector, rigorous federal statutes must be enacted to assure that citizens and police officers alike will not be victimized by reckless exposure to riot control agents.

How is this program to be realized?

Public Pressure

The American public has traditionally displayed a strong revulsion for CBW in all its forms. The ease with which public opinion can be mobilized to resist the handling of chemical weapons is evident to this day (313). The accident at Dugway, Utah in 1968 generated a heavy response that forced the Army ultimately to confess that their nerve gas had killed 6,000 sheep. Earlier, the disposal of toxic chemical wastes from the Rocky Mountain Arsenal by deep-well pumping had been blamed for generating a spate of earthquakes in the Denver area (314). Also, the Army had planned to ship from Denver a million gallons of mustard gas and GB by rail to the Atlantic coast where it would be sunk in a ship some hundred miles off shore (315). But the Army was forced instead to set up "Task Force Eagle," a $14.6 million project to destroy the agents by burning them on the spot. Representative Richard McCarthy commented in retrospect: "The public reaction to this incredibly dangerous plan triggered a series of governmental reviews that offer the possibility of a return to a policy of reason in this area of warfare" (316).

The proposed shipment of the nerve gases GB and VX from Okinawa to

Oregon caused substantial embarrassment to the chemical experts in the Pentagon. The presence of nerve gas on Okinawa was revealed in the summer of 1969 when a leaky container administered a sublethal dose to twenty-four Americans on the island. To molify public opinion on the island, the Pentagon promised to transfer the gas, which also included some mustard agents, to a storage depot at Hermiston, Oregon. This in turn resulted in the formation of a group called PANG—People Against Nerve Gas—and ultimately the governors of both Oregon and Washington filed suit to block the shipment (317). On May 31 the Department of Defense, on orders from President Nixon, agreed to send the gas to Kodiak, Alaska (318). The governor of Alaska pledged to oppose the plan with every means at his disposal (319). A month later the Senate passed a bill intended to require destruction of the agents on the island of Okinawa. The Pentagon then drew up a plan to move the gas to Johnston Island, a transfer that would violate the amendment to the Foreign Military Sales Act which forbids movement of the chemicals to the United States or its possessions (320). The issue still has not been resolved inasmuch as Okinawa officials have objected to detoxification at the present storage depots, although the Army at one time announced the construction of a portable detoxifier that would be brought to the seven gas storage sites in the United States and to those in West Germany and Okinawa (321). Subsequent to the latter announcement, the Department of Defense said the Okinawa gas would be sent to Johnston Island in the Pacific in late 1970 or early 1971.

McCarthy cites other schemes of the Pentagon, such as the testing of nerve gas in Hawaii, various shipment projects, and the like, all of which had to be abandoned as a result of public clamor (323). The August, 1970, sea burial of obsolete stores of nerve gas in the Atlantic east of Cape Kennedy prompted vigorous protest, including legal action, from various local, state, national and international sources (324). In this incident the Army had entombed a large quantity of leaky M-55 rockets, each charged with both chemical warhead and propellant, in concrete coffins. Thus, instead of chemically or physically destroying the GB (and some VX) the Army had combined the substances within a relatively inaccessible structure, an ultimately hazardous procedure that Under Secretary Thaddeus R. Beal said would not be repeated (325). The Environmental Defense Fund and Governor Claude R. Kirk, Jr. of Florida tried through the courts to prevent the disposal. Although they were unsuccessful, conservationists believed they had prevented any future burials of nerve gas at sea (326) inasmuch as the Senate voted eighty-two to one to require CBW agents be rendered "harmless to man and his environment" prior to disposal. The shipment was scuttled on August 18, 1970, in 1,600 feet of water 283 miles off the Florida coast (327).

The sum of these experiences suggests that the American public is capable of dealing with the scourge of CBW provided that objective information can be made available to them. The Women's International League for Peace and Freedom has been very effective in gathering and disseminating at the grass roots level factual information on CBW (328), as has also the American Friends Service Committee (329) and similar organizations.

Scientific Catalysis

Because scientists have been instrumental in the creation of chemical weapons with the potential of mass extermination, this group can and must play a vital role in furnishing the precise data upon which a sound public policy on CBW can be erected. This is a special responsibility scientists have to the public (330). So far as Vietnam is concerned, the scientific community has already made significant contributions to the CBW debate. Individual scientists such as Joshua Lederberg of Stanford University and Matthew Meselson of Harvard have testified in Congress and have otherwise contributed to the movement (331). Meselson says: "Scientists have long had a major influence on CBW programs and policies" (332).

Early in 1966 twenty-nine prominent scientists living in the New England area issued a statement calling on President Johnson to repudiate the "barbarous" use of chemical weapons in Vietnam (333). The spokesman for the group was Dr. John T. Edsall of Harvard. Special problems arising from the military use of herbicides formed the subject of a petition to the president from twelve plant physiologists, dated September, 1966 (334). Later in the same year Milton Leitenberg conceived the idea of a national petition, and Leitenberg, Meselson and Edsall prepared a "presidential letter" (petition). The petition was distributed in the first week of October, 1966, and although a deadline of October 31 was set for signatures, over 5,000 names were obtained within the month. The petition was not publicly released, however, until February 14, 1967 (335). The statement had been officially adopted by the Federation of American Scientists, to whom Dr. Donald Hornig, presidential adviser on science and technology, sent an acknowledgement on March 13, 1967. Jay Orear, then chairman of the Federation, on May 29 wrote to the president complaining that no answer had been received.

The petition made two requests: development of a national policy on CBW, including a reaffirmation of "no first use," and an end to the use of antipersonnel and anticrop chemicals in Vietnam. The Federation has continued to press for extension of the Geneva Protocol to tear gas and has asked for conversion of the biological warfare laboratories to a national testing center for the screening of toxic effects in industrial and agricultural chemicals (336).

The Society for Social Responsibility in Science, an organization with only 600 members, arranged the Orians-Pfeiffer ecology survey in South Vietnam in 1969. The Pugwash conferences, although plagued with elitism, have enabled there to be communication between scientists from different lands.

Among the professional science societies, only the American Association for the Advancement of Science has maintained a consistent interest in chemical warfare in Vietnam, and that interest has depended on constant prodding from Pfeiffer and has been restricted to problems arising from the military use of herbicides. The full story is told elsewhere in this volume (p. 117).

In 1968 E. W. Pfeiffer and I concluded that if the scientific community could be mobilized behind a specific demand to end chemical warfare in Vietnam, the chances of aid from the AAAS would be greatly magnified. The AAAS needed a constituency and a base of support for work in such a politically sensitive area. The specific aid we envisaged was a field study to be carried out on a scale too ambitious for the resources of the private investigator. In the fall of 1968 we organized under the tentative title Scientists' Committee to End Chemical Warfare in Vietnam and circulated notice of a founding meeting to be held December 28 at the time of the annual AAAS convention in Dallas, Texas. Besides Pfeiffer and me, other members of the organizing committee included Meyer Chessin, University of Montana; E. U. Condon, University of Colorado; William C. Davidon, Haverford College; John T. Edsall, Harvard University; Arthur Galston, Yale University; E. Edward A. Hudson, Lane College; A. R. Kruckeberg, University of Washington; Michael McClintock, University of Colorado; Franklin Miller, Kenyon College; and Harry Rubin, University of California. As a consequence of discussions with colleagues at Dallas and with others around the country, the decision was made to change the name of the committee to Scientists' Committee on Chemical and Biological Warfare. An executive committee was appointed consisting of David Baltimore, Massachusetts Institute of Technology; Edsall; Galston; E. James Lieberman, National Institute of Mental Health; McClintock; Richard Novick, Public Health Laboratory, City of New York; Gordon Orians, University of Washington; Robert Rutman, University of Pennsylvania; and Susan Zolla, New York University School of Medicine. Philip Siekevitz of Rockefeller University was appointed treasurer, and Neilands and Pfeiffer were appointed chairman and executive secretary, respectively. John S. Strauss, National Institutes of Mental Health and Edward Herbert, University of Oregon, have since joined the board.

The Scientists' Committee has been especially active in arranging informational meetings in conjunction with the national conventions of professional science societies. Such meetings were held at the 1969 and 1970 sessions of the Federated American Societies for Experimental Biology in Atlantic City and at the 1969 meeting of the AAAS in Boston. On the latter occasion, Ngo Vinh Long, a cartographer and native of Vietnam who had travelled extensively in the defoliated zones, addressed the group as did also John T. Edsall and Representative Richard D. McCarthy. The Committee presented a policy statement to the Arms Control and Disarmament Agency and gave testimony at the hearings on CBW led by Representative Zablocki in 1969 (337).

The most ambitious project undertaken by the Scientists' Committee was a full page advertisement in *Science* magazine, Volume 166, page 950, 1969. This was placed opposite the editorial page and cost about $1,500, paid for by subscriptions from the executive committee. The advertisement called for ratification of the Geneva Protocol without reservations (*i.e.,* herbicides or riot control agents), asked for an ecological study in Vietnam, and solicited membership in the committee. The 1970 slate of officers was comprised of Galston (chairman), Siekevitz (treasurer), and Strauss (executive secretary). The committee publishes a newsletter on a quarterly basis that is circulated to a membership of several hundred American scientists.

It is an interesting coincidence that the *Science* advertisement appeared just four days prior to Nixon's policy statement on CBW on November 25, 1969. Prior to the Boston meeting of the AAAS, Pfeiffer had submitted a resolution in the name of the committee that again requested an end to the use of herbicides in Vietnam and a field investigation of the effects of Operation Ranch Hand. The resolution was presented to the Committee on Council Affairs by Edsall, Galston, and Neilands and was subsequently adopted by the Council of the AAAS. At that meeting the AAAS also set up the Herbicide Assessment Commission to be chaired by Meselson and directed by Arthur H. Westing of Wyndham College, Vermont. A sum of $50,000 was budgeted for the work of the commission. At that particular meeting a vocal contingent of socially motivated students and others seeking peace was instrumental in inducing the AAAS to face up to its responsibilities vis-à-vis chemical warfare in Vietnam.

The activities of the Scientists' Committee on Chemical and Biological Warfare have been recounted here because they illustrate once more that there is no substantial support in the scientific community for chemical warfare. Perhaps patient tilling of this vineyard will bear fruit. The professional science societies can be humanized and made to face their responsibilities, although a range of sensitivities to issues such as CBW can be expected. Thus, the record of the American Chemical Society is not one of great compassion for the suffering of the Vietnamese peasant. Nonetheless, this attitude surely must change if science is to flourish and enjoy public support. As Benjamin De Leon said in the *Bulletin of the Atomic Scientists:*

... scientists must accept moral responsibility for their work. Furthermore, should they fail to respond to this demand of the time, they may very well be overwhelmed by an irresistible wave of popular revulsion. ... at the present level of technological development, the urgent demand in science is to re-introduce the human goals for which it is intended to be used. (338)

There is a second way in which academic scientists can discharge their responsibilities, *i.e.,* through introducing socially relevant topics in their courses. At the Berkeley campus of the University of California in 1969 Charles Schwartz and I taught an interdepartmental course titled "The Social Responsibility of the Scientist." This experiment proved quite successful, and in response to popular demand the lectures were collected and published by The Free Press (339). In the Biochemistry Department we have initiated a course, "Ecological Biochemistry," in which we discuss CBW, herbicides, pesticides, atomic radiation, lead and mercury pollution, smog, "The Pill," the "Abortion Pill," and many other topics at the interface between "classical biochemistry" and society. Students have taken an active role in arranging the content of the courses just described.

Congressional Action

Congress has its own vanguard of workers against chemical weapons and when a sufficient groundswell of public opinion has been generated, this body can be expected to achieve significant results.

Representative Richard D. McCarthy on the House side has been the leading congressional critic of CBW. Representative John Dellenback, a Republican of Oregon, is similarly well informed on the issues. Among others who have spoken out loudly about CBW or who have introduced bills on one or another aspect of the subject are Representatives Robert Kastenmeier of Wisconsin, Edward Koch of New York, Donald Fraser of Minnesota, Benjamin Rosenthal of New York, Edward Roybal of California, Dante Fascell of Florida, and Lester Wolff of New York. Representative Patsy Mink of Hawaii told the 1969 House CBW hearings:

In my opinion we may have already violated the Geneva Protocol by our use of repugnant chemicals like napalm and defoliating agents, and I believe that the President should direct an immediate ban on their use. It is shocking to read accounts of innocent people poisoned, and of birth malformations, resulting from these defoliants which now pollute the Vietnam environment. (340)

These hearings were convened in response to a number of identical resolutions that, even without an organized campaign, were sponsored or co-sponsored by some 108 Members of Congress.

On the Senate side of the Congress the Foreign Relations Committee, under the chairmanship of J. W. Fulbright, is believed to favor a "no gas" interpretation of the Geneva Protocol. Interestingly, Senator Charles Goodell on May 26, 1970, introduced amendment No. 659 to the military appropriations Act for fiscal 1971, a measure to block funds for the procurement or use of either antiplant agents or the equipment required for application of antiplant substances. In the previous year the Senate adopted by a vote of ninety-one to zero an amendment to the defense procurement authorization bill that would establish at least minimum supervision and controls over CBW development and operation (341).

Vietnam may be left with three million war wounded, more than the worst affected nations in western Europe after World War II or the Korean war. The peasant society has been devastated by years of strategic bombing. It would be comforting to salvage something of value from this enormous carnage—the recognition at last that chemical agents must be forever placed outside the bounds of acceptability as legitimate weapons of war.

Summary

The major points of this survey are the following:

1. From the end of World War I through the Roosevelt period the United States had established a record that was consistently in opposition to CBW and in support of the Geneva Protocol, in spite of the fact that the Senate had never given its advice and consent to ratification. In the decades after Roosevelt's death the Department of Defense, possibly with the concurrence of the chief executive, ultimately became sufficiently emboldened to declare that the United States is not bound by the Protocol. During the tenure of President Johnson the Protocol was accepted as customary international law but tear gas and herbicides were exempted after the Department of Defense had first used these chemicals in Vietnam. The claim that tear gas is not prohibited is a departure from the general historical American stance vis-à-vis the Geneva Protocol.

2. Agents CN, DM and CS were introduced in the Vietnam war in late 1964 and first used by the South Vietnamese forces. The public record suggests that the decision to employ gas was made at a "low level" in the United States government and that the use was understood to be on a strictly limited scale. In March, 1965, when news of the initiation of gas warfare traveled around the world, the Johnson administration (a) defended the right of field commanders to employ "nonlethal" gas, (b) stated that the gas would henceforth be used only in situations analogous to riot control, and (c) suppressed the use of the agents for several months.

3. In the fall of 1965 tear gas again came back to Vietnam after a carefully staged demonstration of its "humanitarian" use in the war (see p. 33–34). The incident was preceded by an intensive pro-gas public relations campaign in the United States. The procurement of CS then escalated from about a quarter of a million pounds in fiscal year 1964 to over six million pounds in fiscal 1969. Approximately fourteen million pounds of all forms of CS were requisitioned for southeast Asia during this five-year period. The agent has attained the status of a routine combat weapon, and practically every weapons system in use in Indochina has a CS gas capability.

4. By employing CS in conjunction with conventional firepower and by applying it in confined spaces such as caves, bunkers, tunnels, and shelters, the gas has been used in effect as a lethal military agent.

5. Agents CS and CN are relatively toxic agents; the mortal dose in the human subject is of the same order of magnitude as for certain other war gases. In a poorly ventilated environment an individual can inhale a fatal dose within minutes. Death results from asphyxiation associated with the development of pulmonary edema.

6. Agents CS and CN are active alkylating agents, and in this respect they resemble other chemicals that have been implicated in carcinogenic, mutagenic, and teratogenic reactions. Another war chemical, mustard gas,

is a similarly effective alkylating agent; it is believed to be responsible for a sharp increase in the incidence of cancer in factory workers who prepared the substance during World War II. Despite the massive use of CS at home and abroad, the cellular and genetic effects of the agent have never been ascertained. Both CS and CN cause dermatitis and are sensitizers that may give very serious allergic reactions upon repeated exposure.

7. Riot control agents have been adopted to curb civic unrest in the United States and used in a manner that can be characterized as irresponsible and as a substitute for dialogue and democratic reform. Federal regulations governing the use of "drugs as weapons" are nonexistent.

8. President Nixon's program to ratify the Geneva Protocol has been undermined by the continued use of CS gas and herbicides in Vietnam. A few weeks after the president's announcement of November 25, 1969 that the Protocol would be submitted to the Senate for advice and consent to ratification, the General Assembly of the United Nations by a vote of eighty to three declared that herbicides and tear gas are covered by the treaty. Consequently, eight months after the proclamation from the White House, the Protocol still had not been sent up to the Senate Foreign Relations Committee. Thus has the Department of Defense, in illegally introducing and institutionalizing chemical agents in the Indochina war, effectively sabotaged the ratification of an arms limitation measure that would enhance the security of the peoples of the world.

Acknowledgement

Among all those persons who furnished documentation for this survey or read the manuscript, I wish to mention in particular the contributions of my wife, Juanita.

References

1. John Duffett, ed., *Against the Crime of Silence, Proceedings of the Russell International War Crimes Tribunal,* O'Hare Books, Flanders, N. J., 1968. (Reprinted as a Simon & Schuster–Clarion P.B.)
2. *The New York Times* published articles by their correspondent, Harrison Salisbury, who visited North Vietnam in December and January, 1966–67. These accounts revealed for the first time the civilian bombardment in the DRV but did not elaborate on its extent or the types of weapons used.
3. For complete documentation of the development of chemical warfare from ancient to modern times see the publications of the Stockholm International Peace Research Institute, 166 Sveavagen, 113 46 Stockholm, Sweden.
4. Robin Clarke, *The Silent Weapons,* McKay, New York, 1968.
5. George Bunn, *Wisconsin Law Review,* 375 (1969).
6. *Department of State Bulletin, 16,* Part 2, 726 (1947).
7. Seymour M. Hersh, *My Lai 4,* Random House, New York, 1970.
8. *London Times,* July 1, 1936.
9. *New York Times,* November 26, 1936.
10. Seymour M. Hersh, *Chemical and Biological Warfare, America's Hidden Arsenal,* Bobbs-Merrill, Indianapolis, Ind., 1968; Elinor Langer, *Science, 155,* 174, 299 (1967).
11. George R. Merck, "Report to the Secretary of War," *The Military Surgeon, 98,* 239 (1946).
12. Langer. See ref. 10.
13. Quoted by Matthew Meselson, *Scientific American, 222,* 15 (1970).
14. Hersh. See ref. 10.
15. D. Julea, and I. Popa, *Revista Sanitara Militara, 5,* 845 (1966).
16. World Health Organization Report, *Health Effects of Possible Use of Chemical and Biological Weapons,* 1969.
17. *CBW,* a pamphlet published by the Union of Concerned Scientists, November 16, 1969, at P. O. Box 289, MIT Branch Office, Cambridge, Mass. 02139.
18. Charles MacArthur, testimony before the defense procurement hearings, Part 6, p.129, June, 1969; J. B. Neilands, *American Medical News,* July 7, 1969.
19. *San Francisco Chronicle,* March 23, 1967.
20. Poster published by Clergy and Laymen Concerned About Vietnam, 475 Riverside Drive, New York, N. Y. 10027.
21. *New York Times,* December 3, 1967.
22. *Medical Tribune,* July 8, 1968.
23. *New York Times,* April 14, 1968.
24. *Epidemiological Situation in Vietnam,* a report published in 1968 by the World Health Organization, 1525 23rd Street N. W., Washington, D. C.
25. *San Francisco Chronicle,* March 22, 1968; *New York Times,* March 21, 1968.
26. Letter dated January 8, 1970 from John S. Foster, Jr., Department of Defense, to J. B. Neilands.
27. J. D. Marshall, Jr. *et al., J. Epidem., 86,* 603 (1967).
28. *Baltimore Sun,* April 11, 1967.
29. *Clinical Laboratory Forum,* Vol. 1, No. 1, 1969.
30. *San Francisco Chronicle,* April 24, 1968.

31. *Medical Tribune,* February 15, 1968.
32. Letter dated October 27, 1969 from John Takman, M. D., Stockholm, Sweden, to J. B. Neilands.
33. *Time* magazine (Canada), October 10, 1969.
34. Susumu Hotta, *Dengue and Related Hemorrhagic Diseases,* Green, St. Louis, 1969.
35. *London Times,* November 6, 1967.
36. Duffett. See ref. 1, chapter by Frank Pestana.
37. L. F. Fieser, *The Scientific Method: A Personal Account of Unusual Projects in War and Peace,* Reinhold, New York, 1964.
38. *Chemical and Engineering News,* March 14, 1966.
39. J. B. Neilands, *Asian Survey,* X, 209 (1970).
40. *Baltimore Sun,* March 28, 1967.
41. *Ibid.,* April 11, 1967.
42. *Ibid.,* June 10, 1967.
43. Transcript, *Today Show,* NBC, July 10, 1969.
44. Neilands. See ref. 39.
45. *Washington Post,* March 13, 1965.
46. *San Francisco Chronicle,* February 9, 1965.
47. Frank Harvey, *Air War Vietnam,* Bantam Books, New York, 1967.
48. *New York Times,* March 12, April 9, 1969.
49. Letter from R. R. Holt to *New York Times,* April 9, 1967.
50. *Le Monde,* March 12, 1966.
51. Isabelle Fairhurst, *Manuel of High Explosives, Incendiaries and Poison Gases,* 1942.
52. Abraham Behar. Quoted by Neilands, ref. 39.
53. *San Francisco Chronicle,* March 31, 1969.
54. Duffett. See ref. 1. and "No More Hiroshimas!," *14,* No. 7, December, 1967.
55. John Takman, *Napalm, An International Symposium,* Rabén and Sjögren, Stockholm, 1967.
56. George Wald, *New York Review of Books,* July 2, 1970.
57. Statement, Japanese Scientists' Mission for the Investigation of U. S. War Crimes in Viet Nam, Hanoi, July 31, 1967.
58. *Vietnam Courier,* October 30, 1967.
59. *Ibid.,* April 8, 1968.
60. *New York Times, Boston Globe, Victoria* (B. C.) *Daily Colonist,* May 8, 1970.
61. *Dagens Nyheter,* August 16, 1970.
62. CBW Hearings, Subcommittee on National Security Policy and Scientific Developments, Rep. Clement Zablocki, Chm'n, House Committee on Foreign Affairs, November–December, 1969.
63. R. D. McCarthy, *The Ultimate Folly, War by Pestilence, Asphyxiation and Defoliation,* Knopf (casebound), Vintage (paperback), New York, 1969.
64. *L'Express,* March 14–20, 1966.
65. CBW Hearings. See ref. 62, testimony of Admiral William E. Lemos.
66. Augustin M. Prentiss, *Chemicals in War,* McGraw-Hill, New York, 1937.
67. Bo Sorbo, *Läkartidningen, 66,* 448 (1969) (in Swedish).
68. Rex Applegate, *Riot Control Materiel and Techniques,* Stackpole, Harrisburg, Pa., 1969.
69. Clarke. See ref. 4.

70. Prentiss. See ref. 66.
71. *London Times,* July 21, 1921.
72. Applegate. See ref. 68.
73. Prentiss. See ref. 66.
74. *Field Manual 3–10, Employment of Chemical and Biological Agents,* Departments of the Army, Navy, and Air Force, March 1966.
75. *Field Manual 3–8, Chemical Reference Handbook,* Department of the Army, January, 1967.
76. Applegate. See ref. 68.
77. Prentiss. See ref. 66.
78. *Ibid.*
79. *Special Summary Report on the Toxicology of CN, CS and DM,* Edgewood Arsenal, 1965.
80. *Ibid.*
81. *Field Manual 3–10.* See ref. 74.
82. B. Corson, and R. J. Stoughton, *Am. Chem. Soc., 50,* 2825 (1928).
83. *Ibid.*
84. S. Rose, ed., *CBW, Chemical and Biological Warfare,* Harrap, London, 1968.
85. *Field Manual 3–10.* See ref. 74.
86. *New York Times,* February 3, 1970.
87. Prentiss. See ref. 66.
88. *Special Summary Report.* See ref. 79.
89. Letter from Russell Stetler to the *Guardian,* April 30, 1970.
90. C. L. Punte *et al., Toxicol. and Appl. Pharm., 4,* 656 (1962).
91. David Moore, personal communication.
92. *Effects of Thermally Generated CS Aerosols on Human Skin,* Edgewood Arsenal Technical Report, 4075, 1967.
93. D. A. Weigand, *Military Medicine, 134,* 437 (1969); R. McLean, *Brit. Med. J. 3,* 546 (1969).
94. R. McLean, *Brit. Med. J., 3,* 652 (1969).
95. CBW Hearings. See ref. 62.
96. Weigand. See ref. 93.
97. Sumner Kalman, Seminar, Department of Biochemistry, University of California, Berkeley, May 28, 1970.
98. John McWhorter, personal communication.
99. *San Francisco Chronicle,* July 25, 1969.
100. *Training Circular 3–16* was reprinted by John Takman in Stockholm in March 1970. The manual was photo-offset with two alterations: the insignia of the U. S. War Office was placed on the front, and a message was inserted describing the manual as being "for war criminals by war criminals."
101. Applegate. See ref. 68.
102. *Ibid.*
103. *Ibid.*
104. *Document Concerning the U. S. Chemical Warfare in South Vietnam,* South Viet Nam Committee for the Disclosure of the U. S. Imperialists' War Crimes in South Vietnam, February, 1970.
105. J. S. Tomkins, *The Weapons of World War III,* Doubleday, Garden City, New York, 1966.
106. *Field Manual 3–10,* See ref. 74.

107. United Nations Report No. E. 69.1.24, *Chemical and Bacteriological (Biological) Weapons and the Effects of Their Possible Use,* 1969.
108. Hersh. See ref. 10.
109. McCarthy. See ref. 63.
110. Hersh. See ref. 10.
111. *New York Times,* March 24, 1965.
112. CBW Hearings. See ref. 62, p. 149.
113. *Ibid.,* p. 150.
114. *Ibid.,* p. 224.
115. *In the Name of America,* Clergy and Laymen Concerned About Vietnam, Turnpike Press, Annandale, Pa., 1968; Duffett. See ref. 1.
116. *New York Times,* See ref. 111.
117. Letter dated March 31, 1965, from Deputy Secretary of Defense Cyrus Vance to Rep. R. W. Kastenmeier.
118. *New York Times.* See ref. 111.
119. Hersh. See ref. 10.
120. *New York Times.* See ref. 111.
121. *Ibid.*
122. *Ibid.*
123. *Black Paper,* Volume II, Committee to Denounce the War Crimes of the U. S. in South Vietnam, Vietnam Bulletin, Pålsundsgaten 8, Stockholm Sv, Sweden, November, 1966.
124. Duffett. See ref. 1, p. 330.
125. Document. See ref. 104, statement by Dinh Ba Thi, Deputy Chief of the Delegation of the Provisional Revolutionary Government, 56th Plenary Session, Paris Conference on Vietnam, February 26, 1970.
126. *New York Times.* See ref. 111.
127. *Ibid.*
128. *Ibid.*
129. *Ibid.*
130. *Ibid.*
131. *New York Times,* March 25, 1965.
132. *New York Times.* See ref. 111.
133. *New York Times.* See ref. 131.
134. *Chicago Tribune,* March 30, 1965.
135. Hersh. See ref. 10.
136. *New York Times.* See ref. 131.
137. Quoted by Hersh. See ref. 10.
138. Hersh. See ref. 10.
139. *Wall Street Journal,* January 5, 1966.
140. *London Times,* September 10, 1965.
141. *Ibid.,* September 8, 1965.
142. *Ibid.,* September 27, 1965.
143. Hersh. See ref. 10.
144. *Ibid.*
145. *London Times,* October 9, 1965; see also *In the Name of America,* ref. 115.
146. Hersh. See ref. 10.
147. R. D. McCarthy, Congressional Record, E 6608–10, August 4, 1969.
148. Duffett. See ref. 1, p. 343.
149. *New York Times,* January 4, 1966.

150. *New York Times,* February 22, 1966.
151. *Baltimore Sun,* January 13, 1966.
152. *New York Times,* February 23, 1966.
153. *Christian Science Monitor,* March 28, 1966.
154. *Vietnam Courier,* February 6, 1967.
155. *Black Paper.* See ref. 123.
156. Duffett. See ref. 1.
157. Books on CBW appearing in 1968: Hersh, see ref. 10; Clarke, see ref. 4; Rose, see ref. 84; and Nigel Calder, ed., *Unless Peace Comes,* Viking, New York, 1968.
158. *London Observer,* February 25, 1968, article by John Davy.
159. The conference resulted in the book published by Rose. See ref. 84.
160. *New York Times,* September 10, 1968.
161. *Montreal Star,* April 19, 1969.
162. *Washington Post,* July 24, 1969.
163. *San Francisco Chronicle,* September 29, 1969.
164. *New York Times,* December 6, 1969.
165. CBW Hearings. See ref. 62.
166. Rose. See ref. 84, p. 96.
167. *New York Times,* January 13, 1966.
168. *New York Times,* January 14, 1966.
169. Rose. See ref. 84, p. 93.
170. *Brisbane Courier Mail,* January 13, 1966.
171. Letter from David Neufield to the *Saigon Post,* October 20, 1967.
172. Document. See ref. 104.
173. Prentiss. See ref. 66.
174. Special Summary Report. See ref. 79.
175. CBW Hearings. See ref. 62.
176. *San Francisco Chronicle.* See ref. 99.
177. *New York Times.* See ref. 164.
178. F. J. Brown, *A Study in Restraints,* Princeton University Press, Princeton, 1968.
179. *Newsletter,* Federation of American Scientists, May, 1970.
180. Applegate. See ref. 68.
181. Hersh. See ref. 10.
182. *New Republic,* June 28, 1969.
183. *San Francisco Chronicle,* June 30, 1970.
184. J. P. Adams *et al., Am. J. Bone and Joint Surgery, 48,* 436 (1966).
185. Sumner Kalman, *Pharmacology of Riot Control Agents,* Federation Proceedings, *30,* 84 (1970).
186. United Nations Report. See ref. 107.
187. World Health Organization Report. See ref. 16.
188. Kalman. See ref. 185.
189. N. S. Penneys *et al., New England J. Med., 281,* 413 (1969).
190. *Medical Tribune,* May 20, 1968.
191. *New Republic,* May 11, 1968.
192. *Medical Tribune,* August 15, 1968.
193. Penneys. See ref. 189.
194. N. S. Penneys, Dept. of Dermatology, Univ. of Miami School of Medicine, Miami, Fla., unpublished ms., "Contact Dermatitis due to Chloroacetophenone," 1970.
195. *Medical Tribune.* See ref. 190.

196. Penneys. See ref. 194.
197. *Medical Tribune,* February 23, 1966.
198. R. A. Levine and C. J. Stahl, *Am. J. Ophthalmology, 65,* 497 (1968).
199. R. H. Gwynn and Salaman, M. H., *Brit, J. Cancer 7,* 482 (1953).
200. *Special Summary Report.* See ref. 79.
201. Penneys. See ref. 194.
202. *Medical Tribune.* See ref. 190.
203. *Special Summary Report.* See ref. 79.
204. *Ibid.*
205. S. A. Cucinell, reported in ref. 185.
206. J. B. Nash *et al., Chem. Absrt., 45,* 4344a (1951).
207. Punte. See ref. 90.
208. S. Benzer, *Proc. Natl. Acad. Sc., 47,* 1025 (1961).
209. Cucinell. See ref. 205.
210. J. B. Neilands, *J. Biol. Chem., 208,* 225 (1954).
211. Cucinell. See ref. 205.
212. J. Mackworth, *Biochem. J., 42,* 82 (1948).
213. Letter dated April 27, 1970, from J. B. Neilands (for the Scientists' Committee on Chemical and Biological Warfare) to Health, Education and Welfare Secretary Robert Finch.
214. Letter dated September 8, 1970 from M. J. Ryan, Director of the Office of Legislative Services, Department of Health, Education and Welfare, to J. B. Neilands.
215. Weigand. See ref. 93.
216. CBW Hearings. See ref. 62, p. 464.
217. Applegate. See ref. 68. ·
218. Howard Coleman and Dinah Robinson, Unpublished ms. presented to Prof. Frank Newman titled "The Legal Controls of Tear Gas. A Study in International and Domestic Law," University of California, Berkeley, 1969.
219. J. B. Neilands, *Spokesman,* No. 2, April, 1970.
220. Letter dated November 6, 1969, from B. R. Baker to J. B. Neilands.
221. *Berkeley Gazette,* May 27, 1969.
222. *New York Times,* May 21, 1969; *San Francisco Chronicle,* May 23, 1969.
223. Hilary Rose and Russell Stetler, *New Society,* September 25, 1969.
224. *Nature, 226,* 95 (1970).
225. *Science, 165,* 1240 (1969).
226. *New Scientist,* September 4, 1969; *New Society,* April 9, 1970.
227. *Nature.* See ref. 224. *Science.* See ref. 225.
228. Russell Stetler, "The Battle of Bogside," *Sheed and Ward,* London and Sydney, 1970. See also *Scanlan's 1,* 58 (1970).
229. *London Observer,* August 24, 1969.
230. *Nature, 224,* 746 (1969).
231. *New York Times.* See ref. 86.
232. CBW Hearings. See ref. 62.
233. *New York Times.* See ref. 86.
234. Rose. See ref. 84.
235. Levine and Stahl. See ref. 198.
236. K. E. Jackson and M. A. Jackson, *Chem. Rev., 16–17,* 195 (1935).
237. *Newsletter,* Society for Social Responsibility in Science, September, 1969.
238. Kalman. See ref. 97.
239. *New Republic,* April 13, 1968; *Medical Tribune.* See ref. 190.

240. Sumner Kalman, *California's Health*, September, 1968; *Stanford MD, 8*, No. 3, p. 31, 1969.
241. Quoted by Coleman and Robinson. See ref. 218.
242. *New York Times*, February 22, 1970.
243. Quoted by Coleman and Robinson. See ref. 218.
244. Bunn. See ref. 5.
245. Richard Falk, ed., *The Vietnam War and International Law*, Princeton Univ. Press, Princeton, N. J., 1968.
246. Duffett. See ref. 1.
247. Pestana. See ref. 36.
248. Bunn. See ref. 5.
249. *Ibid.* Also Hersh; see ref. 10.
250. Duffett. See ref. 1.
251. A. Frank Reel, *The Case of General Yamashita*, University of Chicago, Chicago, Ill., 1949.
252. *The Black Panther*, IV, No. 28, June 13, 1970.
253. *New York Times* (editorial), February 26, 1970.
254. Duffett. See ref. 1.
255. *Science, 167*, 1110 (1970).
256. *Look* magazine, April 4, 1967.
257. *San Francisco Examiner and Chronicle*, April 16, 1967.
258. *New York Times Magazine*, February 19, 1967.
259. *Sacramento Bee*, May 17, 1967.
260. *San Francisco Chronicle*, October 19, 1968.
261. *Ibid.*
262. A. A. D'Amato *et al., Calif. Law Review, 57*, 1055 (1969).
263. United Nations Report. See ref. 107.
264. McCarthy. See ref. 63.
265. Bunn. See ref. 5.
266. D'Amato. See ref. 262.
267. *Ibid.*
268. *New York Times*, August 19, 1970.
269. M. Meselson, testimony to the Senate Foreign Relations Committee, April 30, 1969.
270. *Ibid.*
271. *Ibid.*
272. *New York Times.* See ref. 131.
273. *In the Name of America.* See ref. 115.
274. United Nations Report. See ref. 107.
275. McCarthy. See ref. 63.
276. CBW Hearings. See ref. 62.
277. Hersh. See ref. 7.
278. *New York Times*, November 26, 1969.
279. *Ibid.*
280. S. A. Ajl *et al., Microbial Toxins*, Volumes I, II and III, Academic Press, New York, 1970.
281. United Nations Report. See ref. 107.
282. Letter dated December 30, 1969, from John T. Edsall to President Richard M. Nixon.
283. *New York Times*, January 4, 1970.

284. *New York Times,* December 16, 17, 1969.
285. *New York Times,* January 26, 1970.
286. *New York Times,* February 15, 1970.
287. *Ibid.*
288. *San Francisco Examiner and Chronicle,* February 15, 1970.
289. *London Observer,* November 30, 1969.
290. Bunn. See ref. 5.
291. Letter from Philip Noel Baker to the *London Times,* December 3, 1969.
292. Jozef Goldblatt, *Bulletin of the Atomic Scientists, 26,* 13 (1970).
293. *Ibid.*
294. *Ibid.*
295. McCarthy. See ref. 63.
296. Letter dated June 18, 1970, from Lee DuBridge to Jay Orear.
297. CBW Hearings. See ref. 62.
298. *Science, 169,* 454 (1970).
299. Report on CBW Hearings. See ref. 62. See also report of May 17, 1970.
300. *New York Times,* August 20, 1970.
301. *New York Times,* August 21, 1970.
302. CBW Hearings. See ref. 62.
303. Ivan Bennett, *Proc. Natl. Acad. Sc., 65,* 271 (1970).
304. CBW Hearings. See ref. 62.
305. *Ibid.*
306. *Ibid.*
307. *Ibid.*
308. *Ibid.*
309. Letter dated April 12, 1968, from William B. Macomber, Jr., to Rep. L. Mendel Rivers.
310. American Prisoners of War in Southeast Asia, hearings before the Subcommittee on National Security Policy and Scientific Developments, Rep. Clement Zablocki, Chairman, House Committee on Foreign Affairs, April 29, May 1, 6, 1970.
311. Report on CBW Hearings. See ref. 299.
312. CBW Hearings. See ref. 62.
313. Susan Zolla, in *Environmental Effects of Weapons Technology,* SIPI, 30 E. 68th Street, New York, N. Y. 10021, 1970.
314. *Christian Science Monitor,* May 21, 1970.
315. *San Francisco Chronicle,* February 14, 1970.
316. McCarthy. See ref. 63.
317. *New York Times,* April 22, 1970.
318. *New York Times,* May 31, 1970.
319. *Good Times,* June 5, 1970.
320. *New York Times,* August 13, 1970.
321. *New York Times,* August 21, 1970.
322. *San Francisco Chronicle,* September 16, 1970.
323. McCarthy. See ref. 63.
324. *New York Times,* August 7, 9, 1970; *San Francisco Chronicle,* August 8, 1970.
325. Letter by Thaddeus R. Beal, *New York Times,* August 16, 1970.
326. *New York Times,* August 17, 1970.
327. *New York Times,* August 19, 1970.
328. *Four Lights,* XXX, No. 1, January, 1970, WILPF, 2006 Walnut St., Philadelphia, Pa., 19103.

329. See especially the publication *National Action/Research on the Military Industrial Complex,* AFSC, 160 N. 15th St. Philadelphia, Pa. 19102.

330. Theodor Rosebury, *Peace or Pestilence: Biological Warfare and How to Avoid It,* McGraw-Hill, New York, 1949. See also the June, 1960, issue (vol. XVI, No. 6) of *Bulletin of the Atomic Scientists* and the August-September, 1967, issue (vol. 9, No. 7) of *Scientist and Citizen.*

331. M. Meselson, "Man in the News," *New York Times,* November 26, 1969.

332. M. Meselson, *Proc. Natl. Acad. Sc., 65,* 253 (1969).

333. *Chemical and Engineering News,* January 24, 1966.

334. Rose. See ref. 84. See paper by Arthur Galston.

335. *Newsletter,* Federation of American Scientists, *20,* 5, 1967.

336. *News Release,* Federation of American Scientists, January 22, 1970.

337. Testimony of E. J. Lieberman, M. D. See ref. 62.

338. *Bulletin of the Atomic Scientists,* May, 1968.

339. M. Brown, *The Social Responsibility of the Scientist,* The Free Press, N. Y., 1971.

340. CBW Hearings. See ref. 62.

341. *Ibid.*

Chapter 2

Medical Aspects of Antipersonnel Gases

ALJE VENNEMA

In the field of medicine there are two principles that are essential: ethics and scientific discussion of medical problems. Medical ethics protect the patient and in a sense, the doctor. That the doctor shall not disclose the disease of his patient has become an accepted fact. Yet, it is sometimes beneficial to disclose the disease of the patient not only to stimulate scientific discussion and research but to benefit him or others and protect him from the disease. It is for these reasons that the medical problems of certain Vietnamese patients will be discussed.

The provincial hospital of Quang Ngai where these patients were seen is a civilian hospital and falls under the jurisdiction of the Ministry of Health for South Vietnam. The hospital is under the direction of a Vietnamese doctor appointed by the Ministry. In Quang Ngai all four directors since 1964 have been military men. The *Medicin-Chef,* as he is known, reports to the provincial governor who is also a Saigon appointee. In 1964 the hospital had 220 beds, which was almost adequate for the number of patients then seeking attention. After May, 1965, the number of surgical patients gradually increased, conditions in the province rapidly deteriorated, food became more scarce, hygiene and sanitation went rapidly downhill, the number of refugees increased daily, and loss of homes became the order of the day. New additions to the hospital clearly were required. By 1968 the number of beds had increased to 440, and the average daily census was between 550 and 650 patients. The number of admissions was over 1,300 per month on an average. There were 350 surgical and 250 medical patients per month, and the remainder were obstetric, pediatric, and tuberculosis patients.

The hospital serves a population of 700,000 and is situated in the small capital city, the population of which has increased over the last three years from 8,000 to 30,000 owing to the influx of refugees. Scattered throughout the province are ten poorly functioning district dispensaries, understaffed, with the personnel underpaid and not supervised.

The hospital improved greatly from 1960 to 1964 owing to the presence of a "Medico Team" (Medical International Cooperative Organization founded by Dr. Thomas A. Dooley in 1958). Yet, according to Western standards there is no comparison. The wards and clinics consist of brick buildings and sheds, with all facilities highly overburdened. The inflow of patients is often so great and bed space so limited that two patients to one bed is commonplace. Sometimes on the pediatric ward one may see two mothers in one bed each with a child. The beds measure thirty by seventy-three inches. Not only are diseases exchanged; the relatives who are there to feed and nurse the patients are of course quite vulnerable. When night falls, the relatives curl up with the patients or sleep on the floor. If the patients are not too sick when they arrive, the chance that they will be soon after their arrival is great.

The city also has a field hospital, "The First Army Republic of Vietnam Field Hospital." There are in the town one private physician, a Vietnamese who does not concern himself with public medicine; one seventy-three-year-old private Chinese physician, who is retired; and four Vietnamese military doctors.

Two of the military doctors have had one and two years surgical training respectively and perform all the civilian and military surgery as they see fit and desire to do. They spend no more than one or two hours a day in the civil or military hospital. They do fairly good work technically, but have no concept of preoperative and postoperative treatment. They again see the patient on whom they operated about two or three days after the operation. In the meantime the care is left up to the nurse who dares to call the doctor only in an extreme emergency or if the patient is a relative or good friend of the doctor. This attitude seems to stem from class distinction.

Of the other two military doctors, one, the director, is the administrator for both the civilian and military hospitals. He has had two years of training in medicine and is fairly good and quite conscientious but is overburdened. He actually has three jobs: *Medicin-Chef* of both hospitals and the head of the Rural Health Department. The other military doctor, a recent graduate from Saigon, has had no additional training to his schooling and practices very poor medicine for a few hours a day.

All these doctors never leave the town to go into the countryside to see the sick and go on leave quite often. Their time not spent in the hospital is devoted to private practice and pleasure.

Besides the above doctors, there are usually five foreign doctors in Quang Ngai Province. One, an Australian who concerns himself with the primitive Montagnard tribes, belongs to the Missionary Alliance. A second is a Canadian

Colombo Plan physician. There are four Americans: two army doctors from MILPHAP (Military Public Health Assistance Programme) who stay for a year, and two short-term Project Vietnam doctors who spend two months. At times the International Rescue Committee has a doctor in the area. Hence, in total, there are eleven doctors for a population of 700,000 or one doctor per 50,000 persons. Actually, this is not a true estimate, for the Vietnamese doctors do not concern themselves with the rural population, which leaves the foreigners to look after more than 650,000 people. To help screen the more than 300 patients daily at the provincial hospital, there is one health technician with training equivalent to two years of medical school, and a national nurse. ("National" implies a three-year training program in one of five approved hospitals in South Vietnam.) The hospital is staffed with seventeen national nurses and thirteen assistant nurses, each with one year of training. There is one very competent surgical technician who does both major and minor surgery.

One may ask how is it possible that a 440-bed hospital manages to take care of such a huge population. The answer is, it does not! An assortment of reasons besides limited facilities and too few doctors are evident: few can afford to pay the fifty-piaster ride by lambretta to town, few have their own vehicle, and ambulances are nonexistent. The only possibility is to walk or come by bicycle to the hospital.

Many people still believe in primitive remedies. Medicine in Quang Ngai is a curious mixture of the ancient and the modern. There are two private Western pharmacies in town that have all the modern drugs known to Western medicine. Very few patients can afford these even though no prescription is required. The first resort is usually the herb doctor, then the Chinese medicine man with all his exotic concoctions. If these do not work, there is the last resort, the hospital.

Who Are the Patients, and Where Do They Live ?

The patients are Central Vietnamese and live in the province of Quang Ngai. The French who colonized Indochina from 1852 to 1954 did not return to Quang Ngai after the defeat of the Japanese in 1945. When in 1945 Vietnam received independence from Japan, Quang Ngai became a bastion of Nationalism and had until 1954 a Viet Minh government. After the Geneva Accords in 1954, Quang Ngai became part of South Vietnam. Today, less than one-third of the population is under government control.

The province itself is about the size of greater Los Angeles, and has, roughly, a population of 700,000. Geographically, it is mountainous for the most part with a narrow coastal plain along the South China Sea. Located in Central Vietnam it is one of the most densely populated areas in the world. There are more than 1,000 persons per square mile in the inhabited parts; the mountainous areas are not habitable. The coastal plain is twenty miles wide and is intensely farmed for rice and sugarcane. The forested mountains behind the plain are now inaccessible as are many areas of the plain, including the valley rice lands, because of the heavy guerilla infiltration.

Less than 20 per cent of the land is "secure," so-called, by day. At night, no area is secure. The military presence of the South Vietnamese Army, Second Division, the United States Marines and Air Cavalry units, and the South Korean Marines have been able only to maintain the status quo.

In winter the climate is cool, sometimes cold, especially at night, with heavy torrential rains, because this is the season of the wet monsoon. The summer is quite hot, with temperatures regularly around 100° F. The late summer and wet monsoon season are often the season of typhoons and devastating floods, which each year bring disaster to hundreds of people. In 1964, 1965, and 1967, hundreds drowned and thousands became homeless.

There is no large city. The town of Quang Ngai has a population of about 30,000. Industry is virtually nonexistent, except the handicrafts, and what little wealth there is is controlled by a few people. The soil is poor compared to the rest of the country. All these factors combined make this one of the poorest provinces in the land.

Over a period of five years from early 1964 until late 1968, medical and surgical problems were commonplace at the hospital. There were the wounded few in 1964, more in 1965, and many in the following years. There were the medical diseases of infants, children, and adults, and the obstetrical problems. Diseases primarily infectious in origin, such as tuberculosis, encephalitis, pneumonia, dysenteries, cholera, and plague were prevalent as well as the nutritional conditions like vitamin deficiencies, kwashiorkor, marasmus, beri-beri, and cirrhosis. War injuries ranged from small wounds to multiple injuries, be it from bullet, mine, grenade, cannon, or bomb. It was in May, 1965, that the first cases of gas poisoning were seen. Over the ensuing years until August, 1968, twenty-one cases were well documented. Other cases occurred, but no accurate records of these were kept. Consequently, the findings that will be discussed pertain to those twenty-one cases that were well documented (Table 2-1). It should be noted that all fatalities were women and children.

The reason that nine of the twenty-one documented cases died may be explained in three ways: one, the antipersonnel gases behaved on the patients' biochemistry and pathophysiology like the nerve gases; two, repeated inhalation in an enclosed space was cumulative and without the presence of mind to get out of the enclosed space, the patient had no time to recover because he was continuously exposed; and three, the gas exposure was superimposed upon an already diseased lung, *i.e.,* a lung with chronic bronchitis, emphysema, bronchiectasis, pneumonia or superimposed on the general debilitation of the patient, be it from other disease or malnutrition.

TABLE 2–1

The Patients

Date	Name	Age	District	Village	Note
June 3, 1965	Hien TAM	3	Son Tinh	Ba Gia	Died 3 June 1965
	Vo Thi LE	6	—	—	Died 4 June 1965
	Hien PHAT	9	—	—	Home 23 June 1965
	Vuong Thi HOA	32	—	—	Home 23 June 1965
	Vuong Thi MINH	65	—	—	Died 6 June 1965
Oct. 6, 1965	Ho PHAT	4	Son Tinh	Son Kim	Home 8 Nov. 1965
	Le Thi CAM	8	—	—	Died 7 Oct. 1965
	Nguyen Thi LIEN	35	—	—	Home 28 Oct. 1965
	Ho Van SAU	37	—	—	Home 30 Oct. 1965
	Nguyen Thi Kim CHI	32	—	—	Home 1 Nov. 1965
Oct. 12, 1965	Pham Thi LIEU	2	—	—	Died 13 Oct. 1965
	Pham Thi LIEN	33	—	—	Home 29 Oct. 1965
	Vo Thi LAM	32	—	—	Died 13 Oct. 1965
Oct. 7, 1966	Huynh LUONG	14	Tu Nghia	Tu Phuoc	Escaped 9 Oct. 1966
June 23, 1967	Nguyen NAM	8	Nghia Hanh	Nghia Phu	Died 23 June 1967
	Nguyen Thi LUONG	10	—	—	Home 12 July 1967
	Dinh Thi PHONG	30	—	—	Home 25 July 1967
June 24, 1967	Le Thi MAI	60	—	—	Home 14 July 1967
	Nguyen Thi TIEN	10	—	—	Home 25 July 1967
June 26, 1967	Dinh Thi GIA	39	—	—	Died 26 June 1967
June 27, 1967	Mai Thi XUONG	31	—	—	Died 27 June 1967

Physiology

The signs that the patients exhibited support the contention that the action of the antipersonnel gases in an already poor-risk patient is like that of the nerve gases and organic phosphates so frequently used as insecticides. The antipersonnel gases may inhibit the cholinesterase enzyme system, which normally acts at the neuromuscular junction, at postganglionic parasympathetic sites, at the preganglionic sympathetic and parasympathetic ganglion cells, at the adrenal medulla, on somatic motor nerves to skeletal muscle, and on certain tracts of the central nervous system. Cholinesterase is necessary to remove any excess of acetylcholine, which is responsible for impulse transmission at the neuromuscular junction. Because of the continuous destruction of cholinesterase by the antipersonnel gases, acetylcholine accumulates and brings about its adverse effects. It causes among other things a flaccid paralysis similar to that produced by curare. The gases have a short action span and are metabolized or hydrolyzed rapidly. However, continuous exposure reintroduces the substance again and again through inhalation or through the skin. Even though the gas metabolizes quickly, the accumulation of acetylcholine is long-lasting because it does not metabolize quickly. The effects of acetylcholine accumulation leads to the inevitable disruption of all the functions of the parasympathetic nervous system.

There is at first flushing of the skin, and the skin feels warm to touch. A rapid, bounding pulse is noted. Sweating, tearing, and excess salivation ensue. Inspiratory stridor and shortness of breath choke the patient. After a few minutes the pulse rate drops, the heart slows down, and the blood pressure drops. Arrhythmias, *i.e.,* atrial fibrillation and heart block, develop. The signs and symptoms that will hereafter be discussed seem more than likely owing to an excess of acetylcholine.

The Gas Victims

In early June, 1965, during the battle of Ba Gia about twenty kilometers from Quang Ngai, a number of patients arrived at the hospital. They had been hiding in a tunnel in order to shelter themselves from the severe bombardment that went on in the Ba Gia area where the guerillas had launched a battle on May 29 that lasted until June 4. Among the hundreds of dead and wounded, both civilian and military, were three children and two adults (mother and grandmother) who suffered from gas poisoning. They had been exposed to gas the day before their arrival at the hospital. The youngest child was three and moribund. The other children were six and nine years old. The mother was getting over the worst of it. It was through her courage and willpower that she had managed to get the group out of the tunnel and away from the embattled area. The three-year-old died within two hours after arrival, the six-year-old died the next day, and the grandmother two days later. Only the mother and the nine-year-old survived. At the time not much attention was paid to the problems of patients suffering from gas because of the necessity of dealing with hundreds of casualties and disposing of over 300 dead to prevent catastrophic health problems.

In October, 1965, as the activity north of the town increased, on two consecutive occasions a group of five patients and a group of three patients came in from Son Kim village, Son Tinh district. Their story was similar to that of the patients of May, 1965. The group of five were all related. They had constructed for themselves a bunker near their straw hut for protection against artillery fire at night. During the day of October 6, when fighting erupted nearby, they sheltered themselves in the bunker. As they were hiding, a canister of gas was thrown into their bunker, and they were told in English to get out. They did not understand the language and got frightened. They remained inside for a while and later on crawled out and managed to get to hospital by lambretta. Of the first group of five, two were children, one of four years and one of eight. The others were adults—father, mother, and an aunt. One of the children, the child of eight, died the next morning. The four-year-old survived, as did the three adults. Of the second group of three (mother, child and a neighbor) the child was two years old, the mother thirty-three and the neighbor thirty-two. The neighbor was well known at the hospital as she had been a tuberculosis patient for several years. The child and the neighbor died the day after arrival.

In 1966, patients with gas affliction were seen at the district dispensaries outside the town—two in early spring at the Mo Duc dispensary and one in midsummer at Tra Bong. In October, 1966, one case was seen at the provincial hospital—a young boy of fourteen who arrived at 8:00 P.M., retching and vomiting. He had been at the hospital for thirty minutes before I saw him. As I entered the room I saw a sick child in great distress. At first I did not know what I was dealing with until upon examination I touched his skin. My fingers started to burn and my eyes to hurt, and I could not breathe. I had to leave the room and return five minutes later. It was obvious that this was again gas affliction. Treatment was started, and the boy was transferred to an open room. There was no oxygen available at the hospital, and only supportive treatment could be given. During the night he gradually improved. The next morning he took some rice soup; the day thereafter he escaped from the hospital to return home.

During 1967 again several cases were seen; some were admitted to other wards and treated by one of the American doctors. When I questioned him about the cases and asked him for information on the type of gas it was and how it was being used, when, where, and what the hazards were, he stated that he did not know. Upon asking other American officials of the United States Agency for International Development, the Central Intelligence Agency, and other civilians in the area, I was still unable to learn what it was. More satisfaction was obtained from the ordinary soldiers who were very helpful and told of the circumstances under which the gases were used. The gases were used to flush guerillas out of tunnels and hiding places; when an unfamiliar village was entered, each hole that looked suspicious was searched. The soldiers were familiar with the effects of the gas, and many a soldier stated that people got very ill from it. The soldiers did not know what to do in case a patient was very ill except to expose him to the open air. They were also aware that deaths had occurred from gas.

In May, 1967, at noon, three patients were brought to the hospital in a vehicle. As they entered the gate, the driver of the vehicle recognized two of the American doctors who were leaving the hospital by jeep. He stopped them and asked them for assistance. The patients had been exposed to gas that morning and by this time were extremely ill. Both doctors threw a cursory glance at the patients and told the driver they were going to their barracks for lunch and that if the patients were still alive by 3:00 P.M., they might do something. I witnessed this as I was on my way home. The plight of the patients was a terrible one. Two were middle-aged women. Both were severely short of breath, wheezing, coughing, and retching. The floor of the vehicle was covered with vomitus. The driver took them to the ward where intravenous fluids, aminophylline, and atropine were given. An antibiotic was prescribed to treat the aspiration pneumonia both had acquired. One of the women died. The terrible problem was to explain to the Vietnamese the behavior of the American physician.

Nguyen Nam and Nguyen Thi Luong

Nguyen Nam and Nguyen Thi Luong were brother and sister. Nam was eight years old, and Luong was ten years old. They were brought to the hospital at about 6.00 P.M. on June 23, 1967 by a Canadian who worked for the Vietnam Christian Services organization. The girl complained of frontal headaches, burning eyes, blurring of vision, photophobia, and pain in the eyes. She was retching and vomiting, irritable, restless, wheezing, and extremely short of breath. The young boy was foaming at the mouth and comatose. His respiration was depressed with a respiratory rate of 10/min; his blood pressure was 60/20, and his pulse was 60. He did not respond to pain. His temperature was 38.5° C. His pupils were constricted, and there was spasm of the ciliary muscles. The nose exhibited secretions, and there was severe bronchospasm with rales and rhonchi of both lungs throughout. There was laryngeal spasm. The heart sounds were distant; multiple extra systoles were heard. The abdomen felt soft with no masses; there was incontinence of urine; and the muscles exhibited fasciculations.

Immediate treatment for heart failure and pulmonary edema was started but to no avail. The boy's respirations became more depressed. He was gasping for breath. He became cold and developed Cheyne Stokes respira-

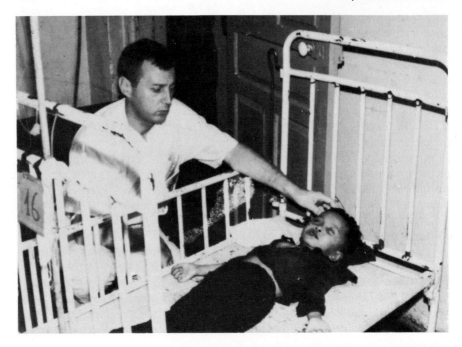

Figure 2–1. Dr. Alje Vennema checks the body of an 8-year-old boy, Nguyen Nam, a victim of tear-gas inhalation. Quang Ngai Hospital, June 23, 1967.

tions. The pulmonary edema became worse, the pulse slowed, tonic and clonic convulsions set in. He developed atrial fibrillation, went into flaccid paralysis, and died at 7.45 P.M., less than two hours after admission. His sister was very ill as well. She was panicky, apprehensive, and severely dyspneic. Her pulse rate was 140 and bounding; her respiratory rate was 25 with a blood pressure of 100/60; her temperature was 39.5° C. Her pupils were constricted; she was sweating and tearing from her eyes. Both lungs exhibited rhonci and rales throughout. Her heart sounds were normal; there were no extra systoles; her abdomen felt soft, and she was not incontinent. Her skin was flushed and felt warm. She was treated for pulmonary edema and pneumonia. Her course in hospital went up and down. She was in hospital for twenty days and had pulmonary edema three times. Finally, the pneumonia cleared up, and she was sent home on July 12.

The same day the two children were admitted a woman named Dinh Thi Phong was brought to the hospital by the Vietnam Christian Service. She was from the same village but not related to the children. She was discharged on July 25 after treatment for pulmonary edema.

On July 13 an elderly woman of sixty and her grandchild of ten were brought to the hospital by the Vietnam Christian Service. They were from

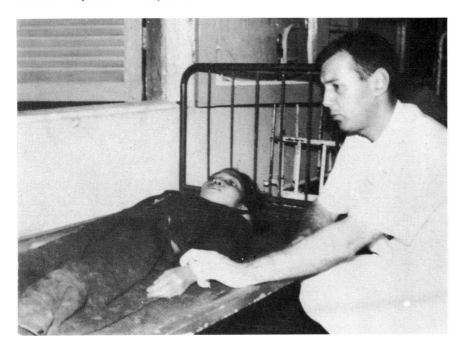

Figure 2–2. Dr. Vennema examines gas victim Nguyen Thi Luong, a 10-year-old girl. Quang Ngai Hospital, June 23, 1967.

the same village and were related to the two children. Though both were very ill and stayed in hospital for twenty and thirty days respectively, they survived. In the outpatient department, where both were followed later on, they had to be treated for chronic bronchitis. Repeated respiratory disease as a complication of parasitosis is very common in Vietnamese children. The child may have had respiratory disease before she was exposed to gas; the same is true for her grandmother. Nevertheless, both were seen frequently thereafter and treated for chronic lung disease.

Treatment of all the cases centered around supportive measures—oxygen when available, intravenous fluids, atropine. When the eyes were involved, atropine was instilled. Activity was completely restricted; even if the patient appeared well, he was kept in bed because the slightest bit of exertion precipitated wheezing and pulmonary edema the first several days after exposure.

The rationale for atropine is that it functions as an anticholinergic and as such stimulates respiration by relaxing the bronchial musculature, inhibits secretions, and suppresses vagal inhibition of the heart. Most patients had a high threshold for atropine and required large dosages. If there has been an anoxic period or a period of depressed respiration, atropine is contraindicated because it releases vagal inhibition and causes atrial fibrillation. Hence, oxygen becomes the main treatment. In case of convulsions valium

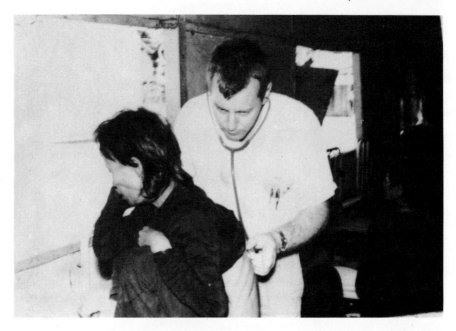

Figure 2–3. Dr. Vennema with Le Thi Mai, a 60-year-old woman treated for gas poisoning. Quang Ngai Hospital, June–July, 1967.

when available should be used to control the seizures. Phenobarbital is contra-indicated because it depresses the respiration even more. Increased dizziness, confusion, visual disturbances, and a cloudy sensorium were sometimes noted as side effects of atropine. In the case of circulatory collapse, a vaso-pressor is contraindicated and a vasodilator should be used. Venosection should be done, and at least 300 cc. of blood removed. The patient must be given antibiotics to combat the always present bronchitis or pneumonia. Atelectasis is a common complication. Steroids were also used; however, the role they played was not clear.

Sequelae of the condition were judged over a period of only one year. Several of the patients who survived did return to clinic and were found to have chronic bronchitis. They were followed for the duration of my stay in Vietnam during which time they managed on periodic broncho dilators and antibiotic treatment of any superimposed infection. In the returnees there was no evidence of emphysema, though this may well ensue as the years go by. Coughing, wheezing, and expectoration of frothy sputum were the main complaints. The patients' lung functions could not be determined except crudely; their forced expiratory phase was markedly prolonged. Some patients did not return for follow up, and it may be assumed that they completely recovered.

The X-ray findings in the acute stage showed a diffuse infiltration of both lungs. If no pneumonia ensued, the lungs cleared after two weeks. The chronic stage changes were those of fibrosis with no evidence of bronchiectasis. Negative X-ray findings after recovery did not of course rule out further disease nor did minimal gas exposure. It has been shown that minimal gas exposure may eventually lead to chronic chest disease and emphysema.

Only two postmortems were done—one on the little boy of eight and the other on a woman of thirty-nine. There was no chance to do a postmortem on the others because relatives objected. Only the chest and abdomen were opened, and gross examination of the lungs was carried out. On postmortem the bodies were dusky. The lungs were distended when the chest was opened and remained distended. The pleural cavities contained serosanguinous exudate, there was no evidence of obstructive emphysema, but there was gross evidence of pulmonary edema. The trachea and bronchi were filled with a serosanguinous exudate. Gross sectioning showed fluid in the terminal bronchioles. The abdomen was opened, but no organs were removed. On gross inspection no abnormalities were seen except that the liver was congested. A small section was taken, but unfortunately the specimens were lost and microscopic section was therefore impossible. One can therefore only guess as to what the effect of the gas really is. It more than likely acts on the epithelium, which gives rise to the exudation of fluid into the alveoli. The postmortem was done at night immediately after death when only the Vietnamese surgical technician and I were present. At that time I was being watched because my criticism of the war was not liked by some of the American personnel in the area.

Here the story ends.

On November 23, 1967, I wrote a letter to Dr. E. W. Pfeiffer recounting the incidents described above. When the letter was released to the press, the incidents were immediately denied by Richard Fryklund, Deputy Assistant Secretary of Defense for Public Affairs, a spokesman for the Pentagon.

In Quang Ngai words of denial were not necessary, for the evidence spoke for itself. Nguyen Nam, Nguyen Thi Luong, and the others who had succumbed could no longer testify. In a Vietnamese hospital there are always many people because the relatives attend to the sick. The wards are open and anyone may walk in or look on. As Nguyen Nam gasped for breath for two hours before he died, many looked on. They knew what caused the child's death. It was gas—and they were the silent witnesses to a tragic story.

PART II

Herbicides

Chapter 3
The Military Uses
of Herbicides
in Vietnam

E. W. PFEIFFER & GORDON H. ORIANS

Following its annual meeting in December, 1969, the American Association for the Advancement of Science (AAAS), America's largest and most prestigious science organization announced:

Harvard geneticist, Matthew S. Meselson, has been named by the AAAS to prepare a detailed operating plan for a future study of the effects of defoliants and herbicides on the land and people in Vietnam. The Council of the AAAS agreed to provide Meselson, a long-time foe of chemical and biological warfare, with up to $50,000 for his one-year study. He will head a committee that will design a long-range study, financed from outside sources (but not the Defense Department), to be conducted in Vietnam by an international team of specialists. (1)

With the many problems arising from the Vietnam war, why is it that the American scientific community, as represented by the AAAS, should be so concerned about this particular aspect of the war in Vietnam? Basically what appears to be involved is the intersection of increasing concern about our general impact upon our environment with the increasing destructiveness of modern war. When we add to these concerns the great uncertainty about the effects of the chemicals used in Vietnam and the fact that they represent a weakening of political and moral restraints against chemical and biological warfare, a serious situation obviously confronts us.

References to this chapter are on page 176.

The concern of the AAAS was first formalized when E. W. Pfeiffer introduced a resolution to the Pacific Division of the AAAS at its Annual Council
Meeting June 15th, 1966. The resolution read:

Whereas, units of the U.S. Department of Defense have used both chemical and
biological warfare agents (as defined by U.S. Department of the Army TM-3216) in
operations against enemy forces in Vietnam; and whereas, the effect of these agents
upon biological systems in warfare is not known to the scientific community; and
whereas, the scientific community has a responsibility to be fully informed of these agents
and their use in warfare because they are a result of scientific research; therefore, be
it resolved that: 1) the Pacific Division of the AAAS establish a committee of experts
in the field of biological and chemical warfare to study the use of CW and BW agents
in Vietnam for the purpose of determining what agents have been used and the extent
of their use and the effects on all biological systems that might have been affected;
2) that the above committee make a public record of their findings at the next meeting
of the Pacific Division of the AAAS. (2)

It was hoped that this resolution would catalyze into effective action the
concern many scientists had long felt about the massive use of certain chemicals
in the war in Vietnam. Uneasiness was first expressed by the Federation of
American Scientists in 1964 when it issued a statement that said in part:

Finally we are concerned with reports of the field use of chemical weapons in
Vietnam. Allegations relating to the use of anti-crop agents under American supervision been officially denied. However, reports that defoliating agents have been
used to destroy protective cover have been confirmed by representatives of the Department of Defense. These charges give rise to the broader implication that the U.S. is
using the Vietnamese battlefield as a proving ground for chemical and biological
warfare. We are opposed to experimentation on foreign soil and also feel that such
experimentation involving citizens of other countries compounds the moral liability
of such actions. (2)

In following years appeals were made to the White House by many individual scientists and groups of scientists. The largest single group of independent
scientists, under the leadership of Dr. John Edsall of Harvard, forwarded a
petition to President Lyndon Johnson in February, 1967. More than 5,000
American scientists, including seventeen Nobel Prize winners and 129 members of the United States National Academy of Sciences, were among the
signers recommending a review of United States policy toward CBW weapons
and urging that an order be issued by the president to stop the use of herbicides in Vietnam. It was typical of the administration that President Johnson
did not even answer these scientists, and the Department of Defense continued
to escalate the use of the chemicals that had so concerned these experts.

The concern of scientists about military use of herbicides arose in large
part from the fear that not enough was known about the effects of these
chemicals on the biota of even our own country to say nothing of the effects
of their massive use, at higher concentrations than obtained in domestic uses,
in a tropical area. This lack of information made it impossible for anyone to
predict the short- and long-term effects of this massive chemical intervention
in the environment in Vietnam.

The Military Uses of Herbicides in Vietnam

But what are these chemicals and how are they used? Accor
Department of Defense three basic types of herbicides are emplo,
military in Vietnam (3). Table 3–1 gives the exact composition, p
gallon of acid equivalent, and the normal application rate of these f
The chemical normally used for jungle defoliation is Agent Orang(＿ ᴜᴜ
mixture of the n-butyl esters of 2,4-D and 2,4,5-T. Agent Orange is dissolved
in an organic solvent such as diesel oil or kerosene before spray application.
It is a general purpose herbicide that produces leaf fall in three to six weeks
and control persisting for seven to twelve months. About 40 million pounds
have been sprayed over 5 million acres during the last nine years (4). Agent
White combines Picloram (picolinic acid) with 2,4-D in a low volatility amine
salt formation. This combination provides relatively longer duration of control
of a wide spectrum of woody plants plus the advantages of more accurate
spray placements where volatility creates problems. Agent Orange is highly

---

TABLE 3–1

Military Use of Herbicides[a]

MAJOR CHEMICALS USED IN SOUTH VIETNAM

Agent Orange: 2,4-D and 2,4,5-T

Composition: A 1:1 mixture of the n-butyl esters of 2,4-dichloro-
phenoxyacetic acid and 2,4,5-trichlorophenoxyacetic acid.
Active Ingredients: 4.1 and 4.4 lb./gal.
Application: Undiluted at 3 gal./acre. Often applied a second time.
Major use: Against forest vegetation.

Agent White: 2,4-D and Picloram

Composition: A 4:1 mixture of the tri-iso-propanolamine salts of
2,4-D and 4-amino-3,5,6-trichloropicolinic acid in water. (Picloram
is the same as Dow Chemical Company's "Tordon"; the mixture
used is the same as Dow's "Tordon-101.")
Active Ingredients: 2.0 and 0.54 lb./gal.
Application: Undiluted at 3 gal./acre.
Major use: Same as for agent Orange.

Agent Blue: Cacodylic Acid

Composition: A 6:1 mixture of sodium dimethyl arsenate and di-
methyl arsenic acid in water. (Cacodylic acid is the same as Ansul
Company's "Phytar-560G.")
Active Ingredients: 3.1 lb. and 0.50 lb./gal.
Application: Undiluted at 3 gal./acre.
Major use: Against rice and other food crops.

TABLE 3–1 (cont'd)

APPROXIMATE EXTENT OF SPRAYING IN SOUTH VIETNAM

Year	Forest Land	Crop Land	Total Land
1962	4,900 acres	700 acres	5,600 acres
1963	24,700	200	24,900
1964	83,500	10,400	93,900
1965	155,600	65,900	221,500
1966	741,200	104,000	845,200
1967	1,486,400	221,300	1,707,700
1968	1,267,100	63,700	1,330,800
1969 (first half)	797,200	38,800	836,000
TOTAL	4,560,600 acres	505,000 acres	5,065,600 acres

[a] U.S. Department of Defense data. The total area of South Vietnam is approximately 42 million acres. Of this, about 7.6 million acres are under intensive cultivation and about 14 million acres are forested (89 per cent semideciduous, 9 per cent mangrove, and 2 per cent conifer).

volatile in the heat of southeast Asia. Agent White is similar to compositions used for aerial spraying of power line rights of way throughout the United States. Agent Blue, cacodylic acid, is a contact herbicide employed for rapid defoliation. It does not kill most broad-leaved (dicotyledonous) species, but it is an effective grass control agent particularly useful in keeping down dense vegetation along roadsides and around military encampments. It is also widely used on rice fields in "enemy controlled" country where it destroys existing crops but does not apparently affect subsequent growth.

Cacodylic acid is a fast-acting contact dessicant that withers vegetation within a few days. The other agents act in a different manner. They mimic the natural seasonal defoliation that occurs in many woody plants by speeding up the process of leaf loss. According to the plant physiologist, Dr. Arthur Galston of Yale University:

... the leaves of deciduous plants are attached to the stem by a narrow stalk called the petiole. Through this petiole runs vascular tissue which conducts water and nutritive materials into the leaf and organic matter out of the leaf. As long as the leaf produces the hormone auxin at a moderate concentration the leaf remains on the plant. In normal concentrations auxin plays a useful role in various aspects of plant growth. If for natural reasons, such as the shortening days of Autumn or for artificial reasons, such as injury to the leaf blade, the production of auxin in the leaf blade ceases or slows down measurably, then a layer of large, weak, thin-walled cells which are easily ruptured is formed at the base of the petiole and results in leaf fall. This layer of large, thin, weak cells is called the abscission layer. The knowledge that lowered auxin levels in the leaf blade results in leaf fall suggested to scientists that deliberate application of hormone antagonists or compounds which lowered auxin levels in the leaf could furnish the means of controlling leaf fall. This suggestion was put to work in agricultural practice many years ago when defoliants were applied to cotton plants several days in advance of harvest of the bolls so that the mechanical cottonpicker would not be clogged by the undesirable leaves. The reverse practice, that of prolonging the retention of leaves and fruits to promote better growth and ripening can be accomplished by spraying with carefully controlled concentrations of substances with auxin hormone activity. If the hormone is too high, undesirable side effects occur which may even kill the plant. (5)

As yet there is disagreement over the effects of these chemicals on the soil and soil microorganisms. Experts at the U.S. Department of Agriculture and Department of Defense conclude that none of the chemicals used will have a detrimental effect on microbial populations in the soil. They point out that the numbers of soil microorganisms capable of inactivating 2,4-D apparently increase when 2,4-D is present in the soil. This probably occurs with 2,4,5-T as well. Picloram does not destroy microorganisms, but it is broken down by microbes relatively slowly.

These official conclusions have been seriously questioned by competent independent scientists. A recent report reveals that the biological activity of picloram is more than 100 times greater than that of 2,4-D and its activity is so sensitive to variations in climate and soil conditions that the margin of safety on edible crops is very low. The U.S. Food & Drug Administration has not licensed picloram for use on a single American crop. In Puerto Rico jungle areas treated with picloram remained essentially bare of trees and shrubs for two years. A report recently released by the Advanced Research Project Agency of the U.S. Department of Defense states that "a detectable residue of picloram was present after one year at all temperature and moisture levels in all soils even at the one-half pound per acre rate." Dr. Arthur Galston, a distinguished plant physiologist at Yale University, points out that there are not any data pertinent to the action of herbicides on the soils of Vietnam. He states that they usually take from 2 to 15 weeks to disappear from the soil in temperate climates after a single application. Some of them may linger for more than a year or do not disappear at all. Microorganisms break down such chemical compounds as 2,4-D and 2,4,5-T, changing their structure. It is not yet known how these molecules break down, but it is possible that phenolic substances are produced. These phenolic substances may promote destruction of natural auxins within a plant. Although the original herbicide has disappeared, it may have been replaced by another substance which is also toxic to plants. (6)

A History of the Use of Herbicides

The history of herbicides extends back at least to the great English naturalist, Charles Darwin, who in 1880 made the first observations that subsequently led plant physiologists to the discovery of growth-regulating materials in plants (7). Darwin observed that plants always bend toward their source of light, and he speculated that the tip of the plant transmitted some substance to the lower part of the plant that produced this directive growth. After years of experimentation by plant physiologists, an extract containing a plant growth substance was finally obtained in 1926. Plant physiologists continued to test and find ever more potent growth-regulating chemicals during the 1930s. They found that some of these chemicals could make apples and pears remain on trees until fully ripe, that some of them induced rooting, hastening the ripening and curing of fruits, and that some even produced seedless tomatoes. The purpose of the research on growth regulators was always to discover more of such useful applications for these synthetic plant hormones.

However, the interest in the use of synthetic plant hormones or growth regulators took a dramatic turn in 1942 when it was discovered that phenoxyacetic acids had powerful effects on the metabolism and growth of plants. E. J. Kraus, head of the Botany Department of the University of Chicago, who had been working for several years on plant growth regulators, recognized that in certain concentrations 2,4-D had toxic properties that could be used for the destruction of crops or the limitation of crop production. He suggested to a special committee on chemical and biological warfare of the National Academy of Sciences that chemicals should be tested for their herbicidal properties. In 1943 Kraus worked out a contract between the University of Chicago and the U.S. Army to study what turned out to be the highly toxic effect of 2,4,5-T on rice. In 1944 the Army decided to step up this work with herbicides, and they made herbicide research a part of the work at what is now Fort Detrick, the chief CBW research center. Thus, the use of herbicides for military purposes was born of basic research, the first application of which was for the benefit of agricultural production. During this period of testing and development, toxicity studies on animals were made to establish the safety of 2,4-D. In fact, Kraus personally consumed one-half gram per day for three weeks of this material and claimed to experience no adverse effects. All these tests were of a short-term nature, and therefore they could potentially reveal only some of the effects of these chemicals.

In addition to the rapid end of the war in 1945, there was another rather important reason why the United States did not do field tests of herbicides in an active theater during World War II. During the war there was a great deal of interest in destroying vegetation in the Pacific Theater. The principal means employed at that time was high explosives. Scientists were asked to investigate chemicals that were available in large quantities in the United States and that could be used for defoliating this vegetation. By June, 1945, the U.S. Army was prepared to recommend the use of certain defoliants in the Pacific Theater. As Dr. Charles Minarik of the Crops Division, U.S. Army Biological Center, Fort Detrick, recalls, "If we used this chemical, we would be accused of conducting poison gas warfare. Therefore, the plan to use chemicals for destroying vegetation in the Pacific Theater was dropped" (3).

In a postwar program, Fort Detrick studied approximately 12,000 chemicals for their defoliating and desiccating activities. Some of these defoliants were tested against tropical vegetation in Puerto Rico. In 1959 a highly significant demonstration of vegetation control was conducted at Camp Drum,

New York, using 2,4-D and 2,4,5-T. The trees in the tested area were denuded over an area of four square miles. Shortly after this successful defoliation test the government of South Vietnam requested the U.S. Army to undertake trials of defoliants for use against guerrilla forces. This request coincided with the first announcement in the United States that, "The Army is experimenting with chemical techniques for stripping jungle areas of foliage to expose guerrilla fighters or other hostile forces and installations" (3). A variety of chemical agents were shipped to the Vietnamese military authorities and were tested between July, 1961 and April, 1962. These tests proved that the esters of 2,4-D and 2,4,5-T killed the majority of the species encountered in Vietnam, providing the herbicide spray was properly applied to the vegetation during a period of active growth. In addition the first aerial application of cacodylic acid showed its promise as a fast-acting desiccant. After these preliminary tests it was recommended that further screening of chemicals and development of application systems be conducted in Thailand or other tropical areas having vegetation similar to that in Vietnam.

It is ironic that the Advanced Research Project Agency (ARPA) of the U.S. Department of Defense turned to the U.S. Department of Agriculture's Crops Protection Branch, Agricultural Research Service to learn in far greater detail about defoliation techniques and how to *destroy* crops. On January 30, 1963, the ARPA issued Order 424 to the U.S. Department of Agriculture. Order 424 directed the Agricultural Research Service to evaluate new herbicides or combinations of herbicides for killing tropical and subtropical vegetation, to develop methods of evaluating herbicides on different woody species, to determine the effects of environment on behavior and effectiveness of toxic herbicides, to determine optimum dates and rates of application, to relate the percentage of defoliation to horizontal and vertical obscuration, to develop methods for improved application techniques that provide better distribution patterns, and to obtain the botanical information needed so that correlations might be made between vegetation indigenous to the continental United States, Puerto Rico, and southeast Asia. This large order was filled by the USDA by November, 1967 (8).

In addition to the Agricultural Research Service, the Forest Service provided assistance to the U.S. Department of Defense in conjunction with its study of defoliation effects. It has been recently brought to light that there were two unsuccessful attempts to provoke massive fire storms in forests that had been defoliated for the purpose of subsequent bombing. The fire storms were to have been created by massive bombing with napalm following the killing of the forest with defoliants (9). Personnel from the Forest Fire Laboratory at Missoula, Montana, were sent to Vietnam to work out the technique to study the fuel properties of Vietnamese forests following defoliation.

In addition to contracting with the U.S. Department of Agriculture, the ARPA of the Department of Defense contracted with the U.S. Army Biological Center at Fort Detrick to conduct research on defoliation and control of tropical forests in Thailand. Let us look at some of the conclusions of these extensive studies as presented by Dr. Fred Tschirley in one of his reports (8). He states that picloram with few exceptions was the most effective herbicide tested for long-term defoliation. Picloram is not equally phytotoxic, and the rate required for effective defoliation varies widely. However, there is a very broad spectrum of woody species that are susceptible to picloram, making picloram particularly appropriate for the defoliation of forest types with high species diversity, such as are frequently found in tropical environments. Picloram also provides greater suppression of lateral and basal dormant buds. In studies of the amounts of picloram and 2,4-D moved about in different areas of the plant, it was shown that picloram was translocated more readily than 2,4-D, and this great mobility within the plant is probably the reason that picloram suppresses dormant buds more effectively than does 2,4-D. Furthermore, it was found that 2,4,5-T is not translocated, that is, moved through the leaves upon which it has been deposited, until the leaves are fully expanded.

Woody plants can also be effectively controlled by making herbicidal applications to the soil. Vegetation control can be obtained for relatively long periods if enough herbicide is used and there is not too much rain. The research indicated that picloram is mobile in the soil but does not degrade rapidly. In heavy clay the picloram remained at phytotoxic levels for long periods of time. Tschirley concluded that considerable regrowth occurs within six months after application of high rates of 2,4-D and 2,4,5-T to foliage. The rate and degree of regrowth are lower when equivalent volumes of picloram are applied. Application of 27 pounds/acre of picloram to the soil in rain forests in Puerto Rico resulted in almost complete destruction of woody vegetation. Within one year after treatment, however, the ground floor was completely covered with grasses and sedges, and woody seedlings were also becoming established. Grasses and herbaceous weeds are almost always the first vegetation types to reinvade an area after treatment with herbicide. In dry areas the grasses and weeds are of low stature, but they may grow as high as ten feet in wet tropical areas. Thus, if defoliation is maintained in a wet evergreen forest, grasses, sedges, and vines will quickly become established on the forest floor.

The Use of Herbicides in Vietnam

Vietnamese military forces conducted several large-scale tests of herbicides in the spring of 1962. At this time United States planes sprayed jungle along High·vay 15 connecting Bien Hoa to the coastal city of Vung Tau. This seventy-mile route had been considered unsafe for months, and government officials had to travel to Vung Tau by air. Following this early test, a high Vietnamese official said:

Defoliant chemicals will also be sprayed on Viet Cong plantations of manioc and sweet potatoes in the highlands. The exact locations of these plantations have already been plotted by aerial surveys. Tests have shown that manioc and sweet potatoes die four days after having been sprayed. These are the two most important food staples for the Communist bands in the mountains. (3)

Additional defoliation tests against mangrove and Nipa palm vegetation of the Ca Mau Peninsula were conducted in August, 1962. In these trials the heavy delta vegetation was sprayed 400 meters back from the edge of the rivers, and the roads were sprayed over a total length of seventy-nine kilometers. The agents used were 2,4-D and 2,4,5-T at the rate of 1.5 and 3.3 gallons per acre. The mangrove vegetation was completely defoliated in about one week. Nipa palm was slower, turning yellow and losing its leaves within five weeks. After five weeks 95 per cent of the leaves had dropped, and the visibility of the ground from directly overhead was increased by 90 per cent according to Army studies. Some of the consequences of this defoliation appeared to be economically beneficial. Following defoliation, the mangrove stands along some of the roads became accessible to the native woodcutters who cut the trees, converted the wood to charcoal, and sold it for fuel. Where the land was suitable after removal of the trees, various crops were planted and cultivated.

Since 1961, when herbicides were first used in Vietnam, military defoliation has become the largest known use of herbicides. This activity has been carried on by the U.S. Air Force, which created the 309th Air Commando Squadron. The first of their aircraft, C123 cargo planes, specially equipped for spray application, came to Tan Son Nhut Airport on November 29, 1961. This group of aircraft was the forerunner of the operation later to be known as Operation Ranchhand.

Military considerations primarily determine how and where and when herbicides will be applied (3). The particular tactical objectives (temporary leaf drop or plant kill) largely determine the type of vegetation treated and therefore the herbicide used. The extent of kill vs. defoliation depends on the herbicide used, the time of the year, and the nature of the vegetation. The rate and nature of revegetation and succession depend in part on whether isolated strips and patches of jungle vegetation are destroyed or whether large contiguous areas are controlled. Spraying cropland gives different ecological effects from those resulting from the defoliation of forests and brushland.

The Midwest Research Institute report, *Assessment of Ecological Effects of Extensive or Repeated Use of Herbicides,* prepared in 1967 at the request of ARPA of the Department of Defense, identifies the following as major defoliation targets:

1. Nipa palm and mangrove woodlands grow in coastal areas in deltas and within reach of the tidal waters along the banks and out into the rivers and canals of South Vietnam. The edges of these waterways are sprayed for a distance of 200 to 300 meters back from the water. Since these are

permanent traffic routes, the objectives include total plant kill and long-term vegetation control. Respraying at yearly intervals is generally required.

2. Rain or moist evergreen forests usually have three stories of foliage with a ground cover of shrubs, vines, and herbs of variable density. These targets are sprayed to create bare stretches surrounding Viet Cong strong-holds so that movement of men or supplies in and out of the area can be observed from the air. This type of target requires rapid defoliation; how-ever, long-term control or permanent kill is not essential.

3. The dense shrubbery and second-growth brush along highways and roads create cover for ambush. These areas are defoliated back into the edge of the forest to deprive the Viet Cong of concealment. At points where Viet Cong are known to have set up road blocks for the confiscation of "taxes," an area 400 meters in extent is cleared to expose such opera-tions for aerial reconnaissance and attack.

4. In the Mekong Delta area, the Viet Cong often secrete caches of ammunition, food, and supplies so well concealed that they are difficult to find on the ground and impossible to detect from the air. Trees, weeds, and underbrush are defoliated to disclose the location of these supply dumps.

5. In areas that have been cleared for villages, buildings, and military posts, heavy grasses and foliage may hide the infiltration of unseen at-tackers. This foliage is treated to hold down the grasses and foliage out to a safe distance. Long-term control is desirable in this application. (3)

In Vietnam both fixed-wing aircraft and helicopters are used for herbicide application. The HU-1B helicopter has been made available to the U.S. Army and to the Vietnamese Air Force (RVNAF) for special types of herbicide applications. The basic spray plane, however, is the twin-engine C-123 air-craft,* equipped with a chemical tank of 1,000-gallon capacity and A/A45y-1 internal defoliation dispensers. Each plane has two wing booms each with fourteen nozzles and a tail boom with eight nozzles. The normal crew consists of pilot, copilot, and a technical specialist who operates the spray console at the back of the plane. The spray equipment is calibrated to discharge the 1,000-gal tank in a five-minute period; however, in case of emergency the tank can be emptied in slightly less than thirty seconds.

As is the case with aerial spraying for civilian applications, the spray run is made as close to the foliage as practical and at a relatively low speed. A normal spray application takes place at about 150 feet at a speed of 130 knots, only seven knots above stall speed. Under these conditions, the spray emerging from the open nozzles is atomized by air turbulence into herbicide droplets ranging from 100 to 400 microns in diameter with an average drop size of about 300 microns. The spray mist from a single plane reaches the forest

---

* These aircraft have recently been modified by the addition of two jet motors.

Figure 3–1. U. S. Air Force C-123 aircraft spraying herbicides over cultivated South Vietnamese fields. Wide World Photos.

canopy in a swath approximately 250 feet wide. However, the pattern of settling is greatly influenced by weather, wind, and thermal currents. The most effective spray results are obtained in the early morning when the air is calm, the spray can settle directly onto the target, and movement to undesired targets is minimized.

Tests have been made to determine the pattern of spray-droplet interception by the various levels of leaves in the forest. In a moist tropical forest in full leaf approximately 80 per cent of the spray droplets are intercepted by the foliage of the topmost canopy. About 14 per cent is caught by the intermediate levels of vegetation; and only 6 per cent reaches the shrubbery and ground.

Spray drift is an important factor in both civilian and military herbicide applications. The fine droplets (200 microns or less) formed when liquid is released from aircraft, are readily affected by air currents. For example, Tschirley found that a 200-micron droplet will drift nine feet while falling twenty feet in a lateral airflow of 1 mile per hour. The farther above the forest the spray is released, the more drift will occur and the more likely it is that the droplets will enter rising air currents. Some drifting of small droplets cannot be avoided. Tests conducted in Thailand established that about 20 per cent of the herbicide drifts or evaporates and lands elsewhere than intended.

The picloram and cacodylic acid mixtures used in Vietnam are considered nonvolatile and should be subject only to wind drift. The *n*-butyl esters of 2,4-D and 2,4,5-T, on the other hand, are highly volatile under both laboratory and field conditions. Even the normally low volatile esters of the chlorophenoxy acids are significantly volatile when sprayed at the temperatures prevailing in Vietnam.

While herbicides were being increasingly used in Vietnam, they were also being tried out against insurgents in Thailand. According to the French newspaper, *Le Monde,* of April 20, 1968, the vice-president of Air America revealed that his planes had been spraying defoliants for the CIA in combat operations against Thai insurgents on the Isthmus of Kra.

One indication of the magnitude of United States defoliation operations in Vietnam by 1967 is given in the following quotations from two authoritative journals. *Science* reported in its August 18, 1967, issue:

Defense Department procurement of defoliant chemicals for use in Vietnam is proceeding at a steady pace. The Pentagon recently announced contracts of $57.7 million to eight companies for the chemical agents. Actual yearly expenditures rose from $12.5 million in fiscal year 1966 to $15.2 million in fiscal 1967. Estimated expenditure for fiscal 1968 is $43.3 million. The companies supplying the defoliants are Dow Chemical, Diamond Alkali, Uniroyal Chemical, Thompson Chemical, Hercules, Monsanto, Ansul, and Thompson Hayward.

Business Week reported in its April 22, 1967 issue that:

The recent increase in defoliation flights—now chiefly in the demilitarized zone, where a major enemy offensive is feared—has forced the Pentagon to grab all supplies of the chemical 2,4,5-T, used as weed killer on highways and other rights-of-way, and on pastures and rangelands.

The Business and Defense Services Administration has been ordered to assure that military orders for 2,4,5-T will be met in full.

According to one industry spokesman, this means that the compound is "all gone." Unless production is greatly expanded, there will not even be enough of the material to satisfy military demands, to say nothing of commercial need. The amount the military seeks is classified but industry speculation puts the figure at four times total U.S. capacity.

In a May 13, 1968 AP story it was reported:

Air Force officials told Congress last week the chemicals required for Vietnam operations in fiscal 1969 will cost $70.8 million, an increase of $24.9 million over the fiscal 1968 figure. . . . The Air Force is preparing to dump 10 million gallons of vegetation- and crop-killing poison over South Vietnam in the year beginning this July. . . . The Pentagon says the chemicals are harmless to humans and animal life and do not make the soil sterile for future growth. (10)

The greatly expanded defoliation program created significant political problems for both the South Vietnamese and American Governments. The *Christian Science Monitor* correspondent, Elizabeth Pond, detailed some of the problems in dispatches from Vietnam on November 25, 1967:

"We are people who live by farming alone and have fallen into a deficient, indigent situation because of the influence of defoliation. American military performed this by planes spreading chemicals and the effect . . . has made various types of fruit trees lose their leaves, ruined fruit, and crops such as green beans, white beans, peanuts, soybeans and black beans lose their leaves, then die. . . . We sincerely request you suggest that the higher authorities send personnel to inspect the crops affected in order to compensate for our losses."

This is the petition that six farmers sent to the American advisor in Kiem Tan District, Long Khanh Province. And they are not alone in their complaint. Some 3,000 similar petitions, each presented by several farmers jointly, already have been filed with the Kiem Tan District Chief. Many of them report crops down by two-thirds in this October-November harvest season.

The cause of this poor crop, the farmers say, is the American defoliation program.

For some the drop means only a loss in profits. The cement houses and the big Roman Catholic churches that have gone up in the past few years testify both to the fertility of the soil here and to the hard work of the North Vietnamese refugees who 10 years ago began wresting this land from virgin forest.

For other, poorer farmers farther north, the drop in production means a reduction in the amount of food their families will eat next year. It appears unlikely that any of the affected farmers will receive cash compensation, despite legal provisions for such payments.

The United States maintains that this is strictly a Vietnamese affair. It gives the South Vietnamese Government funds for payment of war damages to civilians, but it has nothing to do with processing defoliation claims.

On the Vietnamese side, the province chief of Long Khanh has informed his district chiefs that anything over three kilometers from targeted defoliation sites cannot be compensated for, and most of the petitions are therefore automatically shelved as soon as they reach district headquarters.

The fact that the poor harvests of Kiem Tan District this year took place against a general national and regional increase in vegetable production and the fact that various kinds of crops across the board from manioc to beans were affected would also point to defoliants.

The question of whether the crop damage was really the result of defoliation is by now academic, for the farmers of Kiem Tan are all convinced that it is. Whatever the technical analysis, the psychological fallout is an established fact.

As one specialist phrased it, with some bitterness: "It takes years to teach a farmer how to plant properly and then this happens. What does the farmer do when his crop fails—send his daughter into town to be a prostitute? Is this what President Johnson wants?"

The American district adviser in Kiem Tan put it less dramatically, but with equal passion. He's the kind who speaks Vietnamese fluently, spends all his time with the farmers in his district, and indeed, asked to be transferred here from an earlier higher level job that kept him pinned to a desk. He put it this way:

"On the one hand it's my job to make the people feel their government is effective, and on the other hand to help make sure the government really is effective.

"People talk about the elections. They say the hamlet chief doesn't affect them one bit, he doesn't have any power. . . . I wanted to show them their elected officials can have some power, and then something comes along like defoliation and makes me feel like an idiot. It's a typical example of something that really counts, and then the district chief is told that anything over three kilometers cannot be compensated for by the province chief."

Undoubtedly, military benefit was derived from the use of defoliants in the Song Dong Nai operation. Undoubtedly also, however, the aid program of development sponsored by the South Vietnamese Government and the United States in this area was seriously undercut by that same operation. What was missing in this situation was any hardnosed weighing of the one against the other.

Miss Pond further reported:

The United States mission here is in the midst of an interagency review of its defoliation program.

Participating in the review are representatives of the embassy political section, the joint economic office of the embassy and the Agency for International Development and the military command.

How major a review it is depends on whom you talk to.

One source said it is the first real postaudit since initiation of the defoliation operation in 1961.

A few Americans in the political and economic sections here are uneasy, however, about the actual practice of defoliation, about the doctrine and guidelines under which it is carried out.

Given the known sensitivity of crops to even small amounts of jungle defoliants—and given examples like Long Khanh—they are concerned that present controls may not be strict enough to prevent excessive accidental damage to "friendly crops."

Widespread damage to crops—or even widespread conviction on the part of Vietnamese farmers that such damage was occurring, whether justified or not—could blunt agricultural development programs.

It could likewise blunt the whole process of rural reconstruction and nation building in a Vietnam that is still 80 per cent peasant.

John Wilhelm, the military liaison officer for the joint embassy and AID economic office here, is one of the few officials who talks easily—and on the record—about defoliation and its review.

"If it's rice versus men, then spray by all means. But if there is no clear-cut military necessity, and suddenly defoliant is tossed onto an area where there is a vegetable or animal-feed production program, that's not too helpful."

Another civilian source expressed the same thought in different words. "You can't automatically say that if one American life is saved, an action is worth it," he suggested. The saving of these 500,000 American lives is not the primary consideration, or else the logical step would be to take them all home again.

"On the contrary, the United States is deliberately risking half a million American lives in Vietnam to do a job. If an action subverts that purpose, it is not justified.

"If an action alienates Vietnamese peasants from their government and from the Americans sufficiently to prolong the war, then it in fact costs more American lives than it saves. You must ask, How many lives? How much alienation?"

Such reasoning explains the concern with which a few American officials here view defoliation. They simply do not know how much accidental crop destruction there is at present or at what point the harmful side effects from defoliation begin to outweigh the intended benefit. But they want to find out.

One American official in III Corps, the hardest hit of any of the corps by unintended fallout, gave the judgment that virtually every farmer in that corps knows of the defoliation program and disapproves of it. This is perhaps the most important measure of all.

The problems caused by defoliation are further documented by two members of the International Volunteer Services, Don Luce and John Sommer. They spent many years in Vietnam and wrote:

> Defoliation is not a part of pacification, yet it affects pacification efforts, making them very difficult to carry out. While the military has seen it as "resource control," or a way of keeping food from the enemy, the farmers see the "medicine from the sky" as they often call it, as their biggest agricultural problem. The military defoliates the roadsides and canal banks to prevent Viet Cong ambushes, but it is also here that the farmers grow most of their fruits and vegetables so they can get them easily to market. The generals order jungle areas defoliated to destroy the cover for the enemy, yet wind carries the defoliant ten or fifteen miles and it destroys the farmers' bananas, papayas, and coconut trees. The military policy of destroying rice fields in NLF-controlled areas is intended to deprive Viet Cong soldiers of their source of food, but, as in any famine, it is the weak—the women, children, and old men who grow the rice—who suffer most. (11)

The Involvement of the AAAS in the Herbicide Problem

While these problems were arising in Vietnam as a result of the defoliation program, back in the United States the AAAS was trying to grapple with the issue brought before it in Pfeiffer's resolution of 1966. The controversy within the AAAS over the military use of chemical defoliants and herbicides in Vietnam presented a difficult problem because the nature of the ecological impact was bound up with the political controversy surrounding the Vietnamese conflict itself. Representative Emilio Q. Daddario, Chairman of the Subcommittee on Science, Research and Development of the Committee on Science and Astronautics, found the controversy within the AAAS of sufficient importance to ask his subcommittee to prepare a case history of the Vietnam defoliant matter. This study by Congressman Daddario's committee is a concise summary of the actions and interactions between the AAAS members, its officers, and various government bureaucrats. It documents the disturbing fact that as a group American scientists were unable, mainly for political reasons, to take any meaningful steps to gain scientific information on a problem related to national policy. We believe that the ineffectiveness of America's largest science organization in attempting an objective study holds very serious implications for the future of science and its relation to the federal government in this country. For these reasons we present the following abstracts from the Daddario Committee history of the controversy over the assessment of defoliation damage in Vietnam (2).

It was at a meeting of the Council of the Pacific Division, June 15, 1966, that the issue of war use of herbicides first entered the formal policy deliberations of the AAAS. At this meeting, the secretary presented a communication from E.W. Pfeiffer, associate professor of zoology at the University of Montana. It proposed a resolution for consideration by the council, which read:

> Whereas units .of the U.S. Department of Defense have used both chemical and biological warfare agents (as defined by U.S. Department of the Army, TM3-216) in operations against enemy forces in Vietnam; and
> Whereas, the scientific community has a responsibility to be fully informed of these agents and their use in warfare because they are a result of scientific research: Therefore be it
> Resolved, That—
> 1. The Pacific Division of the AAAS establish a committee of experts in the field of biological and chemical warfare to study the use of CW and BW agents in Vietnam with the purpose of determining what agents have been used, the extent of their use, and the effects on all biological systems that might have been affected.
> 2. That the above committee make a public report of their findings at the next meeting of the Pacific division of the AAAS.

The minutes of the meeting reveal that the Pfeiffer resolution had a mixed reception. Eventually, the council decided to refer it—without recommendation—to the national office of AAAS. Even this decision was controversial—being carried by a 9 to 5 vote with several abstentions. During debate on the resolution, members of the council questioned the propriety of having the action taken at a regional meeting, viewed the issue as more properly one for treatment by the National Academy of Sciences, and rejected the proposition in the resolution that the Pacific Division had the means to conduct field investigations in Vietnam.

As president-elect of AAAS, Mr. Don K. Price, dean of the Kennedy School of Government, Harvard University, was chairman of the Committee on Council Affairs in the fall of 1966. In this capacity, he received Professor Pfeiffer's resolution. During the yearend meetings of AAAS, in Washington D.C., the Committee on Council Affairs held a public meeting, at which Pfeiffer and others spoke on the subject of the proposed resolution. After this open session, the committee in an executive session decided to modify the resolution before introducing it as new business before the council. The resolution as redrafted by the committee had received Pfeiffer's approval. Its text at that point read as follows:

> Whereas modern science and technology now give man unprecedented power to alter his environment and affect the ecological balance of this planet; and
> Whereas the full impact of the uses of biological and chemical agents to modify the environment, whether for peaceful or military purposes, is not fully known; and
> Whereas the major users of these agents on a scale sufficiently large to modify

the ecological balance are now the governments of this and other countries. Be it
Resolved, That the American Association for the Advancement of Science—

(1) Expresses its concern regarding the long-range consequences of the use of biological and chemical agents which modify the environment; and

(2) Establishes a committee to study all aspects of such use, starting with the effects of chemical and biological warfare agents, and periodically to report its findings through appropriate channels of the association; and

(3) Volunteers its cooperation with public agencies and offices of government for the task of ascertaining scientifically and objectively the full implications of major programs and activities which modify the environment and affect the ecological balance on a large scale.

The closeness of the division on final adoption of the twice-amended resolution by the Council is indicated by the vote: 125 to approve and 95 opposed. In its final form, as approved, the resolution read:

Whereas modern science and technology now give man unprecedented power to alter his environment and affect the ecological balance of this planet; and

Whereas the full impact of the uses of biological and chemical agents to modify the environment, whether for peaceful or military purposes, is not fully known:
Be it
Resolved, That the American Association for the Advancement of Science—

(1) Expresses its concern regarding the long-range consequences of the use of biological and chemical agents which modify the environment; and

(2) Establishes a committee to study such use, including the effects of chemical and biological warfare agents, and periodically to report its findings through appropriate channels of the association; and

(3) Volunteers its cooperation with public agencies and offices of government for the task of ascertaining scientifically and objectively the full implications of major programs and activities which modify the environment and affect the ecological balance on a large scale.

In its final form, the resolution dealt primarily with the issue of environmental impairment on a global basis, and only very secondarily with military use of herbicides. Also, while Pfeiffer had sought an actual scientific field investigation by qualified ecologists under AAAS sponsorship in Vietnam, the AAAS Council had been content to express concern over the long-range consequences of the use of chemical and biological agents (whether public or private) that modify the environment, to establish a committee to study the general question, and to volunteer AAAS's cooperation with the Federal Government to identify implications of major programs that "modify the environment and affect the ecological balance on a large scale."

The Council action on the amended Pfeiffer resolution was reported to the AAAS membership without any particular emphasis. The first implementing action in response to the resolution was the formation by the AAAS board of directors of an ad hoc committee on environmental alteration, during its meeting March 11–12, 1967. The committee was chaired by Dr. René Dubos, Rockefeller University. Its members included Pfeiffer and Mayer, who had been active in the herbicide issue. When the ad hoc committee reported, in May, it recommended establishment of a continuing AAAS "Commission on the Consequences of Environmental Alteration," and discussed three examples of problems with which the commission should be concerned. These were chemical agents, chemical fertilizers, and waste recycling.

The Committee offered a number of suggestions as to ways in which the proposed Commission should conduct its affairs. In particular, it said:

> On occasion, it may be desirable for the Commission to make arrangements to have studies conducted by others. We recommend that the board of directors [of AAAS] consider requesting the National Academy of Science to arrange a continuing study and scientific record of the effects of chemical and biological warfare agents on soil, biota, and human health.

However, one member of the committee, E. W. Pfeiffer, took exception to this suggestion. In a separate, "minority" statement, he said he did not believe that the National Academy of Sciences was a "truly independent organization of scientists" because it had been identified [in *Science,* Jan. 13, 1967] as a "source of advice for the biological warfare effort . . . and had also been involved in a postdoctoral research fellowship program sponsored by Fort Detrick" [biological warfare research center], for which candidates were "screened by the Academy" and "permitted to describe themselves as having received a NAS–NRC fellowship."

Upon receipt of the ad hoc committee's report, the AAAS board of directors at its meeting in June, 1967, decided to divide the general problem into two parts: one was the general question of the consequences of environmental alteration, and the other the specific question of the use of chemical and biological warfare agents in Vietnam. The board itself agreed to accept responsibility for the next stage of action on the specific question of military herbicide use in Vietnam.

With respect to "the more specific question of the use of chemical and biological warfare agents in Vietnam" the board recognized that "no effective study of the effects of such agents could be carried out in active theater of war without military or other official permission and sponsorship." It therefore instructed the AAAS president (Don Price) and the executive officer (Dael Wolfle) to urge appropriate officers of the Federal Government to arrange for a thorough study under official auspices. Accordingly—

> Conferences on this proposal were held with Frederick Seitz, who is Chairman of the Defense Science Board as well as President of the National Academy of Sciences; Donald Hornig, Director of the Office of Science and Technology; and Donald MacArthur and Rodney W. Nichols of the staff of Robert S. McNamara, Secretary of Defense. Following these conferences, the AAAS president wrote to Secretary MacNamara, urging that a study by an independent scientific institution or committee of both the short- and long-range effects of the military use of chemical agents which modify the environment be authorized and undertaken.

The letter to Secretary MacNamara recognized that "decisions regarding the use of [chemical agents which modify the environment] in various circumstances must be made in the light of tactical and strategic considerations: but that nevertheless, the consequences of their use may have such long-range social, economic, and political consequences, both in Vietnam and on the world scene, that the problem warrants study under the highest responsible political auspices." The letter suggested that the National Academy of Sciences–National Research Council would be an appropriate institution for this purpose; an independent commission responsible to the Secretary of Defense or the President's Science Advisory Committee would be an acceptable alternative. The letter concluded by offering "any assistance it could in such an undertaking, either by sharing in its formal sponsorship, or by advising in the selection of those who are to carry out the study."

The AAAS letter of September 13, 1967, was answered by Dr. John S. Foster, Jr., Director of Defense Research and Engineering, September 20. First, he dealt with the present state of knowledge concerning the "short- or long-term ecological impacts" of the use of herbicides or defoliant chemicals in Vietnam: Whether such impacts existed, and whether they were detrimental or advantageous, he said, was not definitely known. Then he went on—

> Qualified scientists, both inside and outside our Government, and in the governments of other nations, have judged that seriously adverse consequences will not occur. Unless we had confidence in these judgments, we would not continue to employ these materials.

In view of the uncertainties remaining, Dr. Foster said he had taken two steps. One was to commission a "leading nonprofit research institute to thoroughly review and assess all current data in this field." The other was to request the National Academy of Sciences–National Research Council to assemble a group of professionally qualified experts to "review the results of the study and to make appropriate recommendations concerning it." Dr. Foster made clear that he expected no definitive answers from these actions. Instead, they should be considered the first of a number of necessary steps. The study he had commissioned should provide—

(1) A comprehensive compilation of available information;
(2) An assessment of the current information gaps;
(3) Inferences concerning any possible ecological impacts; and
(4) A basis for planning.

Upon completion of this effort, Dr. Foster suggested, there should be a consultation concerning its findings between the Department of Defense and the AAAS leadership, in order to define next steps to be taken. The report was scheduled to be completed by mid-December, to enable its examination by the AAAS Council and board of directors in advance of the association's annual meeting.

Dean Price responded for the AAAS board, October 26. He expressed gratification that the contractor's report and the National Academy of Sciences review would both be available before the AAAS Council meeting in New York City, "between Christmas and New Year's." He also asked Dr. Foster to elaborate on the sources of informed opinion that had led to the conclusion by the Government "that seriously adverse consequences would not occur from the current use of herbicides and defoliants." In reply, November 10, Dr. Foster said the conclusion derived from a "consensus of informed opinion" of some 50–70 individuals, in the absence of "hard data." Nevertheless, he said, "we remain convinced that our judgments were, and are, reasonable and take account of all significant data."

The selection of a contractor to perform the function envisioned by Dr. Foster in his letter of September 20 had already been completed at that time. The contractor was the Midwest Research Institute, located in Kansas City, Missouri.

The MRI report had not been available to the board by the time the AAAS convened in New York City for its 1967 annual meeting. At the AAAS Board meeting, December 29, it became known that the committee on science in the promotion of human welfare, under the chairmanship of Dr. Margaret Mead, had concluded that it had more than enough work already before it, and that the importance of the environmental issues identified by the Dubos committee warranted the establishment by AAAS of a new permanent committee. Accordingly, the board at this same meeting decided to establish a new permanent committee on environmental alteration "and proceeded on the spot to name a few members (some at least of whom were in the room)." The new committee was instructed to "carry on a continuing evaluation of the implications of technological intrusion on environmental processes and their interactions with human population; and, in view of the previously expressed concern of council regarding the use of chemical and biological agents in Vietnam and elsewhere, to request the committee to consider these problems as its initial order of business." The committee was to be under the chairmanship of Dr. David R. Goddard, provost of the University of Pennsylvania, with Dubos, Dr. Barry Commoner of Washington University, and Dr. Athelstan F. Spilhaus, president of the Franklin Institute, initially named as members, with others to be appointed later. The board action was reported to the council a day or two later.

Apparently there was a good deal of pressure on the new committee not only to deal with Vietnamese herbicide usage, but to make it priority business. Before the MRI report was made available to AAAS, the new committee ran into a snag. Several weeks after its formation, the chairman, Dr. Goddard, resigned, as did Dr. Spilhaus. As reported in *Science:*

> Both cited extensive professional commitments as the reason for their resignation, though Goddard, in a telephone interview with *Science,* added, "no sooner was my appointment announced than I started getting pressures from all directions. The emotional overtones were terrific."

In his letter of resignation, Dr. Goddard pointed out that his committee had been formed to deal with a broad range of problems created by environmental alteration, but that the life of this committee was threatened by political pressures over its concern about defoliants in Vietnam. He wrote that many distinguished scientists had prejudged the issue even before the study had started and he concluded that "The political climate within the membership of the AAAS is such that I do not believe that an impartial study can be made."

The review of the MRI report by the National Academy of Sciences (NAS) apparently began November 7 and was completed by January 31, 1968. In the meantime, however, as Dr. Goddard had indicated in his letter of resignation, a discussion of the MRI report's findings had appeared in the New York Times 3 weeks earlier, and had apparently stimulated further excitement over the issue. Treatment of the report by the NAS was somewhat noncommittal.

The report itself was a substantial volume, 369 pages multilithed, referencing 147 persons as information sources, with 52 pages listing 1,500 items of bibliographical references. The report made the following findings:

(1) Direct ecological consequence of herbicide use in Vietnam was the destruction of vegetation, setting a region back to an earlier stage of development, from which the process of restoration would then occur.
(2) Food chains of fauna and heterotrophic plants would be altered.

(3) Phytotoxicity of herbicides in the soil was not a consideration, nor were lethal toxicity to humans or wildlife, or concentration of deleterious chemicals in food chains.

(4) Data on chronic toxicity were incomplete.

(5) Data on aquatic environmental effects of herbicides were inconclusive and mixed—some favorable and some unfavorable.

The report then identified four important areas of uncertainty that remained:

(1) The effect of 2,4-D and 2,4,5-T on water quality.

(2) The possible threat to mammals and birds already approaching extinction.

(3) Micrometerological effects of forest denudation.

(4) Possibility of exposing lateritic soils, such as to result in their hardening and infertility.

In accordance with the understanding between the O.D.D.R. & E. staff and the board of directors of AAAS, the NAS Review Panel was to comment on "the thoroughness and accuracy with which the scientific literature relating to herbicides and their ecological effects had been examined and evaluated."

The NAS assessment (presumably drafted by the Chairman of the Review Panel) noted that the Panel had not functioned as a committee "in the usual sense" because they "did not have an opportunity to meet as a group after the final report was made available." They had, however, "provided specific comments and advice on early drafts of chapters in the report, and after completion of the first full draft, submitted corrections, suggestions for deletions and additions and general comments." The consensus of the Panel was as follows:

(1) Midwest Research Institute has done a creditable job of collecting, correctly abstracting, and citing much of the relevant published information although, under the circumstances, the report could not be expected to cover in a truly comprehensive way so vast a literature.

(2) Of necessity, the preponderance of the material deals with herbicides as they are used in vegetation management in a diversity of situations and environments. On this general topic, abundant data are available. However, the scientific literature provides markedly less factual information on the ecological consequences of herbicide use and particularly of repeated or heavy herbicide applications. The Midwest Research Institute report correctly reflects this disparity.

In transmitting the report to Dr. Foster, January 31, 1968, the President of the National Academy of Sciences, Frederick Seitz, expressed the view that "it is very clear that the compilation of this report is only a first step in investigating further the ecological effects of intensive use of herbicides. Some research in this area is now under way but much more needs to be done." Dr. Seitz indicated that "the Academy will be glad to participate in any useful way in the planning and promotion of such research."

By the latter part of February, 1968, there was a good deal of confusion as to the status of the "technological assessment" that the AAAS had undertaken in response to Dr. Pfeiffer's communication. This state of affairs is well summarized in a paragraph of "Late News" in *Scientific Research:*

The AAAS is handing the report over to its new standing committee, specially formed to investigate uses of chemical and biological agents. Pfeiffer has offered to serve and is now planning to bring pressure on the association to sponsor an extensive symposium on the subject. The Scientists' Institute for Public Information in New York will be enlisted by Pfeiffer, although another group—Physicians for Social Responsibility—has already offered to help. This group has had experience of firsthand field research in Vietnam, having visited hospitals there. "If the AAAS won't sponsor the symposium," said Pfeiffer, "another organization like the International Red Cross or the World Health Organization will be approached." "The symposium would hopefully stimulate people to go into the field and get data on the effects of herbicides. This should include Vietnam in areas which are not continually under fire," Pfeiffer said.

Thus, by the first half of 1968, the problems of conducting a technological assessment by a large association of scientists had been identified as complex and formidable.

There was the importance attached by many leaders of the scientific community to the preservation of the canons of scientific objectity, which meant avoiding resolution by scientists of technical issues into which a considerable element of political controversy had entered.

There was the problem of screening out of the controversy the bias of those who were opposed to all forms of participation by the United States in the Vietnamese conflict, and who rejected out of hand the defoliation program as merely one more manifestation of a program to which they objected on broader political grounds.

There was the tendency of some scientists to regard the organizational relationships of the Department of Defense, the military departments, the personnel with scientific training in Defense posts, and the military contractors and their scientific personnel, as all involved in a conspiracy to defend and justify programs simply on grounds of short-term military expedience.

There was the fundamental difficulty that the sciences contributing to ecology were insufficiently developed to permit definitive findings as to the long-range impact of herbicides even in the United States where they had been used for more than two decades; so that an assessment of repeated and possibly heavier application of herbicide sprays in an altogether different ecology, under the hazardous conditions of a diffused guerrilla warfare, posed insuperable problems of definitive assessment.

An assessment of the use of herbicides in Vietnam required (a) financial resources to mount an expedition; (b) military support for it—to gain entry to the combat area and receive protection while conducting its onsite examination, and (c) staffing by recognized scientists unconnected with any aspect of the defoliation program to establish objectivity and maintain credibility. It had become apparent that the MRI report was only the first step toward such an assessment. While it had eliminated a number of questions it had raised or underlined others. But there appeared to be a growing consensus that further investigation was needed.

One expression of this need came from Dr. Pfeiffer. After the annual meeting of the AAAS in New York, he said: "I am very disturbed and very disappointed."

There have been outright attempts to kill the project completely [he went on]. Are American scientists capable of making an independent study or not? So far the situation has been up in the air. You cannot get the AAAS board of directors to commit themselves to such a study, and I don't think the average AAAS member knows that the study was ever being considered.

He regarded the use of defoliant chemicals in Vietnam as a "burning issue" and said: "I hope the new committee can send a group to Vietnam, and that it will include people who are concerned with this issue."

Dean Price saw the role of AAAS somewhat differently:

Our role is far from finished [he said]. This is a slow process. My own opinion is that we had the choice between the kind of operation that would call for a large staff and large sums of money to do firsthand field research. The AAAS has never done this. We operate by committees and review field work done by others. To do field work in the combat zone is even more difficult.

We could have mounted a protest movement which would have achieved little and which would have been opposed violently by the overwhelming majority of our members. The other way was to get the best scientific study done, and then have a committee of hard scientific competence to review it.

When the MRI report, and the accompanying assessment by NAS, reached the offices of AAAS, early in February, the association was unable to take any immediate action because there was no continuing group in session. However, in March, the board of directors met and voted to accept directly the responsibility to review the MRI report. Arrangements were made to have copies of both the report and the NAS assessment provided to all members; in addition, the AAAS staff was asked to send copies to a number of consultants to secure their comments and advice.

The precise function of the AAAS in relation to the MRI report is not clear. From the point of view of most board members, the important question was the broad, long-range condition of the human environment. The military use of herbicides in Vietnam was decidedly secondary. The latter issue was also so inflammatory that any AAAS committee asked to study both the general environmental condition and the specific issue of Vietnamese herbicide usage, would be under great pressure to deal primarily with the secondary issue. Experience had shown the difficulty of organizing a committee willing to accept both issues.

In mid-July, 1968, the Board of Directors of the AAAS issued its own policy statement on the use of herbicides in war. . . .

In the basic statement, the board expressed the conviction that "many questions concerning the long-range ecological influences of chemical herbicides remain unanswered." One of these was the extent of long-term deleterious effects of the forest defoliation in Vietnam. They also questioned the use of arsenicals on crops and the "ultimate route taken by arsenical compounds in plants, soil, and animals." Accordingly, they did not "share the confidence expressed by the Department of Defense . . . that seriously adverse consequences will not occur as a result of the use of herbicidal chemicals in Vietnam, insofar as arsenical compounds are concerned." They also took account of the "serious concern expressed by scientists in Vietnam over long-term environmental consequences of the military use of herbicides." Because of the uncertainties in available evidence of these consequences, said the board, "such charges cannot now be answered unequivocally."

Accordingly, the board recommended—

That a field study be undertaken under the auspices and direction of the United Nations, with the participation of Vietnamese scientists and scientists from other countries, and with cooperation, support and protection provided by the contending forces in the area. This study, which could well be supplemented by experimental work elsewhere, should provide a detailed environmental analysis of the long-range effects of the agents used and of the steps necessary to assure optimum future productivity of the environment for the welfare of its inhabitants.

Further, we urge that the maximum possible amount of relevant data be released from military security, so that the scientists conducting the study may know the areas affected, the agents used, the dates applied, and the dosages employed.

We express especial concern about the use of arsenical herbicides in Vietnam, and urge that their use be suspended, if it has not already been stopped, until the ultimate fate of the degraded arsenical compounds can be . . . reliably determined.

We recognize the difficulties involved in the proposed field study; however, it is our hope that the feasibility of such a study may be increased as a result of the current peace talks in Paris.

Finally, we hope the recommended study can be initiated promptly and we proffer the good offices of the association in helping to plan it and to publicize its findings.

Following the AAAS board meeting, letters were sent out July 19, 1968, over the signature of Dr. Dael Wolfle, executive officer of the AAAS, to the Secretaries of State and Defense, and to the Secretary General of the United Nations. . . . The response, August 5, signed by José Rolz-Bennett, Under Secretary General for Special Political Affairs, indicated that the Secretary General offered assurances " . . . that the matter of chemical and bacteriological weapons is receiving his very close attention."

The response of the Department of State, dated September 3, signed by Charles E. Bohlen, Deputy Under Secretary, took note of the fact that "there are differences of opinion on the use of certain chemicals even among the members of this distinguished group." It recalled that limited studies already made by Government agencies, had "failed to reveal serious ecological disturbances." It acknowledged, however, that "the ultimate effect of these herbicides can be determined definitively only by long-term studies." Accordingly, it favored such a long-term study in Vietnam. However—

Such studies in combat areas are obviously difficult at present. The United States will be happy to cooperate in responsible long-term investigations of this type as soon as practicable. The participants should be selected on the basis of their scientific competence to insure acceptance by the scientific community.

The AAAS letter to the Secretary of Defense expressed gratification at the MRI survey. But it noted that ". . . on a number of points information is lacking or insufficient."

The [AAAS] board has concluded that a study should be conducted of the long-term effects of the use of chemical defoliants on the ecology of Vietnam, and has proposed that that study be carried out under the U.N. auspices. A majority of the members of the board have added a supplementary recommendation that the United States assume responsibility for such a study if the United Nations is unable to do so.

The reply to Wolfle's letter to the Department of Defense, dated August 24, was signed by John S. Foster, Jr., Director of Defense Research and Engineering. It expressed gratification at the interest of the AAAS board, and repeated the earlier assurance that herbicides would not be used if competent opinion found them to have seriously adverse consequences. The letter continued—

. . . On balance, we continue to be confident that the controlled use of herbicides will have no long-term ecological impacts inimical to the people and interests of South Vietnam. . . .

We are, of course, continuing our investigations and surveys, I believe we have consistently taken a responsible and openminded approach to the herbicide program of the Department of Defense. As soon as peaceful conditions return to Vietnam and systematic scientific investigation becomes feasible, we will support additional studies in all ways that are legal and proper.

One official action that seems relevant to the calls for an immediate on-the-spot survey of the effects of repeated use of herbicides on the Vietnamese ecology was an assessment under State Department auspices in Saigon during September, 1968. Apparently no single vector was responsible for motivating this assessment; rather, it was the culmination of a number of unrelated developments:

The request by the AAAS board of directors that brought in the United Nations, as well as the Department of State;

The fact that Dr. Fred H. Tschirley of the U.S. Department of Agriculture, at the request of the Department of State, had made ecological observations earlier in the year in some areas of Vietnam where herbicides had been used;

The fact that the AAAS board of directors was still in communication with the Department of Defense on the herbicide issue;

The apparent concern of officials of the Agency for International Development (AID) over occasional instances of inadvertent damage to crops from military herbicide spraying operations;

The drumfire of propaganda from Hanoi and Peking, charging the use of "poisonous" herbicides (which the Vietcong guerrillas apparently accepted at face value);

The possibility that "world public opinion" had been influenced by Communist allegations that required contradiction from well-documented sources;

The possibility that South Vietnamese officials and public required some degree of formal reassurance.

The more extensive assessment by the Department of State that took place during 1968, under the sponsorship of Ambassador Elsworth Bunker, was reported in Saigon by the U.S. mission, September 18; the text of the basic press release was as follows:

In keeping with the U.S. mission's policy of continually monitoring the U.S. role in Allied herbicide operations in South Vietnam, Ambassador Ellsworth Bunker established a special interagency committee earlier this year to make a comprehensive review of the program. . . .

According to the findings of the committee, the use of herbicides around base perimeters, along lines of communication, and against enemy infiltration routes, staging and base areas has, both in terms of offensive and defensive action, reduced the number of men and amount of equipment required for combat missions, secured material and facilities, and, most importantly, helped to save the lives of many Vietnamese and Allied personnel.

The military benefits of the use of herbicides against enemy food sources in food-scarce highland areas in I, II, III Corps, the only areas where such operations are conducted, was more difficult to assess. There was, however, considerable evidence that food shortages for which herbicide operations were partly responsible, have created logistical problems for the enemy by causing him to divert human and other resources to noncombat activities.

Economic costs were found to be sizable. The principal cost was in lost or damaged timber reserves and merchantable timber, particularly in war zone D where security conditions have not permitted salvage efforts. There were other, minor economic losses for accidental damage to various crops due to spray or vapor drift, equipment failure, and emergency jettisoning of herbicides. The committee considered it within the capability of the GVN and the USG, however, to reduce and eliminate some of the economic costs of the program, principally through salvage operations and reforestation.

Thus, in weighing the overall costs, problems and unknowns of the herbicide programs against the benefits, the committee concluded that the latter outweigh the former and that the programs should be continued.

When the AAAS membership convened at Dallas, at the close of 1968, the status of the controversy over military use of herbicides in Vietnam was as follows:

The Department of Defense had released considerable technical information assertedly relevant to its conclusion that no "seriously adverse consequences" resulted from military herbicide usage; and had given assurance that the assessment program was continuing.

The AAAS board of directors had urged specific reductions in the program, and had not revised this recommendation upon receipt of DOD information.

AAAS had been unable to find a way to enlist the resources of the U.N. in the conduct of an on-the-spot study; the study performed by DOD at the insistence of the AAAS had been limited to the open literature, and had not involved the collection of onsite data; the State Department's release of data in Saigon had not quieted those who sought onsite data.

Accordingly, in the annual meeting of the AAAS Council, in December 1968, the board of directors announced that the AAAS "would participate in a study of the use of herbicides in Vietnam." An account of the council's response to this announcement, carried in *Science,* was as follows:

> In a heated meeting in an overheated room on Monday, the board's inclusion of Vietnam in its original resolution was challenged by council members. The attack was opened by James H. Ross, representing the Nature Conservancy, who said that the board should concern itself with other environmental hazards and should not single out Vietnam. A resolution expressing the agreement of the council with the sense of the board resolution to conduct a study of the use of herbicides in Vietnam, but advising changes in the language of the board's original resolution so as to delete mention of Vietnam, was passed overwhelmingly. In passing such a resolution, the council was taking a position similar to that adopted at the 1966 AAAS meeting in Washington, D.C.
>
> In accordance with this advice from the council, the board revised its resolution to read as follows:

> "It is the sense of the board that the association, looking not only to the effects of the wartime use of herbicides, but also to the opportunities for the peacetime reconstruction of the agriculture and economy of affected areas:
>
> (1) Determines that it shall be a purpose of the association to bring into being the most effective possible field study of the potential long- and short-term ecological risks and benefits to the areas affected;
>
> (2) Specifically directs the AAAS staff to convene, as soon as possible, an ad hoc group involving representation of interested national and international scientific organizations to prepare specific plans for conduct of such a field study

and with the expectation that the AAAS would participate in such a study within the reasonable limits of its resources."

By the end of June, 1969, it appeared that the AAAS had virtually exhausted its initiatives. The association had obtained assurances from the Department of Defense that herbicide usage would be continually assessed. A general policy had also been established that there should be no long-range and seriously adverse consequences of such usage. Both the Departments of State and Defense had promised support for a postwar ecological investigation of long-range consequences of the military use of herbicides in Vietnam. The United Nations had agreed to sponsor a full-scale international meeting of world scientists on environmental quality. The issue of chemical and biological warfare had been referred by the General Assembly to the 18th National Disarmament Conference in Geneva for consideration as a part of its permanent agenda. Technical cautions had been expressed by the AAAS board concerning the treatment of large areas or blocks of territory; the issues of biodegradability, toxicity, heavy application, and repeated application had been made publicly visible.

On the other hand, the operational role of the AAAS in making ready for long-sought postwar assessment had not yet been defined. Although pledging its support and assistance, the board and council had taken no steps to mobilize AAAS resources for this purpose. A substantial membership roster had been recruited for the new AAAS committee on Environmental Alteration, but the staff of AAAS had made clear that it was not expected to spearhead the effort.

There was available no indication that its future program would include the design of an ecological survey of herbicide effects in Vietnam or even the development of criteria that such a survey would need to satisfy. It remained to be seen whether its membership could preserve both stability of leadership and forward momentum.

The annual meetings of the American Association for the Advancement of Science provided an opportunity for the scientific politicization of the issue. Once the council of the AAAS had adopted a resolution bearing somewhat on the relationship of herbicides to the human environment, those concerned with the use of herbicides in Vietnam continued to keep the question of this war use alive among the membership and the leadership of the association. An attempt was made to separate the thorny political question of military herbicides from the broader, but less inflammatory technical issue of "environmental alteration" . . . But the AAAS board of directors had not assumed leadership in defining what form this assessment should take. By June, 1969, neither those who favored nor those who opposed defoliants in Vietnam had given a clear indication as to what the ecological questions were or how they should be answered.

Thus for a variety of reasons, the AAAS did not appear to be able to take a leadership position in obtaining an ecological assessment of the herbicide program in Vietnam. However, as a result of funds made available by the Society for Social Responsibility in Science, we were able to make a trip to Vietnam in March, 1969, to learn as much as we could about the effects of defoliants.

The Ecology of Vietnam

In preparation for our trip we studied the literature on the ecology of Vietnam because the effects of herbicides and defoliants cannot be understood without some knowledge of the vegetation of the region and the factors that produce it. The vegetation of an area is the result of the climate, soil types, and other physiographic features of that particular region, modified to a greater or lesser degree by the activities of man.

The general physiography of Vietnam is that of great plains and plateaus rising to mountain ranges with peaks upwards of 6,500 feet in altitude. About 85 per cent of the total land mass of Vietnam is made up of the highland mountainous region which descends gradually to the east via sandstone and limestone tablelands to a narrow coastal plain to the east and to the south of the Mekong River Delta, an alluvial lowland seldom over twenty feet above sea level. The entire region is drained by a network of both large and small rivers and their tributaries, most of which flow in a southerly or southeasterly direction. The estuaries of the larger rivers form extensive deltas covered with a distinctive mangrove woodland vegetation. Some of these rivers are navigable for considerable distances into the interior.

South Vietnam is about 700 miles long and 150 miles wide at its maximum breadth with a total area of 66,000 square miles, somewhat less than half the area of the state of Montana. About 18 million people live in South Vietnam, principally in the coastal plains and southern peninsula.

The climate of South Vietnam is dominated by the monsoons, which are seasonal winds blowing from one direction during part of the year and from another direction during the remaining months. During the northern summer, low pressure develops over the Asian continent, producing a landward flow of moist maritime air over southeast Asia. Conversely, during the winter high pressure develops over central Asia, producing a flow of cool, dry air southward over the southern fringes of the continent. In South Vietnam the rainy season begins in April and ends in October and is followed by a long and severe dry season from November to March. Along the narrow coastal plains of Central Vietnam the rainy season, influenced by typhoons in the South China Sea, may extend into January. In the lowlands of South Vietnam the overall annual rainfall averages about eighty inches (2,000 mm) but it is impossible to obtain a second crop of rice without irrigation because of the length and severity of the dry season. Rain can be expected about 150 days each year. Except in mountainous areas, temperatures are high throughout the year with no frost at lower elevations. Mean air temperatures are about 80°F with a typical daily high near 90°F and a nightly low in the low seventies.

In the Mekong Delta more than 90 per cent of soils are recent alluvial ones with a clay texture (12). In the alluvial plains of Central Vietnam lighter texture soils and loams sometimes occur. Since they are not yet highly leached, alluvial soils are used for rice production and play a predominate role in

Vietnam's agriculture. Certain of the alluvial soils, especially those of the mangrove swamps, have such a high salt content that growing rice is not possible. In the southern part of the country, above the alluvial soils, are soils formed from sandstone. They occur in all climatic zones of the lower part of the country and generally are composed of sand with a weak humus layer sometimes present. The natural vegetation, normally a dense brush, may be absent in moving dune areas. These types of soils have a low agricultural value even though they are not laterized. Laterization is discussed below.

Tropical soils and the factors that produce them are poorly known as compared to temperate soils. In general it is true that the nature of the underlying rock exerts a greater effect on mature soil types in the tropics. Also, because of the torrential nature of the rains and the intensity of the sun's heat, the tropical soil system is a very fragile one, easily disrupted by human activity.

Forests soils of Vietnam, like soils elsewhere in the wet tropics, are highly leached. Under the prevailing high temperatures, however, the clay minerals in the soil decompose rapidly to provide a supply of new bases to replace those leached out during the rainy season. For this reason the soils are not acidic as might otherwise be expected. For the same reason the supplies of dead plant materials that reach the forest floor are rapidly decomposed and the nutrients made available to other plants. Therefore there is little accumulation of litter or humus on the surface of these soils.

Under conditions of high temperature and non-acidity it is the silica fraction of the soil that is most readily leached downwards, leaving behind the iron oxides that give these soils their characteristic red color. The process producing these iron-rich, silica-poor soils is known as laterization and these soils are referred to as lateritic soils. If the laterization process continues long enough, the soil may be converted into a hard substance known as laterite composed entirely of iron oxides. Soil scientists do not yet understand why true laterite is not more widespread than it is, but it may be the result of the fact that only on very flat surfaces does the soil remain in one place long enough for the process to be completed. Moreover, on soils derived from rocks such as sand-stone or quartzite, laterization does not appear to occur at all. Some of these soils, known as podzols, may even be very acidic and have well developed litter layers.

A widespread soil type in Vietnam is the red and yellow podzols. They are formed from a wide variety of acidic parent materials such as acid rocks or alluvial sediments. Most of these soils are under broad-leaf and pine forests or savanna, and their main agricultural use is for shifting rice cultivation; although in population centers they are often used for cultivation of peanuts, sweet potatoes, and the like. Some truck farming is done in these areas. Gray podzolic soils are predominantly found on terraces of old alluvial sediments. They are limited to areas of an annual rainfall of more than 1,400 mm and have a leached horizon. They are found in areas with a flat or, at most, undulating relief. The natural vegetation is generally an open forest. These are usually poor soils; but when fertilized, they are excellent for rubber, and they carry some of the most productive plantations.

The extensive lateritic soils in Vietnam are developed largely as the weathering products of basalt. The natural vegetation found on the lateritic soils is evergreen seasonal forest or savanna that is used in large part for shifting rice crop cultivation—the slash and burn practice called "rai." The rice yields may be very good. The larger part of Vietnam's rubber and coffee plantations are found on these soils, and there are in certain areas extensive cultivation of a wide variety of food crops.

The vegetation of Vietnam is as varied as might be expected, given the diversity of climate and soil types. There is much information on the flora of the region and its economic potential. For almost ninety years Vietnam, Cambodia, and Laos (formerly collectively called Indochina) were under French administration. Both French and native botanists, ecologists, and foresters made large plant collections and extensive ecological and silvicultural studies. According to French botanists, there are more than 1,500 species of woody plants in Vietnam; therefore, many of these forests associations are exceedingly complex.

The major forest formations in Vietnam have been characterized as follows: evergreen, broad-leaf rain or moist forests (true rainforest is confined mainly to the lower and middle elevations on mountain slopes); dipterocarp forest, probably the most extensive type covering about 50 per cent of the total forested area; mixed deciduous forests, usually heavily cut over and quite open; dry evergreen forest, concentrated especially along the river streambanks; montane forests containing oak, frequently mixed with conifers at middle and upper elevations; coniferous forests, in which species of pine form rather extensive stands in the uplands; swamp forests, consisting of mangrove woodland (in coastal areas, in deltas and around river estuaries), stands of Nipa palm (also in deltas and tidal reaches growing with the mangroves) and fresh water swamps generally in the interior; savannahs—open or sparsely wooded and dominated by a ground cover of coarse grasses; thorn woodland consisting of shrubs and small to medium sized trees often mixed with bamboo to form a very dense tangle difficult to penetrate; and bamboo breaks, frequently forming dense fringes along banks of streams and rivers which develop rapidly in abandoned tilled land or when clearings are made in most types of forests. (3)

Owing to the seasonal pattern of rainfall in Vietnam wet evergreen forests are largely restricted to mountain areas where precipitation is higher and evaporation rates are lower than in the lowlands. These forests have not been studied nearly as extensively as the lowland forests of Vietnam, but they contain several valuable timber species and have been exploited for many years in all accessible areas.

The most widespread forest type in lowland Vietnam, occurring on most soil types subjected to desiccation during the dry season, is the so-called dipterocarp forest, dominated by several genera of trees of the wood-oil family *(Dipterocarpaceae)*. The dipterocarp forest is a deciduous or seasonal type in which many to most of the trees shed their leaves either entirely or in part during some period of the dry season. As is typical for tropical regions, most of the trees flower during the dry season. These tall forests range from moderately dense to open, depending on soil conditions and disturbance, and will typically contain four to five leaves above every point on the ground, that is, an acre of forest contains four to five acres of leaves. There is often a dense underbrush of shrubs. Grasses are abundant in clearings and stream banks in addition to small palms and cycads. These forests occur on plains and hill slopes and are not selective as to soil types or elevation except that they seldom reach an altitude of 3,000 feet. Bamboos are frequent in the lower story. This type of forest is the most predominant and the most extensive type in Vietnam. The lateritic soils upon which it is primarily found have a profound effect on the composition and structure of this forest type. There are many species of dipterocarp trees that grow in this type of forest, and some are of large dimensions and have long figured in the domestic and international markets. Extensive areas in dipterocarp forests have been cleared for rice culture. Also, the constant demand over many decades for durable timbers for heavy construction, for railroad ties, and as a source of fence posts and firewood has been a heavy drain on this forest.

The mangrove forest, an evergreen plant community primarily controlled by edaphic factors, is a specialized association found along narrow coastal belts and in deltas and estuaries below the high tide mark. It is the result of constantly changing conditions brought about by the accumulation of silt transported and deposited by streams and rivers, by the tidal movement of salty or brackish water around estuaries, and by the effect of wave action on the deposition of silt, sand, and mud along sea coasts. The canopy of the mangrove swamp forest is generally of uniform height and ranges from light to dark green so that a mangrove woodland is readily distinguishable from the air by the general hue of the foliage. The mangrove forests of Vietnam, though they contain up to twenty different species of trees and shrubs, are dominated by trees of the genera *Rhizophora, Bruguiera,* and *Avicennia,* which form a dense almost impenetrable tangled evergreen mass of trees ranging in height from 10 to 50 feet.

In South Vietnam mangrove forests cover a large area of about 1,800 square miles along the south coast from Ca Mau to Vung Tau. A tree that is closely associated with the mangrove community is the Nipa palm *(Nipa fruticans)*. This species, with a short trunk and pinnate leaves that may be fifteen to twenty feet long, also forms small clumps in rice fields or extensive stands along the landward side of mangrove forests. It grows best in brackish estuarine areas where fresh water mixes with slightly saline water.

Bamboos of several genera are a conspicuous feature of the landscape of Vietnam. They are giant grasses that are among the most conspicuous plants that colonize recently disturbed areas. Some are fire resistant and are difficult to eradicate although they can be chemically controlled to some extent. Following clear-cutting or burning of the forest the site is soon restocked by new bamboo developing from the subsurface rhizomes that have survived fire or other damage. To promote natural regeneration of the forest the bamboos have to be cut repeatedly or eradicated by means of herbicides. Certain bamboo species invade clearings that remain fallow following the shifting agriculture that has long been practiced in southeast Asia. Because of their vigorous growth, bamboos may supress regeneration of other plants, even including tree species. Clearing of evergreen rain or moist forest creates conditions favorable for the establishment of bamboo, especially breaks of *Bambusa.* Soon after flowering and seeding, the break regenerates from new combs sprouting from the underground rhizomes or from seedlings. Thus, a regular rhythm characterizes the development and replacement of the bamboo break.

Of what value are these various vegetation types to the people of Vietnam? The uninformed person is likely to call tropical forests "jungles," a term that connotes a useless mass of vines and palm trees with no commercial or esthetic value. However, this is certainly not the case in Vietnam where the people make extensive use of many of the different species of plants found in the different vegetation types. The forests of Vietnam serve as sources of timber for fuel and as thatch and so on for houses. For instance, the leaves of the Nipa palm are dried and stitched to form a thatch material that is both light and effective and that forms the sides, partitions, and roofs of houses. Nipa palm leaves are also utilized for such purposes as umbrellas, sunhats, raincoats, coarse baskets, mats, and bags.

Many of the trees of the dipterocarp forests are commercially valuable. *Dipterocarpus,* classified by American foresters as second grade timber, is resistant to both weathering and termites. It is useful for general construction, as we use Douglas fir, and for planks in the construction of riverboats or sampans. It is used for veneers, plywood, and for the interior construction of houses. Another common hardwood, *Lagerstroemia,* is one of the best woods in Vietnam for building boats because it bends well and is resistant to insects, termites, and vibration. It is also considered suitable for general construction. Another high grade timber tree is *Pterocarpus.* This is considered a luxury wood in Vietnam because it has a fine grain, is hard and heavy, takes a good polish, is susceptible to only slight shrinkage, and is resistant to insect attacks. It is considered an excellent wood for the manufacture of high grade furniture and for fine carpentry and cabinetwork. As was pointed out above, in addition to the hardwoods and the palms, the mangroves that we have described in some detail are used as a source of firewood and charcoal by the people of Vietnam.

Before we examine the effects of the recent massive destruction of these forests by the American chemical attacks, it is important to remember that much of the forested area of Vietnam has been devastated by man for many centuries. To quote a recent study by Williams:

First savage or semi-savage people occupied the land and destroyed the forest without discrimination. After that came the Annamite who in spite of a more advanced civilization regarded the forest as capable of regenerating itself indefinitely and gave no thought to its protection. Despite ample rainfall and other favorable conditions for their growth the forests were unable to reestablish themselves after prolonged periods of destruction. As a result, much of the vegetation that formerly covered Southern South Vietnam consists mainly of secondary growth and is interspersed with scattered stands of primary forests. Most of the burning of the forest in Central Vietnam, that is in the highlands, is done for shifting cultivation, the Rai System, widely adopted throughout Southeast Asia. In this process thousands of acres of forests are burned each year, followed by the planting of crops mainly for food. After two or three harvests the patches are abandoned. Soon a series of grasses, particularly *Imperata,* and weeds develop. Even in normal times this practice of slash and burn is difficult to suppress among the tribes in the mountain areas, although it can be controlled to some degree in the plains where people are in closer contact with authorities. In some instances during a single year the inhabitants of a large village may destroy a considerable area of forest within a radius of ten to fifteen miles. Bamboo breaks are also destroyed by fire. The effect of this deforestation over a long period is evident also in Central and North Vietnam. Here there is a gradual increase of uncultivated land along the bases of mountains caused by erosion of soil from the bare upper slopes filling up the stream beds, with consequent floods. (13)

How do these forests respond to such devastation? To understand this we should look briefly at what is known as "forest succession." When a primary forest is disturbed by felling or burning, a number of factors are changed radically. Removal of the vegetative canopy increases the average illumination at the ground level from about three per cent of full sunlight to 100 per cent. It gets cooler at night and hotter during the day, and the minimum atmospheric humidity is lowered. Exposure to sun and air alter the properties of the soil. Where there are steep slopes, the rate of erosion of the surface soil layers will increase. An increase in soil temperature leads to a rapid disappearance of what little humus was there to begin with. The subsequent vegetation that develops is better adjusted to the altered microclimate and soil conditions and to the changed conditions of the habitat than is the original forest vegetation.

The first phase of successional growth following the disturbance of dense humid forest in southeast Asia is usually dominated by weeds and grasses. Though most of these plants are perennials, such sites are rapidly invaded, often within a year, by shrubs, followed by small softwooded trees. Alternatively, the succession may lead almost directly from the herbaceous stage to trees. These invading trees have very soft wood and grow to tall heights very rapidly. They begin to flower and fruit when they are still very young. Little is known of the time needed in the tropics for the secondary or successional stages to develop into a climax forest. The problem is made more intractable by the fact that as yet there are no reliable techniques for aging tropical trees.

The Ecological Effects of the Military Use of Herbicides in Vietnam

DIRECT EFFECTS ON VEGETATION

The assessment of the ecological consequences of the defoliation program in Vietnam made by Fred H. Tschirley provides the first steps in our attempts to untangle the complex problem of the response of forest systems to defoliation. In his report he writes:

The principal ecologic danger imposed by repeated treatments with herbicides is that saplings and poles present in the lower story, and then seedlings, may be killed. If that happens in large areas, natural reseeding may be a problem. Dipterocarp seeds are disseminated by the wind and thus would be expected to be among the first tree species to repopulate an area. Seeds of other species, dependent on dissemination by small mammals and rodents and by birds, would probably not spread as rapidly. Seeds of some species would undoubtedly remain viable in the soil and would germinate after the last in a series of multiple treatments. Many species in the family *Leguminosae* have that capability. Less is known about seed characteristics in other families. Turrill reported it has been proved at Rothamstead that seeds of arable weeds remained viable in soil under pasture after 300 years in one area and 30 to 40 years in others.

The greatest danger resulting from repeated defoliation treatments in Vietnam is that such areas will be invaded by bamboo. The presence of bamboo is the most constant feature of the semideciduous forests I saw in Vietnam. Species of large bamboo (the most common being *Dendrocalamus strictus* and *Bambusa arundinacea* according to a local RVN forester) are particularly apparent in areas where the "rai" (slash and burn) system of agriculture has been practiced. But bamboo is not limited to areas that were previously cleared of trees. A small-stemmed bamboo is present as an understory in many forested areas and can be seen frequently where trees have been defoliated. In addition, the small bamboo *Schizostachyum sollingeri,* ten to fifteen feet high, was present in the forest of all the camps I visited. The presence of bamboo in Asian forests is well documented. Aerial observations in RVN suggest that it first invades new areas along routes of more favorable moisture supply. From there it can spread throughout the forest.

The defoliation program has caused ecologic changes. I do not feel the changes are irreversible, but complete recovery may take a long time. The mangrove type is killed with a single treatment. Regeneration of the mangrove forest to its original condition is estimated to require about 20 years.

A single treatment on semideciduous forest would cause an inconsequential ecologic change. Repeated treatments will result in invasion of many sites by bamboo. Presence of dense bamboo will then retard regeneration of the forest. The time scale for regeneration of semideciduous forest is unknown. Available information is so scanty that a prediction would have no validity and certainly no real meaning. Most of the defoliation treatments in the semideciduous forests have been made in strips along lines of communication. The ecologic effect of defoliation in those areas would not be as severe as in areas where large blocks have been treated.

If it were not for the probable invasion by bamboo of severely defoliated areas in the forests of Vietnam, I am reasonably certain that the successional progression to a secondary forest would proceed without undue retardation. A reason for feeling so is based on data I obtained from plots in Puerto Rico that were treated at the rate of 3, 9, and 27 pounds per acre as follows: picloram, 5-bromo-3-*sec*-butyl-6-methyluracil [bromacil], 3-6-dichloro-*o*-anisic acid [dicamba], 3-(3,4-dichlorophenyl)-1,1-dimethyl-urea [diuron], (2,3,6-trichlorophenyl)acetic acid [fenac], and 2,4-bis(isopropylamino)-6-(methylthio)-*s*-triazine [prometone] applied to the soil. Two years after treatment, the plots were examined for the presence of seedlings. Many of the secondary forest species and several primary forest species were present as seedlings. In addition, there was no apparent differential effect of the six herbicides. (14)

We arrived in Saigon on March 16, 1969, to begin our studies. Our work would not have been possible without the cooperation of many different people. As we reported in our article in *Science*:

We are grateful to the U.S. Embassy, Army, Navy, and Air Force, the Rubber Research Institute of Vietnam, Plantations Michelin, and the many Vietnamese biologists, both in governmental and nongovernmental positions in their country for their cooperation and hospitality. All information which we requested from the Department of Defense that did not carry a security classification was made available to us.

Because rubber plantations are one of the most important sources of foreign capital in Vietnam and since the rubber tree *Hevea brasiliensis* is particularly susceptible to damage by defoliants, especially 2,4,5-trichlorophenoxyacetic acid (2,4,5-T), we interviewed plantation owners concerning defoliation damage. The Rubber Research Institute of Vietnam, a private research corporation, has made careful observations of the nature and extent of damage to rubber trees and has carried out some experiments to find ways of minimizing the loss to defoliants. The data in the files and publications of the Institute, kindly made available to us by the director, Jean-Paul Poliniere, were invaluable to us in learning more about effects of defoliation on rubber trees. Also, during a visit to the research station of the Institute, we were able to observe recent damage to trees by defoliants and to view pictures of trees damaged and killed by previous defoliations. Officials of the Michelin Plantations also provided us with data from their files on the nature and extent of herbicide damage to rubber trees on one of their plantations.

The Faculty of Science, University of Saigon, and government agencies concerned with plants and animals, such as Ministries of Fisheries, Forestry, and Agriculture, are staffed with biologists trained primarily in France and the United States. By means of interviews with them we were able to assess their concerns, find out what kinds of studies have been initiated, explore ways of helping them launch future studies, and to gather information they had collected which was relevant to our mission. (15)

Through the cooperation of the U.S. Department of Defense, we visited the 12th Air Commando Squadron, called "Operation Ranchhand," situated at the large air base at Bien Hoa. Ranchhand is responsible for the actual application of the herbicides but does not decide where and when the defoliants will be used. We arrived at the "Ranch," as the troops call it, and were treated to a most hospitable welcome by the commander of the squadron and his pilots. We were awakened for breakfast at 5:00 A.M., then adjourned to the briefing room where the targets were pinpointed and the flight orders were issued. At the briefing we were informed that the first mission would be a "heavy suppression mission." This meant that intelligence had learned that we could expect ground fire directed at our planes from the target area. We would, therefore, rendezvous with fighter bombers that would accompany us on the mission to suppress antiaircraft ground fire in the target area. We took off in C-123 (Provider) aircraft from the Bien Hoa Airbase at about 7:45 A.M. and approximately forty minutes later were flying toward the target area at about 4,500 feet altitude. The target was located in a vast expanse of country that looked like a great uninhabited swamp. Nipa palms and other trees of uncertain identity grew among the reeds. We were later informed that the target was in the Plain of Reeds northwest of Saigon near the Cambodian border. The target area was marked by smoke bombs, and we dove from our altitude at 4,500 feet to about 100 feet above the ground at the maximum descent allowable by the aircraft. There were seven aircraft in our flight, and they were staggered so that the spray from each plane overlapped the spray from the plane ahead of it. As we leveled off, one could see the spray emerging from the nozzles on the wings and the tails of the planes ahead of us. From our location between the pilot and copilot we were able to see the operation readily. As we flew just above tree level, hundreds of herons, egrets, and storks flew up in front of us and we may have hit some of these birds as we flew through them. At the beginning of the run our escort of F-100 fighter bombers, going at tremendous speed, dropped cluster bomb units on either side of the target area. These produced large explosions and clouds of smoke in our path. The subunits then exploded in smaller balls of red fire looking like sparklers and spreading the antipersonnel pellets designed to keep down the heads of the antiaircraft gunners below us. Nevertheless, as we reached the end of the run and were running out of defoliant, the sergeant back in the fusilage called over the intercom that our aircraft was receiving bullets and that pieces of metal were flying all over inside the aircraft. An electric line and a hydraulic line were cut, but no serious damage was done to the essential functions of the aircraft. We then climbed rapidly back to 4,500 feet and returned to Bien Hoa without further incident.

In view of the fact that these planes fly very low and comparatively slowly, it seems quite certain that a number of them have been lost to ground fire, but the number is classified. Upon arrival at Bien Hoa we were debriefed and learned at that time that one of the aircraft during our flight had jettisoned its entire 1,000 gallons at the end of the target through the emergency exhaust valve because the spray nozzles would not function.

We had the opportunity to observe at rather close range the effects of the spray operations on mangrove forests during a trip with armed naval patrol boats through the cooperation of the U.S. Navy. We left the naval base at Nha Be a few miles south of Saigon to make a patrol through the channels in the delta of the Nha Be river (an area known as the Rung Sat Special Zone) that are used by freighters coming up from the South China Sea to supply Saigon. The two boats of our patrol were high-speed, heavily armored vessels with two heavy machine guns fore and aft and two lighter caliber machine

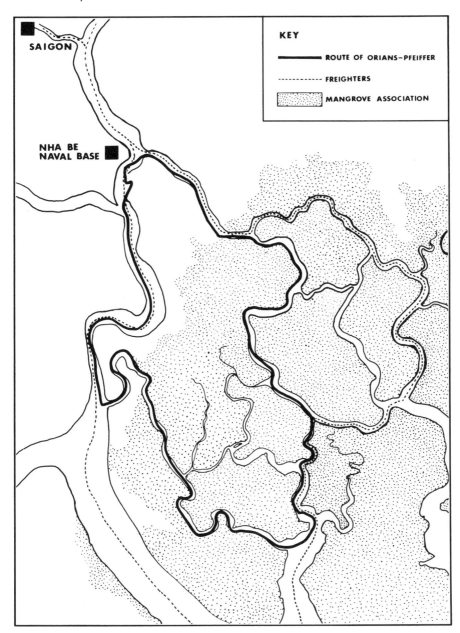

Figure 3–2. Map showing the route taken by the Orians and Pfeiffer patrol through the channels in the delta of the Nha Be River (Rung Sat Special Zone).

Figure 3–3. Gordon Orians (left) observing the defoliated mangroves in the Rung Sat Special Zone from the deck of an armed river-patrol boat. Photo by E.W. Pfeiffer.

guns amidships. We were issued steel-helmets and flak-jackets and, despite the heat, we soon donned these uncomfortable articles of apparel. The reason for all this was that the Rung Sat Special Zone was considered to be National Liberation Front territory, and there had been many attacks by soldiers of the NLF against both Saigon-bound freighters, and U.S. Navy patrol craft.

On the basis of our observations during the sixty-five-mile trip through the region we were able to:

... confirm Tschirley's report that the trees which are collectively known as mangroves are extremely susceptible to the action of defoliants and that one application at the normal rate employed in Vietnam is sufficient to kill most of the trees. Most of the areas we visited by boat on the Rung Sat Peninsula ... were still completely barren even though some of the areas had been sprayed several years earlier. Only in occasional places was there any regeneration of mangrove trees. We observed no growth of the saltwater fern *Achrosticum aureum* which often invades mangrove areas. . . . Although our observations were limited to what we could see from the boats with binoculars, there is reason to believe that the timetable may be somewhat longer than this. Possibly conditions for seed germination are not now very good in the defoliated forests. The unusual soil conditions of mangrove forests may result in a failure of the herbicides to be decomposed. If the molecules remain bound to the soil particles, they

Figure 3–4. Defoliated mangrove association in the Rung Sat Special Zone. The trees have been killed by the herbicide. Photo by G. H. Orians.

might influence seed germination for a long time. Alternatively, seed dispersal into the areas is difficult because of the large areas in which mature trees have been killed. Many of the areas, as a result of continued soil deposition under the trees, are flooded only at the highest of high tides, and seeds must be transported for long distances from the river channels under very unfavorable conditions. It cannot be excluded that reestablishment of the original forest may be impossible except along the edges of the river channels and backwaters. (15)

While we were in Vietnam, we were unable even to walk around in a defoliated upland hardwood forest because of security conditions. However, during our stay in Saigon, we met Barry R. Flamm, Chief of the Forestry Division of USAID in the Republic of Vietnam, who described to us in some detail experiments he had carried out in South Vietnam to attempt to determine some of the effects of the defoliant chemicals on hardwood forests. He also showed us many photographs of defoliated forests. In March, 1968, Flamm installed forest inventory sample areas at three locations in Tay Ninh and Binh Long provinces. These locations were at Thien Ngon, Katum, and Tong Le Chon Special Forces Camps. The site at Thien Ngon was selected as representing a single herbicide treatment in 1966 in a moist semideciduous forest. Katum was selected as an area of heavy herbicide treatment in a moist semideciduous forest. Katum had received two applications over a two-year period.

The site at Tong Le Chon was selected as representing a single herbicide treatment in 1966 in a *Lagerstroemia* forest. A deliberate attempt was made to have all three sample areas located on the same broad soil type. All trees $11\frac{1}{2}$ inches in diameter at breast height (DBH) were classified as saw timber. Trees from $3\frac{1}{2}$ to $11\frac{1}{2}$ DBH were classified as poles. Reproduction was estimated by counting stems ranging from twenty inches high to 3.4 inches DBH. Each saw timber was identified, and diameter and merchantable height were measured. The condition of the tree and log was judged, and the cause of damage was estimated. From the results of this study Flamm concluded that at Thien Ngon economic loss and permanent damage to the forest was relatively light (16). However, a second treatment within the next year would probably kill the seedlings and saplings already present and necessary to restock the stand. Marketable timber, heavily damaged by the first treatment, would probably suffer heavy mortality from a subsequent treatment. At the Katum site Flamm concluded that the two treatments of herbicides applied to this area had severely damaged the saw-timber-sized trees and their seedlings and saplings. The ground cover had substantially changed, with an increase in grass cover. The Tong Le Chan study revealed that *Lagerstroemia* was very susceptible to herbicides. All the trees for which data were recorded were completely defoliated or had less than 25 per cent of their crown remaining. However, during a second trip to this area, a check of the inner bark of many specimens showed a high percentage still alive. All the trees recorded as dead may not in fact have been dead, and some may have later recovered. Flamm concluded from his study:

Light to moderate mortality occurs in forest stands following one application of herbicides. After one year, all trees killed by defoliation remained sound and salvageable. Reproduction representative of the over-story is found in adequate numbers. Two treatments in successive years result in heavy mortality of sawtimber and loss of reproduction. Grasses appear to increase and it can be expected that bamboo will also increase. Evaluation of damage is difficult during the dry season. When possible, evaluation should be made during the rainy season. Follow up examinations should be made this summer, particularly of the *Lagerstroemia* stands, to check estimates of mortality. Log salvage operations should commence the second year following initial herbicide application, as mortality can be judged accurately at this time and logs remain sound. Permanent forest areas receiving two or more treatments of herbicides should be planned for reforestation.

EFFECTS ON RUBBER PRODUCTION

In talks with officials of the Michelin Plantations and the Rubber Research Institute of Vietnam, we learned much about the effects of defoliation on the growth and production of rubber trees in Vietnam. Damage to rubber trees in Vietnam has been extensive.

During 1967–68, the Institute staff visited over 200 different plantations in the provinces of Bien Hoa, Binh Duong, Gia Dinh, Hau Nghai, Long Khanh, Phuoc Tuy, Tay Ninh, and Binh Long. (This covers most of the area between the rice-growing areas of the Saigon and Mekong River deltas and the mountainous central part of the country.) On this extensive area of approximately 130 by 40 kilometers, all plantations reported damage by defoliants. More than 40,000 hectares planted with rubber trees were defoliated at least to the extent of 10 percent. It is difficult to estimate the total amount of damage resulting from defoliation. Plantation owners might possibly submit exaggerated claims, but there is no doubt that the damage has been considerable. For example, Plantation de Dautieng of the Michelin Company has been affected by defoliants three times since 1965. In all cases, the defoliant has not been applied directly to the rubber trees, but has been carried by the wind from applications in the general area. Few trees were killed but, by measuring the drop in latex production due to stoppage of tapping, decreased yield of lightly damaged trees, and costs of cutting and trimming back partially killed trees, the company estimates that the damage amounted to $27,835 in 1965, $37,479 in 1966, and $27,844 in 1967. . . .

The yield of rubber per hectare is decreasing. In 1960, rubber plantations in Vietnam yielded 1066 kilograms of dry rubber per hectare (on plantations of more than 25 hectares). In 1967, the yield had dropped to 793 kilograms per hectare. In contrast, in Malaysia the yield in 1960 was 758 kilograms of dry rubber per hectare, but had risen to 1007 kilograms per hectare in 1966. The decrease in yield in Vietnam is due to a combination of circumstances such as the cessation of tapping forced by military action, less experienced labor and less thorough control in the field, herbicide damage, lack of general upkeep of plantations and the cutting of rubber trees along roads where about 3000 hectares have already been cut. The relative importance of each factor seems impossible to assess. It is a fact that they are all the consequence of the war.

The total yield of rubber in Vietnam has also declined. In 1960 77,560 tons of dry rubber were produced. Rubber exports amounted to $48,000,000 which was 56 percent of South Vietnam's total exports for that year. In 1967, the yield had dropped to 42,510 tons of dry rubber, which considering the devaluation of the piaster, amounted only to $12,800,000. Inasmuch as other exports suffered even more heavily, this diminished amount (26 percent of the 1960 exports) made up 72 percent of South Vietnam's exports, which had decreased to $17,800,000 or 20.8 percent of the 1960 exports.

If a rubber tree is completely defoliated by herbicides, the Institute recommends that planters stop tapping until its new leaves are fully grown. Because it takes a month for a new leaf to grow to full size from the time of breaking of bud dormancy and because dormancy is not usually broken immediately after defoliation, the minimum period of stopping is about 2 months. The maximum period of stoppage is, of course, permanent if the tree is killed. If tapping is not stopped while the tree is defoliated, there is competition between growth of new leaves and yield within the tree, and the future health of the tree is jeopardized. In a number of cases where trees were not killed, tapping has been stopped for as long as 1 year. If only some of the leaves are lost, tapping can be continued, but there is a drop in latex production after a lag of about 1 month. The loss, over a period of a year, has been estimated to be sometimes as much as 30 percent of the normal yield of latex. At current prices that amount of loss reduces profit from about $90 per hectare per year to nothing. As a consequence, most of the small plantations have been unable to stay in business. Only the large planters, with solid financial backing, can afford to remain in operation despite the war (15).

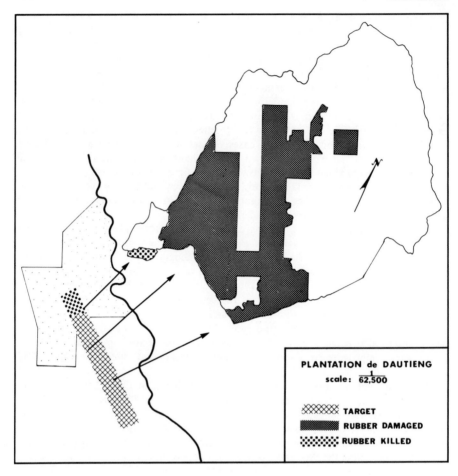

Figure 3–5. Target areas and areas of rubber trees on Plantation de Dautieng affected by defoliation in February, 1965, as indicated by Plantations Michelin. Wind direction is indicated by arrows.

Though few studies have been made of the physiological effects of 2,4-D and 2,4,5-T on trees it is known that:

... the defoliant is absorbed through the leaves of the trees and is carried down through the phloem within 24 hours, and symptoms of defoliation appear within a few weeks after spraying. The distance the defoliant travels down the tree is a function of the dosage received, and the Institute people have assessed this by the simple device of cutting into the trunk of the trees at different heights to investigate the flow of latex. Necroses are also clearly visible in the sectioned trunks, many of which we examined in the laboratories of the Institute. As might be expected, the smaller the rubber tree, the more readily it is killed by defoliants. Research in Malaysia has shown that a wide range of concentrations of the *n*-butyl ester of 2,4,5-T killed rubber seedlings in 6 weeks. Accidental defoliations in Vietnam indicate that trees less than 7 years old can be killed by the dosages used in military operations, but that older trees normally recover. Nevertheless, all trees on 100 hectares on Plantation Ben Cui were killed by herbicides in 1965, despite the fact that the trees were 33 years old. From such occurrences, the Rubber Research Institute concluded that repeated defoliations threaten the very existence of rubber culture in Vietnam.

In spite of such evidence, Chemical Operations Division, United States Army, claims that rubber trees cannot be killed by defoliants. According to our observations, although we do not claim expertise in this field, damage to rubber production is severe. The Rubber Research Institute, which does not itself maintain any plantations and cannot be accused of bias on that account, seems to be in an excellent position to conduct further research into the physiological effects of defoliants on trees. Funds are urgently needed for this purpose. (15)

CROP DESTRUCTION PROGRAM

In addition to the spraying of chemicals to defoliate trees there is a large program designed specifically to destroy crops.

When we were in Vietnam, we discussed the crop destruction program with American officials, and some of them expressed the view that it was very successful because some captured soldiers from the areas that had been attacked were seriously undernourished, some to the extent of being stretcher cases at the time of capture. However, Dr. Jean Mayer, a distinguished Harvard nutritionist and at the present time the president's adviser on nutrition, has stated that the main effect of crop destruction in Vietnam is the starving of children (5). He said that children make up 60 to 70 per cent of the country's population, and they are the first to die of starvation due to the United States' military crop destruction program. He pointed out that older people are the next to suffer from food denial. The older people are followed by babies because mothers aren't able to nurse their babies owing to the lack of food. Men and adolescents fair the best because bands of armed men are able to seize whatever food there is available in an area that is undergoing food denial programs. Dr. Mayer believes that history has repeatedly shown that starvation methods have never defeated an army but have only succeeded in killing many innocent people.

Stories in *The New York Times* of December 20 and 21, 1965, had this to say about this aspect of the use of herbicides:

There is a complex system of political and military controls on the crop destruction program. The program which began last Spring has touched only a small fraction, 50–75,000 acres of the more than 8 million acres of cultivated land in South Vietnam. This is the intention of policy-makers. Although the VC control or at least contest 70 per cent of the land area of the nation, crop destruction missions are aimed only at relatively small areas of major military importance where the guerrillas grow their own food or where the population is willingly committed to their cause. Officials say that no herbicide missions have been flown or will be flown in heavily populated areas. There has been no crop destruction for example in the Mekong Delta. There is concern that any attempt to destroy crops in heavily populated areas dominated by the VC could only send a new flood of displaced Vietnamese to join South Vietnam's 730,000 refugees. It is also suggested that unless the herbicides were applied on a vast scale, a move that would probably be politically impermissible, it could have little effect in heavily populated areas. There is just so much food in the Delta that crop destruction missions here would have no real military value, one official said. Destruction operations are intended primarily for food fields, and such Viet Cong base areas as War Zone D north of Saigon and in areas where growers are considered willing Viet Cong supporters. Some Viet Cong units are devoting as much as 50 per cent of their man power to growing food. Food shortages have become so acute in Central Vietnam that some analysts expect the enemy to shift more of its military activity towards the north Vietnamese border to ease the supply of provisions.

Table 3-1 shows that the program of crop destruction, which began on a modest scale, rapidly escalated so that the total number of acres had reached several hundred thousand by 1969.

The South Vietnamese Government often warns the population in the area that is to be attacked with crop destroying chemicals. The following is a text of a leaflet picked up by a Vietnamese farmer:

The Government of the Republic of Vietnam has adopted the use of defoliant which will ruin your rice crop and other crops in the field. This has been necessary as your rice fields are located in areas supplying food to the Viet Cong. However you should not be disappointed as the Government will compensate for all damages done to your rice crop. Meanwhile the Government will help evacuate you to other places with food, lodging, and clothing provided until next harvesting season, if you so desire. (5)

In addition to crops deliberately destroyed, there has been widespread destruction of fruit trees and vegetables in "friendly" areas. We were able to observe the results of an accidental defoliation in the town of Ho Nai. We saw damage to several species of trees in this town, which is very close to the American airbase at Bien Hoa. Many fruit trees had recently been damaged by defoliants. The characteristic sign was the presence of curled, dead leaves on the trees. Most of the damage was on the south side of the trees suggesting that the spray was carried into the village by means of southerly winds. Villagers told us that spray had hit them about one week previous to the time that we visited them. The Chemical Operations officers of the U.S. Army reported to us that a defoliation aircraft had dumped its chemicals at the end of the runway at nearby Bien Hoa Airbase the same day the Honai residents had observed the spray. Residents of Ho Nai claim that they had been affected by defoliation missions seven times within the past year.

Arthur Galston writes:

In a survey of defoliant action in the Bien Hoa area on March 4, 1965, observers noted that considerable damage was done to trees and bananas. This damage was recognized as evidently due to drift from defoliation spraying. At Tan Hiep village beans were damaged presumably not from aerial spraying but from a buffalo turbine

Figure 3–6. The crown of a jack-fruit tree in the Catholic refugee village of Hanoi near the U.S. airbase at Bien Hoa. The leaves are characteristically curled and brown after having been killed by an accidental drift of herbicides. Photo by G. H. Orians.

sprayer. In this area alone approximately 500 complaints or requests for compensation had been filed with hamlet chiefs for transmission to the province chief through channels. Beans and water spinach are recognized as the major susceptible crops especially between May and November. On December 13, 1965, three aircraft flew over Thoi Andong village of Phong Phu District spraying defoliant extensively. Maturing watermelon only 20 days from full maturity was seriously damaged as were rice, vegetables and fruits. Crops in the adjacent villages of Phuce Thoi and Tuyen were also heavily damaged. The entire area is supposed to be secure from the U.S. point of view and thus should not have been sprayed at all. Con Son, an island 1/2 kilometer from Can Tho, was subjected to defoliation treatment six times during June through December, 1969. Papaya, jackfruit, milkfruit, coconut, watermelon, mustard cabbage and beans were adversely affected. At An Nghiep hamlet, bean, cabbage and tomato were adversely affected. The damage ranged from 40 to 100 per cent rendering the crops unprofitable for harvesting. Some farmers also decided not to replant thus amplifying the economic loss. (5)

While we were in Vietnam, we discussed at considerable length the method for payment of damage claims, and we tried without success to learn how much had been paid. However, the Vietnamese to whom we talked all agreed that payments are minimal. We were told by Vietnamese that people who file claims with the government are often threatened with imprisonment if they continue to press their claims. Many others do not attempt to file claims because they feel that it will be of no use. United States officials, for their part, argue that most claims are fraudulent. It was our conclusion that significant quantities of defoliant are regularly carried by the wind over broad areas of crop land in the Republic of Vietnam. We concluded that the extent of the damage caused by drifting spray had contributed significantly to the deterioration of relations between many Vietnamese and Americans. The United States military was finally realizing the damage caused by wind drift from targets into friendly areas, and we were informed that Agent White was being used increasingly in the Delta region because of its low volatility.

EFFECTS OF HERBICIDES ON ANIMALS

As zoologists, we were particularly interested to learn of the effects on animal life of the defoliation program in Vietnam. The fauna of southeast Asia includes a great viariety of species, some rare and quite unique. Jean Delacour, probably the foremost authority on the birds of Indochina, writes that the birds of Vietnam constitute one of the richest and most fascinating avifaunas on earth (17). He states, "I also hope that the Vietnamese people will understand that a marvelous natural treasure has been entrusted to them and will take all wise and necessary steps to preserve it for future generations." Nearly 600 species of birds have been seen in Vietnam, but the combined effects of the war and modern economic development threaten the future of many of them.

Among the mammals of Vietnam are many large species, including elephants, tigers, wild boar, deer, rhinoceros, and primates, some of them unique to the area, such as the Douc Langur and the Indochinese Gibbon. These primates are classified by the International Union for the Conservation of Nature as endangered species. The Douc Langur, a monkey that lives almost entirely upon leaves, is one of the most colorful of all mammals. The beautiful Indochinese gibbon is almost completely arboreal and feeds on fruits, buds, leaves, insects, and birds' eggs. The dependence of this gibbon upon undisturbed forest is described by a French zoologist as follows:

The Gibbon is so highly specialized that he becomes an unsurpassed virtuoso acrobat in the high forests, which are his natural environment, but at the same time he is entirely dependent on this environment. The different apes of the macaco species only need brushwoods and undergrowth left over by men, and even dare to approach cleared lands and human habitations when looking for profitable spoil. The Gibbon, on the contrary, needs free space for his bounds and also a network of branches thick enough for his rebounds. He also needs a floor of branches between the ground and the sky, above the undergrowth and the huge trees surpassing it. He finds all this in the intermediate floors of the tropical forest with its three levels of vegetation. The branches and leaves, some very tall and some of middle height, join and entangle, united by the creepers which ramify on a level of 20 to 30 meters' height. This is where the ferns, the orchids, and the lycopodia find the best conditions of light, humidity, temperature and hygrometry. This hanging garden, at the same time light and sheltered, airy and confined, dense and closed, dominated by widespread ramifications of unequally distributed giant trees, is the Gibbon's world. Here he is roaming, here is his play ground, his exercise grounds, this is the place where he picks up his food, where he sleeps and rests. The micro-climate of this forestial floor, sifting and regulating the two climates between which it is interposed, fits the Gibbon perfectly.

All these dwelling conditions are to be found in the forest of high trees and only there, in the great thick and evergreen forests. (18)

There are also rare bovine species like the kouprey, a cow that was not even discovered until 1936 and is limited to a few hundred individuals. This animal is of particular interest because it is apparently the form of wild cow to which our domestic cattle are most closely related. The International Union for the Conservation of Nature states that the kouprey is dependent upon forest glades and savannas. Because this type of habitat occurs relatively rarely in the Indochinese peninsula, the range of this ungulate is necessarily limited. It has been observed in only two regions of Cambodia and has also been noted in the area between Kontume and Ben Mei Thuot in South Vietnam. Undoubtedly its former distribution included the entire zone of forested glades in central Indochina, that is to say, northern and eastern Cambodia and western Vietnam. Estimates of remaining numbers of kouprey vary from 700 to 800 in 1938 to 200 in 1964.

The gaur and banteng are other bovines that occur in Southeast Asia. According to the American expert, Professor C. H. Wharton, these wild cattle inhabit savanna grasslands and humid deciduous forests. Much of their range is heavily defoliated regions of Vietnam. One subspecies of gaur is limited to only some 300 individuals.

Two other large mammals in danger of extermination in Vietnam are the the Sumatran rhinoceros and the brow-antler deer. All these endangered species depend upon relatively undisturbed vegetation for both food and cover, and therefore the elimination of vegetation will quickly wipe them out. An unknown number are also shot by soldiers and native hunters.

In the marine and fresh waters of Vietnam there is a great variety of invertebrate life, some of which, such as cuttlefish, mollusks, shrimp, and crabs, are very important commercially. There is also a very great variety of fishes, some of them being unique physiologically in that they are tree climbers getting their oxygen through the air as well as water. Others hibernate in mud during the dry season. The food chains, pathways through which food energy moves through herbivores and carnivores, will be altered by the defoliation of the vegetation that is the starting point of all of these pathways. Because herbicides do not ordinarily concentrate in animal tissues as do some of the chlorinated insecticides, intense concentration resulting from passage through different animals probably does not occur. Much more important are the direct effects of habitat destruction. Alteration of the structure and species composition of the vegetation, even if the changes appear subtle to the un-informed human observer, may cause profound changes in the animal life. Some animals are dependent upon specific plant species and others, like the Gibbon, are restricted to vegetation of specific structural characteristics. Tschirley also made a few observations on the possible effects of defoliation upon animal life of South Vietnam. After his visit to Vietnam, he stated: "The effect of defoliation on animal population is truly unknown," and he speculated about the possible effects on the food chain of killing the mangrove (14). Assuming that carnivorous fish would be near the top of the food chain, Tschirley speculated that disruption of the lower links in the chain might be expected to reduce fish populations. However, he then quoted statistics from the fisheries branch of the U.S. Agency for International Development that indicated that the fish catch has been increasing in Vietnam. He concluded that "the statistics on the fish catch give a strong indication that the aquatic food chain has not been seriously disturbed." Nevertheless, we do not know where the fish were caught or anything about possible changes in fishing effort. Therefore, these gross statistics are difficult to interpret.

Tschirley questioned men in Special Forces Camps about animals that they had seen in treated areas, and the men indicated that birds, deer, elephants, and monkeys were still present. There were no reports of any bovines, and Tschirley writes, "It is surely possible that such rare bovines such as the Kouprey, Gaur and Banteng have been eliminated from the defoliated areas in War Zone C and D but I suspect that bombing, artillery fire, human presence, and hunting have had a far greater effect than defoliation."

Although we were able to obtain some quantitative data about animals, it was obvious to us that not much can be learned about effects of defoliation on animal life without intensive long-term studies. During our trip through the defoliated mangrove swamps of the Rung Sat Special Zone, we were able to get some estimate of the effect upon bird life in that area. With binoculars we counted the total number of species of birds and of individuals that we saw during the sixty-five-mile journey. It was very impressive that we did not see a single species of insectivorous or fruit-eating bird with the exception of barn swallows that were wintering in the area from the north. This is, of course, highly unusual because the mangrove swamps of the tropics, whether in America or Asia, are known to be very rich in bird life under normal circum-stances. We saw a considerable number of fish-eating birds, although even their numbers were less than we would expect under normal circumstances. In the two-hour trip we saw oriental darter, grey heron, large egret, little egret, intermediate egret, Javan pond heron, stork, black-winged kite, osprey, whimbrel, little tern, and white breasted kingfisher. All these except the kite, which feeds on small mammals, are fish-eating birds. The only other vertebrate animal that we encountered in this defoliated mangrove area was a large crocodile lying on the bank of a small channel.

Although we were unable to obtain any data on the status of invertebrates in the Rung Sat area, we concluded that the ecology of their habitat must have changed very greatly due to defoliation. The stripping of the leaf cover allows for much greater illumination with resultant changes in soil temperature and moisture and also permits precipitation to have a much greater direct impact on the soil, thus affecting the living conditions of invertebrates, such as crustaceans and mollusks.

In our discussions with Vietnamese we received one report of sick and dying birds in forests following a defoliation attack. This report was made to us by a captain in the ARVN who was an amateur ornithologist. He had moved into a forested area shortly after a defoliation mission, and he stated that he was able to pick up paralyzed birds at will. He informed us that the people often go in after defoliation attacks upon forested areas because they can capture birds easily following these attacks. We also received reports of a large number of deaths among small pigs in a large pig farm near Saigon, including deaths from abortions. These deaths were attributed by Vietnamese to the drift of defoliants from target areas to the north. The director of the Institute of Fisheries of the Republic of Vietnam told us that he had received reports that the incidence of disease among fresh water fishes is increasing. It appears that a sickness, characterized by many small, round, dark spots on the muscles of the affected fish, formerly of rare occurrence, is now widespread, especially at the beginning of the rainy season when the fish invade the rice fields. The taste is supposedly adversely affected, although poor people continue to eat even the diseased fish. The director of the Institute of Fisheries was carrying out studies to determine whether the incidence of this disease had particularly increased in those areas where defoliation was extensive. In this connection it should be pointed out that Holden working in England has shown that 2,4-D and 2,4,5-T are toxic to certain types of fish (19). He determined that the LD_{50} (the dose required to kill half the experimental animals during a forty-eight-hour exposure) for salmonids during a twenty-four-hour exposure to 2,4-D is 0.5 ppm. Thus, if the fish of Vietnam are as susceptible to 2,4-D as salmonid fish are, one could expect a very high mortality because the LD_{50} as determined by Holden is less than the rate of application of 2,4-D in Vietnam. In addition, the shallow waters of the rice fields provide conditions under which high concentrations of herbicides might be expected to occur.

In discussions with an army medical entomologist in Saigon we learned that he was concerned that defoliation of the mangrove swamps may affect the epidemiology of malaria such that the incidence of this disease is increased. He stated that some types of malaria-carrying mosquitoes show a preference for better illuminated areas, and thus the stripping of the leaves from the mangroves could increase reproduction of these malarial vectors and thereby increase a problem that is already serious in South Vietnam due to the spread of a very virulent form of malaria, *Plasmodium falciparum.*

There has been widespread concern in the United States about the use of Agent Blue in Vietnam. It is cacodylic acid that contains a high percentage of arsenic but in nontoxic form as applied. We were able to get some indication of the effect of this agent upon animal life in discussions with Army personnel at the Tan Son Nhut Airbase in Saigon. The perimeter of this base is sprayed by hand several times each year with Agent Blue in order to prevent growth of high grass. Despite the fact that this area has been treated for many years, there is still a high population of rats in the area. Because of the plague problem there is an active attempt to keep the rat population to a minimum. A trapping crew is permanently engaged in obtaining animals for medical examination. Each night they put out about 100 snap traps and thirty live traps. During the period from January 3, 1969 to March 19, 1969, they had trapped 613 rats and 8 viverrids (weasel-like predators of rodents). We concluded that Agent Blue was not having direct toxic effects on these species of mammals. We also accompanied a bird netting team from the University of Saigon on two trips to a previously sprayed brushy area near Bien Hoa. We found high population of birds that were behaving as expected at the end of the dry season, that is, they were singing and defending territories.

In concluding this discussion on the direct effects of defoliation on animals, it should be understood that habitat destruction, which defoliation produces, usually is the equivalent of death for the animals who were in that habitat. The idea that animals can move to other nearby areas is untenable, because there is good ecological evidence to suggest that tropical forests hold the maximum number of individuals that the habitat will support. Reduction of these habitats decreases the populations of their characteristic animals by an equivalent amount. It is not true that forest species can live successfully in the greatly modified conditions one finds in even partially defoliated forests. Defoliated forests cannot be reinhabited by typical species until the basic food resources are reestablished, and it is impossible to say how long this will take.

Though field data are meager, 2,4-D may also affect certain animals indirectly because of its effect on plant metabolism. It has been shown that certain plants, such as sugar beets, after treatment with relatively low amounts of 2,4-D may accumulate abnormally large quantities of nitrates in their leaves (20). If cattle eat these leaves, they may die from a peculiar type of nitrogen poisoning. In the intestinal tract of cattle and other animals the nitrates from the ingested leaves of the treated plants are changed to nitrites that are then absorbed into the blood and block the ability of the blood to carry oxygen to the tissues. This has been found to produce death, or in pregnant mothers it may lead to abortion. This is one of the reasons why dairy cows are not permitted to graze in areas treated with 2,4-D for at least two weeks after the application of this chemical. It would be important to know whether the water buffalo and cattle that are so common in Vietnam have been affected in this manner.

The Department of Defense has consistently maintained that the chemicals dumped on Vietnam for crop destruction and defoliation are harmless, and it emphasizes that they are common garden-variety chemicals used routinely in the United States. It is certainly true that for many years the herbicides applied in Vietnam have been used in many ways for a variety of nonmilitary purposes in the United States and elsewhere. In Montana for instance, many thousands of acres of desert have been sprayed to kill the sagebrush and convert the rangeland to grass production. Agent 2,4-D has also been used for thinning trees that have regenerated in areas following forest fire burns. In Washington state herbicides are used to suppress the growth of alder and encourage rapid invasion of conifers. However, the maximum rates at which these chemicals are applied are much lower than the rates at which they are used in Vietnam. There are also many regulations and precautions taken which cannot, of course, be followed in the war-time environment in which herbicides are used in Vietnam. In the United States boards have been set up in areas to be sprayed to implement the control practices, determine the need for supervision, and check that proper procedures have been followed. In one operation in Montana, for instance, the Forest Service is reported to have taken precautions to protect the range and watershed in the area (21). Livestock were kept off the treated area for ten days to allow the chemical to decompose completely. The water was protected because spray areas were adjusted to avoid streams. Streams adjacent to the treated areas were sampled periodically for the chemicals.

In 1967 the Midwest Research Institute Report, on the basis of a literature survey, summarized available information about the problem of the toxic effects of herbicides as follows:

The possible toxic hazards involved in the aerial spraying of herbicides in Vietnam are of concern to scientists and to the public. As mentioned elsewhere in this report the herbicides being used for defoliation of forest areas or for crop destruction are Orange, White, and Blue. After examining the voluminous toxicity data and the actual rates at which these chemicals have been applied, we can make the following observations: 1. The direct toxicity hazards to people and animals on the ground is nearly nonexistent. 2. Destruction of wildlife, food and wildlife habitats will probably affect wildlife survival more than any direct toxic effects of the herbicides. 3. The application of Orange or White alongside of rivers and canals, or even the spraying of the water area itself at the levels used for defoliation, is not likely to kill the fish in the water. 4. Food produced from land treated with herbicides will not be poisonous or significantly altered in nutritional quality. If residues of a more persistent herbicide such as picloram should carry over to the next growing season it would retard plant growth rather than concentrate some toxic residue in the crop. 5. Toxic residues of these herbicides will not accumulate in the fish and meat animals to the point where man will be poisoned by them. 6. The primary ecological change is the destruction of vegetation and the resulting ecological succession in the replacement of this vegetation. (2)

Such was the Department of Defense's optimistic report upon the possibility of poisonous effects of the herbicides. After many years of civilian uses of herbicides, during which no serious adverse consequences had been recognized, it seemed that John S. Foster, Jr., Director of Research for the Department of Defense, was on fairly safe ground when he said:

> Qualified scientists, both inside and outside our government, and in the governments of other nations, have judged that seriously adverse ecological consequences will not occur (from use of herbicides and defoliants in Vietnam). Unless we had confidence in these judgments, we would not continue to employ these materials. (2)

Nevertheless, since the publication of these reassuring statements about the lack of toxic effects on animals, new evidence has been obtained suggesting that animals and humans may indeed be sensitive to herbicides. In a story of March 15, 1970, *The New York Times* states as follows:

> In the last several months, reportedly on instruction from Washington, the U.S. Military Command and the U.S. Embassy have formed a special committee to review the effects of the defoliation program especially on humans. The South Vietnamese Government regards the entire subject as taboo. Vietnamese newspapers have been suspended for publishing articles about birth defects allegedly attributed to the defoliants, and the Public Health Ministry declines to provide any statistics on normal and abnormal births. However, the concern felt among the Americans is shared by many South Vietnamese scientists, physicians, health officials, and villagers interviewed in a three weeks survey of the effects of the program. Saigon's leading maternity hospital, TuDu from which rumors of an increase of abnormal births emanate periodically, has not even compiled annual reports of statistics for the last three years. Recent monthly figures show an average of about 140 miscarriages and 150 premature births among approximately 2,800 pregnancies, but the hospital is not prepared to say whether this represents an increase and, if so, what the cause might be.
>
> A high Agriculture Ministry official said: "I don't think the Americans would use the chemicals if they were harmful."
>
> He conceded that his ministry had made no tests and asserted that his experts had been unable to get any information about the defoliants from the Defense Ministry which considers such data secret. The main defoliant compounds and some information about them are available in the United States.
>
> Last Oct. 29, President Nixon's science adviser, Dr. Lee A. DuBridge, announced that, as a result of a study showing that one of the defoliants used, 2,4,5-T, had caused an unexpected high incidence of fetal deformities in mice and rats, the compound would henceforth be restricted to areas remote from population.
>
> That directive appears to be ambiguous in South Vietnam for military spokesmen assert that 2,4,5-T continues to be used only in "enemy staging areas"—by definition populated regions.
>
> Don That Trinh, Minister of Agriculture from November, 1967 to May, 1968, and for 10 years professor of agronomy at Saigon University, said that while he was Minister, the Defense Ministry "would try to conceal the defoliant products from me."
>
> "I did not believe in defoliation," he added.
>
> According to one of the Vietnamese directors of a Government research laboratory in Saigon: "We didn't know anything before the United States started spraying. It was only when we received complaints from the livestock people that we started getting interested." But, he added, there are still no Vietnamese studies.

Even the village of Tanhiep, 20 miles north of Saigon, on which 1,000 gallons of defoliants were jettisoned on Dec. 1, 1968, has not been the object of attention or study.

An American C-123 flying out of Bienhoa air base, northeast of Saigon, developed engine trouble shortly after takeoff. To lighten the craft, the pilot sprayed the full load of chemicals over Tanhiep and nearby Binhtri in 30 seconds instead of the usual 4 minutes 30 seconds, which spreads the defoliant at the rate of three gallons an acre in unpopulated areas.

The defoliant involved according to the United States command, was a 50–50 mixture of 2,4-Dichlorophenoxyacetate, or 2,4-D, and 2,4,5-Trichlorphenoxyacetate, or 2,4,5-T, in an oil base. It is one of the three compounds the military says it uses here, the others being a Dow chemical product called Tordon 101, a mixture of amine salts of 2,4-D and Picloram, and an arsenic compound of cacodylic acid.

No physicians visited Tanhiep to examine the people after their exposure, which like eight similar emergency dumpings since 1968—some over unpopulated forests—was not made public by the United States command.

A United States Air Force medical team visited Binhtri shortly after the spraying and, according to American district officials, found the villagers had suffered no ill effects. There was no later inquiry.

Mrs. Tran Thi Tien of Tanhiep, who says she has four normal children, is convinced that the malfunction of her son, who still looks like a newborn at 14 months of age, "must be due to the chemicals I breathed."

Her neighbors, Mrs. Nguyen Thi Hai and Mrs. Tong Thi An, blame the spraying for the fact that their children, one year and 20 months old respectively, still crawl instead of walk.

Nguyen Van Nhap, a farmer, complains of suffering bouts of fever, sneezing and weakness.

"I was working in the field when the spray came down," Mrs. Tien said through an interpreter. "I felt dizzy, like vomiting and had to stay in bed three or four days."

Many other villagers reported feeling the same sensations as Mrs. Tien, but, except for the two children described as retarded in learning to walk, no other abnormal children, were described to visitors at the village of 1,200 residents.

Tran Van Dang, a farmer in neighboring Binhtri, recalled that three days after the spraying two villagers, Tam Ten and Mrs. Hai Mua, died after suffering respiratory difficulties and trembling. The next day, he said, a third villager, Mrs. Hai Nuc, died after showing similar symptoms. Mr. Ten was an old man and could have been expected to die soon anyway but the two others, Mr. Dang said, were middle-aged and seemed healthy.

Such complaints are not limited to Tanhiep and Binhtri, where villagers were admittedly exposed to concentrated doses of defoliant—though just how concentrated has not been established.

In Bienhoa city, 10 miles from Tanhiep, any defoliant in the air drifts down from the heavily sprayed battle areas to the north.

Dr. Nguyen Son Cao says he finds a clear correlation between the days when there is spraying and the number of patients who come in with respiratory ailments, mostly sneezing and coughing.

Dr. Cao, who has been practicing in Bienhoa for 21 years, said he had also noticed that in the last two to three years the number of miscarriages among his patients had doubled.

"These women are convinced that they are the victims of the chemicals," he said. "I only suspect there could be relationship. This suspicion is well known. The increase in miscarriages is very, very significant."

However, the manager of another clinic reported no increase in miscarriages for the last several years.

Another story in *The New York Times* of February 8, 1970, describes the feelings of the people of Globe, Arizona, about 2,4-D and 2,4,5-T and its relation to their health. The attitudes of these Americans toward the herbicides is remarkably similar to those we have just quoted from the Vietnamese villagers:

In the area of Globe, Arizona, where spraying has occurred in the adjacent National forests, the incidence of miscarriages has gone up in the area, a number of women have suffered from internal hemorrhaging and several have had to undergo hysterectomies. The evidence is not conclusive but the women blame the spray. The head of the range station in Globe, Arizona, who supervised the spraying, said that the chemicals used were not harmful and that directions for their use had been followed closely. But the local residents do not agree. The chemicals are the same as those used in Vietnam and are generally known as Orange. Mrs. Willard Shoecraft, a local architect and poet, showed a visitor copies of a Department of Agriculture publication on pesticides. The publication stated that safe tolerance levels had never been established with either 2,4,5-T or Silvex. Moreover, the publication warned that neither chemical should be used in the water intended for irrigation, crop spraying or domestic and animal water supply. The warning was also present on the labels of the pesticide cans. One of the residents stated, "If they try to spray again, we'll shoot them down. We realize we'll lose but we'll lose either way. They've done so much damage that if they spray again life won't be worth living. We wouldn't have anything left."

In England similar questions were being raised about some of these herbicides. A story in the *London Times*, April 12, 1970, states in part:

Only a week ago Mr. Jenson learned that the Forestry Commission, Britain's largest users of herbicides, had sprayed 2,4,5-T in the New Forest to kill off brambles. He returned to the forest clearing where he had been painting last August. "Nothing is growing there now," he said. "Everything had literally been razed to the ground. The trunks of young trees have gone to powder."

Mr. Jenson and his vet now suspect that 2,4,5-T was responsible for the (Mr. Jenson's) dog's death. Their fairly unscientific conclusion becomes more significant when events on the Isle of Wight are taken into account. Two dogs—a golden retriever and a boxer—have died in mysterious circumstances. Both had been for walks in forests only recently sprayed with 2,4,5-T by the Forestry Commission. Symptoms were similar and when the other owner, Mr. James Robert, sent his retriever's remains to Leeds University for examination the cause of death was again inexplicable.

Local publicity around the strange deaths produced further worrying information from the islanders. For instance, tiny forest birds have been found dead or flapping about blind while forest walkers have come across the bodies of ground animals. This phenomenon has only appeared since the Commission began its programme to spray 700 acres of the island with 2,4,5-T.

And to add to the concern, forestry workers have been complaining of skin rashes, boils and acne after exposure to the chemical. If they do not wear respirators when spraying, some of the men are overcome with headaches, nausea and unsteadiness.

Evidence is now available implicating 2,4,5-T and 2,4-D in the deaths of over 100 reindeer and many miscarriages during the fifth month of pregnancy of these animals in Swedish Lapland in May, 1970. This case is particularly disturbing because the herbicide treatment occurred the previous summer. It may be that at the very low temperatures of that area herbicides may be much more persistent than they are at lower latitudes where most studies of persistence have been made.

The South Vietnam National Liberation Front has expressed in the March 1, 1970, issue of its journal *South Vietnam, The Struggle,* its opinions about the use of herbicides in Vietnam. It claims that the defoliants are used primarily to deprive the population of their livelihood by destroying "crops and harvest, cattle and poultry . . . and have caused many deaths." This journal states that during the first ten months under the Nixon administration 905,780 hectares were sprayed, mostly in the Mekong Delta, and that 285,740 people were affected. The report claims that many people went blind or deaf, suffered cessation of lactation and miscarriages. It also says that the soil has been made sterile, flooding is increasing, water is polluted, and serious effects have occurred to birds and fish.

Do these reports indicate toxic effects of the herbicides, or do they represent hasty public reaction to inconclusive circumstantial evidence? The answer it not easy to uncover because determining the toxicity of any chemical is not a simple matter. In order to answer the question: "Is a substance like 2,4,5-T toxic?" we must find out the following. First, does the chemical accumulate in the bodies of animals and reach concentrations that could either kill those animals or sicken people who eat the animals? The chemical DDT is a classic example of an agent that is concentrated in the tissues of animals and accumulates to the point of lethality. Many birds have died from accumulation of DDT in their tissues. A second question of very great importance is that of the carcinogenicity of herbicides and the possibility that at some future date a large increase in the incidence of human, animal, or fish cancer might result from the use of herbicides. Third is the problem of teratological effects, pathological changes occurring during embryonic development. Another area of concern is the possible human toxicity that may result from skin absorption, contact with the eyes, or through inhalation of herbicide aerosols by persons who may inadvertently be sprayed with them as might occur during the defoliation of forests in Vietnam. Last, there is the possibility that herbicides may have a mutagenic effect, that is, they may cause changes in the genetic character of the cells of animals and/or plants.

The first indications that some of the herbicides were indeed toxic came in the fall of 1969, when *The New York Times* reported on October 3 that the federal government was taking action to restrict the use of 2,4,5-T. This action resulted from laboratory tests conducted by the Bionetics Research Laboratories in Bethesda, Maryland for the National Institutes of Health. These tests showed that there was a higher than expected number of deformities in the offspring of mice and rats given relatively large oral doses of the chemical. The Departments of Agriculture and Interior promised to stop the use of 2,4,5-T in their own private programs in populated areas or where residues from use could reach man, and the Department of Defense promised to restrict the use in Vietnam of 2,4,5-T to areas remote from the population. Subsequently, it was learned that the federal government had been forced to release this report because of the activities of independent scientists, among them Arthur W. Galston. Galston told *The New York Times* that the government covered up the report on birth abnormalities in rats while promptly releasing two others that showed that the 2,4,5-T was neither carcinogenic nor mutagenic. Galston said that he and other scientists got wind of the suppressed report. They went to Washington, talked with people in government and let it be known that they had the report. Apparently President Nixon's science adviser, Dr. Lee DuBridge, had not known about the report until Galston and others visted him. It was after this that DuBridge issued his statement on the restrictions on the use of 2,4,5-T.

Even after taking action on the use of 2,4,5-T the government was reluctant to reveal the reasons for its action. Thomas Whiteside points out:

From the beginning, it seems, there was an extraordinary reluctance to discuss details of the purported ill effects of 2,4,5-T on animals. Six weeks after the publication of the DuBridge statement, a journalist who was attempting to obtain a copy of the full report made by Bionetics and to discuss its details with some of the government officials concerned encountered hard going. At the Bionetics Laboratories, an official said that he couldn't talk about the study, because "we're under wraps to the National Institutes of Health"—the government agency that commissioned the study. Then, having been asked what the specific doses of 2,4,5-T were that were said to have increased birth defects in the fetuses of experimental animals, the Bionetics official cut off discussion by saying, "You're asking sophisticated questions that as a layman you don't have the equipment to understand the answers to." At the National Institutes of Health, an official who was asked for details of or a copy of the study on 2,4,5-T replied, "The position I'm in is that I have been requested not to distribute this information." He did say, however, that a continuing evaluation of the study was under way at the National Institute of Environmental Health Sciences, at Research Triangle Park, North Carolina. A telephone call to an officer of this organization brought a response whose tone varied from wariness to downright hostility and made it clear that the official had no intention of discussing details or results of the study with the press. (9)

Galston has calculated that human beings in Vietnam could ingest fifty or more milligrams per day per kilogram of body weight of 2,4-D and 2,4,5-T from rain-fed cisterns and ponds after aerial spraying. If they ingested this amount and were as sensitive as rats, this would be a dose adequate to produce malformed offspring to Vietnamese women. It is quite possible for the Vietnamese to ingest significant amounts of these chemicals because much of their drinking water is collected from the roofs upon which defoliant chemicals are deposited following a defoliation attack. The water from the roofs is washed into large earthenware cisterns where it is stored for drinking during the dry season.

The reaction of Dow Chemical Company and certain Department of Agriculture officials to these studies was predictable. Dow Chemical maintained that the sample studied for teratogenicity contained an abnormal amount of a contaminant, Dioxin, and that the material used in Vietnam undoubtedly did not have this contaminant. Dr. Ned Baily and T. C. Byerly of the Department of Agriculture argued in *The New York Times* of April 8, 1970, that tests showing bad effects of the herbicide were preliminary and that the Department had found nothing requiring cancellation or suspension of such registered use. However, on April 16, 1970, the *Washington Post* reported that the matter had been settled conclusively.

> The agriculture department will declare, possibly today, that liquid formulations of the herbicide, that is 2,4,5-T, are "an imminent hazard" to human health. It will forbid their use around the home, on lakes, ponds and ditch banks, and on food crops. A spokesman said that existing supplies down to the retail level will be recalled.
>
> Deputy Defense Secretary David Packard stated that the use of Orange is being suspended in Vietnam and that agent White will be used instead.

FDA scientist Dr. J. Verrett crystallized a 2,4,5-T so free of the Dioxin contaminant that none of it could be detected. She showed that this pure substance causes significant deformities in both chick embryos and hamsters. Thus, not only the contaminant but also the pure herbicide itself could cause birth abnormalities. Dr. Verrett also testified that a mixture of 2,4,5-T and 2,4-D (Agent Orange) caused animal deformities such as skeletal deformities in the limbs and eye region of the skull as well as a disease called the edematous syndrome. She reported that doses as low as 10 ppm of Agent Orange did this to chick embryos. Her testimony was of particular interest to us because we had sent Dr. Verrett the Agent Orange for testing. It had been given to us by the chemical operations officer at Tan Son Nhut Airbase during our visit to Vietnam. It has, therefore, been proven that the material dumped upon Vietnam contains an agent or agents that are highly teratogenic. We also forwarded a sample of this agent to Dr. Steven Rose, a British biochemist, who reports that Agent Orange as used in Vietnam is "grotesquely contaminated and includes in addition to 2,4,5-T and 2,4-D, 17 other contaminants, each one of which may be toxic."

In addition to teratogenic possibilities, 2,4-D and 2,4,5-T have long been known to produce a skin disease called chloracne among workers in the factories that have produced these chemicals. There have also been cases of what is called neuropathy among people who have been exposed to 2,4-D. The following is a summary of such a case taken from the *Journal of the American Medical Association* of November 7, 1959:

Severe sensory and motor symptoms necessitated hospitalization of three patients. In each case the disorder began some hours after the use of 2,4-D to kill weeds. The symptoms continued through a period of days until pain and paralysis were severe. Disability was protracted and recovery was incomplete even after the lapse of years. There was little doubt that the neurological damage was done by the absorption through the skin of spilled 2,4-D. Since there is no antidote or other specific treatment for 2,4-D poisoning this herbicide should be used with caution.

Does the Use of Herbicides in Vietnam Constitute Chemical Warfare?

An important question facing scientific and government circles, indeed all citizens, is the status of herbicides under the Geneva Protocol of 1925, which prohibits the first use in war of "asphyxiating, poisonous or other gases and of bacteriological methods of warfare." President Nixon stated on November 25, 1969 that it was his Administration's policy to urge ratification of this Protocol by the Congress of the United States (22). However, he urged the omission of both the riot control agents and herbicides stating that they should not be classified as chemical or biological warfare agents. In doing this, President Nixon followed the lead of the Department of Defense that was set forth by Dr. John S. Foster, Jr. in a letter to Senator Jacob Javits. Dr. Foster said:

Let me state unequivocally that there is no chemical or biological warfare being conducted in Vietnam. While riot control agents and herbicides are chemical substances as are many other items and articles of common use throughout the world they are not CBW agents. This fact was established without rebuttal by presentation for international view by our representative to the United Nations General Assembly. Relevant parts of Ambassador Nabrit's speech on December 6, 1966, are as follows: "It would be unreasonable to contend that any rule of international law prohibits the use in combat against an enemy for humanitarian purposes of agents that Governments around the world commonly use to control riots by their own people. Similarly the Protocol does not apply to herbicides which involve the same chemicals and have the same effects as those used domestically in the U.S., Soviet Union, and many other countries to control weeds and other unwanted vegetation."

This view expressed in 1966 by the United States government has recently been rejected by a majority of the members of the United Nations when they voted eighty to three to include riot control gases and herbicides as CBW agents. It remains to be seen whether the United States Congress will accept the Nixon administration's desires to exempt these herbicides from classification as CBW agents and thus prevent their use in future war.

In a letter to *The New York Times* on December 9, 1969 Philip Noel-Baker describes a conversation he had with Henri Bonnet, Ambassador of France to the United States, at the Geneva Conference of 1925. M. Bonnet said, "Oh, yes; the form of words they've got is good. It prohibits every kind of chemical or bacterial weapon that anyone could possibly devise. And it has to. Perhaps some day a criminal lunatic might invent some devilish thing that would destroy animals and crops."

But the trends of history are such that crop-killing chemicals were accepted by most Americans as perfectly normal and permissible to use. Distressing as this might seem, it is the natural result of American foreign policy. After all, if it is better to be dead than Red, it is presumably better to be poisoned or deformed than Red. Under this view environmental destruction and human illness are part of the price we must pay to defend ourselves. Ultimately, this is where the real problem lies.

References

1. *Science, 167,* 36 (1970).
2. *A Technology Assessment of the Vietnam Defoliant Matter,* a report of the Subcommittee on Science, Research and Development of the Committee on Science and Astronautics, U. S. House of Representatives, August 8, 1969.
3. *Assessment of Ecological Effects of Extensive or Repeated Use of Herbicides,* Midwest Research Institute contract DAHC15–68–0119 with Advanced Research Projects Agency of the Department of Defense, 1967.
4. *Science, 168,* 453 (1970).
5. *Scientist and Citizen,* August-September, 1967.
6. E. W. Pfeiffer, *Science Journal,* February 1969.
7. Gale E. Peterson, *The Discovery and Development of 2, 4-D,* in *Agricultural History.*
8. *Response of Tropical and Subtropical Woody Plants to Chemical Treatments,* USDA contract # 424 with ARPA of USDOD, 1967.
9. T. Whiteside, *Defoliation,* Ballantine, New York, 1970.
10. *Missoulian,* May 13, 1968.
11. Don Luce and John Sommer, *Viet Nam—The Unheard Voices,* Cornell University Press, Ithaca, N. Y., 1969.
12. F. R. Moorman, *The Soils of the Republic of Vietnam,* Ministry of Agriculture, Saigon, 1961.
13. Much of the information on the flora of Vietnam and its uses has been obtained from Llewelyn Williams, *Forests of Southeast Asia, Puerto Rico, and Texas,* Agric. Research Service, USDA contract # 424 with ARPA of USDOD, 1967.
14. F. H. Tschirley, *Science, 163,* 779 (1969).
15. G. H. Orians and E. W. Pfeiffer, *Science, 168,* 544 (1970).
16. B. R. Flamm, *A Partial Evaluation of Herbicidal Effects to Natural Forest Stands Principally in Tay Ninh Province,* USAID, Saigon, 1968.
17. P. Wildash, *Birds of South Vietnam,* Chas. E. Tuttle Co., Rutland, Vt. and Tokyo, 1968.
18. Jean Boulbet, *Nokor Khmer,* Oct.–Dec., 1969. Phnom Penh, Cambodia.
19. A. V. Holden, *J. Inst. Sew. Purif.,* 361 (1964).
20. L. M. Stahler and E. I. Whitehead, *Science 112,* 749 (1950).
21. *Missoulian,* July 18, 1968.
22. *Chemical-Biological Warfare: U. S. Policies and International Effects,* report of the Subcommittee on National Security Policy and Scientific Developments of the Committee on Foreign Affairs. House of Representatives, May 16, 1970.

Chapter 4

Herbicidal Damage to Cambodia

ARTHUR H. WESTING

Cambodia has the misfortune of being next to Vietnam. The troubles resulting from this circumstance are legion. It was one of the consequences of Cambodia's unfortunate geographical location that afforded us the opportunity to obtain a brief, first-hand indication of the impact that the massive, widespread, and indiscriminate application of herbicides has on land and people in a rural, tropical setting.

Although the United States has during the past decade flown over 30,000 sorties applying heavy dosages of herbicides to millions of acres in neighboring South Vietnam, virtually none of this area is accessible for study by concerned biologists owing to the singular lack of success of the United States' "pacification" program.

When it became known that Cambodia's southeastern border province of Kompong Cham (the so-called Fishhook area) had been subjected to major herbicidal attack during the spring of 1969, Professor E. W. Pfeiffer of the University of Montana seized upon this potential opportunity to supplement his earlier observations in South Vietnam.[1] Owing to the unsettled border conditions, the tenuous diplomatic relations between Cambodia and the United States, the general reluctance of Cambodia to have outside observers anywhere in the country—*e.g.*, all foreign correspondents were barred (1)—and other factors, negotiations to visit the afflicted area did not bear fruit for many months.

To condense a long and involved story, Pfeiffer and I, accompanied by

---

[1] See Chapter 3.

References to this chapter are on pages 202–205.

two Frenchmen. Dr. Jean Lavorel (a biophysicist with the Centre National de la Recherche Scientifique) and M. Léon Matarasso (a lawyer with the Centre International pour la Dénonciation des Crimes de Guerre) finally arrived in Phnom Penh on Christmas Eve, 1969. Because we were guests of Prince Sihanouk, our subsequent study received the full cooperation and logistical support of his various ministers. Moreover, M. Min Sarim, Director General of State [Rubber] Plantations (and a professional forester), was assigned to us as a guide for all our field expeditions.

The subsequent destruction of the entire sprayed area by intensive bombing, shelling, and other ground action might make the present report seem academic. However, this report attempts to document, at least in part, the impact an herbicidal attack has on a rural, tropical habitat, its people, and their economy. As such, it is the first to do so. (This report is also the first to be published to detail herbicidal damage to rubber trees.)

It is most important to bear in mind throughout the description that follows that the damage described was (or could have been) the result of ten sorties or less of the type of which neighboring South Vietnam has experienced over 30,000.

Unfolding of the Event

The herbicidal damage to Kompong Cham Province occurred between mid-April and mid-May of 1969 and covered over 173,000 acres, of which about 24,700 were severely affected.[2] The damage was in part the result of atmospheric drift from across the border, where heavy military applications were being made in the neighboring South Vietnamese province of Tay Ninh (War Zone C). However, a significant portion of the damage could be attributed to actual aerial application in direct violation of the Cambodian border.

The event received remarkably little coverage in the United States. What follows is a brief chronology of the diplomatic and political aspects of this story.

On May 19, 1969, the Cambodian Minister of Foreign Affairs transmitted an indignant letter of protest to the United States (through the French Embassy in Phnom Penh), demanding a cessation of the herbicidal attacks and reparations for the damages sustained. Then on May 23, Prince Sihanouk described

---

[2] Most data presented in this chapter were originally in metric units. The most frequently used conversions were:
  1 hectare = 2.471 acres
  1 kilogram = 2.205 pounds
  1 meter = 3.281 feet
  1 kilometer = 0.6214 mile
  1 kilogram per hectare = 0.8922 pound per acre
  1 liter = 0.2642 gallon
The monetary exchange used was: 1,000 Riels = $28.57

the "unprecedented catastrophe" at a press conference in Phnom Penh. At that early stage he estimated the damages to be in excess of $5.7 million, according to Reuters, or $7.1 million according to Agence France-Presse, and he threatened suit in the World Court should the United States refuse to pay compensation (2). On May 26 the Permanent Representative of Cambodia to the United Nations provided the president of the United Nations Security Council with a preliminary account of the tragedy. This was distributed to all members of the Council (3) and, in similar form, to all permanent members of the United Nations. The May issue of *Kambuja* carried a brief, illustrated account (4).

On June 3, 1969, revised damage estimates totaling $8.7 million (5) were forwarded to the United States, again through the French Embassy in Phnom Penh. This information was then circulated on June 18 among all members of the United Nations Security Council (6) and subsequently made public on November 6 by the Agence Khmère de Presse (A.K.P.), the official Cambodian press agency.

The first indication of the affair in the American press was brief dispatches in the *Washington Post* on June 4 (7) and *The New York Times* on June 5 (8). The *Post* article discounted Cambodian claims of mortality to vegetation and of widespread diarrhea, colitis, and vomiting among the local populace. Referring to United States government "sources," the article categorically denied (1) that United States military incursions across the border had in fact occurred, (2) that the defoliants in use by our military could even kill plants, and finally (3) that the defoliants could cause any human ailments. The *Times* article quoted the United States Department of State as insisting that at no time had United States herbicidal operations come closer to Cambodian territory than three miles. This article did reveal a quite surprising United States request for permission to inspect the allegedly sprayed area and the even more surprising Cambodian accession to this request. Cambodia's agreement is noteworthy in view of the fact that she had broken off diplomatic relations with the United States in 1965, following repeated United States violations of her eastern border (9).

The U.S. State Department inspection did indeed materialize (10), the team making a secret report of its observations on July 12, 1969 (11), a copy of which was received by Cambodia in the following November. (This remarkably objective and frank report was made available to us by the Government of Cambodia upon our arrival there in December.) In brief, the report was devoted largely to damage to rubber, slightly to damage to fruit trees and other vegetation, and virtually not at all to injury to livestock, other animals, or humans. It confirmed the Cambodian damage estimates, realized that it was too early for a final assessment (recommending such for the summer of 1970), and concluded that a portion of the damage was "probably caused by a direct spray application." (We subsequently found out that the State Department team had underestimated the extent of plant mortality, but it must be recalled that they visited the area only two months after the spraying, and shortly after the onset of the growing season, and thus too soon to make a reliable final evaluation.)

Negotiations to prepare for the reestablishment of diplomatic relations between the United States and Cambodia were initiated in June of 1969 (12) and finally culminated in the arrival of the U.S. Charge' d'Affaires in August (13). This action emphasizes the inscrutability of international diplomacy when one considers that just shortly before these events Cambodia had recognized the Provisional Revolutionary Government (*i.e.*, the "Viet Cong") as the true government of South Vietnam (14).

On November 22 our newly established embassy in Phnom Penh received revised damage claims amounting to $ 12.2 million—and on February 16, 1970, received an urgent request to agree to send a second inspection team so that final damages could be assessed and the claim settled.

It must be stressed that very little of the above chronology was (or is) public knowledge. At the time of our departure for Cambodia in December, an alert reader depending upon *The New York Times* for his information on world affairs would have been able to find but two items, both brief, incomplete, superficial, and understated (15). This is a sad commentary on our press in view of the fact that this affair involved not only United States violation of the neutrality of another nation but also a serious disturbance of its shaky national economy and precarious balance of foreign trade. Even more important, it brought about at least the temporary devastation of the rural economy of some 30,000 peasants eking out a livelihood as subsistence farmers and rubber tappers over an area of some 173,000 acres.

The evaluation of the Cambodian herbicide damage by the U.S State Department team did not see the light of day here until our return from Cambodia when its findings were briefly alluded to in conjunction with our findings (16).

The Cambodian damage claim has not yet been acted upon by the United States, although I was informed by our State Department on March 3, 1970, that the United States position on the claims was "in the final stages of preparation," but that its report might not be made public. The overthrow of Prince Sihanouk (17) and the subsequent turmoil have of course eclipsed the herbicide matter in importance. Indeed, the very same area in question (the Fishhook area) has been the scene of heavy, repeated saturation bombing and ground battle, and it now appears to be largely devastated (18). Moreover, it must be noted that information reaching us from the area is unreliable since news of the border region via South Vietnam is suppressed by the United States (19) and probably also by South Vietnam (20); furthermore, the news emanating from Cambodia is censored by that government (21).

Objectives of the Trip

Concern over ecological disturbance of man's environment has grown enormously over the past several years. Herbicides and other pesticides have come under particular fire owing to their potential ability to do serious, long-range, and partially unpredictable harm to the over-all balance of nature. It has become increasingly evident that this balance of nature is crucial to the well-being and ultimate survival of man and all other living things (22).

When even the so-called moderate (or "recommended") herbicide dosages used domestically come under fire (23), it is small wonder that the massive dosages used by our military over extensive areas of South Vietnam have aroused such bitter protests from a segment of the intellectual and scientific communities (24). These protests are, of course, reinforced by and confounded with considerations of the more direct harm to human health (both immediate and long-range) that the herbicides might inflict upon the local population, and of the moral issues involved in denying food to civilians apparently to try to make it less available to the enemy (25).

Unfortunately, the state of the art of ecology is such that, despite the informed intuition of thousands of scientists,[3] very little can be said with persuasive authority about the consequences of a massive introduction of herbicides into a humid, tropical ecosystem, and even less about the impact

---

[3] "Thousands of scientists" is no figure of speech. In early 1966, 29 scientists and physicians signed a protest petition [*Science, 151*:309], shortly thereafter endorsed by 93 more [*Science, 152*:15]. Later that year, 12 plant physiologists prepared another petition [*BioScience, 17* (1):10], and this was shortly followed by still another one signed by 22 scientists [*Science, 153*:1508; *Bull. Atomic Scientists, 22* (9):39–40]. Yet a further resolution was added to the list by 121 Japanese ecologists [*Science, 162*:513–514] and then another by some 2,000 Japanese biochemists [*Soc. Social Responsibility Sci. Newsltr., 182*:4]. The culmination of the various domestic efforts was the transmission to the President in early 1967 of the 22-scientist petition mentioned above, now bearing over 5,000 signatures, representing scientists from at least 40 states (plus D.C. and P.R.) and including 17 Nobel laureates and 129 members of the National Academy of Sciences. This petition was never publicly acknowledged by the White House [*Science, 155*:302; 813; A. H. Westing, *New Republic, 157* (3):35 (1967)] until three years later [June 18, 1970].

Additionally, a number of scientific bodies have registered one form or another of relevant protest, among them the Federation of American Scientists as early as 1964 [*Bull. Atomic Scientists, 20* (8):46–47; *24* (7):31–32] and again in May 1970; the American Association of Scientific Workers in 1966; the American Anthropological Association [*Science, 155*:302]; the Society for Social Responsibility in Science in November 1967 and again in March 1970 [*Soc. Social Responsibility Sci. Newsltr., 204*:2]; Physicians for Social Responsibility in June 1964 [*Science, 155*:302]; the Scientists' Committee on Chemical and Biological Warfare in December 1968, August 1969, December 1969, and April 1970; and the American Association for the Advancement of Science [*Science, 155*:856; *161*:254; *167*:1152].

Moreover, it is of interest to add that at least 82 of the world's nations (including the U.S.S.R.) have publicly renounced the military use of herbicides [N.Y. *Times*, November 26, 1969, p. 17; December 11, 1969, p. 13; December 18, 1969, p. 6].

this will have on the local inhabitants—their health and their subsistence economy.

Thus, we took it upon ourselves to obtain some preliminary, first-hand insights into the impact military applications of herbicides might have in southeast Asia, a task apparently unfeasible to do adequately in South Vietnam, at least until the cessation of hostilities, and perhaps not even then, depending upon the outcome of the war. (While we were in Cambodia, the American Association for the Advancement of Science, after a number of hesitant steps, at the end of 1969 recognized the necessity for a major investigation of the over-all problem and laid the groundwork for appropriate study (26).)

The paucity of information, indeed the shroud of mystery surrounding the details of the actual attack upon Cambodia, made a second objective necessary, attempting to recreate what actually had happened. Another objective was to make an independent evaluation of the extent of damages for comparison with other evaluations that had been made. (A final objective, one of particular concern to the two Frenchmen and not developed here, was to clarify the implications of the event as it pertained to international law and the violation of Cambodian neutrality.)

What Seems To Have Occurred

Our observations of the herbicidal damage and their subsequent evaluation would have been enormously facilitated by a precise knowledge of when, how often, with what, and with how much the area had been sprayed. Who actually did the spraying and for what reason would have also been of more than passing interest. As it was, we knew with a high degree of confidence only where the spraying had occurred and in a more general way, when it had occurred. The answers to the "what with," "how much," "who," and "why" questions are still largely in the realm of informed guesswork or conjecture.

The geographical limits of damage were established by the Cambodians (5), verified by the State Department team (11), and again verified by us (27). This information is presented in Figure 4–1.

The time of application was given by the Cambodians as falling between April 19 and May 9, 1969 (5), apparently based largely upon the onset of injury to the vegetation. A later Cambodian report gives the dates as April 19 to May 12 (6). Thus, the attack occurred at the end of the dry (dormant) season. Eyewitness accounts of aircraft application have been mentioned (27), but the authenticity of these accounts can be debated. The time of application is in part confused by the fact that some of the damage had resulted from drift across the border and some from direct overflight.

The chemicals applied have not been established with certainty, although the characteristic vegetational responses observed seem to limit the possibilities to the hormonal-type herbicides exemplified by the chlorine-substituted

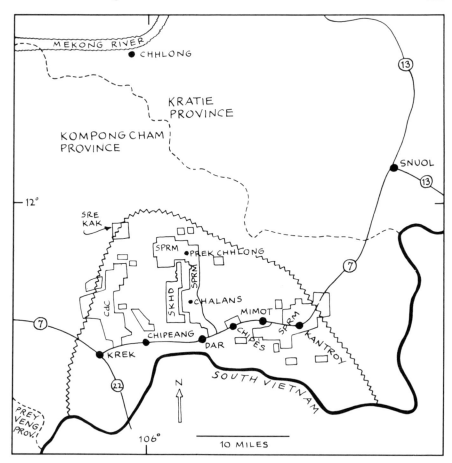

Figure 4–1. Portion of Kompong Cham Province, showing area sprayed April–May, 1969. Zigzag line indicates limits of damage. Only rubber holdings of over 25 acres are shown; hundreds of smaller plantations are scattered through the affected area. Map by A. H. Westing.

phenoxy alkanoic acids. This class of herbicides is systemic in its action, being absorbed and translocated by the vegetation treated. These substances have a profound influence on growth and differentiation, possibly acting through an effect on the transfer of genetic information. They cause erratic and uncontrolled overgrowth, flower, fruit, and leaf abscission, branch dieback, temporary sterility, and other ill effects. In some instances, death of the plant follows.

Of the herbicidal mixtures in general use at that time by United States forces in southeast Asia, either or both Agents Orange (2,4-D plus 2,4,5-T) and White (2,4-D plus Picloram) are suggested by the observed plant responses, and Agent Blue (sodium dimethyl arsenate) is precluded. More detailed information on Orange, White and Blue, the three major herbicidal agents in use by the military, may be found in Chapter 3 and in the literature (28). Admirers of Lewis Carroll will be pleased to learn that the Pentagon, in concert with our National Security Council, recently decreed that these agents are not to be considered as chemical warfare agents (29).

Basing their conclusion on observations of plant response (and limiting their choice to the above three agents), the Cambodian investigators suggested that the herbicide had been Agent Orange (5). The State Department team did not commit itself on the herbicides used but implied that Agents Orange and/or White may have been responsible (11). Certainly, either or both these agents could have been responsible for the damage that resulted from over-the-border drift from the Tay Ninh Province operations. The region in question, which is just across the border and is known as War Zone C, has been the object of massive herbicidal attack on a number of occasions, including the spring of 1969 (11).

We concluded that it was most likely that Agent Orange had done the damage or the major portion of it, although we could not preclude Agent White with certainty (27). Our conclusion was based largely upon the relative persistences of the two agents. Whereas Agent Orange (*i.e.*, its more persistent component, 2,4,5-T) disappears within a matter of weeks or months at the most (30), Agent White (*i.e.,* its more persistent component, Picloram) can persist for months or even years (31). Some crops planted in fields treated with Picloram five years prior to planting still grow abnormally (32).

Our examination of annual garden crops planted subsequent to the attack revealed no definitive abnormalities. The numerous evidences of residual damage to those herbaceous and woody perennials growing at the time of the attack—such as sterility in pineapple[4] and guava, premature abortion in custard apple, or distorted fruits and leaves in papaya—might have been the result of herbicidal persistence in soil or plant but were more probably after-effects of the original treatment on the then-dormant buds. Moreover, the slight original damage to banana and mango (5) and their essential recovery at the time of our visit would suggest Agent Orange because banana (33) and mango (34) are both rather sensitive to Picloram.

The herbicidal dose rates involved are another question to which there is no simple answer. The Cambodian investigators did not speculate on this matter. The State Department team estimated the dose rate in the hardest hit areas to have been in the range of 0.5 to 1.0 pound per acre (11). According to C. E. Minarik, they based this estimate on the extent of observed damage to banana (35). I consider this value to be underestimated, for the reasons given below.

---

[4] See scientific names of biota in the Glossary.

The usual rates employed by the United States forces in South Vietnam for Agent Orange are 25.5 pounds of active ingredients per acre, an order of magnitude greater than for roughly comparable domestic uses. Although there is almost no published information on the subject, it appears that one typical application in Vietnam defoliates virtually all the upland forest species within a few weeks of attack. Roughly 90 per cent of the trees eventually recover although branch dieback is evident in some species. The remainder are killed. If the area is subjected to a second attack within a year or so, mortality rises to 50 per cent or greater, depending upon species composition. Because bamboos and other grasses are relatively immune to these herbicides and some are aggressive colonizers, a heavily damaged upland forest community is likely to be replaced by these weed species. This will, in turn, upset the animal community the area supports. There are several recent reports of herbicide-caused damage to South Vietnam (36).

We attempted to estimate the possible dosages involved on the basis of the selectivity and duration of the damages incurred. Dicotyledenous (broad-leafed) plants are generally far more sensitive to Agent Orange (or White) than are monocotyledenous plants (grasses, palms, and the like) (37) and small, herbaceous plants are generally more sensitive than large, woody ones. However, no hard and fast generalizations can be made in this regard since there are some pronounced differences in sensitivity among species within a genus and occasionally even among varieties within a single species. (There are, of course, also differential responses by the same plant to different herbicides.) As already mentioned, experience in South Vietnam has shown that a significant proportion of the perennials found there can recover at least in part from one application of the heavy dosages employed by the military.

In the central, most severely afflicted zone of the Cambodian damage area, we were told that in the spring there had been widespread defoliation of virtually all the dicotyledenous plants. On the other hand, such monocotyledons as grasses, bamboo, sugar palm, and betel-nut palm had been virtually unaffected. Coconut and banana (two monocotyledons) and papaya (a dicotyledon) had exhibited slight injury; mango (another dicotyledon) had exhibited virtually no sign of damage.

At the time of our inspection, eight months and one growing season later, we found that most jack fruit, many kapok trees, and some guava trees (all dicotyledons) had died in the interim. On the other hand, banana, coffee, and teak (coffee and teak being dicotyledons and the teak initially completely defoliated) appeared to us to be entirely normal. Some varieties of rubber (a dicotyledon), *e.g.*, TR.1600, had succumbed, whereas others, *e.g.*, PB.86, had recovered to a considerable extent. In forested areas, with a highly divers species composition, roughly 10 per cent of the overstory trees had been killed.

These and similar observations described below compare closely with experience of herbicide damage in South Vietnam (11) and in other tropical locations (34), leading me now to suggest that at least portions of the central area might have received a dose approaching that routinely applied in South Vietnam, and thus higher than that suggested earlier (11,27). The eastern and western zones of damage showed lesser degrees of injury, possibly the result of drift but possibly owing to lower rates of direct application. A reasonable guess (but only a guess) is that these peripheral areas had been subjected to dosages of the order of 1 per cent to 10 per cent of that received by the central portion.

The total quantity of herbicide application in Cambodia (assuming the agent to have been Orange) was very conservatively estimated by us to have been 77,000 pounds of active ingredients (based on the exceedingly modest area-wide average application rate of 0.4 pound per acre) (27). Perhaps a more realistic estimate would be a figure ten-fold higher, although to support such an estimate rigorously at this late date would be difficult.

Aircraft normally used by United States forces in southeast Asia for spray missions (and accounting for about 80 per cent of all military applications in South Vietnam) carry a payload of 7,900 pounds of active ingredients each (38). The State Department team concluded that there had been only five missions, apparently totaling twenty-nine aircraft, from which across-the-border drift could conceivably have occurred (11). Assuming (lavishly) that each of these inadvertently spread 10 per cent of their payloads to Cambodian territory, such drift would account for 23,000 pounds. The remaining 54,000 pounds then represents the payloads of seven aircraft (sorties) making direct overflights. Actually, as I have inferred above, the number of aircraft was probably higher. It should be mentioned here that an early Cambodian report (4) alludes to eight separate missions and another (5) to at least seven (neither, however, specifying the number of aircraft).

I must stress again that our scant knowledge of what actually occurred, together with the limited knowledge of the effects of spraying and rates of recovery under the conditions in question, make the above estimates rather uncertain. For example, the possibility exists that helicopters were used (some of which are known to be rigged for spraying).

Finally in this section, I shall briefly indulge in speculation about who actually did the spraying and for what purpose. As already mentioned above, the first official United States government reaction to the Cambodian disclosure of the event was a categorical protestation of innocence (7,8). The State Department investigating team, although convinced of the high probability of direct overflight and despite its apparent access to U.S. Air Force mission records, was aware of no spray mission over Cambodia (11). Personal conversation with one of the members of that team revealed, moreover, that his conversations with Air Force personnel of the 12th Special Operations Squadron (the one responsible for most herbicide usage in South Vietnam) convinced him that this outfit was innocent of the affair (39). However, in the meantime it has become clear that the United States was, indeed, responsible. A U.S. State Department official, has testified before a House committee that "the greatest part of the damage was caused by a deliberate and direct over-flight of the rubber plantations" (40). We have presented evidence elsewhere for the unlikeliness of the Cambodian attack having been due to a navigational or similar error (27), which need not be elaborated upon here in view of the State Department's admission of deliberateness.

The above information makes it possible to advance the theory that the CIA (or some similar United States agency that might have been active in southeast Asia) was responsible for the herbicidal attack. Our conversations with highly placed Cambodian government officials disclosed that they were convinced of continuing clandestine United States operations in Cambodia aimed at the harassment, disruption, and eventual overthrow of the Sihanouk regime (41). Such a supposition is not too far-fetched because CIA activities within Cambodia have since been made public (42). There is even reason to believe that CIA agents had infiltrated the Cambodian Army (43) which did, indeed, subsequently overthrow the Sihanouk government (44). Moreover, the area in question has in the past been the scene of at least several clandestine U.S. Special Forces missions (45), possibly in the belief that it contained the main Viet Cong Army Headquarters (Central Office for South Vietnam or COSVN) as once claimed by our president (46) but since disclaimed by our commanding general in South Vietnam (47). Furthermore, it appears that the CIA has a spray capability (48).

The Damaged Region

Up-to-date information on Cambodia's land and people, particularly information broken down by provinces or regions, is hard to find. Those seeking detailed data are referred to two recent bibliographies (49) as well as to a very useful, heavily annotated atlas (50). There is also a limited number of descriptive texts particularly worthy of mention for one reason or another (51). A monograph exists dealing specifically with Kompong Cham Province (52). One readily available map of Cambodia exists (53).

The province of Kompong Cham, with its 2.4 million acres and roughly estimated population of 880,000, contains about 6 per cent of Cambodia's land surface but roughly 14 per cent of its population (50). Its capital has an estimated 29,000 inhabitants, boasts a new technical university, and is the site of an important Mekong River crossing. The province contains (more accurately, contained) a number of large rubber processing factories, the largest at Chup and the second largest at Mimot (Mémot), and is the home of the Cambodian Rubber Research Institute (Institut des Recherches sur le Caoutchouc au Cambodge [IRCC]). There are also an agricultural research station, a textile mill, and a tobacco processing plant.

Although rubber is the major product of the province, rice, corn, coffee, jute, kapok, and fish also contribute to its domestic economy. The rural population, although employed in the production of these products, is tied very closely to the land. Each family depends for its subsistence on individual small kitchen gardens and associated fruit trees. The people are grouped in hundreds of small hamlets that spot the flat to rolling countryside. Except where the forests have been displaced by rubber, the terrain is largely forested.

Our own observations were made in small, low-flying aircraft and by intensive on-site investigations by automobile and on foot. We flew over and visited both unsprayed and sprayed areas in Kompong Cham Province. Any and all areas we wished to visit were freely open to us for purposes of inspection, interviewing, and photography. We were able to interview and inspect the records of several large plantation directors, their staffs, and workers as well as the technical personnel of local research stations. We also visited a number of small villages. All this was supplemented by interviews with various government officials in Phnom Penh. There was no language barrier because French (and often English) was understood almost everywhere and because a Cambodian (Khmer) interpreter was always available to us as needed for communication with uneducated local inhabitants.

Damage to Rubber Trees

The southeastern border country in question had been largely un-inhabited jungle (dipterocarp forest of amazing diversity) until the French established a number of large rubber plantations there beginning in 1921 (54). Today, Cambodia has a total of about 123,000 acres planted to rubber, of which about 95 per cent is in Kompong Cham Province. The 116,000 acres of rubber in the province, representing about 5 per cent of its total area, are largely held in about five major ownerships. Most of the remainder are scattered among a thousand or more tiny, privately owned family plantations of only a few acres each. These small holders sell their crude latex to one of the major companies with processing facilities, from whom they also receive assistance in rubber culture.

Up-to-date methods of culture and exploitation together with highly favorable climate and soil conditions have combined to give this region the highest latex yields per unit area in the world. Moreover, according to Gilbert Deconinck, a plant pathologist with the IRCC, none of the serious rubber diseases that are of major concern in other parts of the world are presently a factor in Cambodia. The one recent exception was pointed out by K. G. McIndoe in his description of rubber in neighboring South Vietnam: ". . . the only. . . 'disease' of real concern is that caused by man himself, namely defo-liation chemicals applied from the air—and this certainly is widespread" (55).

The processing plant at Chup (the nation's largest, handling about half of all latex produced in Cambodia) is surrounded by what may be the world's largest rubber plantation (Compagnie du Cambodge). Until its recent pillage and destruction (56) the factory was a showplace of automation and of gleaming stainless steel. The second largest processing plant, at Mimot, has also been destroyed (57).

Rubber occupies only 2 per cent of Cambodia's total agricultural lands, 1 per cent of its work force, and 6 per cent of its internal production values (58). On the other hand, rubber represents more than one-third of Cambodia's export values, vying only with rice as the nation's number one export commodity (rubber occupying first place in dollar value four out of ten times in the most recent decade for which data are available) (58). Thus with a minimum of land and labor, rubber has been, before the most recent rape of this resource, a major hard currency earner, carrying a lion's share of Cambodia's means for attaining a favorable balance of trade.

Rather accurate damage estimates from the herbicide operations are possible thanks to the detailed growth, yield, and other cultural and economic records kept by the major rubber companies as well as by the Institut des Recherches sur le Caoutchouc au Cambodge (IRCC). The IRCC is a semi-official research agency of international renown supported in part by the government and in part by a plantation association. It is well equipped and competently staffed by professionally trained scientists, both Cambodian and foreign, who represent various pertinent disciplines, including agronomy, genetics, plant physiology, and plant pathology. Long-term data are available on a variety-by-variety and block-by-block basis with respect to tree growth, disease resistance, windfirmness, latex yield, latex quality, and so forth.

The area afflicted by herbicides (see Figure 4–1) covers about 38,300 acres of rubber (5). Thus, about 32 per cent of the nation's rubber and a somewhat higher proportion of the nation's trees actually in production are affected. Of the damaged area, about 24,700 acres, or 65 per cent, were damaged rather heavily. Major holdings of several companies were extensively damaged. Among them were the plantations at Chalang (Chalong), Prek Chhlong, Kantroy (Kantreuy), and Mimot owned by the French Société des Plantations Réunies de Mimot (SPRM); the plantation at Dar owned by the French Société Khmère d'Hévéaculture de Dar (SKHD); the plantation at Krek owned by the French Compagnie du Cambodge; and the plantation at Srekak owned by the Société des Caoutchoucs de Srekak. Also affected were the medium-sized state-owned plantation at Chipès and the medium-sized privately owned cooperative at Chipeang, the latter involving about 500 people (see Figure 4–1). Saddest of all, many hundreds of tiny, privately owned plantations scattered throughout the area received the full fury of the attack.

Quite a number of rubber varieties (clones, in the strict sense) are in current production in Cambodia; some are no longer in favor but are still being tapped because the period of remunerative yield is only now being reached by the longest-established plantings. In the larger holdings, rubber is managed in 250-acre units (blocks) under a regular cycle of removal and reestablishment. The trees come into production at age six or seven years and are usually replaced at age forty to fifty. According to very recent information I have received from Dr. W. L. Resing, some 90 per cent of all rubber planted in

Cambodia since 1955 (on both large and small holdings) has been about equally divided among three major varieties: GT.1, PR.107, and PB.86 (59). In the zone of damage, each variety occupies about 11,000 acres. However, portions of the damage zone also support plantings predating 1955. Chief among these older trees are BD.5 and AVROS.50 (each covering about 1,650 acres) plus lesser areas of AVROS.49 and TJIR.1. Additionally, there are small plantings within the damage zone of numerous other varieties, some old and some recent.

Of the total area of rubber damaged (38,300 acres), about 28,000 acres, or 73 per cent, were over six to seven years old at the time of spraying, and they thus were in production (5).

The different varieties of rubber in the area appeared to have a wide range of sensitivity to the herbicides used (see Figure 4–2).[5] Thus, GT. 1 (representing about 29 per cent of the trees in question) and AVROS. 50 (representing about 4 per cent) were originally 90 to 100 per cent defoliated. They have subsequently experienced major branch dieback and have been slow to recover their vigor. Branch dieback of seven to ten feet or more was quite common at the time of our visit. Young individuals of these two varieties, as well as those growing under adverse soil conditions, had in many instances died during the eight months following spraying. IRCC records showed that latex production for these varieties in the half year following spraying was reduced by as much as 70 to 80 per cent. The complement of leaves that we observed, the first refoliation, was somewhat abnormal in appearance. According to Chai Kim Chun, a biochemist with the IRCC, the dry rubber content (DRC) of the latex flowing at the time of our visit was subnormal.

PR.107 (also representing about 29 per cent of the affected trees) was found to be somewhat less sensitive than GT.1 or AVROS.50, all the above-described effects having occurred to a somewhat lesser degree on it. PB.86 (again representing about 29 per cent) had been least affected by the herbicides and had recovered to a large extent after one growing season.

TR.1600 (of which very little is planted) was the most sensitive of all varieties, and almost all these trees had died prior to the time of our visit. Almost as severely affected were BD.5 (representing about 4 per cent of the trees) (see Figure 4–3) and TJIR.1 (of which there was very little).

Over-all, the IRCC has conservatively determined that the May to November, 1969, latex production of the sprayed rubber trees was reduced by an average of 35 to 40 per cent. This together with other estimated damages represents a total present and future economic loss, according to the IRCC, of $11.0 million, broken down as follows (5):

---

[5] J.-P. Polinière, Co-director, Vietnamese Institute for Agro-industries, has suggested to me that differential sensitivities might at least in part have had a phenological rather than physiological basis [personal communication, August 14, 1970].

Figure 4–2. Aerial view of rubber trees sprayed April–May, 1969, as they appeared in December, 1969. Note the differential sensitivities of different varieties. Location: just northeast of Krek. Photo by A. H. Westing.

Rubber in production (28,000 acres) $7.6 million (69%)
Young rubber (10,200 acres)   2.7 million (25%)
Added cultural costs   0.7 million (6%)

We judged these figures to be reliable since we were impressed by the detail and accuracy of the records kept by the IRCC and the large plantations and by the obvious competence and integrity of the professional personnel involved. It should be added that this opinion was shared by the State Department team that had made the earlier inspection (11). Our own rough calculations indicated the Cambodian figures to be conservative.

It is important to point our some of the difficulties involved in arriving at an early estimate of total present *and future* losses. For one thing, there is no past experience to fall back on, so that estimates based only on one growing season of recovery are somewhat uncertain. Whereas PB.86 may be back to essentially normal production within another year, GT.1 may well level off at only 80 per cent of normal production within another two or three years. Presumably PR.107 will be intermediate in its rate of recovery. The

Figure 4–3. An herbicide-sensitive rubber variety (BD.5) sprayed April–May, 1969, as it appeared in December, 1969. Note that it experienced virtually total mortality. Location: just east of Mimot. Photo by A.H. Westing.

death of some GT.1 and PR.107 trees will preclude full recovery of normal production per unit area until their normal time of replacement at about age forty or fifty. Moreover, many of the very young blocks, established during the past few years, were decimated regardless of variety (60); thus the larger plantations in the affected area will largely lack these several age classes. This and the possible need for earlier replacement of mature blocks (owing to possible earlier senility, *i.e.*, earlier drop in latex production) will unbalance the normal rotational cycles for decades to come. An added handicap is that some of the budwood gardens (the source of the cion material for the reestablishment of the clonal varieties) were badly damaged.

One of the more serious indirect problems that has resulted from the herbicidal defoliation is the production of a luxuriant understory of weeds throughout the affected area, resulting from greatly increased illumination of the forest floor. These weeds not only compete for the limited soil nutrients and water but also enormously increase the fire hazard during the dry season. Indeed, we inspected the disastrous results of one fifty-seven-acre wild fire caused by just this situation; the weed-fueled fire caused the death of all the rubber trees in the burnt-over area. The weeds were being cut in part, but according to E. Pellegrin (Director-General of the SPRM holdings) financial limitations preclude adequate control. As noted above, 6 per cent of the $11.0 million rubber damage estimate represents the calculated extra cultural costs which largely stem from the direct and indirect consequences of enhanced weed growth following herbicidal action.

One problem, not considered in calculating the damage estimate, occurs when tapping must be continued almost unabated for pressing financial or social reasons, despite the weakened condition of the trees. This unfortunate circumstance, found at holdings sprayed in their entirety or almost so, prevents the injured trees from recovering as rapidly as they might if they were left alone for a year or two, and is likely to lead to an increased rate of mortality. Although this situation affects a few of the larger plantations, the really devastating impact of this problem is on the private smallholders.

The vast majority of the families comprising the 30,000 or so inhabitants of the affected area depend upon tapping as their prime source of cash income. Although only a minority are smallholders, those working for the large companies have been adversely affected as well. These tappers are all paid on the basis of amount of latex collected daily, and with a drop in latex yield, they earn minimal wages as a result.

Another potential danger should be mentioned, although we observed no indication of it during our visit. The dead branch stubs and the weakened condition of the trees may serve as a court for infection and result in future increases in fungal or insect depredations.

Damage to Food Crops and Other Vegetation

A large variety of garden crops (both agricultural and horticultural) were devastated in the seemingly endless number of small villages or hamlets scattered throughout the affected area. Virtually all of the approximately 30,000 local inhabitants are subsistence farmers. These people, dependent for their ultimate well-being upon their own produce, saw their crops then growing literally wither before their eyes. Indeed, it was the widespread death of the vegetables and other food plants in the kitchen gardens that heralded the rest of the damage to the area. These farmers' then current crops of vegetables of numerous kinds, of pineapples, of guavas, of jack fruit, of papayas, and of many, many more, were simply destroyed.

Some of the other more important food crops largely wiped out at the time were durian, manioc, tomato, several types of beans, cauliflower, and custard apple, according to Hing Un, Cambodia's Director of Agriculture.

Food plants that seemed to be only little or moderately damaged by the herbicides included taro, ginger, banana, orange, longan, mango, sapodilla, sugar palm, betel-nut palm, and coconut palm. Of these, at the time of our visit, coconut was showing a moderate measure of delayed injury that had not originally been expected. A number of annual crops were largely spared because for the most part they had not yet been planted. Rice and corn, although somewhat resistant to herbicides anyway, fall into this category.

At the time of our visit, the annual plants that had been planted subsequent to the spraying seemed to be normal in appearance. However, pineapple plants looked healthy but were refusing to bear. The new papaya crop was small, and the fruits and leaves were somewhat distorted on a number of the plants. Some guava trees had died in the interim between spraying and our visit, and none of those that had persisted were as yet bearing. The custard apples were for the most part not yet bearing either. Lychee trees, apparently not an important crop locally, had suffered severe dieback and were not yet bearing.

The locally important jack fruit trees (which it was anticipated by the U.S. State Department team (11) would mostly recover) had, unfortunately, for the most part died by the time we went there. Indeed, the dead jack fruit trees stood—and stand—beside virtually every rural home in the area as grim reminders of the "poison from the sky" (see Figure 4–4). The Cambodians estimated that some 45,100 jack fruit trees were killed or severely damaged (5). Conversely, the banana plants seemed completely normal again, and the manioc trees (shrubs) seemed to be recovering well (although we found some of the new fruits to be abnormal in shape).

Kapok trees, whose fibers provide a small cash crop for the local inhabitants, were largely killed in village after village. The few surviving trees were not yet bearing their fiber-producing fruits.

Figure 4—4. Rural dwelling with dead jack fruit, a most herbicide-sensitive tree. The area had been sprayed in April—May, 1969, and the photograph was taken in December, 1969. Note that the papaya tree to the left has recovered. Location: near Chipès. Photo by A. H. Westing.

The sprayed area supports a number of small plantations besides rubber, among them 290 acres of banana, 220 of pineapple, 30 of orange, 120 of coffee, and 970 of teak. The Cambodian damage estimates for these are presented below. We inspected one area producing coffee and another one supporting a stand of young teak. The teak, although largely defoliated at the time of the attack (5), indicated no sign of damage. The coffee also appeared healthy. However, the possibility exists that the final product will be impaired because 2,4-D treatment can impart a bad flavor to the bean (61). The pineapple, one of the most valuable fruits grown in the region, was, as already noted, not bearing.

The forested portions between the plantations and villages in the affected area presently support only a scattering of commercially usable timber trees of a variety of species. Although many of the few tall timber trees had been defoliated initially, most seemed to be slowly recovering at the time of our visit (primarily through the production of adventitious shoots). We did observe some dead individuals of two commercial species of dipterocarp, lumbor and phdiec. From aerial photographs I took, it can be estimated that roughly 10 per cent of the dicotyledenous trees had succumbed. This is actually a conservative estimate because from a distance one can be fooled by the epiphytes that inhabit the crowns. Bamboo species had been left untouched by the initial spray (5) and were also growing robustly at the time of our visit; bamboos are a notoriously difficult group to kill with herbicides (62).

Total damage to crops other than rubber has been estimated by the Cambodians to approximate $1.2 million (5).

It can be added here that we observed no evidence of increased erosion or of soil hardening via laterization and no evidence of change in the level of the water table or of any other physiographic factor. Nor did discussions with Sor Thay Seng, Cambodia's Chief of Agronomy, suggest such damage that we might have overlooked. We did not find or hear of any evidence of weather modification. The possibility does exist, of course, that living or nonliving components of the local ecosystem had been modified in some subtle way that our cursory examinations would not have disclosed. For example, the total biomass was diminished, at least for a time. This may have resulted in a net loss of nutrients—and thus of productivity—because the living portion of a tropical ecosystem comprises a very important reservoir in the over-all nutrient budget (63).

Damage to Livestock and Other Animals

All our interviews with the local inhabitants disclosed that village livestock became ill for a period of several days soon after spraying. Although the larger animals (water buffaloes, cattle [zebus], and mature pigs and sheep) became only mildly ill and all apparently recovered, some of the smaller ones (chickens, ducks, and young pigs) suffered more severely and in some cases were reported to have died. The domestic mammals were described as having digestive problems, whereas the domestic birds became partially paralyzed for a time. From elsewhere it is known that exposure to 2,4,5-T or 2,4-D reduces both egg production and poultry weight (64). Apparently many wild birds became disabled and could be captured easily. It was also reported to us that a number of small dead birds were found at the time. It is stated in the Cambodian investigators' report that bovines were reluctant to feed on herbage that had been sprayed, and it is suggested that this might have been due to the odor (5).

The literature on veterinary toxicology of herbicides is extensive and has been reviewed a number of times (65). A perusal of this literature does not seem to provide clear confirmation of the symptoms noted above. However, one report from South Vietnam presents an account similar to the ones we received (66). It has further been suggested in South Vietnam that a now-prevalent fish muscle disease might be the result of herbicides (67). The same observers have described specialized bird population declines in certain habitats.[6]

Eastern Cambodia in general had earlier experienced quite a substantial increase in a variety of wildlife, apparently driven out of Vietnam by the defoliation and other ravages of the war. According to Suon Kaset, Director General of Waters, Forests, and Game, these included muntjacs and other species of deer, wild cattle (gaurs, bantengs, and some koupreys), elephants, a number of monkey species, and wild pigs. With the current turn of events, one can but wonder whether they will soon run out of places to which to escape.

Effect on Human Health

Many of the local inhabitants we interviewed spoke of widespread temporary diarrhea and vomiting, particularly among infants and to a lesser extent among the general adult populace. At Chipeang, Buoy San (director of the local plantation) told us that water was trucked in for a time following spraying to provide uncontaminated water for the children. In those instances where the people depended largely upon deep wells for their domestic water supply, e.g., at Mimot, we received no report of human digestive problems.

Similar reports have come from neighboring South Vietnam (68). One cautionary note must be added, however. While in Cambodia we interviewed Le Van Hai, an elderly Vietnamese farmer from My Tho (Dinh Tuong) Province, South Vietnam. He described to us in some detail the effects on him and his family of an herbicidal attack on his village, Thanh Binh, in February, 1969. It soon became clear that his village had been subjected both to herbicidal chemicals and CS-2 gas[7] and that he was attributing the effects of both to herbicides.

Although not generally appreciated in the past (69), 2,4,5-T and/or associated impurities (the so-called dioxins, particularly 2,3,7,8-tetra-chlorodibenzo-*para*-dioxin) are now known to possess toxic, abortive, and teratogenic (fetus damaging) effects in small mammals (70). They are suspected of having produced similar effects in humans in South Vietnam (71). This supposition has gained a modicum of support from several items in the popular press (72) and from a recent progress report of the Children's Medical Relief International (73). As a result, we interviewed at some length Dr. Charles Bosquet, director of the hospital at Mimot, the largest hospital in the affected area. This hospital serves some 15,000 people and handles about 200 local patients a day. We also inspected his detailed hospital patient records (monthly summaries) for 1968 and 1969. This investigation, however, revealed no

[6] See chapter 3.
[7] See chapter 1.

Figure 4–5. Arthur H. Westing (left) and E. W. Pfeiffer being welcomed by Cambodians living in the Mimot region of Eastern Cambodia which had been defoliated in April–May, 1969.

increase in the incidence of any malady requiring hospitalization during or subsequent to spraying and no increase of malformation in newborns. Our negative findings are, of course, not definitive owing to the very small sample involved. There are only about fifty local births per month, with one congenitally malformed infant every two months, on the average. Thus, there were only a very small number of infants (about 200) born up to the time of our visit who had been *in utero* at the time of the herbicidal attack—and a much smaller number (about 75) if only certain periods during gestation (*e.g.*, weeks six to twelve) are prone to herbicidal damage. Moreover, only a very narrow range of chemical concentration could be expected to produce a congenital malformation; greater concentrations would result in a miscarriage, no records of which were available to us.

Effect on Economic Welfare

The 173,000 acres of land that were sprayed accounts for 7 per cent of the area of Kompong Cham province and contains an estimated 30,000 inhabitants (about 3 per cent of the population of the province). As already noted elsewhere, the affected area contains about 38,300 acres planted to rubber. This represents 32 per cent of the province's rubber and 30 per cent of all Cambodia's. Although the damaged rubber covers only 22 per cent of the total area sprayed, it accounts for the primary source of livelihood for the area's residents. Virtually all of the families in the area appear to depend upon small subsistence farms, working additionally as tappers or in the processing plants or in other rubber-related employment. All wages are determined by the amounts collected or produced and thus were drastically diminished. The economic losses owing to rubber damage are detailed above; they were estimated to total $11.0 million. I calculate the actual exportable loss of rubber during the first growing season following spraying to approximate $7.5 million, thereby reducing Cambodia's total value of exports of all items for 1969 by roughly 12 per cent.

The loss caused by damage to cultivated vegetation other than rubber which contributes to the gross national product (but is not exported) has been estimated as follows by the Cambodians (5):

Jack fruit (45,100 trees)	$386,000
Durian (7,700 trees)	441,700
Rambutan (4,300 trees)	73,400
Banana (290 acres)	13,900
Pineapple (220 acres)	192,900
Orange (30 acres)	18,500
Coffee (120 acres)	16,100
Teak (970 acres)	69,400

To the above can be added injury to natural forest stands, estimated to amount to $25,000, bringing the total non-rubber damage estimate to $1.2 million and the grand total of vegetational damage to $12.2 million.

The damage estimates presented above were relatively easy to determine and represent the loss to the internal and external agricultural economy of the region and nation. On the other hand, what is essentially impossible to calculate is the enormous hardship and suffering of a people who depend for their well-being and survival on their own produce. As described above, the annual crops of the local inhabitants were largely devastated, as were a significant portion of their perennial crops. With much of the food supply for one year destroyed, and sources of cash income drastically reduced, with virtually no welfare assistance from the government,[8] and with strong cultural and other restraints on relocating, one can only guess at the resulting privation.

Conclusion

Our mission was a sad one, a mission whose *raison d'être* we wish had never occurred. We felt particularly grieved about the innumerable direct and indirect losses suffered by the innocent local populace. We were able to see at first hand how particularly pernicious this type of military action is for people whose very existence is so closely tied to the land. And now that since the time of our visit the whole area we came to know has been utterly destroyed by the full impact of the spreading air and ground war, our sadness has turned to a feeling of despair.

Prior to the most recent turn of events, the damage, though serious enough, had been finite in time, space, and degree. Cambodia's economy had been hurt, some French investments had been adversely affected, and the local population had been caused suffering. However, recovery would have been largely a matter of time, effort, and a little money (*i.e.*, "little" by United States standards). The annual crops were already back to normal at the time of our visit; the perennial crops would have been back to normal in a few years, or at most decades. Cambodia was at the time of our visit still a free and relatively peaceful nation working hard to establish economic viability independent of the United States and struggling to remain as neutral and uninvolved as its geographic position and military weakness could conceivably permit. Certainly, its extent of cooperation with the Viet Cong seems to have been greatly exaggerated by our government (74). Until the coup and subsequent events, Cambodia could have been considered modestly prosperous by southeast Asian standards. It was the only nation in the region without a population problem; it was an exporter of rice; and its people were friendly, healthy, and happy. It is thus a tragedy that our President did not share Senator Mike Mansfield's insights toward Cambodia, which indicated Mansfield's confidence in the policies of that nation under Prince Sihanouk, policies that according to Mansfield could have maintained this former oasis of peace in a war-torn southeast Asia to our benefit as well as to the benefit of the peoples of Cambodia (75).

In closing, I shall quote briefly from a most perceptive account of Cambodia by a recent Australian visitor, Maslyn Williams, who was able to capture the spirit of Cambodia as I felt it and as it may never be again (76):

---

[8] Joseph Elder, University of Wisconsin, who happened to visit Mimot shortly after the devastation (on May 29, 1969), has informed me that Prince Sihanouk had provided approximately $8,000 of immediate relief, to be divided among the smallholders of the region [personal communication, March 25, 1971].

There is, then, a tranquil and soothing beauty about this wide, flat landscape such as I have not seen in any other country—a strangely placid lack of extravagance in this vista that has no sharp shapes, no startling landmarks, no vivid brilliance to shake the senses into ecstacies. Nothing that man has done seems to clash with what was in the beginning (there are no colorful trimmings, no decorating excesses). It is, I think, a particularly Buddhistic tranquility, achieved by the elimination of everything unnecessary. It is a beauty that never for an instant loses its gentle, terrible sense of endless resignation.

Acknowledgements

My main debt of gratitude is to the many Cambodians at all levels of responsibility and in all walks of life, from whom we received such friendly welcomes, willing cooperation, and gracious hospitality wherever we went. Their unassuming modesty, their simple pleasures, and their love of nature were all infectious.

Our mission could not have been completed without the active support of Prince Norodom Sihanouk, Chief of State; His Excellency Ung Hong Sath, Vice President of the Council of Ministers; Chuon Saodi, Minister of Agriculture; Min Sarim, Director General of State Plantations; Suon Kaset, Director of Waters, Forests, and Game; Hing Un, Director of Agriculture; and Sor Thay Seng, Chief of Agronomy. Min Sarim must be singled out for his continuing efforts in our behalf.

Among our hosts and guides in Kompong Cham Province, I should like particularly to thank Dr. W. L. Resing, Director of the Institut des Recherches sur le Caoutchouc au Cambodge (IRCC); Gilbert Deconinck, IRCC; Chai Kim Chun, IRCC; Buoy San, Director of the cooperative plantation at Chipeang; Som Khom, Director of the Société Khmère d'Hévéaculture at Dar; E. Pellegrin, Director General of the Société des Plantations Réunies at Mimot (SPRM); C. Audureau, Assistant Director of SPRM; and Dr. Charles Bosquet, Director of the hospital at Mimot.

Finally, my trip was an intellectually stimulating event and a singular pleasure because of my three fellow travellers: Léo Matarasso of Paris, Jean Lavorel of Gif-Sur-Yvette, and Bert Pfeiffer of Missoula. To them, my greetings!

References

1. *New York Times,* December 8, 1969, p. 6.
2. *Egyptian Gazette,* Cairo, May 25, 1969, p. 4; *Le Monde,* Paris, May 25–26, 1969, p. 7.
3. United Nations Security Council Document No. S/9224 (1969).
4. *Kambuja,* Phnom Penh, *5* (50), p. 112 (1969).
5. Min Sarim, Hing Un, Suon Kaset, Sor Thay Seng, Ho Tong Lip, W. L. Resing, and M. Berrier, *Rapport du Comité Chargé du Constat et de l'Evaluation des Dégâts dûs aux Épandages des Produits Défoliants par les Avions Américano-Sudviet-namiens,* Ministry of Agriculture, Phnom Penh (1969). [Original report dated May 16; subsequent additions dated July 10, November 17, and December 9, 1969.]
6. United Nations Security Council Document No. S/9263 (1969).
7. *Washington Post,* June 4, 1969, p. A18.
8. *New York Times,* June 5, 1969, p. 4.
9. *New York Times,* May 4, 1965, p. 1; *Livre Blanc des Agressions Américan-Sud-vietnamiennes Contre le Cambodge 1962–1969,* Ministry of Foreign Affairs, Phnom Penh (1970).
10. *Chemical and Engineering News, 47* (28), p. 27 (1969); *New York Times,* August 5, 1969, p. 10.
11. C. E. Minarik, J. B. Shumate, N. G. Vakili, and F. H. Tschirley, *Report on Herbicide Damage to Rubber and Fruit Trees in Cambodia,* U. S. State Department, Saigon (1969).
12. *New York Times,* July 3, 1969, p. 1; August 5, 1969, p. 10.
13. *New York Times,* August 16, 1969, p. 12.
14. *New York Times,* May 10, 1969, p. 5.
15. *New York Times,* June 5, 1969, p. 4; August 5, 1969, p. 10.
16. *Brattleboro* [*Vt.*] *Daily Reformer,* January 11, 1970, p. 7; *Los Angeles Times,* January 14, 1970, pt. 1, p. 4; *New York Times,* January 14, 1970, p. 4.
17. *New York Times,* March 19, 1970, p. 1; *et seq.*
18. *New York Times,* April 15, 1970, p. 3; April 30, 1970, p. 5; May 2, 1970, p. 1; May 5, 1970, p. 1; May 7, 1970, p. 1; *et seq.*
19. *Washington Post,* April 6, 1970, p. A1; *New York Times,* April 30, 1970, p. 4.
20. *New York Times,* February 1, 1970, p. 3.
21. *New York Times,* April 1, 1970, p. 3.·
22. R. Carson, *Silent Spring,* Houghton Mifflin, Boston (1962); R. L. Rudd, *Pesticides and the Living Landscape,* University of Wisconsin Press, Madison (1964); N. W. Moore, *Advances in Ecological Research, 4,* p. 75 (1967); K. Mellanby, *Pesticides and Pollution,* rev. ed., Collins, London (1970).
23. A. H. Westing, *Effects of 2,4,5-T on Man and the Environment,* U. S. Senate Committee on Commerce (1970), p. 76.
24. A. W. Galston, *Scientist & Citizen, 9,* p. 122 (1967); *New Scientist, 38,* p. 583 (1968); *BioScience, 20,* p. 405 (1970); E. W. Pfeiffer, *Scientific World, 12* (6), p. 16 (1968); *Science Journal, 5* (2), p. 33 (1969); *Biological Conservation, 2* (2), p. 149 (1970); R. E. Cook, W. Haseltine, and A. W. Galston, *New Republic, 162* (2), p. 18 (1970); A. H. Westing, *Friends Journal, 16,* p. 193 (1970); *Natural History, 80* (3), p. 56 (1971); J. B. Neilands, *Asian Survey, 10,* p. 209 (1970); I. F. Stone, *I. F. Stone's*

Weekly, Washington, *17* (23), p. 1 (1969); N. Chomsky, *New York Review of Books, 13* (12), p. 3 (1970).

25. J. Mayer and V. W. Sidel, *Christian Century, 83,* p. 829 (1966); A. H. Westing, *Friends Journal, 16,* p. 193 (1970); *New York Times,* July 12, 1971, p. 27.

26. *Science, 167,* p. 37; p. 1104 (1970); *171,* p. 43 (1971) [*cf.* Appendix X].

27. A. H. Westing, E. W. Pfeiffer, J. Lavorel, & L. Matarasso, *Report on Herbicidal Damage by the United States in Southeastern Cambodia,* Phnom Penh (1969); in *Defoliation,* Ballantine, New York (1970), p. 117. Also in *Withering rain,* Dutton, New York (1971), p. 151.

28. *Employment of Riot Control Agents, Flame, Smoke, Antiplant Agents, and Personnel Detectors in Counterguerrilla Operations,* U.S. Department of the Army Training Circular No. TC 3–16 (1969) [*cf.* Appendix III]; W. B. House, L. H. Goodson, H. M. Gadberry, and K. W. Dockter, *Assessment of Ecological Effects of Extensive or Repeated Use of Herbicides,* Midwest Research Institute, St. Louis (1967).

29. *Washington Post,* January 31, 1970, p. A5.

30. M. L. Montgomery and L. A. Norris, *U. S. Forest Service Research Note,* No. PNW–116 (1970).

31. M. G. Merkle, R. W. Bovey, and F. S. Davis, *Agronomy Journal, 59,* p. 413 (1967); G. R. Harvey and J. D. Mann, *Scientist and Citizen, 10,* pp. 165, 221 (1968); D. D. Hemphill, *Down to Earth, 24* (1), p. 2 (1968–1969).

32. W. H. Vanden Born, *Canadian Journal of Plant Science, 49,* p. 628 (1969).

33. R. R. Romanowski, Jr., J. A. Crozier, J. S. Tanaka, and R. C. Barba, *Hawaii Agricultural Experiment Station Technical Progress Report,* No. 162 (1967).

34. F. H. Tschirley, *U. S. Agricultural Research Service Publication,* CR–13–67 (1968).

35. C. E. Minarik, U. S. Department of the Army, personal communication, June 18, 1970.

36. F. H. Tschirley, *Science, 163,* p. 779 (1969); G. H. Orians and E. W. Pfeiffer, *Science, 168,* p. 544 (1970) [*cf.* Chapter 3]; A. H. Westing, *BioScience, 21* [in press] (1971); *Journal of Forestry, 69* [in press] (1971).

37. D. L. Klingman and W. C. Shaw, *U.S. Department of Agriculture Farmers' Bulletin,* No. 2183 (1962).

38. F. Harvey, *Air War: Vietnam,* Bantam, New York (1967).

39. F. H. Tschirley, U.S. Agricultural Research Service, personal communication, January 31, 1970.

40. T. R. Pickering, *Chemical-biological Warfare: U.S. Policies and International Effects,* [*I*] *Hearings,* [*II*] *Report,* U.S. House of Representatives Committee on Foreign Affairs (1970), p. [I] 198.

41. See also: M. Williams, *Land in Between: the Cambodian Dilemma,* Wm. Morrow, New York (1970); R. Johnson, *American Friends Service Committee Newsletter,* Cambridge, Massachusetts, No. 8, p. 1 (1970).

42. *New York Times,* January 28, 1970, p. 1; March 22, 1970, p. 17.

43. *Le Monde Diplomatique,* Paris, *193,* p. 12 (1970); N. Chomsky, *New York Review of Books, 14* (11), p. 39; (12), p. 43 (1970).

44. *New York Times,* March 19, 1970, p. 1; *et seq.*

45. *New York Times,* May 3, 1970, p. E2.

46. *New York Times,* May 1, 1970, p. 1.

47. *New York Times,* June 3, 1970, p. 1; see also: June 7, 1970, p. 1.

48. *Le Monde,* Paris, April 20, 1968, p. 2; *Los Angeles Times,* January 4, 1970, p. E10.

49. Mekong Documentation Centre of the Committee for Coordination of Investiga-

tions of the Lower Mekong Basin, *United Nations Economic Commission for Asia and the Far East Publication*, Bangkok, No. WRD/MKG/INF/L.211 (1967); M.L. Fisher, *Massachusetts Institute of Technology Center for International Studies Publication*, No. C/67–17 (1967).

50. Engineer Agency for Resources Inventories and Tennessee Valley Authority, *Atlas of Physical, Economic and Social Resources of the Lower Mekong Basin*, United Nations, New York (1968).

51. W.G. Burchett, *Mekong Upstream: a Visit to Laos and Cambodia*, Seven Seas Publishers, Berlin (1959); F.P. Munson, K.W. Martindale, D.S. McMorris, K.E. Parachini, W.N. Raiford, and C. Townsend, *Area Handbook for Cambodia*, rev. ed., U.S. Department of the Army Pamphlet No. 550–50 (1968); R. Prud'homme, *Économie du Cambodge*, Presses Universitaires de France, Paris (1969); M. Williams, see Ref. 41.

52. L. Loubet, *Monographie de la Prov. de Kompong Cham*, Phnom Penh (1963) [not seen].

53. *Viet Nam, Cambodia, Laos, and Thailand*, National Geographic Society, Washington (1967).

54. F.P. Munson *et al.;* R. Prud'homme; see Ref. 51.

55. K.G. McIndoe, *Development & Resources Corporation Vietnam Working Paper*, New York, No. 3 (1969).

56. *New York Times*, May 24, 1970, p. 1; May 25, 1970, p. 1.

57. *Guardian*, New York, *22* (33), p. 13 (1970).

58. R. Prud'homme, see Ref. 51.

59. W.L. Resing, Directeur, Institut des Recherches sur le Caoutchouc au Cambodge (IRCC), personal communication, March 19, 1970.

60. See also: F.W. Hutchison, *Journal of the Rubber Research Institute of Malaya, 15*, p. 241 (1958).

61. G. Wrigley, *World Crops, 14*, p. 412 (1962).

62. H.J. Cruzado, T.J. Muzik, and W.C. Kennard, *Weeds, 9* (1), p. 20 (1961).

63. G.M. Woodwell, *Science, 168*, p. 429 (1970); F.B. Golley, J.T. McGinnis, R.G. Clements, G.I. Child, and M.J. Duever, *BioScience, 19*, p. 693 (1969).

64. N. Dobson, *Agriculture*, London, *61*, p. 415 (1954–1955).

65. N.-E. Björklund and K. Erne, *Acta Veterinaria Scandinavica, 7*, p. 364 (1966); S. Dalgaard-Mikkelsen and E. Poulsen, *Pharmacological Reviews, 14*, p. 225 (1962); V.K. Rowe and T.A. Hymas, *American Journal of Veterinary Research, 15*, p. 622 (1954); J.M. Way, *Residue Reviews, 26*, p. 37 (1969); see also: P.A. Condon, *U.S. National Agricultural Library List*, No. 87 (1968).

66. *Scientific Research*, New York, *4* (12), p. 22; (13), p. 26; (15), p. 5 (1969).

67. G.H. Orians and E.W. Pfeiffer, see Ref. 36.

68. W.G. Burchett, *Vietnam: Inside Story of the Guerilla War*, 3rd ed., International Publishers, New York (1968).

69. S. Dalgaard-Mikkelsen and E. Poulsen; J.M. Way; see Ref. 64; W.J. Hayes, Jr., *Annals of the New York Academy of Science, 160*, p. 40 (1969).

70. K.H. Schulz, *Arbeitsmedizin Sozialmedizin Arbeitshygiene*, Stuttgart, *3* (2), p. 25 (1968); E.M. Mrak, W.J. Darby, *et al.*, *Report of the Secretary's Commission on Pesticides and their Relationship to Environmental Health*, U.S. Department of Health, Education, and Welfare (1969); T. Whiteside, *Defoliation*, Ballantine, New York (1970); K.D. Courtney, D.W. Gaylor, M.D. Hogan, H.L. Falk, R.R. Bates, and I. Mitchell, *Science, 168*, p. 864 (1970).

71. *Scientific Research,* New York, *4* (23), p. 11 (1969); *Medical World News, 11* (9), p. 15 (1970); *Health Aspects of Chemical and Biological Weapons,* World Health Organization, Geneva (1970).
72. *Tin Sang,* Saigon, June 22, 25, 26, 28, 29, and 30, 1969; *Le Monde,* Paris, January 2, 1970, p. 4; *New York Times,* March 15, 1970, p. 14.
73. Children's Medical Relief International, New York, *Progress Report, January 1 to March 31, 1970.*
74. *Is Cambodia Next?,* Russell Press, Washington (1967); M. Williams, see Ref. 41; A. H. Westing, *New Republic, 162* (13), p. 28 (1970).
75. M. Mansfield, *Perspective on Asia: the New U.S. Doctrine and Southeast Asia,* U. S. Senate Committee on Foreign Relations (1969).
76. M. Williams, see Ref. 41.

PART **III**

Appendixes

Appendix I

The Geneva Protocol of June 17, 1925, and a List of the 98 Signatory States

Protocol Prohibiting the Use in War of Asphyxiating, Poisonous or Other Gases, and of Bacteriological Methods of Warfare, Geneva, June 17, 1925

The undersigned plenipotentiaries, in the name of their respective Governments:

Whereas the use in war of asphyxiating, poisonous or other gases, and of all analogous liquids, materials or devices, has been justly condemned by the general opinion of the civilized world; and

Whereas the prohibition of such use has been declared in Treaties to which the majority of Powers of the world are Parties; and

To the end that this prohibition shall be universally accepted as a part of International Law, binding alike the conscience and the practice of nations;

Declare:

That the High Contracting Parties, so far as they are not already Parties to Treaties prohibiting such use, accept this prohibition, agree to extend this prohibition to the use of bacteriological methods of warfare and agree to be bound as between themselves to the terms of this declaration.

The High Contracting Parties will exert every effort to induce other States to accede to the present Protocol. Such accession will be notified to the Government of the French Republic, and by the latter to all signatory and acceding Powers, and will take effect on the date of the notification by the Government of the French Republic.

The present Protocol, of which the French and English texts are both authentic, shall be ratified as soon as possible. It shall bear to-day's date.

The ratifications of the present Protocol shall be addressed to the Government of the French Republic, which will at once notify the deposit of such ratification to each of the signatory and acceding Powers.

The instruments of ratification of and accession to the present Protocol will remain deposited in the archives of the Government of the French Republic.

The present Protocol will come into force for each signatory Power as from the date of deposit of its ratification, and, from that moment, each Power will be bound as regards other Powers which have already deposited their ratification.

In witness whereof the Plenipotentiaries have signed the present Protocol.

Done at Geneva in single copy, this seventeenth day of June, One Thousand Nine Hundred and Twenty-Five.

States Parties to the Protocol for the Prohibition of the Use in War of Asphyxiating, Poisonous or Other Gases and of Bacteriological Methods of Warfare, Done at Geneva June 17, 1925

States which have deposited instruments of ratification, accession, or continue to be bound as the result of succession agreements concluded by them or by reason of notifications given by them to the Secretary-General of the United Nations:

Argentina—May 12, 1969
Australia—January 22, 1930[1ab]
Austria—May 9, 1928[1ab]
Barbados[1ab2]
Belgium—December 4, 1928[1ab]
Botswana[1ab2]
Brazil—August 28, 1970
Bulgaria—March 7, 1934[1ab]
Burma[1ab2]
Canada—May 6, 1930[1ab]
Central African Republic—
   July 31, 1970[1ab]
Ceylon—January 20, 1954
Chile—July 2, 1935[1ab]

China—August 7, 1929
China, Dem. People's Rep.—
   August 9, 1952[1ab]
Cuba—June 24, 1966
Cyprus—December 12, 1966
Czechoslovakia—August 16, 1938[1b]
Denmark—May 5, 1930
Dominican Republic—December 8, 1970
Ecuador—September 16, 1970
Estonia—August 28, 1931[1ab]
Ethiopia—September 18, 1935
Fiji[1ab2]
Finland—June 26, 1929
France—May 9, 1926[1ab3]

Gambia, The—November 16, 1966
Germany, Federal Republic—April 25, 1929
Ghana—May 3, 1967
Greece—May 30, 1931
Guyana[1ab2]
Holy See—October 18, 1966
Hungary—October 11, 1952
Iceland—November 2, 1967
India—April 9, 1930[1ab]
Indonesia—January 26, 1971
Iran—July 4, 1929
Iraq—September 8, 1931[1ab]
Ireland—August 18, 1930[1ab]
Israel—February 20, 1969[1ab]
Italy—April 3, 1928
Ivory Coast—July 27, 1970
Jamaica—July 31, 1970
Japan—May 21, 1970
Kenya—July 6, 1970
Latvia—June 3, 1931
Lebanon—April 17, 1969
Lesotho[1ab2]
Liberia—April 2, 1927
Lithuania—June 15, 1933
Luxembourg—September 1, 1936
Madagascar—August 12, 1967
Malawi—September 14, 1970
Malaysia—December 10, 1970
Maldive Islands—January 6, 1967
Malta—October 15, 1970
Mauritius—January 8, 1971
Mexico—March 15, 1932
Monaco—January 6, 1967
Mongolia—December 6, 1968[1b]
Morocco—October 13, 1970
Nepal—May 9, 1969
Netherlands—October 31, 1930[1c4]
New Zealand—January 22, 1930[1ab]

Niger—April 19, 1967
Nigeria—October 15, 1968[1ab]
Norway—July 27, 1932
Pakistan—June 9, 1960
Panama—December 4, 1970
Paraguay—January 14, 1969
Poland—February 4, 1929
Portugal—July 1, 1930[1ab]
Romania—August 23, 1929[1ab]
Rwanda—June 25, 1964
Saudi Arabia—January 27, 1971
Sierra Leone—March 20, 1967
Singapore[1ab2]
South Africa—January 30, 1930[1ab]
Spain—August 22, 1929[1ab]
Swaziland[1ab2]
Sweden—April 25, 1930
Switzerland—July 12, 1932
Syrian Arab Republic—
    December 17, 1968[1d]
Tanzania—April 22, 1963
Thailand—June 6, 1931
Tonga[1ab2]
Trinidad and Tobago—
    November 30, 1970
Tunisia—July 12, 1967
Turkey—October 5, 1929
Uganda—May 24, 1965
Union of Soviet Socialist Reps.—
    April 5, 1928[1ab]
United Arab Republic—
    December 6, 1928
United Kingdom—April 9, 1930[1ab5]
Upper Volta—March 3, 1971
Venezuela—February 8, 1928
Yemen Arab Rep.—March 17, 1971
Yugoslavia—April 12, 1929[1b]
Zambia[1ab2]

[1] a,b,c,d With reservations to Protocol as follows:
   [a] binding only as regards relations with other parties.
   [b] to cease to be binding in regard to any enemy States whose armed forces or allies do not observe provisions.
   [c] to cease to be binding as regards use of chemical agents with respect to any enemy State whose armed forces or allies do not observe provisions.
   [d] does not constitute recognition of or involve treaty relations with Israel
[2] By virtue of agreement with former parent State or notification to the Secretary-General of the United Nations of succession to treaty rights and obligations upon independence.
[3] Applicable to all French territories.
[4] Applicable to Surinam and Curaçao.
[5] It does not bind India or any British Dominion which is a separate member of the League of Nations and does not separately sign or adhere to the Protocol. It is applicable to all colonies.

Appendix II

Chemical Properties of CN, DM, and CS

TABLE A II-1

General Properties of CN, DM, and CS [a]

Agent	Name	mp °C	Solubility	Odor	Irritation limit mg/m³	Tolerance limit mg/m³	Lethal exposure[b] mg-min/m³
					(one minute exposure time)		
CN	chloroacetophenone or ω-chloroacetophenone	54	sol. in alcohol, ether; insol. in water	apple blossom	0.3–1.5	5–15	8,500–25,000
DM	diphenylaminochlor- arsine or adamsite	195	sol. in benzene; insol. in water	none	0.1	2–5	15,000–30,000
CS	o-chlorobenzylidene- malononitrile or o-chlorobenzal- malononitrile	95	sol. in alcohol, ether; insol. in water	peppery	0.05–0.1	1–5	25,000–150,000[c] 40,000–75,000

[a] Unless otherwise specified, data are from U.N. Report No. E. 69.1.24, 1969. See reference (107) on page 96 in *Harvest of Death*.
[b] Determined for laboratory animals. For example, a concentration of 850 mg per cubic meter gives a 50 per cent kill in the population at 10 minutes exposure in the case of CN.
[c] *London Observer*, August 24, 1969.

TABLE A 11–1 (cont'd)

Technical Properties of CN, DM, and CS [a]

Agent	Molecular weight	State at 20°C.	Vapor density (air−1)	Density gm/cc	Freezing point (°C.)	Boiling point (°C.)	Vapor pressure mm	Volatility mg/m^3	Flash point	Decomposition temperature (°C.)	Heat of vaporization cal/gm	Median lethal dosage mg-min/m^3
CN	154.59	Solid	5.3	1.32 at 15°C. (solid)	54 to 55	244 to 245	0.0054 at 20°C.	105 at 20°C.	High enough not to interfere with military use	Stable to boiling point	98	About 11.000 (estimated)
DM	277.57	Yellow to green solid	Forms little vapor	1.65 (solid) at 20°C.	195	410	Negligible	Negligible	None	Above boiling point	54.8	15.000
CS	188.5	Colorless solid	—	—	93 to 95	310 to 315	—	—	—	—	—	25,000 for resting men

Table A II-1 (cont'd)

Agent	Median incapaciting dosage mg-min/m^3	Rate of detoxification	Eye and skin toxicity	Rate of action	Physiological action	Protection required	Stability	Decontamination	Means of detection in the field	Use
CN	80	Rapid	Temporary severe eye irritation; mild skin irritation	Instantaneous	Lacrimatory; irritates respiratory tract	Protective mask	Stable	Aeration in open; soda ash solution or alcoholic caustic soda in closed spaces	M-nitrobenzene and alkali in white dot/band tube of detector kits	Training and riot control agent
DM	22 for 1-min exposure; 8 for 60-min exposure	Rapid in small amounts	Irritating; relatively nontoxic	Very rapid	Like cold symptoms plus headache, vomiting, nausea	Protective mask	Stable in glass or steel	None needed in field; bleach or DS2 in confined spaces	None	Training and riot control agent
CS	10 to 20	Rapid; sublethal in 5 to 10 minutes	Highly irritating; not toxic	Instantaneous	Highly irritating; but not toxic	Protective clothing	Stable	Water, 5% sodium bisulfite, and water rinse	None	Training and riot control agent

a U.S. Departments of the Army and the Air Force Technical Manual, *Military Chemistry and Chemical Agents*, TM 3–215/AFM 355–7 (Washington, D.C.: U.S. Govt. Print. Off., December 6, 1963). Table 1, facing p. 101 [extraction].

Appendix III

Excerpts from *Department of the Army Training Circular 3–16,* **April 9, 1969**

* TC 3-16

TRAINING CIRCULAR⎰   HEADQUARTERS
                                    DEPARTMENT OF THE ARMY
NO. 3-16   ⎱   Washington, D.C., *9 April 1969*

EMPLOYMENT OF RIOT CONTROL AGENTS, FLAME, SMOKE, ANTIPLANT AGENTS, AND PERSONNEL DETECTORS IN COUNTERGUERRILLA OPERATIONS

		Paragraph	Page
Chapter 1.	INTRODUCTION		
Section I.	General	1-3	2
II.	Considerations of weather and terrain	4-6	2
Chapter 2.	RIOT CONTROL AGENTS, EQUIPMENT, AND MUNITIONS		
Section I.	Technical aspects	7-9	6
II.	Concepts of employment of riot control agents	10-20	17
III.	Employment of riot control agent munitions and equipment	21-34	27

[Pages 43–85 inclusive deleted–Ed.]

*This circular supersedes TC 3-16, 11 July 1966.

CHAPTER 1
INTRODUCTION

Section I. GENERAL

1. Purpose. This training circular provides guidance on the employment of riot control agents, flame, smoke, antiplant agents, and personnel detectors in counterguerrilla operations. It emphasizes the principles and techniques compatible with the environment, type of operations, and nature of the enemy. It will also assist in conducting realistic training based on materiel available and type of operations.

2. Scope. *a.* This training circular provides a consolidated source of information on the technical aspects and employment concepts for experimental and recently standardized items of equipment and munitions and for recently developed field expedients. It consolidates and supplements the limited amount of information on this materiel which is published in the form of maintenance packages, draft technical bulletins, and other miscellaneous publications. This training circular repeats information presented in other Department of the Army publications only as required for clarity and consistency.

b. A listing of the standard items of materiel which are being used in the field but for which employment is not unique to counterguerrilla operations is included at the beginning of each chapter where applicable. These items are listed in appendix B with references to Department of the Army publications which cover tactical and technical training information.

c. The general guidance offered in this training circular is oriented toward the environment and combat conditions of Southeast Asia and is applicable without modification to both nuclear and nonnuclear warfare.

d. The information in this training circular is also applicable to internal defense and/or internal development operations.

3. Changes and Comments. Users of this training circular are encouraged to submit recommended changes and comments to improve the publication. Comments should be keyed to the specific page, paragraph, and line of the text in which the change is recommended. Reasons will be provided for each comment to insure understanding and complete evaluation. Comments should be prepared using DA Form 2028 (Recommended Changes to Publications) and forwarded direct to Commandant, U. S. Army Chemical Center and School, Fort McClellan, Alabama 36201.

Section II. CONSIDERATIONS OF WEATHER AND TERRAIN

4. General. Chemical activities are characterized by dependence on weather and terrain conditions. These conditions are wind speed and direction, temperature gradient, air temperature, humidity, precipitation, amount and type of vegetation, terrain contour, and type of soil. FM 3-10 and TM 3-240 discuss the effects of these conditions in detail. Since this publication is oriented toward combat conditions in Southeast Asia, it is necessary to consider the general climatic conditions and peculiarities in that part of the world. An understanding of the type of weather that may be expected and its effects on the terrain and vegetation will provide valuable information for employing riot control agents, flame, smoke, antiplant agents, and personnel detectors effectively for maximum immediate, intermediate, and long-range effects.

5. Description of Weather and Terrain in Southeast Asia. *a. Weather (Meteorological) Factors.*

(1) Most of North Vietnam has a humid subtropical climate with dry winters and wet summers. The countries of Laos, Thailand, Cambodia, and the areas of South Vietnam and North Vietnam west of an imaginary line between the cities of Vinh in North Vietnam and Pleiku and Nha Trang in South Vietnam are in the tropical savanna climatic region of Southeast Asia (fig 1). Temperatures are strictly tropical in the south, but merge into subtropical temperatures in the Gulf of Tonkin provinces. The rainfall brought by the southwest monsoon (fig 1) during the months of May through August is moderately heavy.

(2) Burma and the area east of the imaginary line between the cities of Vinh, Pleiku, and Nha Trang to the China Sea (fig 1) have a tropical rainy climate and receive sufficient rainfall throughout the year to support the tropical rainforest type of vegetation; however, the precipitation is seasonal. It is heavy from September to December due to the northeast monsoon (fig 1) and light for the remainder of the year when winds are mostly offshore. The temperatures during the summer often exceed 100° F. The winter months bring a drop in temperature, but the cold weather is usually accompanied by fogs. Table 1 shows a comparison of the climates in different parts of Southeast Asia.

b. Terrain Factors.

(1) The natural vegetation in Southeast Asia ranges from dense tropical jungles, with overhead canopy in excess of 80 percent, to tall shrubs or scrub forests, to tall grass (often called elephant or marsh grass), to cultivated fields.

(2) In wet rainforest regions, as in Southeast Asia, where precipitation exceeds evaporation, the water carries much of the soluble material (lime) from the soil and leaves it oversupplied with iron and aluminum compounds. Rainforest soils are among the earth's least productive soil groups and are quickly exhausted when subjected to continuous cropping. In contrast to the rainforest soils, the alluvial soils in the regions of rivers are highly fertile in nature. The delta regions of the Mekong, Chao Phraya, Red, and Irrawaddy Rivers are characterized by this type of soil. In these areas the ground is rich in mineral plant food and is favorable for continuous cropping.

(3) The lowlands and delta regions of Southeast Asia are mainly utilized in the production of rice, but other products include cotton, sugarcane, and coconuts. Tea, tobacco, rubber, and coffee are grown in the well-drained intermediate levels, and cereals and beans are grown in the higher valleys. The rugged mountain areas are well forested with broadleaf evergreen and deciduous trees, mainly sandalwood and teakwood.

6. Effects of Weather and Terrain. Almost all areas of Southeast Asia are conducive to guerrilla operations. The dense rainforest jungles in the mountainous highland regions and the tall marsh grasses, inland rivers, and canals of the river delta regions offer numerous hiding places and avenues of escape to the guerrilla. Extensive employment of riot control agents, flame, smoke, and antiplant agents should be considered to achieve the element of surprise and to reduce concealment. The primary factor affecting the employment of riot control agents, flame, smoke, and antiplant agents is the micrometeorology of the specific region under consideration. Factors affecting the micrometeorology of a region include the synoptic situation (general weather of the area), topography, vegetation, and type of soil. FM 3-10 and TM 3-240 discuss these micrometeorological factors in detail.

TC 3-16

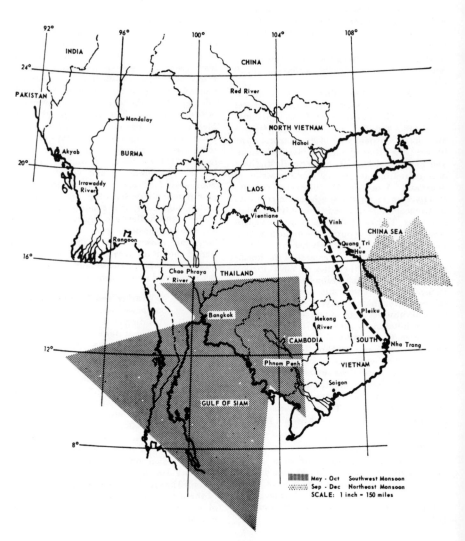

Figure 1. Southeast Asia.

TC 3-16

Table 1. Climates of Southeast Asia

Tropical savanna and tropical rainy climate of Southeast Asia	Mean temperature (°F.)			Average precipitation (inches)		
	Year	Coolest month	Warmest month	Year	Wettest month	Driest month
Burma:						
Rangoon.................	81	Jan 77	Apr 88	100	Jul 21.4	Jan 0.21
Mandalay...............	86	Jan 71	Apr 90	33.1	May 5.3	Jan 0.1
Akyab.....................	78	Jan 70	May 84	204	Jul 53.7	Jan 0.1
Cambodia:						
Phnom Penh............	....	....	....	55.8	Oct 10.9	Jan 0.2
Thailand:						
(Central)................	....	....	....	60	....	
North Vietnam:						
Hanoi.....................	74	Jan 62	Jun 85	63	Jul 13.4	Jan 0.9
South Vietnam:						
Saigon....................	81.9	Dec 78.8	Apr 85.8	77.4	Sep 13.4	Feb 0.1
Quang Tri...............	....	....	....	99.0	Nov 22.0	Feb 2.1
Hue........................	77.7	Feb 67.5	Jun 85.1	117	Oct 26.3	Mar 1.8
Nha Trang..............	80.3	Jan 75.5	Aug 84.1	54.0	Nov 13.8	Apr 0.9

TC 3-16

CHAPTER 2
RIOT CONTROL AGENTS, EQUIPMENT, AND MUNITIONS

Section I. TECHNICAL ASPECTS

7. General. *a. Role of Riot Control Agents.* Riot control agents are playing an increasingly important role in the conduct of counterguerrilla operations. Standard riot control munitions are considered; however, this section deals specifically with recently developed munitions which complement the riot control munitions now in the supply systems.

b. Standard Marking Systems. The standard munitions marking system for a nonpersistent effect riot control agent is one red band on a gray background. The marking system for a persistent effect incapacitating agent is two red bands on a gray background.

c. Evacuation or Disposal to Prevent Enemy Use. Authority for evacuation or destruction of munitions or equipment must be obtained from the responsible local commander. Destruction or disposal of munitions must be accomplished as directed in TM 9-1300-206.

8. Standard Munitions and Equipment. Information on the technical aspects and tactical use of standard materiel in *a* through *g* below is available in current Department of the Army publications. (See app B.)

   a. ABC-M7A3 CS Riot Hand Grenade.
   b. ABC-M25A1 CNI Riot Hand Grenade.
   c. ABC-M25A2 (CN1, CS1) Riot Hand Grenade.
   d. M2A1 Chemical Grenade Projection Adapter.
   e. M3 Riot Control Agent Disperser.
   f. M4 Riot Control Agent Disperser.
   g. M5 Riot Control Agent Disperser.

9. Experimental and Recently Standardized Munitions and Equipment. *a. Grenade, Hand, 8 to 12 Seconds Delay, CS, XM54.* The XM54 grenade (fig 2) is a standard M7 series CS grenade fitted with an 8- to 12-second delay fuze that allows the grenade to be dropped from altitudes of approximately 1,500 feet. It may be hand-dropped from aircraft or launched with a rifle grenade launcher adapter. The body of the grenade, constructed of thin sheet metal, is 6.35 centimeters in diameter and 14.6 centimeters high. The grenade is fitted with a delay fuze and filled with 115 grams of CS pellets and 185 grams of pyrotechnic mix. Weight of the grenade is 454 grams (1 pound). Area coverage of the M7 series and XM54 CS grenades is as follows:

No. of grenades	Temperature gradient	Wind speed (km/hr)	Area coverage (m)	Effective downwind travel (m)
1	Lapse to neutral	15 to 24	100 to 150	35 (approx)

b. Cartridge, 40mm, CS, XM674. The XM674 CS cartridge (fig 3) is a hand- or launcher-fired burning-type CS munition. The cartridge consists of an aluminum alloy tube, or barrel; a plastic launcher adapter; and a firing cap. The XM674 is 22.4 centimeters long and 4.1 centimeters in diameter, and weighs about 340 grams. A rubber body inside the barrel contains a CS/pyrotechnic mix of 50 grams of CS and 50 grams of pyrotechnic mix. When fired, the rubber CS projectile is propelled to the target by a black powder charge in the cartridge barrel. After a 3.2-second delay, the CS/pyrotechnic mix ignites and CS is emitted through four emission holes in the rubber body. The XM674 may be hand-fired using the firing cap, pistol-fired by the AN-M8

TC 3-16

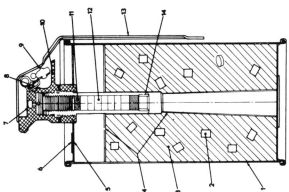

1. Body assembly
2. CS pellets
3. Fuel mixture
4. Starter mixture
5. Emission holes
6. Pressure-sensitive tape
7. Primer

8. Striker spring
9. Striker
10. Fuze
11. First-fire mixture
12. Delay mixture
13. Safety lever
14. Ignition mixture

Figure 2. Grenade, hand, 8 to 12 seconds delay, CS, XM54.

7

TC 3-16

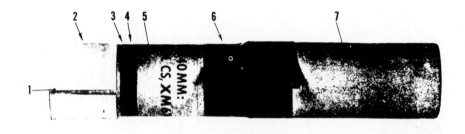

1. Cartridge barrel	4. Identification band (brown)
2. Launcher adapter	5. Nomenclature decal
3. Identification band (red)	6. Waterproof pressure-sensitive tape
	7. Firing cap assembly

Figure 3. XM674 CS riot control cartridge.

pistol (less firing cap and plastic adapter), or fired by the M79 grenade launcher using the plastic launcher adapter. Average range is 70 meters; burning time is 12 to 36 seconds. Refer to TM 3-1310-244-10, which accompanies the munition, before use. Failure to observe all safety precautions may result in injury to personnel.

c. *Base Ejection CS Cartridges.*

(1) *105mm tactical CS cartridge, XM629.* The XM629 CS cartridge (fig 4) is a semifixed, base-ejecting round designed for use in 105mm howitzer cannons M52A1, M101A1, M102, and M108. The main components of the round are a projectile containing four CS/pyrotechnic-filled canisters, a cartridge case containing a propelling charge, and a variable time fuze. Each canister contains 374 grams of CS/pyrotechnic mix. The fuze functions at a preset time or upon impact, and has a safety adapter which permits arming after traveling a minimum distance of 200 feet (61 meters) from the muzzle of the weapon. See table 2 for tabulated data.

(2) *4.2-inch tactical CS cartridge, XM630.* The XM630 CS cartridge (fig 5) has the same ballistic characteristics as the 4.2-inch M329A1 HE cartridge. The main components of the round are the projectile, the ignition cartridge with a propelling charge, four canisters, and a variable time fuze. The

CS/pyrotechnic-filled canisters burn for approximately 1 minute. The time fuze functions at a preset time or upon impact. See table 2 for tabulated data.

(3) *155mm tactical CS projectile, XM631.* The XM631 CS projectile is designed for use in 155mm howitzers M44A1, M114A1, M123A1, and M109. It has the same ballistic characteristics as the M107 155mm HE projectile. The main components of the round (fig 6) are the projectile containing five CS/pyrotechnic-filled canisters and an M548 variable time fuze. The projectile may be fired with M3, M4, or M4A1 propelling charges. See table 2 for tabulated data.

d. *Cartridge, 40mm, CS, XM651E1.* The 40mm XM651E1 CS cartridge (TM 3-1310-243-10) is similar in appearance to other 40mm cartridges, but is slightly longer and has a flat nose (fig 7). The projectile houses a fuze and contains approximately 53 grams of CS/pyrotechnic mix. The cartridge is fired from the M79 grenade launcher *only.* See table 2 for tabulated data.

e. *Grenade, Pocket, CS, XM58.* The XM58 CS pocket grenade (fig 8) is a small lightweight grenade designed for pocket carry. It is 9.2 centimeters long and 3.3 centimeters in diameter, and weighs about 120 grams. The grenade consists of a two-piece body assembly which contains 42 grams of CS/pyrotechnic mix.

Table 2. Tactical CS Cartridges

Designation	Type	Weight Entire round	Weight Projectile	Length	Caliber	Filling Type	Filling Wt	Burning time	Maximum range	Type fuzing	Minimum arming distance	Optimun. height of burst
XM629....	¹B. E., semifixed	19 kg	14.5 kg	81.7 cm	105mm	CS/pyro-technic	1.5 kg	60 sec (avg)	13,600 m	MTSQ	61 m	100 to 150 m
XM630....	¹B. E., mortar	—	11.8 kg	65.3 cm	4.2 in.	CS/pyro-technic	1.8 kg	60 sec (avg)	5,650 m	MTSQ	61 m	100 to 150 m
XM631....	¹B. E., separate loading	—	44 kg	60.4 cm	155mm	CS/pyro-technic	4.4 kg	90 sec (avg)	15,000 m	MTSQ	61 m	100 to 150 m
XM651E1.	Fixed	282 g	205 g	11.4 cm	40mm	CS/pyro-technic	53 g	25 sec	²400 m	Point deto-nating	30 m	NA

¹Base ejecting.
²Maximum accurate range of XM651E1 for point targets, 200 meters.

There is one emission hole centrally located in the bottom of the body, and it is covered with pressure-sensitive tape. The grenade uses a 1- to 3-second delay safety lever fuze. CS is emitted for 12 to 20 seconds. Hand-throwing range is about 45 meters.

f. M106 Riot Control Agent Disperser (Mity Mite). The M106 disperser (fig 9) is a commercial agricultural duster-sprayer modified for military use. It has a blower capacity of 450 cfm of air and is issued with a 6-foot-long neoprene tube (not shown) for blowing air to force CS or smoke from burning-type grenades throughout tunnels or underground fortifications. Its capacity is adequate for small tunnels (200 to 500 feet long). The M106 is capable of dispersing micropulverized agent CS1 or liquid antiplant agents from a 3½-gallon plastic hopper. A 2-foot-long hose is used when spraying liquids or dispersing CS1 in the open. The M106 is powered by a 2-stroke-cycle gasoline engine. The fuel tank holds enough fuel to operate for approximately 20 to 25 minutes. See TM 3-1040-254-13 for additional data.

g. Launcher and 35mm Cartridges, Tactical CS, 16-Tube, E8. The E8 launcher (fig. 10) is a man-portable, expendable munition which can be emplaced, sighted, and fired by one man. The munition system consists of a launcher module and a firing platform with carrying harness and backpack attached. The E8 weighs approximately 34 pounds. The launcher module is watertight and contains 64 E23 35mm cartridges in 16 tubes of 4 each. The E8 may be fired electrically or manually. Electrical binding posts and a lanyard are located in the firing well on the side of the module. The firing platform provides a stable base from which to fire the munition. The E23 35mm CS cartridges which are propelled from the launcher are filled with 38 grams of CS/pyrotechnic mix (40 percent CS). When the mix is ignited, CS is expelled through an off-center hole in the end of the cartridge, which causes it to skitter. Each cartridge has a 5- to 6-second delay fuze, and the CS/pyrotechnic mix burns for 10 to 15 seconds. The cartridges contain different amounts of propelling charge to give a wider dispersion in the target area. Range to center of impact is 150 meters. Refer to TB 3-1310-255-10; *do not attempt to operate the E8 without referring to this TB.* See table 3 for tabulated data.

Table 3. E8 Tactical CS Cartridge Launcher

Weight....................	15.5 kg (34 lb)
Filling.....................	CS/pyrotechnic mix (38 grams/cartridge)
Burning time, each cartridge....	10 to 15 seconds
Impact pattern........................	Elliptical
Pattern width (meters)..............	40
Range in meters (at 35 to 45 degrees elevation):	
Maximum..........................	250
Minimum..........................	75
Center of impact.................	150

h. Canister Cluster, Tactical CS, 50-lb, E158R2. The E158R2 canister cluster (fig 11) consists of eight plastic modules heat-sealed together and a fuzing system. Each plastic module contains 33 CS canisters and a black

TC 3-16

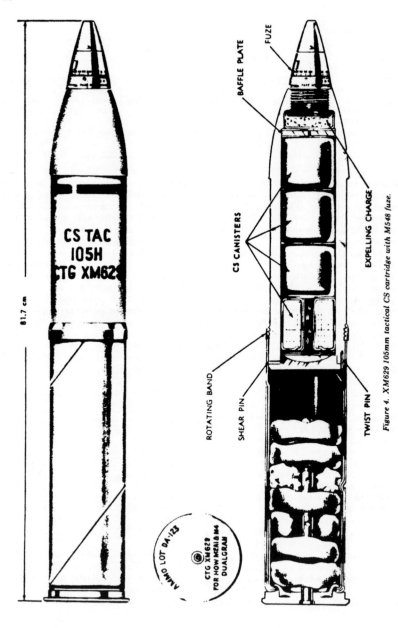

Figure 4. XM629 105mm tactical CS cartridge with M548 fuze.

81.7 cm

CS TAC
105H
CTG XM629

AMMO LOT DA-123
CTG XM629
FOR HOW M2A1 & M4
DUALGRAM

FUZE

BAFFLE PLATE

EXPELLING CHARGE

CS CANISTERS

ROTATING BAND

SHEAR PIN

TWIST PIN

10

TC 3-16

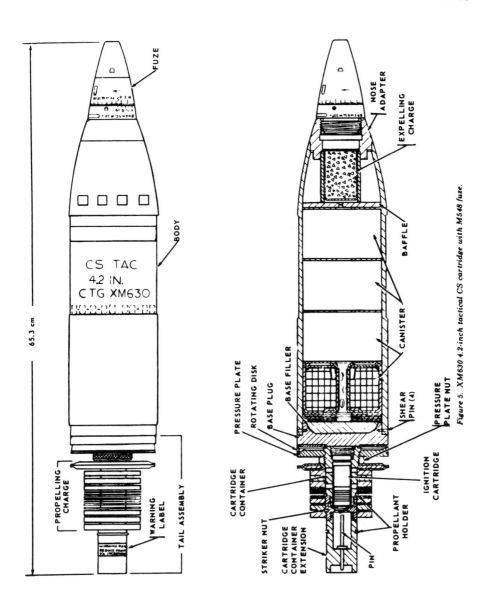

Figure 5. XM630 4.2-inch tactical CS cartridge with M548 fuze.

11

TC 3-16

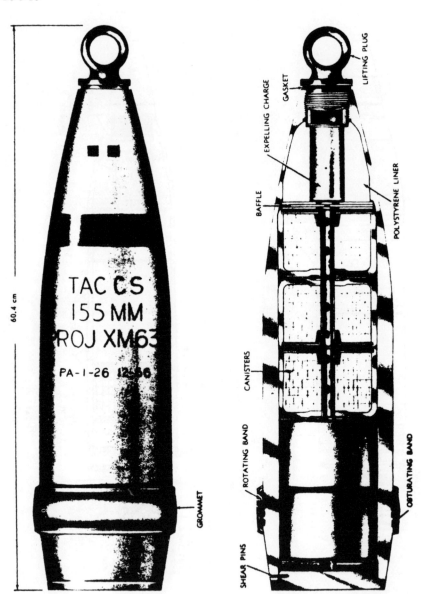

Figure 6. XM631 155mm tactical CS projectile.

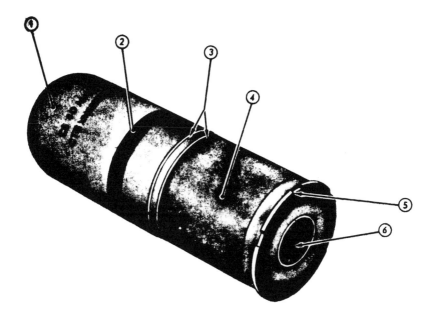

1. Ogive
2. Red band
3. Rotating bands

4. Cartridge case
5. Identification notch
6. Percussion primer

Figure 7. XM651E1 CS 40mm cartridge.

powder charge. Each canister is approximately the size of a flashlight cell and filled with CS/pyrotechnic mix. A mechanical time initiator permits airdropping of the cluster from various altitudes between 700 feet (213 meters) and 4,000 feet (1,215 meters). When the cluster functions, the modules are blown apart, scattering the CS canisters over the target area. The black powder charge which separates each module also ignites the canisters. After a 5- to 6-second delay, they begin disseminating CS. Pressure from the burning CS/pyrotechnic mix builds up and propels the cartridge along an erratic path as it escapes. CS is emitted for 7 to 19 seconds. The cluster is 68.5 centimeters long

and weighs about 21.4 kilograms (47 pounds). See TM 3-1325-232-12 and table 4 for tabulated data.

i. Canister Cluster, Tactical CS, XM15. The XM15 canister cluster is similar to the E158R2 canister cluster (fig 11) in appearance and function, except that a mechanical time fuze is permanently assembled to the XM15 (fig 14). The fuze can be set for a delay up to 10 seconds and must be used with the bombing table provided in the instruction booklet which accompanies the munition. See table 4 for tabulated data.

j. Canister Cluster, Tactical CS, 130-lb, E159. The E159 CS canister cluster (fig 12)

TC 3-16

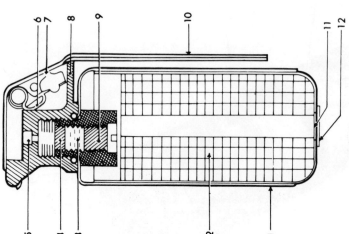

1. Body assembly
2. CS/pyrotechnic mixture
3. Delay mixture
4. First-fire mixture
5. Primer
6. Striker spring

7. Striker
8. Fuze body
9. Ignition mixture
10. Safety lever
11. Emission hole
12. Pressure-sensitive tape

Figure 8. Grenade, pocket, CS, XM58 (left); cross-sectional view (right).

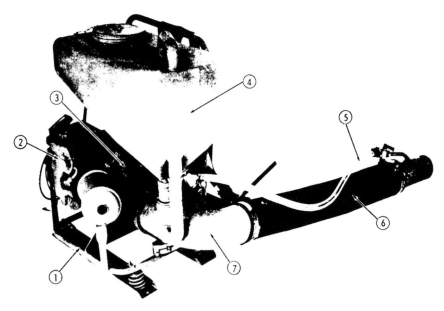

1. Frame assembly	4. Hopper assembly
2. Power unit	5. Liquid tube
3. Blower gearbox assembly	6. Air duct
7. Elbow assembly	

Figure 9. M106 riot control agent disperser (Mity Mite).

consists of two E158R2 clusters held together by a strongback assembly. The E159 is externally mounted on low-performance fixed-wing or rotary-wing aircraft. It can be delivered by UH-1 type helicopters equipped with the M16 armament sub-system. It is dropped electrically or mechanically from 14-inch bomb shackles at speeds up to 350 knots. The E159 does not have a time fuze initiator and must be dropped in accordance with its provisional bombing tables. Either mechanical or electrical initiation by the pilot activates the explosive bolt, which allows the E158R2 clusters to separate from the strongback assembly. Release from the strongback initiates the fuze bar of each E158R2. The remainder of the functioning cycle is identical to that of the E158R2. The E159 is 158 centimeters long and weighs 59.1 kilograms (130 pounds). See TM 3-1325-230-12, which accompanies the munition; also see table 4.

k. Canister Cluster, Tactical CS, 130-lb, XM165. The XM165 canister cluster (fig 13) consists of two XM15 canister clusters held together by a strongback assembly. The XM165 is similar in appearance and functioning to the E159 canister cluster, except for certain improvements in the fuzing system. Each XM15 canister cluster resembles an E158R2 cluster (fig 11), except that a mechanical time fuze which can be set for a 1- to 10-second delay is permanently assembled to the XM15 (fig 14). Therefore, it can be employed at various altitudes, using the bombing table in the instruction booklet which accompanies the munition. See table 4 for additional data.

15

TC 3-16

Table 4. CS Tactical Canister Clusters

Nomenclature	Weight	Length (cm)	Burning time (sec)	Optimum altitude (ft)	Area coverage (m²) (approximate)
E158R2, XM15....	21.4 kg (47 lb)	68.5	7 to 19	1,500	6,500
E159.....................	59.1 kg (130 lb)	158	7 to 19	600	9,000
XM165.................	59.1 kg (130 lb)	158	7 to 19	1,500	9,000

l. Fuze and Burster, Bomb: XM925 System. The XM925 system is used to burst a CS-filled drum when delivered by air (fig 15) and consists of an XM923 impact fuze, a burster assembly, and a drum cover. An arming wire, or lanyard, is included to permit arming of the fuze after it leaves the aircraft. A locknut is provided for securing the burster to the drum cover through a prepunched hole. The XM923 fuze has a vane arming feature. When the arming wire separates from the bomb, the vane is free to turn. After 15 to 20 turns of the vane, the fuze is armed. The fuze is omnidirectional and detonates upon impact with the ground. See TM 3-1325-237-10, which accompanies the munition system.

m. Riot Control Agents CS1 and CS2. Riot control agents CS1 and CS2 are micro-pulverized powder forms of riot control agent CS (o-chlorobenzalmalononitrile) that may be used in applications where longer durations of effectiveness are desired than can be achieved with burning-type CS munitions.

(1) *CS1* is a micropulverized mixture of 95 percent pure CS and 5 percent silica gel aerogal. On open terrain under normal weather conditions, CS1 is effective for approximately 14 days.

(2) *CS2* is CS1 which has been treated for water resistance. The result is a powdered riot control agent which resists weathering, flows freely, and has improved persistence.

n. Dispenser System, Aircraft, XM27. The XM27 dispenser system is designed to be used on low-performance aircraft to deliver a line source of agent CS. The system (fig 16) is composed of an XM18 dispenser (Air Force SUU-14/A bomb dispenser) and 72 XM54 CS 8- to 12-second delay hand grenades. The dispenser is 204.8 centimeters long and weighs

122 pounds when loaded (50 pounds, empty). It consists of six aluminum tubes bound together at the front by a nose fairing and at the middle by an aluminum skin. There are 12 grenades in each tube, for a payload of 144 grenades. An electrical firing system controls ejection of the CS grenades from the tubes. In the attack of targets, the dispenser is flown at an altitude of 1,500 feet and speeds up to 300 knots. The altitude is fixed by the time delay fuze of the XM54 grenade. The dispensers are mounted externally in pairs, one on each side of the aircraft. See table 5 for additional data.

o. Aircraft Dispenser CBU-30/A. The CBU-30/A dispenser system (fig 17) may be employed by high- or low-performance aircraft to deliver an intense line source of CS. The dispenser is an SUU-13/A downward ejection dispenser fitted with 40 dispenser tubes which are fired in sequence by an electrical firing system. The dispenser tubes are loaded with 32 CS canisters, each approximately the size of a flashlight cell. As the dispenser tubes are ejected, the canisters are scattered over the target area. The system may be mounted on high- or low-performance aircraft equipped with standard suspension fittings. See table 5 for tabulated data.

p. M3 2.75-Inch Rocket Launcher System. CS grenades (M7A2, M7A3, or XM54) may be dispersed by use of the adapter kit for the 2.75-inch rocket launcher (fig 36) described in paragraphs 43e and 50b. A CS screen may be produced by utilizing the technique described in paragraph 43e for producing a smoke screen. The XM54 8- to 12-second delay CS grenade may be employed at absolute altitudes up to 1.500 feet. The M7 series CS grenades must be dropped at altitudes of 200 to 500 feet, since these grenades have no delay feature. Burning-

Table 5. CS Dispenser Systems

Designation	Aircraft type	Type of grenade	No of grenades per dispenser	Altitude (optimum) (ft)	Airspeed (knots)	Refill-able by user	Dispersion pattern	Length of pattern
M3 launcher adapter system.	UH-1 series	M7 series, M8, M18.	168	Up to 500	50 to 100	Yes	Line source	1,000 meters (approx)
		XM54	168	1,500	50 to 100	Yes	Line source	1,000 meters (approx)
XM27 dispenser system.	UH-1 series	XM54	72	1,500	0 to 300	No¹	Line source	280 meters at 90 knots
CBU-30/A........	Tactical fixed wing	E49 canisters	1,280	100 to 600	500+	No	Line source	1,100 meters (long) by 61 meters wide at 450 knots

Dispensers must be salvaged through channels after firing

type grenades fitted with flotation devices may also be employed by the M3 system.

q. Dispenser and Bagged Riot Control Agent, Helicopter, CS2, XM28. The XM28 dispenser (fig 18) is designed to be sling-loaded beneath the UH-1 series helicopter. It consists of a rectangular aluminum alloy container fitted with tail fins and a sling cable system. The body of the dispenser contains 19 separate, sealed containers, each holding about 110 paper bags filled with CS2. The bags are emptied from each container by electrical release of a door, and burst when they hit the ground.

r. Mask, Protective, Riot Control Agent, XM28E4. The XM28E4 protective mask (fig 19) resembles the M22 civil defense mask in appearance. The XM28E4 is constructed of silicone rubber, which is more flexible and resistant to permanent set than is the natural rubber of the ABC-M17. The lenses are constructed of clear, flexible silicone rubber and are large enough to permit good peripheral vision. It is designed for protection against riot control agents *only*. The mask is lightweight (mask and carrier weigh about 1½ pounds), comfortable, and compact. In its carrier the XM28E4 measures approximately 20.3 x 12.7 x 6.4 centimeters (8 x 5 x 2½ inches) and may be carried on the person attached to any convenient webbing. No spectacle inserts are provided. The replaceable filter elements are enclosed and thus kept dry in the rain. Since there is no voice-mitter, clarity of speech is limited but satisfactory. See TM 3-4240-269-12 for additional data.

Section II. CONCEPTS OF EMPLOYMENT OF RIOT CONTROL AGENTS

10. General Considerations. *a. Introduction.* The employment of riot control agents (CS, CN) in counterguerrilla operations is most feasible in tactical situations characterized by close combat in which rapidly responding systems are essential and permanent effects are undesirable. Riot control munitions can be used tactically to temporarily disable hostile troops, to suppress their fires, or to cause them to abandon their positions. Offensively, riot control agents can be used to "flush out" unprotected enemy troops from concealed positions or to reduce their ability to maneuver or use their weapons. Defensively, riot control munitions can be integrated into defensive perimeters to provide rapid CS delivery in case of enemy attack. Regardless of the purpose of employment, units employing riot control agents must coordinate with, or at least notify, adjacent and/or potentially affected friendly units of the planned agent dissemination. The essential requirements for the employment of riot control agents are—

(1) The concentration of agent must be

TC 3-16

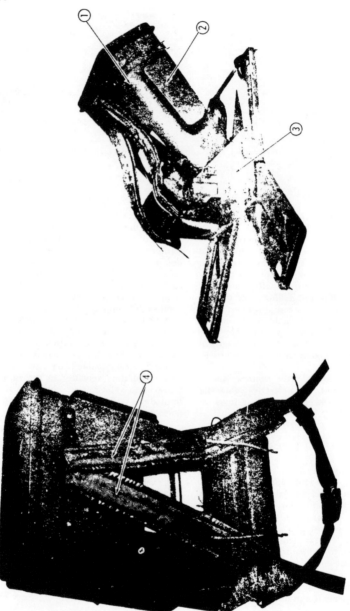

1. Launcher module   3. Firing platform
2. Firing well   4. Carrying harness

Figure 10. E8. 16-tube, tactical CS launcher and 35mm cartridges.

18

TC 3-16

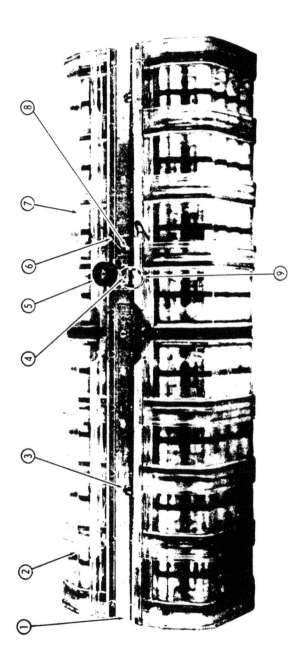

1. Fuze bar assembly
2. Module
3. Junction block
4. Fuze assembly
5. Red safety cap
6. Fuze arming wire
7. Loop
8. Spring loaded detonator slide
9. Safety cotter pin

Figure 11. E158R2 50-lb tactical CS canister cluster.

19

TC 3-16

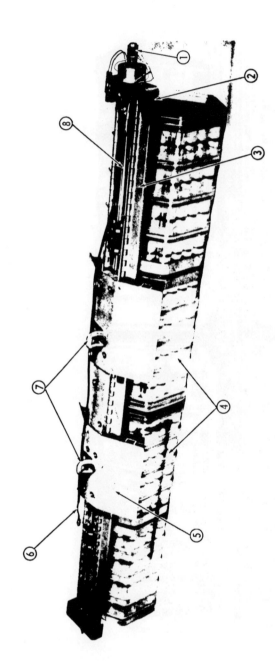

Figure 12. E159 tactical CS canister cluster.

1. Explosive bolt assembly
2. Spring-loaded end clamps
3. Strongback assembly
4. E158 clusters
5. Arming wire
6. Electrical wiring harness
7. Suspension lugs
8. Tie rod

TC 3-16

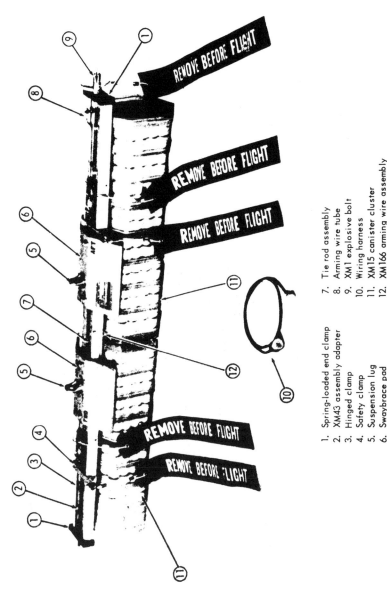

1. Spring-loaded end clamp
2. XM43 assembly adapter
3. Hinged clamp
4. Safety clamp
5. Suspension lug
6. Swaybrace pad
7. Tie rod assembly
8. Arming wire tube
9. XM1 explosive bolt
10. Wiring harness
11. XM15 canister cluster
12. XM166 arming wire assembly

Figure 13. XM165 tactical CS canister cluster.

21

TC 3-16

1. Fuze bar assembly   3. Module
2. Time delay scale   4. Arming wire
              5. Safety wire

Figure 14. Mechanical time fuze, XM15 CS canister cluster.

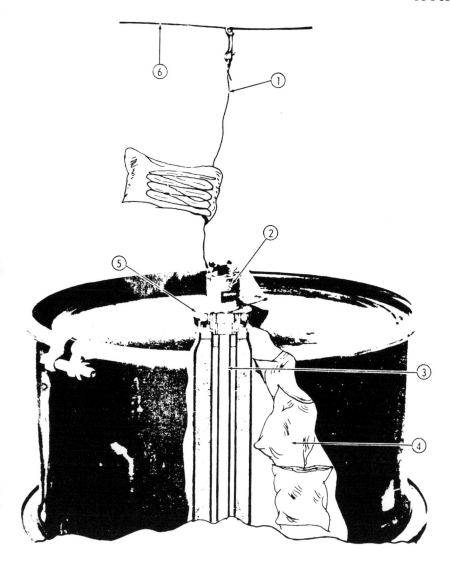

1. Arming wire, or lanyard
2. XM923 fuze
3. Burster assembly
4. Vaporproof bags of CS1 or CS2
5. Locknut
6. Static line

Figure 15. Cross section of CS-filled drum with XM925 system installed.

TC 3-16

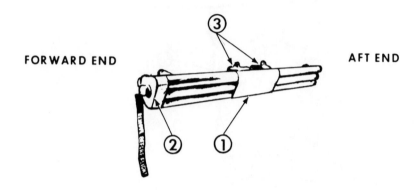

FORWARD END   AFT END

1. Aluminum skin   2. Nose fairing
3. Suspension lugs

Figure 16. XM18 dispenser of XM27 dispenser system.

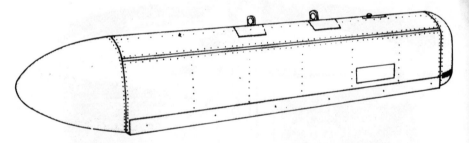

Figure 17. Aircraft dispenser CBU-30/A (SUU-13/A dispenser with CS dispenser tubes).

dense enough over the desired target to be intolerable to unmasked personnel.

(2) The concentration must be extended around the target periphery in sufficient quantities so that escape (by closing eyes and/or holding breath) is difficult.

(3) The concentration must be capable of being established within a short time (1 minute or less).

b. Operational Techniques. Employment of certain riot control agents may be effective or marginal, depending on the operational conditions encountered. The degree of effectiveness is dependent on the employment concepts and

techniques that are established.

(1) *Marginal systems.* Riot control agent CN is considered generally inferior to agent CS for combat operations, except where incapacitation is desired for a longer time after cloud passage. CNC (liquid form of CN) will not penetrate a rainforest canopy in sufficient quantities to achieve a significant concentration under the canopy. Dissemination of micropulverized CS (by any means) above the canopy is ineffective because the particles will not penetrate the canopy quickly and in sufficient amounts to achieve an effective agent concentration. Some concentration will

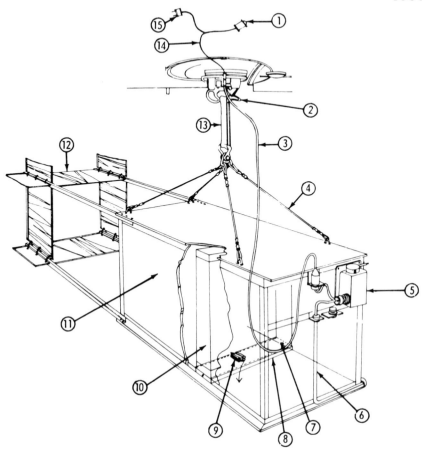

1. Pushbutton firing switch	8. Door
2. Aircraft cargo hook	9. CS-filled paper bag
3. Power cable assembly (outer)	10. Cardboard container
4. Sling cable	11. Dispenser
5. Intervalometer	12. Tail fins
6. Wire leads to each explosive detent	13. Nylon sling
7. Explosive detent	14. Power cable assembly (inner)

15. Rubber cap plug

Figure 18. XM28 dispenser attached to helicopter.

25

TC 3-16

Figure 19. XM28E4 riot control agent protective mask.

be achieved at the forest floor level, but it will vary from 10 to 60 percent of the above-canopy concentration and will reach the forest floor level approximately 20 minutes after cloud passage above the canopy.

(2) *Effective systems.* Dissemination of agent CS in the form of an aerosol of fine particles at ground level (or within fortifications and tunnels) on a well-defined target area is the most effective technique for riot control agent employment. This may be achieved by aircraft- or ground-delivered systems. In jungle (or under canopy) operations against ground-level targets, the best results are achieved by dropping the air-delivered system directly on the target. In open or lightly wooded areas, all munitions and delivery systems may prove effective. Sufficient numbers of munitions must be employed to insure the buildup of a sufficient agent concentration.

11. Preparation of Landing Zones (LZ's). CS fire may be coordinated with HE fire in preparation of LZ's when enemy presence is suspected. Riot control agents should suppress hostile fire or cause it to be ineffective if the enemy is unprotected. A determined enemy might not flee from a well-established position. The riot control agent should be disseminated just prior to troop landing. The troops and aircraft crews must be equipped with protective masks so that the assault can take place with an effective agent cloud in the area.

12. Situations Involving Mixed Populations. In addition to use against unmasked hostile forces, CS munitions may be employed as a most effective weapon choice against a target area containing mixed friendly-hostile or neutral-hostile populations where casualties are to be minimized. Care should be taken not to drop CS/pyrotechnic-filled munitions on buildings with thatched roofs. These munitions may ignite flammable structures.

13. Against Dug-in Enemy. Unmasked enemy troops in bunkers or trenches are vulnerable to CS when conventional fires often are ineffective. The enemy forces, surprised by the use of CS against them, may flee to escape its effects. A determined enemy force may choose to remain in position, but his firepower will be reduced, or be relatively ineffective, since he cannot keep his eyes open.

14. Flushing Tunnels. Riot control agents may be used to cause evacuation of tunnel systems. Generally, blowers such as the M106 disperser (Mity Mite) are required to force the agent through the tunnel.

15. Discouraging Entry Into Tunnels. Micropulverized CS may be dispersed within underground installations to restrict reoccupation and use of the facility as long as the agent remains effective.

16. Aiding in Perimeter Defense. Riot control agents may be integrated into a perimeter defense to cover likely avenues of approach.

17. Canalization. Riot control agents may be used to canalize unmasked hostile personnel into routes, avenues, or positions in which attacking forces can execute preplanned schemes of maneuver with less enemy resistance.

18. Blocking Actions. Riot control agents may be used to impede the escape of enemy forces.

19. Retrograde Movements. Riot control agents may be used as a means of breaking contact when a unit's position becomes untenable. Also, an isolated unit may employ these munitions as a means of route clearance and/or flank security in a particularly vulnerable area on the route of withdrawal.

20. River Crossings. Riot control agents may be integrated into hasty or deliberate river crossings to discourage enemy action such as sniper fire or ambush during the crossing.

Section III. EMPLOYMENT OF RIOT CONTROL AGENT MUNITIONS AND EQUIPMENT

21. General. This section discusses the application of experimental riot control munitions and equipment to the concepts of employment discussed in section II of this chapter and suggests techniques of employment. Users are urged to submit after-action reports on all

TC 3-16

experimental munitions.

22. Employment of CS Hand Grenade, 8 to 12 Seconds Delay, XM54. The XM54 CS grenade is intended for use in aircraft dispenser systems, such as the M3 rocket launcher (para 43*e*) or the XM27 dispenser (para 9*n*). It may also be dropped by hand from low-performance aircraft. The delay element allows the aircraft to fly at altitudes up to 1,500 feet above the ground while dispersing the grenades. The XM54 may also be fired from a rifle using an M2A1 grenade projection adapter. *Care should be exercised in firing the grenade short distances, because the delay element could cause it to be picked up and thrown back.*

23. Employment of Base Ejection Tactical CS Cartridges, XM629, XM630, and XM631. *a. Concepts of Employment.* The XM629 105mm and XM631 155mm tactical CS cartridges provide artillery battalions with the capability of delivering riot control agent CS to point targets. The XM630 4.2-inch tactical CS cartridge affords some infantry battalion commanders a means of providing close riot control agent support to maneuver elements, provided 4.2-inch mortars are organic to the unit. These cartridges are adaptable to many of the concepts of employment discussed in section II of this chapter, and are particularly suitable for the following uses:

(1) *Preparatory CS fire.* In this role, CS is intended to flush the enemy from his entrenched, hard fortifications into the open.

(2) *Preparatory airstrikes followed by CS, followed by conventional artillery.* Airstrikes or artillery may soften or destroy the hard fortifications and suppress ground fire prior to the use of CS fire.

(3) *Preparatory fires using conventional HE and CS fired simultaneously.* The CS and HE are interspersed throughout the target area to gain maximum surprise and to suppress ground fire just prior to landing an assault force.

(4) *Reconnaissance by fire.* In this role, CS is fired into areas of suspected enemy troop concentrations and may cause the enemy to reveal his position.

(5) *Defensive fires.* CS fire may be integrated into the planned fires of defensive positions as an on-call measure to deter or disrupt attacks on outposts or other isolated defensive bases, base camps, defended structures, hamlets, or villages.

b. Techniques of Employment.

(1) *Adjusting point.* Normally, the observer should select an adjusting point well upwind of the target area. However, if the wind speed is negligible (as in jungle terrain), the target area will become the adjusting point.

(2) *Adjustment.* Normal forward observer procedures for adjustment of shell HC smoke are adaptable for adjustment of shell CS. Adjustment could begin with shell HE or WP, entering fire-for-effect when within approximately 100 meters of the adjusting point. However, experienced observers may adjust from one round and enter fire-for-effect, with minor corrections made to keep the target area well covered as long as necessary. A mechanical time fuze provides better area coverage than a point detonating fuze by allowing better dispersion. A height of burst of approximately 100 meters should provide adequate dispersion of the canisters. However, lower heights of burst may be desirable or necessary, depending on the situation. When a high trajectory presents the danger of empty projectiles falling among friendly troops, a lower trajectory, and lower height of burst will cause earlier impact and may eliminate the danger.

(3) *Number of rounds.* The number of rounds to be fired will depend on the size of the area to be covered. The fire direction center can determine the approximate number required to establish an initial concentration of CS. The observer must then determine if further adjustment or replenishment is necessary, depending on any changes in the situation and the desired length of time to maintain the concentration. With a negligible wind speed, the initial concentration may remain effective for 10 to 20 minutes before it dissipates. For some airmobile operations, this may be a sufficient duration of effectiveness, with no replenishment of the agent required. Delivery may be by means of one or more pieces firing continuously or volley fire.

24. Employment of Cartridge, 40MM, CS, XM651E1. *a. Concepts of Employment.* The

40mm CS XM651E1 cartridge provides a CS delivery capability within range of the M79 grenadier. The cartridge is especially useful in the following situations:

(1) *Attack of hard targets.* The XM651E1 CS cartridge may be fired into hard targets, such as caves, bunkers, tunnels, or foxholes, to reduce enemy fire. The M79 grenade launcher provides the accuracy to make this concept feasible from safe distances.

(2) *Offensive operations in mixed population areas.* The M79 grenade launcher may also be used to deliver CS into buildings to flush out occupants in cases where hostile and neutral or hostile and friendly persons are in the structure, causing all to vacate without harm to neutrals or friendlies. This technique may be particularly effective in clearing built-up areas, such as entire sections of a city.

(3) *Ambushes, patrols, and raids.* Patrols and raiding parties, such as long-range reconnaissance patrols and combat ambush patrols, may use CS fired from the M79 grenade launcher to break contact with pursuing hostile forces.

(4) *Perimeter defense.* The 40mm CS cartridge provides the M79 grenadiers on defensive perimeters with a means of reinforcing other fires.

(5) *Convoy counterambush situations.* Fired from helicopters, trucks, or armored personnel carriers, the 40mm CS cartridge may be used to assist the counterambush. The cartridge should be employed as soon as possible after enemy contact is made.

(6) *Reconnaissance by fire.* The 40mm CS cartridge may be fired into suspected enemy positions in the path of a friendly advancing element, especially into suspected ambush sites. This may abort the ambush by causing the enemy to reveal his presence.

b. Techniques of Employment.

(1) The XM651E1 cartridge is intended for use against any target vulnerable to CS. The cartridge is fired *only* from the M79 grenade launcher (TM 9-1010-205-12) and is especially effective when fired into an enclosed area.

(2) Maximum accuracy is obtained at ranges up to 200 meters. Area targets can be engaged at ranges up to 400 meters.

(3) The experienced grenadier, once he has fired the CS cartridge for familiarization, will be able to apply "Kentucky windage" to successive rounds.

(4) The projectile will penetrate window glass or up to 3/4-inch-thick pinewood at 200 meters and release CS after penetration. It will also function against other materials such as earth, gravel, brush, sandbags, and bamboo. Firing the cartridge into water will increase the dud rate and decrease the amount of CS disseminated. When fired into buildings that are easily penetrated, the projectile should enter at a point near the ground to prevent it from passing completely through the building.

25. Employment of Cartridge, CS, XM674. The XM674 CS cartridge (Handy Andy) is designed to be fired by hand, by AN-M8 pistol, or by M79 grenade launcher. It is employed similarly to the XM651E1 cartridge (para 24) at an average range of 70 meters. The correct hand-firing position is shown in figure 20. See TM 3-1310-244-10 for additional information.

26. Employment of M106 Riot Control Agent Disperser (Mity Mite). *a. Concepts of Employment.* The M106 Mity Mite is useful for —

(1) Forcing evacuation of a tunnel.

(2) Discouraging entry into a tunnel.

(3) Locating entrances and vents of a tunnel.

(4) Generating an agent cloud in the open.

(5) Dispersing insecticides or antiplant agents.

b. Techniques of Employment. The M106 riot control agent disperser is available to the infantry unit commander. Each company-sized unit should have a two- to four-man tunnel flush and search team, which would normally operate the Mity Mite. An operation and maintenance manual, TM 3-1040-254-13, accompanies the M106 and should be read carefully prior to operation. Training the team to operate the Mity Mite may be accomplished in about 2 hours.

(1) *Forcing evacuation of a tunnel.*

(a) When the M106 is used in conjunction with a riot control agent to force unmasked personnel from a tunnel, air is directed through the 6-foot tube into the tunnel opening which has been sealed with a

TC 3-16

Figure 20. Hand-firing position for XM674 CS cartridge.

poncho or tarpaulin cover (fig 21). The riot control agent is introduced into the tunnel by raising an edge of the poncho or tarpaulin cover and dropping burning riot control agent grenades into the entrance at intervals of 2 to 4 minutes. If a large tunnel system is encountered, more than one M106 may be operated simultaneously at a tunnel entrance.

(b) The time required for a riot control agent cloud to penetrate all parts of a tunnel system is dependent upon the number of blowers used, the size and length of the tunnel, and the number of entrances and vents which cannot be sealed. The agent cloud will travel through a typical tunnel with no branches at a speed of approximately 15 meters per minute when one blower is used.

(c) As the agent cloud traverses the tunnel system, some of it will escape from other entrances or vents. (If the agent cloud is difficult to see, an occasional smoke grenade may be dropped into the tunnel entrance to make the cloud more visible.) If possible, these openings should be closed as soon as they are discovered to prevent escape of the cloud from the tunnel, or additional blowers may be installed in them and operated as described in *(a)* above.

(d) It is desirable to continue dropping riot control agent grenades into the tunnel at intervals of 2 to 4 minutes as long as the M106 is operating; however, if this is not possible, operation of the M106 may continue after any number of grenades have been dropped into the tunnel. In any event, the M106 should be kept in operation until the entire tunnel system has been penetrated by the agent cloud.

(2) *Operating procedure at tunnel entrance.*

(a) Check the surrounding area and the tunnel entrance for boobytraps.

(b) Place the M106 on the ground approximately 1 meter from the edge of the hole.

(c) Place the end of the flexible tube in the tunnel entrance.

(d) Lay a poncho or tarpaulin cover over the entrance and on top of the flexible tube. Position the cover so that the entrance hole and at least 2 feet of the tube are covered. (If a poncho is used, the flexible tube may be placed through the head hole and the hood strings

TC 3-16

tied tightly around the tube as shown in figure 21.)

(e) Seal the cover in place over the hole with loose dirt. Push the cover under the sides of the flexible tube and place loose dirt around it to hold it in place.

(f) Start the engine of the M106 and set the throttle to run at maximum speed. If the unit creeps on the ground because of vibration, place it on some loosened earth or place some heavy object, such as a sandbag, stone, or tree branch, on the frame. Occasionally check the throttle setting.

(g) Don the protective mask. With M106 operating, remove the safety pin from a single riot control agent grenade. Lift one corner of the cover, drop or throw the grenade into the tunnel entrance, and reseal the hole by placing earth or any available object on the corner of the cover that was raised.

(h) If any of the agent cloud escapes from under the cover or around the tube, place more loose dirt on the cover at the points of leakage.

(i) Every 2 to 4 minutes, drop or throw an additional riot control agent grenade into the tunnel entrance to produce a continuous

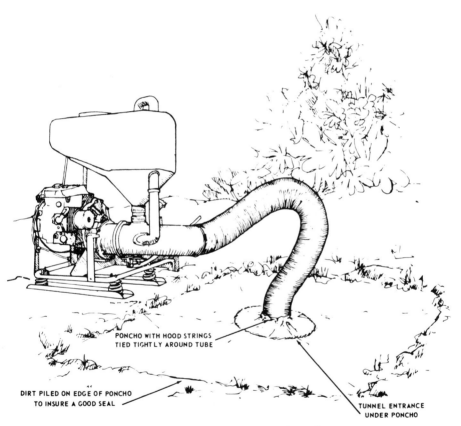

PONCHO WITH HOOD STRINGS
TIED TIGHTLY AROUND TUBE

DIRT PILED ON EDGE OF PONCHO
TO INSURE A GOOD SEAL

TUNNEL ENTRANCE
UNDER PONCHO

Figure 21. Use of poncho with M106 riot control agent disperser.

TC 3-16

cloud in the tunnel.

(3) *Discouraging entry into a tunnel.*

(a) A lingering deterrent may be produced in a tunnel entrance by using riot control agent in a dry form (CS1 and/or CS2). The hopper of the M106 holds approximately 10 pounds of dry agent (CS) which may be dispersed through the outlet tube into the entrance within 3 or 4 minutes. This will produce heavy contamination of the tunnel surfaces near the entrance and will discourage entry by unprotected personnel for a period of about 14 days.

(b) This operation may be performed in conjunction with forcing the evaluation of a tunnel (b(1) above), by filling the hopper of the M106 with dry agent and blowing it into the tunnel. If desired, the 2-foot tube and nozzle may be installed on the blower outlet to direct dry agent into a tunnel entrance without using a cover. The M106 may be carried on the back during the latter operation.

(4) *Locating all entrances and vents of a tunnel system.* To determine the extent of a tunnel system, follow the procedure described for forcing evacuation of a tunnel (b(1) above), using smoke grenades or pots instead of riot control agent grenades. Since a tunnel must have vents throughout its length, their locations and the extent of the tunnel system may be determined by using this procedure.

(5) *Generating a cloud in the open.* Dry agent may be dispersed with the M106 riot control agent disperser. The 2-foot flexible tube with nozzle is used for this operation. The concentration is regulated by use of the dust control lever, as described in TM 3-1040-254-13. The M106 may be operated in this manner while it is on the ground, mounted on a vehicle, or carried on the back.

(6) *Dispersing liquids for antiplant or insecticide operations.* The 2-foot tube with nozzle must be used when dispersing liquids. This operation may be performed with the M106 on the ground, mounted on a vehicle, or carried on the back. Individuals dispersing insecticides should wear protective masks.

c. *Safety Precautions.* The following safety precautions must be taken prior to employment of the M106 riot control agent disperser:

(1) In tunnel-flushing operations, the en-

trance to the tunnel and the area immediately surrounding the tunnel entrance must be thoroughly searched for boobytrap devices.

(2) In tunnel-flushing operations, security personnel should be positioned in all directions (360 degrees) around the tunnel entrance to protect the operators from enemy fire and to observe escaping enemy or to detect smoke escaping from tunnel vents and entrances.

(3) All friendly personnel should be masked when riot control agents are being used in tunnel operations or to generate a cloud in the open.

(4) When burning-type grenades (HC smoke or CS) are used in a tunnel or other inclosed space, they may cause asphyxiation to personnel in the tunnel because of oxygen depletion and carbon monoxide buildup. *A field protective mask will not protect against this condition.* A self-contained breathing apparatus (such as the M15 compressed air breathing apparatus) must be worn for tunnel exploration after smoke grenades or smoke pots are used.

27. **Employment of Launcher and 35MM Cartridges, Tactical CS, 16-Tube, E8.** a. *Employment Concepts.* Within technical limitations, the employment of the E8 tactical CS munition is limited only by the imagination of the user. It may be incorporated into the scheme of maneuver of small unit tactical operations where a short-range, high-angle-fire weapon is applicable. Examples of situations where it is particularly adaptable are —

(1) *Static defense positions.* E8 munitions can provide valuable defensive fires when integrated into the perimeter defensive fires and manmade barriers of hasty, deliberate, or fixed installations and of villages (or hamlets). As time allows, a number of E8 munitions may be emplaced some distance from the position to cover likely avenues of approach as an initial deterrent to the advance of hostile forces. Because of the nature of the munition, command firing is desired. If trip-wiring is deemed necessary to warn of the approach of hostile forces, consideration must be given to the possibility of accidental discharge of the munition and the resultant downwind effects.

(2) *Ambushes and raids.* The E8 munition may be used effectively as an ambush support

weapon against foot or mobile elements when the mission is to capture individuals or equipment. The psychological impact of night ambush with CS may be heightened by the use of trip flares which tend to hold and confuse the hostile forces. The effects of CS will then allow ambushing forces to take prisoners.

(3) *Counterambush situations.* The E8 may be used to supplement other weapons to counter an ambush of foot or motorized elements. The E8 munitions should be fired as soon as possible after enemy contact. E8 munitions may also be used for reconnaissance by fire; that is, to fire into suspected or likely ambush areas prior to entering them.

(4) *Against mixed populations.* The E8 may be used when hostile forces are mingled with a neutral or friendly population where casualties must be minimized.

b. *Techniques of Employment.*

(1) *General.* The E8 is a short-range weapon that produces a shock-action psychological effect (the loud noise and rapid cloud buildup), as well as a riot control agent concentration. It is designed to be rapidly fired either singly or in groups against small area targets or point targets. The widely scattered dispersion of the E23 submunitions over the target area makes the E8 relatively independent of meteorological conditions. When employing the E8 munition, regardless of the type of emplacement, the following must be considered:

(a) *Covering the target.* Sufficient munitions should be employed to cover completely the periphery of the target to make the use of escape routes difficult.

(b) *Employment in depth.* Sufficient munitions should be employed against moving targets (e.g., men fleeing the area) to thoroughly blanket the area of possible movement.

(c) *Timely exploitation.* Once the E8 munition has been employed and during the period of confusion when the surprise action, agent effects, and the white cloud have reduced the effectiveness of masked and unmasked hostile personnel, there must be timely exploitation of the situation by friendly forces. Additionally, there must be sufficient reserve (additional) munitions to refresh target concentrations depleted by wind drift or to fill any gaps caused by delivery error.

(2) *Static employment.* When emplaced as part of a defensive perimeter, the E8 may be fired by either command electrical or command lanyard methods, with preference given to electrical methods of fire. It may be emplaced on top of buildings or bunkers, or adjacent to either with the firing lines running into the structures. Lanyard methods of fire increase the possibility of accidental detonation due to personnel tripping over the cord. The angle of fire differs with the intended role of the weapon. Some munitions are placed in the vertical or 90° position so that the submunitions fall directly on the friendly position in case of overrun by enemy troops. Other munitions may be set up in positions at any elevation, with minor adjustments being made by angling the firing platform of the weapon.

(3) *Mounted on wheeled vehicles.* E8 munitions may be mounted and secured on the front bumper, on the .50 caliber M6 ring (on a plywood platform), or on the cargo bed of the truck at various angles. The E8 is always lanyard-fired by the vehicle commander.

(4) *Mounted on armored personnel carriers.* The munition may be mounted and secured on top of the APC or kept inside and, if needed, placed through the gunner's hatch and aimed and lanyard-fired by the gunner.

(5) *Mounted on tanks.* The E8 may be mounted and secured on the forward edge of the tank or on the turret so that it may be traversed into any direction of fire and lanyard-fired by the tank commander.

(6) *Limitations.* The following limitations affect employment techniques of the E8.

(a) *Range.* The short range of the E8 munition limits its application. In offensive action against an alert or mobile hostile force, it will, in many instances, be impossible for the friendly unit to emplace the E8 munition within range without detection and vulnerability to small arms fire. The best application of the munition is in situations in which the enemy moves within the range of pre-emplaced munitions.

(b) *Weight.* The weight of the munition (approximately 34 pounds) must be considered if an individual is to carry it for any distance in difficult terrain.

(c) *Time lapse from firing to effective CS*

TC 3-16

concentration. Depending upon the proficiency of the carrier and the location of the target sector, there will be a time lapse of 10 to 30 seconds during which the individual carrier emplaces and fires the E8 tactical CS munition. Preplacing the munition (on vehicles or structures) reduces employment time. In all cases of employment, there is a time lapse (approximately 30 seconds) from munition firing to agent buildup to an incapacitating level on the target.

(d) Size of force employing munition. Units smaller than platoon-size have insufficient personnel to provide high-volume fires and to launch maneuver elements if, simultaneously, they attempt to mask and employ CS. Therefore, a platoon is considered to be the minimum sized ground force that can employ the E8 munition effectively in counterguerrilla tactical operations against appropriate targets.

(e) Terrain. Because the E8 munition is a high-angle-fire weapon, it should not be used in dense jungles; however, it may be fired into wooded areas or fields from open locations, such as trails or paths, or from an open side into a jungle.

28. Employment of Canister Clusters, Tactical CS, E158R2, XM15, E159, and XM165. *a. General.* The E158R2, XM15, E159, and XM165 munitions may be delivered by fixed- or rotary-wing aircraft and may be used in offensive or defensive operations. The munitions complement and supplement other methods of CS or conventional HE fire. Maximum effectiveness is realized only under effective air-ground coordination. The uses for these munitions and the techniques for employing them are limited only by the imagination of the user. The three most important employment considerations are to insure that sufficient munitions are employed to completely cover the periphery of the target, to employ the munitions in sufficient depth so that target personnel are unable to leave the area, and to employ the munitions discriminately (timely exploitation) while maintaining a reserve to refresh target concentrations.

b. Employment Concepts. The E158R2, XM15, E159 and XM165 munitions are adaptable to many of the concepts of employment discussed in section II of this chapter. They should especially be considered for use in the following situations:

(1) *During offensive exploitation operations* when the objective is to gain physical control of the target area and its population with minimum casualties. This may be particularly effective during attack of a mixed population target when the village or hamlet must be seized and casualties must be minimized.

(2) *As preparatory fires* to flush the enemy in the open.

(3) *For reconnaissance by fire* in areas where enemy presence is suspected or confirmed but exact locations are not pinpointed.

(4) *In conjunction with airborne personnel detector (APD) operations,* the E158R2, XM15, E159, or XM165 can be dropped by trailing gunships over suspected enemy positions located by the APD to assist in visual sightings by causing enemy movement.

c. Techniques of Employment.

(1) *Delivery systems.* The E158R2, XM15, E159, and XM165 systems can be employed from a variety of aircraft (table 6) at speeds up to 350 knots. The E159 and XM165 are dropped electrically or mechanically from standard bomb shackles of fixed-wing aircraft, or rotary-wing aircraft equipped with the M16 armament subsystem, at speeds up to 350 knots. The E158R2 and XM15 are hand-dropped from fixed- or rotary-wing aircraft. For most missions, the utility helicopter is the aircraft of choice. A cargo helicopter may be desirable when a large payload must be delivered quickly into a small area. Observation and armed/attack helicopters can be used, but are normally limited in availability and payload capacity. The number of munitions which can be carried depends on the aircraft used. The E159 and XM165 depend on availability of bomb shackles. The number of E158R2 or XM15 munitions which can be carried depends on the amount of cargo space available in the aircraft. The recommended load for a UH-1 series aircraft is eight. Doorway positioning of four clusters per door allows ease of movement by the operator for predrop check. Approximately three personnel are required per helicopter in addition to the aircraft crew. Two

Table 6. Delivery Aircraft for E158R2, XM15, E159, and XM165 Munitions

Service	E159 XM165 Dropped from bomb racks	E158R2 XM15 Hand-dropped
Army..........	Light fixed-wing aircraft, armed/attack helicopters (with M16 armament subsystem).	Light fixed-wing aircraft, light observation helicopters, utility helicopters, or cargo helicopters.
Air Force....	Propeller-driven tactical aircraft.	—

men act as bombardiers, one on each side. The third man is located where he can assist in preparation of the clusters for airdrop by the bombardiers. A single sortie, or several sorties, can be used to deliver the munitions. Multiple sorties are more adaptable when replenishment of the agent cloud is necessary.

(2) *Bombing techniques.*

(a) *Accuracy of delivery.* This is dependent on pilot judgment and practice, using the bombing tables available. The E159 does not contain adjustable time fuze initiators and must be dropped in accordance with the bombing tables in TM 3-1325-230-12. The XM165 is activated by time fuze initiators and must be air-dropped in accordance with the provisional bombing table in the instruction booklet which accompanies the munition. The E158R2 and XM15 are activated by adjustable time fuze initiators. Setting instructions are found in TM 3-1325-232-12 for the E158R2, and in the accompanying instruction booklet for the XM15. No sighting device is available to assist the pilot in obtaining accuracy. Accuracy is dependent on pilot experience in dropping objects from his particular aircraft. When dropping the munitions from UH-1 series aircraft, the pilot flies at a selected absolute altitude and at a selected indicated airspeed, lining up the target between his feet as he views it through the chin bubble. He gives the signal for the bombardier to release the clusters. For the E158R2, recommended absolute altitude is 700 to 1,500 feet and recommended airspeed is 60 to 80 knots. Altitudes above 1,500 feet cause considerable bombing inaccuracies. Accuracy may be developed by practicing with a sandbag weighing about 50 pounds, to which a smoke grenade is attached

to mark the point of impact.

(b) *Method of attack.* The E158R2, XM15, E159, and XM165 munitions are designed for "on target" methods of attack. Off target and downwind effects are considered bonus effects.

(3) *Effects.*

(a) These munitions systems are effective for jungle operations. The submunition penetrates the heavy, dense canopy and functions on the forest floor. The dispersion pattern of these submunitions in temperate forests is roughly circular, 100 meters in diameter. The E158R2 cluster should provide an incapacitating (intolerable) concentration of CS over an area of approximately 6,500 square meters, and the E159 or XM165 should provide an incapacitating concentration over an area of approximately 9,000 square meters. With wind speeds less than 2 kilometers per hour and neutral stability conditions, which generally occur in jungle areas, the agent may persist in effective concentration from 10 minutes to several hours.

(b) The impact velocity hazard of the canisters and assembly parts will not result in lethal impact effects if a combat-equipped individual is struck by them. However, the impact velocity of unfunctioned modules or the strongback assembly of a mechanically released E159 or XM165 can result in lethal effects.

(c) The CS canister cluster systems are area weapons rather than point target munitions. When they are used in close support roles, unprotected friendly troops within several hundred meters may be affected, as well as the enemy. Friendly elements should be equipped with protective masks when CS canister clusters are used in close support roles. Using units, in some cases, have limited their use to not less than 300 meters from unprotected friendly troops.

(d) Malfunctioned canister clusters can provide a source of CS to the enemy. To reduce this possibility, an HC smoke grenade can be attached to each cluster, and the pin pulled as it leaves the aircraft. Thus if a malfunction occurs, the smoke marks the point of impact. Armed/attack helicopters can then fire into the area to detonate the cluster.

TC 3-16

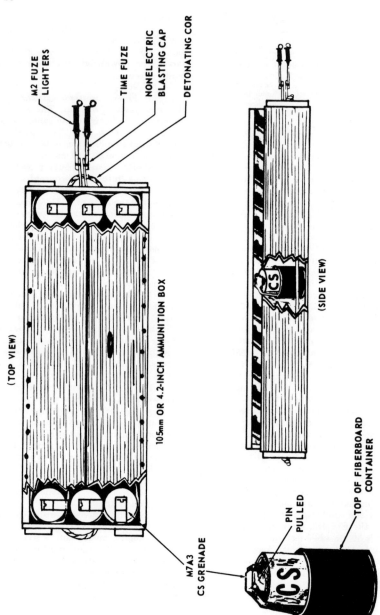

Figure 22. Field expedient CS grenade cluster.

(TOP VIEW)

M2 FUZE LIGHTERS

TIME FUZE

NONELECTRIC BLASTING CAP

DETONATING COR

105mm OR 4.2-INCH AMMUNITION BOX

(SIDE VIEW)

CS

M7A3 CS GRENADE

PIN PULLED

TOP OF FIBERBOARD CONTAINER

36

29. Field Expedient CS Grenade Clusters. When tactical CS clusters are not available or are in short supply, field expedient grenade clusters such as that shown in figure 22 are useful. (Figure 22 depicts only a suggested construction.) The systems are most adaptable to the use of M7 series CS grenades. The dispersion pattern is roughly circular, about 50 meters in diameter.

30. Employment of Fuze and Burster, Bomb, XM925 System. The XM925 system (fig 15) is specifically designed to be used as a bursting system for aerially delivered 55-gallon drums containing riot control agent CS1 or CS2. TM 3-1325-233-10, which accompanies the munition, provides a bombing table giving proper time settings for various drop altitudes. See also paragraph 31b(3) for use of the XM925 system with CS1 and CS2.

31. Employment of Riot Control Agents CS1 and CS2. *a. Employment Concepts.* Riot control agents CS1 and CS2 are capable of providing a degree of persistency not obtainable with burning-type CS munitions. The powder, when dispersed by various means, remains in the area and is effective until it is weathered away or physically removed by decontamination methods. Its effects can be reduced by covering it with earth, but disturbances such as walking, digging, or other activity can produce recurring effects, depending on depth of burial and amount of weathering which has taken place. Riot control agents CS1 and CS2 are suitable for purposes such as:

    (1) Discouraging entry into tunnels.

    (2) Aiding in perimeter defense.

    (3) Airdrop using XM925 system.

  b. Employment Techniques.

    (1) *Discouraging tunnel entry.*

      (a) CS1 or CS2 can be blown into tunnels by using the M106 Mity Mite as described in paragraph 26. One or more Mity Mites can be used, depending on the size of the tunnel system. The outlet hose must be long enough to force the agent well into the tunnel entrance.

      (b) Individual bags of CS1 or CS2 may be placed on detonating cord which is strung throughout the tunnel system. When detonated, the detonating cord ruptures the bags and disperses CS in the tunnel. The bags are best placed at key points in the tunnel, such as at intersections, in storage rooms, and in hiding places, as well as inside the entrances.

      (c) With either of the methods discussed in *(a)* and *(b)* above, the tunnel entrances should be closed by appropriately placed charges or other effective means to reduce the effects of weathering. Bear in mind that agent CS1 is not as resistant to weathering as CS2.

    (2) *Aiding in perimeter defense.* Agent CS1 or CS2 can be dispersed on foliage and along trails near a defense perimeter. Intruders may be caused to give away their location while attempting to escape the agent effects. In this role, the agent remains effective in most cases for periods of 1 to 3 days, depending on the weather.

    (3) *Airdrop using XM925 system.* Aerially delivered CS1 or CS2 can be used to restrict the use of routes of communication and supply to unprotected enemy troops. The 55-gallon shipping container in which the CS is packed is fitted with the XM925 burster system and loaded aboard an aircraft. A suggested loading plan for CH-47 aircraft is shown in figure 23. The CH-47 Chinook can be fitted with a rack and roller system to facilitate delivery of the drums (see fig 24 for construction details). Four racks are bolted end to end for use in a CH-47 aircraft as shown in figure 23.

    (4) *Airdrop using field expedient bursting systems.* If the XM925 system is not available, field expedient burster systems (fig 25) are often used. These systems can be of various constructions as shown in figure 25, but a few guidelines should be followed:

      (a) The system must be reliable. Malfunctions reduce the effectiveness of CS on the target and also provide the enemy with a source of riot control agent. Reliability can be improved by dual priming of the bursting charge.

      (b) If the drums are prepared for airdrop and stored for future use, waterproof components should be used in the bursting system, particularly if the containers are stored in the open.

      (c) The system should incorporate a fuzing system which can be initiated by a lanyard. The lanyard is attached to the aircraft and arms the bursting system not less

TC 3-16

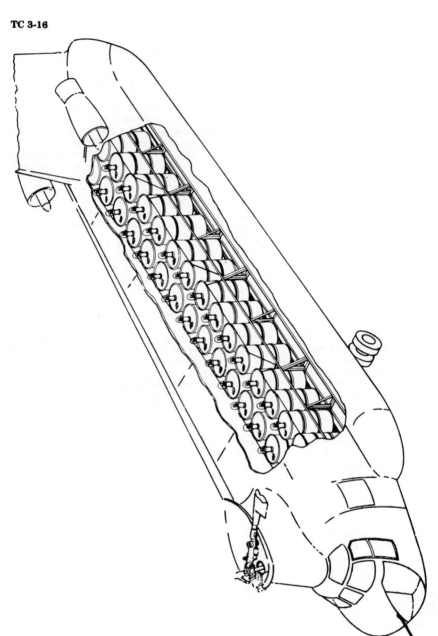

Figure 23. Loading plan for CH-47.

38

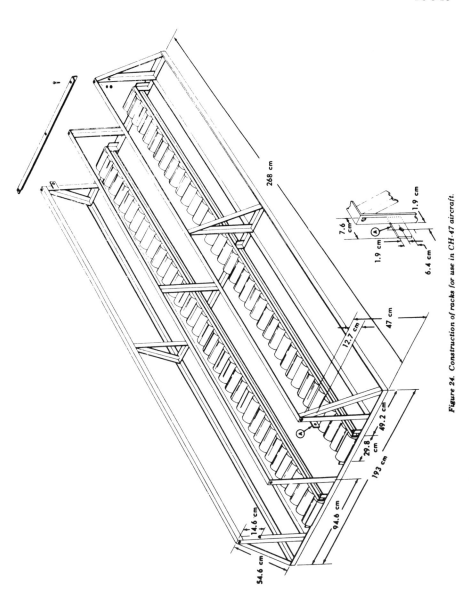

Figure 24. Construction of racks for use in CH-47 aircraft.

TC 3-16

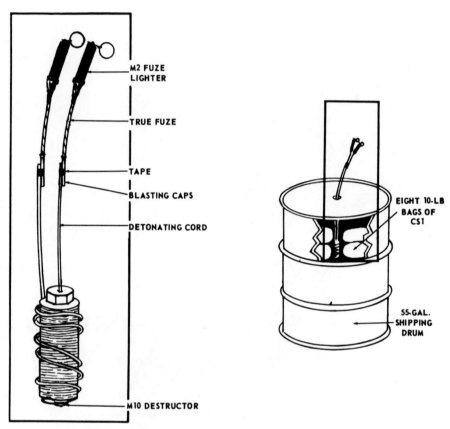

M2 FUZE
LIGHTER

TRUE FUZE

TAPE

BLASTING CAPS

DETONATING CORD

EIGHT 10-LB
BAGS OF
CS1

55-GAL.
SHIPPING
DRUM

M10 DESTRUCTOR

Figure 25. Field expedient bursting system for 55-gallon drums of CS1 or CS2.

than 20 feet from the aircraft after exiting.

(5) *Decontamination.* Equipment that becomes contaminated with powdered CS can be decontaminated by brushing off loose agent and scrubbing with soapy water. Personnel who become contaminated during filling or dispersing operations should decontaminate themselves by taking a cold shower followed by a hot soapy shower, if time and tactical situation permit. If showering facilities are not available, CS should be flushed off the skin with water.

(6) *Persistency of CS1 and CS2.* The length of time the micropulverized CS remains on the ground varies with weather, terrain, and the reason for employment. CS will remain in sufficient concentration to *restrict* movement of unmasked personnel only for a few days. An unmasked, determined enemy can cross a contaminated area if he is willing to endure the discomfort. The use of CS will restrict enemy *occupation* of terrain for a longer priod of time than it will restrict his ability to traverse it.

32. Employment of Grenade, Pocket, CS, XM58. The XM58 CS pocket grenade provides very limited CS capability because it burns only for a short time and forms a small-sized agent cloud. Its size and weight, however, allow many of these grenades to be carried for use at various times instead of one M7A3 CS grenade. Long-range reconnaissance patrols may find the XM58 useful for breaking enemy contact or for impeding pursuit by the enemy.

33. Employment of Dispenser, Aircraft, XM27 and CBU-30/A. *a. Employment Concepts.* The XM27 and CBU-30/A systems are adaptable to many of the concepts discussed in section II of this chapter, and are particularly suitable for the following uses:

(1) *Preparation of landing zones,* where CS may be used in coordination with HE fire to suppress possible enemy fire prior to the landing of a ground force.

(2) *Against mixed populations* where casualties must be minimized.

(3) *Close support of ground elements* in contact with dug-in enemy troops. Use of CS may cause enemy fire to cease or become relatively ineffective if enemy troops are unprotected.

b. Employment Techniques.

(1) The XM27 dispenser can be employed from low-performance aircraft, such as UH-1 series helicopters (fig 26) and fixed-wing aircraft fitted with standard suspension lugs and electrical connections. The XM27 system is

Figure 26. XM27 dispenser mounted on a helicopter, right rear view.

designed to be employed at altitudes up to 1,500 feet and at speeds up to 300 knots. The dispensers are employed in pairs — one mounted on each side of the aircraft.

(2) The CBU-30/A dispenser may be employed from either low- or high-performance tactical fighter aircraft, such as the A1E or F100 aircraft. It may be employed at altitudes from 100 to 600 feet and at speeds over 500 knots. At a 500-foot absolute altitude and at 450 knots, the dispenser should produce an agent cloud about 1,091 meters long and 61 meters wide.

(3) Both dispenser systems produce intense line sources of agent CS. Off-target methods of attack allow the wind to carry the CS across the target area. High wind speeds will require frequent replenishment of the agent cloud, depending on the duration of effectiveness required. When wind speeds are negligible, as in jungle terrain, on-target methods of attack may be appropriate. Area coverage may be provided by several sorties or by subsequent passes over the area.

34. Employment of Dispenser and Bagged Riot Control Agent, Helicopter, CS2, XM28. *a. Employment Concepts.* The XM28 dispenser system may be employed to contaminate selected areas of terrain with riot control agent CS2 to interdict and harass enemy supply and communication routes, base camps, assembly areas, and suspected routes of withdrawal.

b. Employment Techniques. The XM28 system is designed to be aerially delivered by UH-1 series helicopters.

(1) When employed along a linear route, the XM28 will cover an area approximately 210 meters long by 30 meters wide when released at a 1,500-foot absolute altitude and 70-knot airspeed.

(2) Accuracy of delivery is determined mainly by operator experience since no bombing sight is provided. The operator may be either the pilot or another crew member. Whether or not an extra passenger-operator can be carried will depend on the load-carrying ability of the particular aircraft, since the dispenser (loaded) weighs 1,025 pounds. Practice drops of smoke grenades can be used to estimate the release point required to place the bags on the target area. Release of one or two dispenser containers should provide minor corrections, if necessary. If more than one sortie is being flown, subsequent adjustment can be made based on results of the initial sortie.

(3) Meteorological conditions do not have the same overall effect on the XM28 system that they have on burning-type munition systems. CS2, once it is on the ground, is not likely to be blown by the wind to other areas. Some CS will become airborne when the bags burst, causing downwind drift to a distance determined by wind speed. Friendly troops downwind of the target area should be equipped with protective masks. Wind speed may also affect the point of impact of the bags after they are released from the dispenser. Corrections from the initial containers of a dispenser, or from the initial sortie, may be used to apply a subsequent correction.

Appendix **IV**

Excerpts from the Department of State's Transcript of Secretary Dean Rusk's News Conference on the Initiation of Gas Warfare in Vietnam

We are not embarking upon gas warfare in Vietnam.

There has been no policy decision to engage in gas warfare in Vietnam.

We are not talking about agents or weapons that are associated with gas warfare, the military arsenals of many countries. We are not talking about gas that is prohibited by the Geneva Convention of 1925, or any other understanding about the use of gas.

Now, we can understand the concern around the world and in this country about the specter of gas warfare. These memories go back to World War I, when tens of thousands were killed or maimed by what might be called "military gases."

This is not involved here.

We are talking about a gas which has been commonly adopted by the police forces of the world as riot control agents—gases that are available commercially and have been used on many occasions, some in this country and on many occasions in other countries.

Now, why is tear gas a part of the equipment of police forces?

It is because police forces would like to be able to use the minimum force that is required for the maintenance of law and order. It is a minimum instrument. And my information is that certain situations arose in South Vietnam where this problem presented itself.

On one occasion, for example, the Vietcong had seized a village, was holding the villagers in hostage and was firing through these villagers at mixed crowds outside the village.

The decision was made to employ tear gas to try to deal with that situation as a riot-control type of problem in order to avoid the problem of whether to

Reprinted from *The New York Times,* March 25, 1965.

259

use artillery or aerial bombs that would inflict great damage upon innocent people.

Now, it may be that there was a failure in full explanation, in briefing or reporting from Saigon on this matter. The initial reports tended to stimulate problems which were not present. For example, the use of the word "experimentation" suggested that something new and esoteric and weird might be involved here. This is not the case.

But we are reminded, when something of this sort comes up, of the nature of the war in South Vietnam.

It isn't a comfortable and easy war. It isn't a war that is going to be decided by troops on parade with blank cartridges.

It is a mean, dirty, struggle carried out without regard to ordinary norms of conduct by the Vietcong.

Those who are concerned about tear gas, I would hope, would be concerned about the fact that during 1964 over 400 civilian officials were killed and over a thousand were kidnapped in South Vietnam—village chiefs, school-teachers, public health officers.

Among other civilians, 1,300 were killed, over 8,000 were kidnapped. But entire villages have been kidnapped and burned to the ground, when families of those who were in the armed forces were kidnapped and held hostages.

There is nothing more urgent, from the point of view of the United States, than that peace be restored to that country as quickly as possible. And peace can be restored if Hanoi would stop infiltrating military trained personnel into South Vietnam, stop the sending of arms into South Vietnam and stop directing these operations aimed at taking over South Vietnam against the wishes of the people of that country.

Now, these are the essential policy aspects of the problem. We do not expect that gas will be used in ordinary military operations.

Q. Mr. Secretary, to clear up one point, in view of the propaganda furor that has been raised over the use of gas, is any consideration now being given to the thought of not using gas any longer?

A. Well, this is again a problem of general practice among nations. In situations of riot control or situations analagous to riot control, these police instruments undoubtedly will be used. They have been used in many countries and again will be used.

But I think that a good deal of the international reaction has been based upon the first impressions that somehow we were moving into gas warfare, that somehow weapons were being used contrary to the Geneva Convention. This is not the case.

And I would hope that second thoughts, of which we have already had some evidence, that second thoughts would realize that the issue that was involved here was the minimum force that was required under the circumstances where otherwise innocent people would be very severely punished in a circumstance over which they themselves had no control.

Q. Mr. Secretary, it is true, sir, that you referred to tear gas whereas many of the stories, of course, refer to nausea gas. Could you clarify the point on that?

A. The tear gas family, which is available through commercial firms to police forces in this and other countries, includes some gas that produces nausea. I understand that on one incident, in one incident out there that there was some admixture of these two types of gases.

Q. Mr. Secretary, can you clarify as to whether there was a policy decision in the United States over the use of these gases? And could you also say whether the forces in the field have authority to use these at any time of their choosing?

A. We have known, of course, that gases of this type are available to the South Vietnamese Government. They had other similar weapons left over from French days out there, I gather.

So that we knew those weapons were there. We know that they have been used in riot-control situations. We were not specifically asked in Washington on the day before any one of these incidents whether we approved the use of this particular weapon.

Now, here was a situation where they tried to meet the problem with a minimum of violence that would deal with the situation. . . .

Q. Mr. Secretary, you mentioned at the start the use of this in December and January, I believe. Were you saying by this it has not been used since January?

A. It has not been used, as with gases of any type, police or military. There are operational limitations upon their use. I mean—as a matter of fact, in the three incidents which have been reported, it wasn't very effective. When the wind blew it away it was dissipated. It didn't achieve the purpose.

Q. Mr. Secretary, as a result of the great public interest and excitement over this issue during the last two days, have any new directives or policy decisions been issued to the authorities, the American authorities, in Vietnam for dealing with this problem?

A. No new directives have been issued. The anticipation is, of course, that these weapons be used only in those situations involving riot control or situations analogous to riot control.

Appendix V

Editorial from *Chemical and Engineering News*, Newsletter of the American Chemical Society, Advocating Chemical Agents for Guerrilla Warfare

---

Chemical Agents for Guerrilla Warfare

REPORTS FROM VIET NAM SUGGEST
USES FOR MILD BUT EFFECTIVE MATERIALS

The abolition of war is one of man's most pressing goals, but where war exists reason and knowledge ought to be used in any way possible to reduce its awfulness.

The U.S. is involved with a war and is not likely to get disengaged easily or quickly. Excluding here any arguments over whether or not the U.S. should be active in the Vietnamese war, there is some worth in arguing for more forthright use of chemical and biological agents in guerrilla warfare now going on. Chemical warfare has been engulfed in a haze of horror through propaganda and ignorance; yet it could likely mitigate dreadful aspects of what we read about in news stories from Viet Nam. In the midst of some of those reported actions, any of a number of militarily effective chemical agents would have been less atrocious.

In the cave and tunnel warfare of the jungles there seem to be significant but little-tested possibilities for the use of well-tested riot-control agents (used on mobs in the U.S. and elsewhere) and other incapacitating agents. They produce temporarily disabling respiratory and eye irritation and nausea. These

Reprinted from *Chemical and Engineering News*, Vol. 43, August, 16, 1965, p. 7. Copyright 1965 by the American Chemical Society and reprinted by permission of the copyright owner. See also: "Let's get tear gas back into action" (editorial), *Journal of the Armed Forces*, October 9, 1965 and "The case for tear gas" (editorial), *Navy*, October, 1965. In a resolution adopted September 15, 1970 and directed to the Senate Foreign Relations Committee, the Board of Directors and Council of the American Chemical Society urged ratification of the 1925 Geneva Protocol. The resolution did not consider the status of herbicides and tear gas (*New York Times*, Sept. 16, 1970).

are sublethal, in the sense that they do not normally cause death or permanent damage, but it appears that they could produce needed results. To flush all parties out of protective hiding, temporarily unfit for combat yet able to return to their previous state of health, seems a desirable alternative to the indiscriminate slaughter that comes of throwing grenades into caves where there may be not only enemy guerrillas but also civilians including women and children. Defenseless civilians could be sorted out unharmed, and Viet Cong aims of setting up material for atrocity propaganda could thus be frustrated. The propaganda that could be made over use of sublethal chemicals would be without factual basis of disregard for human life.

When sublethal chemical agents were used a few months ago there was widespread unfavorable public reaction. The display of indignation appears to have caused the U.S. leaders to back down rather than to proceed with a more conclusive demonstration of the comparatively harmless efficacy of the unpleasant gas being used. A frequent argument against mild chemical agents —other than the reactions of blind horror in ignorance—is based on the fear that they will lead to use of increasingly vicious products. In the light of comparable possibilities with missiles and explosives, this seems, on the 20th anniversary of Hiroshima, a doubtful argument.

RICHARD L. KENYON

Appendix VI

Text of the November 25, 1969 Policy Statement of President Richard M. Nixon on Chemical & Biological Warfare

Soon after taking office I directed a comprehensive study of our chemical and biological defense policies and programs. There had been no such review in over 15 years. As a result, objectives and policies in this field were unclear and programs lacked definition and direction.

Under the auspices of the National Security Council, the Departments of State and Defense, the Arms Control and Disarmament Agency, the Office of Science and Technology, the intelligence community and other agencies worked closely together on this study for over six months.

These Government efforts were aided by contributions from the scientific community through the President's Scientific Advisory Committee.

This study has now been completed and its findings carefully considered by the National Security Council. I am now reporting the decisions taken on the basis of this review.

As to our chemical warfare program, the United States:

Reaffirms its oft-repeated renunciation of the first use of lethal chemical weapons.

Extends this renunciation to the first use of incapacitating chemicals.

Consonant with these decisions, the Administration will submit to the Senate, for its advice and consent to ratification, the Geneva Protocol of 1925, which prohibits the first use in war of "asphyxiating, poisonous of other gases and bacteriological methods of warfare."

The United States has long supported the principles and objectives of this protocol. We take this step toward formal ratification to reinforce our continuing advocacy of international constraints on the use of these weapons.

Biological weapons have massive, unpredictable and potentially uncon-

Reprinted from *The New York Times,* November 26, 1969.

trollable consequences. They may produce global epidemics and impair the health of future generations. I have therefore decided that:

The U.S. shall renounce the use of lethal biological agents and weapons, and all other methods of biological warfare.

The U.S. will confine its biological research to defensive measures such as immunization and safety measures.

The D.O.D. has been asked to make recommendations as to the disposal of existing stocks of bacteriological weapons.

In the spirit of these decisions, the United States associates itself with the principles and objectives of the United Kingdom Draft Convention, which would ban the use of biological methods of warfare. We will seek, however, to clarify specific provisions of the draft to assure that necessary safeguards are included.

Neither our association with the convention nor the limiting of our program to research will leave us vulnerable to surprise by an enemy who does not observe these rational restraints.

Our intelligence community will continue to watch carefully the nature and extent of the biological programs of others.

These important decisions, which have been announced today, have been taken as an initiative toward peace. Mankind already carries in its own hands too many of the seeds of its own destruction. By the examples we set today, we hope to contribute to an atmosphere of peace and understanding between nations and among men.

Appendix VII

United Nations General Assembly Resolution 2603 A(XXIV) of December 16, 1969 Extending the Geneva Protocol to Tear Gas and Herbicides

The General Assembly,

Considering that chemical and biological methods of warfare have always been viewed with horror and been justly condemned by the international community;

Considering that these methods of warfare are inherently reprehensible, because their effects are often uncontrollable and unpredictable and may be injurious without distinction to combatants and non-combatants and because any use would entail a serious risk of escalation;

Recalling that successive international instruments have prohibited or sought to prevent the use of such methods of warfare;

Noting specifically in this regard

that the majority of States then in existence adhered to the Geneva Protocol of 17 June 1925,

that since then further States have become Parties to that Protocol,

that yet other States have declared that they will abide by its principles and objectives.

that these principles and objectives have commanded broad respect in the practice of States, and that the General Assembly, without any dissenting vote, has called for the strict observance by all States of the principles and objectives of the Geneva Protocol;

Recognizing therefore, in the light of all the above circumstances, that the Geneva Protocol embodies the generally recognized rules of international law prohibiting the use in international armed conflicts of all biological and chemical methods of warfare, regardless of any technical developments;

Mindful of the Report of the Group of Experts, appointed by the Secretary-General of the United Nations under General Assembly resolution 2454 A (XXIII) of 20 December 1968, on chemical and bacteriological (biological) weapons and the effects of their possible use, (A/7575);

266

Considering that this Report and the Foreword to it by the Secretary-General adds further urgency for an affirmation of these rules and for dispelling, for the future, any uncertainty as to their scope and, by such affirmation, to assure the effectiveness of the rules and to enable all States to demonstrate their determination to comply with them;

Declares as contrary to the generally recognized rules of international law as embodied in the Geneva Protocol the use in international armed conflicts of any chemical agents of warfare: chemical substances, whether gaseous, liquid, or solid, which might be employed because of their direct toxic effects on man, animals or plants, and any biological agents of warfare: living organisms, whatever their nature, or infective material derived from them, which are intended to cause disease or death in man, animals or plants, and which depend for their effects on their ability to multiply in the person, animal or plant attacked.

In favour.—Afghanistan, Algeria, Argentina, Brazil, Bulgaria, Burma, Burundi, Byelorussian Soviet Socialist Republic, Cameroon, Central African Republic, Ceylon, Chad, Colombia, Congo (Brazzaville), Congo (Democratic Republic), Costa Rica, Cuba, Cyprus, Czechoslovakia, Dahomey, Dominican Republic, Ecuador, Equatorial Guinea, Ethiopia, Finland, Gabon, Ghana, Guatemala, Guinea, Guyana, Haiti, Honduras, Hungary, India, Indonesia, Iran, Iraq, Ireland, Ivory Coast, Jamaica, Jordan, Kenya, Kuwait, Lebanon, Lesotho, Libya, Maldives, Mali, Mauritania, Mauritius, Mexico, Mongolia, Morocco, Nepal, Niger, Nigeria, Pakistan, Panama, Peru, Poland, Romania, Rwanda, Saudi Arabia, Senegal, Somalia, Southern Yemen, Spain, Sudan, Sweden, Syria, Togo, Trinidad and Tobago, Uganda, Ukrainian Soviet Socialist Republic, Union of Soviet Socialist Republics, United Arab Republic, United Republic of Tanzania, Upper Volta, Yemen, and Yugoslavia.

Against.—Australia, Portugal, United States of America.

Abstaining.—Austria, Belgium, Bolivia, Canada, Chile, China, Denmark, El Salvador, France, Greece, Iceland, Israel, Italy, Japan, Laos, Liberia, Luxembourg, Madagascar, Malawi, Malaysia, Netherlands, New Zealand, Nicaragua, Norway, Paraguay, Philippines, Sierra Leone, Singapore, South Africa, Swaziland, Thailand, Tunisia, Turkey, United Kingdom of Great Britain and Northern Ireland, Uruguay, and Venezuela.

*Draft resolution A was adopted by 80 votes to 3, with 36 abstentions.**

---

* Subsequently the representative of Cambodia informed the Secretariat that had he been present he would have voted in favour.

Appendix VIII

United States Policy on the Use of Tear Gas in War: Excerpt from a Survey Prepared for the Foreign Affairs Division, Legislative Reference Service, Library of Congress, and Published in the May 17, 1970 Report of the Subcommittee on National Security Policy and Scientific Developments, House Committee on Foreign Affairs, on Chemical– Biological Warfare: U.S. Policies and International Effects

Trends in U.S. Policy and Practice : A Summary

From the foregoing review of international negotiations and the U.S. role therein, of U.S. policy statements, and of the record of actual U.S. practice, it is evident that U.S. policy and practice with regard to the use of tear gas have undergone a significant evolution in a number of ways. First, in regard to the Geneva Protocol, U.S. policy has evolved over the past 40-odd years in three distinct stages. The earliest period, which lasted more than three decades, encompasses U.S. failure to ratify the protocol followed by an attitude of almost complete indifference. During the second stage, it was stressed that the United States would support the "principles and objectives" of the protocol, with no indication of any move toward formal ratification.

The final stage in U.S. policy toward the protocol is marked by the President's recent announcement, in which the United States proclaims its intention to submit the treaty to the Senate for approval of ratification. This latter phase is qualified by the declared intention of the United States to reserve its ratification in such a way as to permit the use of lethal chemical weapons in retaliation only. The question of ratification of the protocol by the United States is expected to raise the issue whether the United States will consider the terms of the protocol binding in regard to the use of tear gases, herbicides, or other temporarily disabling chemical weapons.

Second, one can mark a certain development in the general policy and practice of the United States in regard to the use in war of tear and temporarily disabling gases. In the early history of chemical warfare, the record of actual U.S. practice shows that no tear gas was employed, and U.S. policy declarations on the particular issue of using tear gas were vague or nonexistent. This abstinence in practice and vagueness in declared policy have evolved to a stage in which not only are these types of chemical agents used in war, but also their use is officially justified in carefully delineated terms.

During this period of evolution, United States spokesmen have used language in which they have increasingly used the terms "gas warfare" and "chemical warfare" to be synonymous with the use of chemical weapons in war that have either lethal or prolonged incapacitating effects. The President's declaration of policy of November 1969 is applied to "incapacitating" in addition to "lethal" chemical agents. It excludes so-called "riot control" agents, a term which is applied to tear gases and other gases having only temporary or non-lasting effects and which are widely used for domestic law enforcement purposes. The definitions which the United States has applied to such terms as "chemical warfare," "incapacitating agents," and "riot control agents" are not necessarily accepted by other countries. In fact in some instances the terms used by the United States appear to be in conflict with those used by other governments and international organizations.

In the justifications which the United States has made for the military application of tear gas in Vietnam, there is evidence of an evolution in the purposes for which they are employed. Initially, Secretary Rusk and other spokesmen of the executive branch described the operations as "riot control types of problems," that is, situations in which innocent or friendly personnel were intermingled with the enemy. Secretary Rusk avowed that tear gas was not intended for "ordinary military operations."

The current stage is one in which, as Admiral Lemos described it, tear gas is employed as a "normal component of combat power." While the use of tear gas was previously justified on the grounds that it saved innocent lives, it is now conceded that it can contribute to enemy casualties. Although this application is denied as deliberate, such use is justified on the grounds that it enables American military operations to be carried out more efficiently; that is, with minimum losses for both American and allied forces. In other words, tear gas is now considered a normal combat weapon which is used primarily like other combat weapons to destroy the enemy or to save American lives. The "riot control" rationale has faded into the background, although the term is still used.

To some extent the course adopted by the American Executive in seeking ratification of the Geneva Protocol, accompanied by a new statement of policy regarding . . . chemical and biological weapons, is one of compromise. It is an attempt to reap the political advantages of the adoption of a new policy which includes ratification of the Geneva Protocol and at the same time retain for the United States a category of weapons which it considers to be militarily advantageous. In short, it appears that a trade-off is involved. Certain sacrifices are made in terms of both political and military benefit, but at the same time the policy seeks to maximize other political and military benefits. Whether this mix of political and military advantage and disadvantage will be accepted or changed in some way by the U.S. Senate, how the Senate will shape its final decision, and how the resulting product will be received by the other parties to the Geneva Protocol—all at this moment are questions still to be answered.

Charles R. Gellner
Leneice N. Wu

Appendix **IX**

Message of President Richard M. Nixon and Attached Report of Secretary of State William P. Rogers on Submission of the Geneva Protocol to the Senate, August 19, 1970

President Nixon's Message

With a view to receiving the advice and consent of the Senate to ratification, I transmit herewith the protocol for the prohibition of the use in war of asphyxiating, poisonous or other gases, and of bacteriological methods of warfare, signed at Geneva June 17, 1925. I transmit also the report by the Secretary of State which sets forth the understandings and the proposed reservation of the United States with respect to the protocol.

In submitting this protocol for approval, I consider it desirable and appropriate to make the following statements:

The United States has renounced the first use of incapacitating chemical weapons.

The United States has renounced any use of biological and toxin weapons.

Our biological and toxin programs will be confined to research for defensive purposes, strictly defined. By the example we set, we hope to contribute to an atmosphere of peace, understanding and confidence between nations and among men. The policy of the United States Government is to support international efforts to limit biological and toxin research programs to defensive purposes.

The United States will seek further agreement on effective arms-control measures in the field of biological and chemical warfare.

Today, there are 85 parties, including all other major powers, to this basic international agreement, which the United States proposed and signed in 1925. The United States always has observed the principles and objectives of this protocol.

Reprinted from *The New York Times,* August 20, 1970.

271

I consider it essential that the United States now become a party to this protocol, and urge the Senate to give its advice and consent to ratification with the reservation set forth in the Secretary's report.

Secretary Rogers' Report

I have the honor to submit to you, with the recommendation that it be transmitted to the Senate for advice and consent to ratification, the protocol for the prohibition of the use in war of asphyxiating, poisonous or other gases, and of bacteriological methods of warfare, signed at Geneva June 17, 1925. The United States proposed the protocol in 1925 and submitted it to the Senate in 1926. Although the Senate never voted on the question of ratifying the protocol, which was returned to the President in 1947, the United States has always supported its principles and objectives and has pledged itself internationally to observe these principles. At present there are 85 parties to the protocol, the most recent of which, Japan, became a party on May 21, 1970. The United States is the only major military power which is not a party.

Recent support of the principles and objectives of the protocol was given by the United States in 1966, 1968 and 1969 at the United Nations. The United States has voted in the General Assembly for resolutions which called for "strict observance by all states of the principles and objectives of the protocol" and invited "all states to accede to" the protocol.

The protocol prohibits the use in war of asphyxiating, poisonous or other gases, and of all analogous liquids, materials or devices and bacteriological methods of warfare. The protocol is the basic international agreement in this field, and its principles have been observed in almost all armed conflicts since 1925 by parties and non-parties alike.

While the protocol itself speaks in terms of flat prohibitions on the use of chemical and bacteriological agents in war, 39 states (including France, the Union of Soviet Socialist Republics, and the United Kingdom) have ratified or acceded with reservations. The reservations of most of the reserving states assert that the protocol is binding on them only with respect to other parties to the protocol and limit the prohibitions to no first use.

It is proposed that the Senate give its advice and consent to ratification subject to a reservation as follows:

"That the said protocol shall cease to be binding on the Government of the United States with respect to the use in war of asphyxiating, poisonous or other gases, and of all analogous liquids, materials or devices, in regard to an enemy state if such state or any of its allies fails to respect the prohibitions laid down in the protocol."

This reservation would permit the retaliatory use by the United States of chemical weapons and agents, but would not limit in any way the protocol's prohibition with respect to biological weapons.

Ratification of the protocol as qualified by the proposed reservation would put the United States in the following position:

Unlike France, the Union of Soviet Socialist Republics, the United Kingdom, and most other reserving states, the United States would not assert by reservation a limitation of its obligations under the protocol to the parties thereto.

Like France, the Union of Soviet Socialist Republics, the United Kingdom, and other reserving states, the United States would reserve the right to use the prohibited chemical agents in retaliation against any enemy state if such state or any of its allies fails to respect the prohibitions laid down in the protocol.

Unlike France, the Union of Soviet Socialist Republics, the United Kingdom, and all but one other reserving state, the United States would not assert by reservation the right to use bacteriological methods of warfare in retaliation.

The United States considers that the term "bacteriological methods of warfare" as used in the protocol encompasses all biological methods of warfare and the use in warfare of toxins however produced.

It is the United States' understanding of the protocol that it does not prohibit the use in war of riot-control agents and chemical herbicides. Smoke, flame, and napalm are also not covered by the protocol.

The subject of arms control as it relates of chemical warfare and biological warfare is of continuing and increasing importance in the international field. At the 1969 summer session of the Conference on the Committee on Disarmament, the United Kingdom presented a draft convention establishing a comprehensive ban on the development, production, stockpiling, and use of biological methods of warfare. In accordance with your announcement of November 25, 1969, that the United States would associate itself with the principles and objectives of that draft convention, we have taken an active role in its negotiation. Other proposals on the subject of chemical and biological warfare have also been introduced in the United Nations General Assembly and the Conference of the Committee on Disarmament by other governments.

Members of the Conference of the Committee on Disarmament have indicated the need for universal adherence to the protocol as a condition precedent to agreement on more comprehensive measures.

The United States should become a party to the protocol to strengthen the general prohibitions on the use of chemical warfare and biological warfare and to facilitate our participation in the formulation of new arms control provisions in this area.

Appendix **X**

Herbicides in Vietnam: AAAS Study Finds Widespread Devastation

The AAAS team that has been investigating the military use of herbicides in Vietnam believes the American spraying program has caused "extremely serious harm" to the land and to some of the peoples of the war-torn country. The team has also come up with evidence of rather shocking deficiencies in the precautions taken by U.S. military authorities to protect civilian populations from needless attack under the Army's crop destruction program.

These and other findings were made public last week when the AAAS Herbicide Assessment Commission, headed by Harvard biologist Matthew S. Meselson, presented a preliminary report to the AAAS annual convention in Chicago. Meselson was appointed by the AAAS board in December 1969 to prepare a detailed plan for determining the impact of herbicides on the land and people of Vietnam. Operating under a budget of $80,000, he and his colleagues reviewed the pertinent literature, consulted with numerous experts, and made a 5-week inspection tour of South Vietnam this past summer. Their formal reports to the AAAS annual convention were guardedly conservative in tone, but their findings added up to a charge that the military use of herbicides has been considerably more destructive than anyone had previously imagined. Among the assertions:

One-fifth to one-half of South Vietnam's mangrove forests, some 1400 square kilometers in all, have been "utterly destroyed," and even now, years after spraying, there is almost no sign of new life coming back.

Perhaps half the trees in the mature hardwood forests north and west of Saigon are dead, and a massive invasion of apparently worthless bamboo threatens to take over the area for decades to come.

The Army's crop destruction program, which seeks to deny food to enemy soldiers, has been a near total "failure," because nearly all the food destroyed would actually have been consumed by civilian populations, particularly the Montagnard tribes of the Central Highlands.

There is no definite evidence of adverse health effects, but further study is needed to determine the reason for a high rate of stillbirths in one heavily sprayed province and for an increase in two particular kinds of birth defects which were reported at a large Saigon hospital and which were coincident with large-scale spraying.

The AAAS team made no effort to assess the military usefulness of herbicides and, thus, came to no official conclusion as to whether the program should be continued. But individual members of the AAAS team clearly felt that the damaging consequences they had uncovered called the value of the program into question. Last November two members of the team sent to the highest U.S. officials in Saigon and Washington a letter challenging the basis of the crop destruction program. And at the AAAS convention, Arthur H. Westing, a botanist and commission member, urged that the herbicide program be phased out immediately because of the ecological and economic damage it is causing. Meselson, the head of the study, told *Science* in an interview that, while there is no proof that the herbicide program has caused substantial medical harm to the people in South Vietnam, there is no question that it has caused "extremely serious harm" both to the land and to the Montagnards who have been deprived of food.

Not everyone who heard the data presented by Meselson and his colleagues was prepared to draw the same conclusions from the evidence, however. Biologist Kenneth V. Thimann, herbicide specialist and AAAS board member, said that nothing he had heard had changed his opinion, expressed publicly in 1968, that the Army's use of chemicals "for defoliation of forest cover probably represents a military device for saving lives that has an unprecedented degree of harmlessness to the environment." And Brig, Gen. William W. Stone, Jr., who recently retired as director of chemical and nuclear operations for the U.S. Army, said that he personally still believes that "our use of herbicides had not created any permanent ecological damage of any significance in Vietnam."

WHITE HOUSE REACTS

Nevertheless, the study seems already to have achieved a political impact. On 26 December, the very day the AAAS convention opened, the White House, which had previously been informed that Meselson would denounce the crop destruction program, announced that authorities in Saigon were "initiating a program for an orderly, yet rapid, phase-out of the herbicide operations." The White House said that, during the phase-out period, the use of herbicides would be restricted to the perimeter of U.S. bases or to "remote, unpopulated areas." Further information supplied to reporters indicated that authorities planned to use up the existing stockpile of herbicides on these two restricted

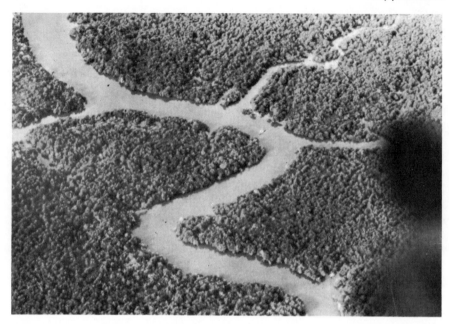

Figure A–X–1. Aerial photograph of a mangrove forest approximately 50 miles east of Saigon that has not been sprayed with herbicides. Mangrove forest areas occupy approximately 2800 square kilometers in South Vietnam. They are an important source of wood for fuel and charcoal, and provide food and nursery grounds for fish and crustaceans. Photo taken in South Vietnam by AAAS/HAC, August, 1970.

uses and then drop the spraying program entirely, probably   next spring.

Though the White House made no mention of the AAAS, several knowledgeable Washington operatives—including Herbert Scoville, Jr., former deputy director of the Central Intelligence Agency and a former arms control official, and Representative Richard D. McCarthy (D-N.Y.), a key activist on the herbicide question—suggested that the AAAS study had been a major factor spurring the White House announcement. But lingering doubts remained about the sincerity of White House intentions. Both Scoville and McCarthy argued that, if the herbicide program is bad enough to be dropped, it should be dropped immediately, instead of after the existing stockpiles are used up. And Scoville questioned whether restricting the herbicides to "remote, unpopulated areas" would really end the destruction of civilian crops since the Army has contended all along that it only destroys crops in "remote, unpopulated areas." In an apparent effort to spur still faster action, the AAAS council adopted a resolution commending the government for its announcement but urging that there be an "immediate discontinuation" of herbicide spraying in Indochina.

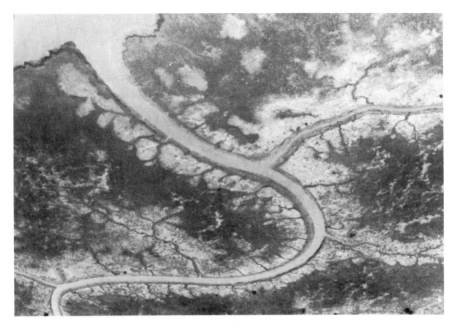

Figure A–X–2. Aerial photograph of a mangrove forest sprayed with herbicides sometime before 1968. A few surviving trees may be seen near the top of the picture. The large dark areas are deposits of humus laid down by the vegetation that once occupied the area. Photo taken in South Vietnam by AAAS/HAC, August, 1970.

LARGE SPRAYING PROGRAM

The herbicide program in Vietnam has been operating for almost a decade now, and it has developed into a sizable operation over the years. The program began in an experimental way in 1961, became operational in 1962, and then grew rapidly to a peak in 1967, before declining somewhat in 1968 and 1969. Over this 9-year period, about one-seventh of the land area of South Vietnam —equal in size to the state of Massachusetts—has been treated with herbicides, most of it sprayed from low-flying C-123 cargo aircraft that made more than 19,000 individual spray flights between 1962 and 1969. About 90 percent of the herbicide was dropped on forest land and about 10 percent on crop land.

The chief herbicide used against forests has been Agent Orange, a mixture of 2,4-D and 2,4,5-T, but the use of Orange was ordered stopped last April because of laboratory tests indicating that 2,4,5-T is teratogenic. The next most commonly used agent against forests has been Agent White, a mixture of 2,4-D and picloram, while the herbicide most commonly used against crops has been

Agent Blue, a solution of cacodylic acid, which is an arsenic compound. The AAAS board expressed particular concern in 1968 about the use of arsenicals on crops.

Several brief studies of the herbicide program have been made in recent years, some by the military or by the U.S. mission in Vietnam, and others by the forestry branch of the U.S. Agency for International Development, by an expert from the Agricultural Research Service, and by such nongovernment scientists as Gordon H. Orians and Egbert W. Pfeiffer, who visited Vietnam for 2 weeks in 1969. But Meselson and his colleagues seem unquestionably to have conducted the most extensive independent analysis yet made. Their study was intended to come up with some preliminary findings and to result in the preparation of a detailed plan for determining more accurately the short- and long-term consequences of the use of herbicides on the land and people of South Vietnam. Meselson and his colleagues reviewed the pertinent litera-ture, solicited information and advice from more than 200 experts in this country and elsewhere, held a 5-day conference with 23 experts at Woods Hole, Massachusetts, and then conducted on-site inspections in South Vietnam for a 5- to 6-week period in August and September. Those making the trip to Viet-nam included Meselson, a professor of biology at Harvard who has long played a major role in assessing the impact of chemical and biological warfare; Westing, a forestry specialist and chairman of biology at Windham College, Vermont, who had previously studied the impact of defoliation in Cambodia; John D. Constable, professor of surgery at Harvard Medical School, who had made two previous health surveys in Vietnam; and Robert E. Cook, Jr., a graduate student in ecology at Yale. The team's observations extended into several areas not previously studied and, in some instances, differed significantly with prior reports. The key findings were as follows:

Crop Destruction

The AAAS team conducted what appears to be the first independent, nongovernmental study of the crop destruction program and concluded that it has been a failure because of poor intelligence.

Some 2000 square kilometers of land have been sprayed to destroy crops. At the request of the AAAS team, specialists on Vietnam in the Agriculture Department estimated that this entailed destruction of enough food to feed 600,000 persons for a year. The anticrop spraying has been largely confined to the food-scarce Central Highlands, which has a population of only about 1 million, mostly Montagnards, a tribal people disliked by the lowland Viet-namese who are active in helping to plan the spraying missions.

The AAAS team was twice flown over an area in Quang Ngai province where crop destruction operations had been conducted only a few days before. They were accompanied by the chemical operations officer who had planned the mission, and they were assured by him that the fields destroyed were growing food for the enemy. The reasons given for this assessment were that the target area was virtually uninhabited (supposedly less than eight persons per square kilometer); the area under cultivation had expanded strikingly in recent years; the cultivated area was much larger than needed to support the supposedly small indigenous population; and there were numerous terraced rice fields—which indicated the presence of the enemy, since the native Montagnards supposedly don't practice terracing.

All four contentions, the AAAS team later concluded, were in error. Though the officer said there were no dwellings below and none could be seen from the air, aerial photographs taken by the AAAS team and a map issued in 1965 both indicate more than 900 dwellings in the area—suggesting a population of more than 5000, or about 180 persons per square kilometer. Moreover, the boundaries of cultivated fields seen in the photographs compared closely with the boundaries on the 1965 map, indicating no major crop expansion over the past 5 years. The AAAS team concluded that the land under cultivation was just about enough to support the people apparently living there. They also learned from other military sources that the Montagnards in question have grown rice on terraced fields for a long time. Summing up, the AAAS team said: "Our observations lead us to believe that precautions to avoid destroying the crops of indigenous civilian populations have been a failure and that nearly all the food destroyed would actually have been consumed by such populations."

In the give-and-take of debate at the AAAS convention, it was also learned that several classified studies conducted under military auspices since 1967 have come to a similar conclusion. The one major classified study which came to an opposite conclusion and asserted that the program was hurting the enemy but was having little impact on civilian food supplies was marred, according to Meselson, by a simple error in arithmetic, which threw its results off by a factor of 100.

The AAAS team also concluded that continuation of the crop destruction program would have "devasting consequences for the Montagnard peoples," not only by depriving them of food, but also because of their animist beliefs. Interviews with Montagnard refugees whose lands had recently been sprayed revealed that they regard the spray operations as the manifestation of an evil spirit. Some abandon their land in the belief that it has fallen under a curse; others destroy their water buffalo, the chief source of wealth, believing them to be infected or feeling a sacrifice is needed.

Brig. Gen. Stone, in attempting to rebut the AAAS team's findings, claimed that the Army's "best intelligence" indicated that the houses seen in Meselson's photographs were unoccupied. He said the fields were most likely cultivated by persons under Vietcong control, since the fields had been sprayed at least once annually for several years and the native Montagnards, fearing evil spirits, would presumably have moved off the land if they had been cultivating it. Stone also said the fields are obviously important to the Vietcong because the enemy has allowed its hidden antiaircraft guns to give away their positions in order to fire at the spray planes. However, Meselson cited evidence indicating that the dwellings were indeed occupied. The matter was left unresolved.

TOTAL ANNIHILATION

Mangrove Forests

The AAAS team seems to have been the only group in recent years to conduct an investigation on the ground in the devastated mangrove forests along the coast southeast of Saigon. For some unknown reason, virtually the entire plant community is killed outright by a single spraying, leaving a "weird and desolate" scene of "total annihilation." Furthermore, again for an unknown reason, herbicide attack appears to prevent the reestablishment of any new plant community. The AAAS team that went in on the ground found that what had previously appeared, from the air, to be regeneration was actually a few surviving plants from the previous stand. The only sign of new life was a few worthless ferns and shrubs that had invaded the area—the fern being considered a serious pest elsewhere in Southeast Asia. This lack of new plant life was deemed one of the most significant findings of the AAAS study by Fred H. Tschirley of the Agricultural Research Service, who had conducted an earlier study of defoliation in Vietnam. "It was surprising to me—I didn't expect it," Tschirley told *Science*. "I had assumed regeneration would be taking place." Westing said the sprayed areas seem impervious to recolonization by plants for at least 6 years, and estimated it will take decades to restore them. The AAAS team also detected the beginnings of erosion along the waterways of the mangrove area, but it is too early to tell how serious this problem will become.

Whether the destruction of the mangrove forests matters in a significant way has not been completely established. Westing acknowledged that the mangrove areas are "inhospitable, seemingly impenetrable, and outwardly unimportant." However, they do serve as home for tens of thousands of people; they serve as a source of firewood and charcoal; they provide cover and food for various birds, fish, and crustaceans; and they continually build up and stabilize the shoreline. The AAAS team recommended that an attempt be made to estimate what impact the loss of mangroves would have on the fishing industry, before deciding how much of the former mangrove area should be replanted to tidal forests and how much devoted to other purposes.

Tropical Hardwood Forests

The AAAS team was unable to get into these forests on the ground, as some previous investigators had, but the team inspected the forests from the air in a wide arc north and west of Saigon, from Cambodia to the sea. The team's most important finding was an "eyeball" observation that more than half of the forest in three provinces over which they flew was "very severely damaged," with the trees dead and bamboo or tenacious grasses spreading over the ground

Figure A–X–3. Ground view of mangrove forest area approximately 50 miles east of Saigon that had been treated with herbicides sometime before 1968. Photo taken in South Vietnam by AAAS/HAC, August, 1970.

in their place. The extent of destruction and of bamboo invasion far exceeded previous estimates that perhaps 10 percent of the trees were being killed in areas sprayed once. The team learned from Vietnamese forestry experts that the invading bamboo species is almost certainly worthless and expensive to eradicate.

Westing, the team's forestry expert, was unable to make the aerial inspection trip. He therefore put together his report, using previously published data that is more conservative than the "eyeball" impressions of his colleagues. Westing concluded that about 35 percent of South Vietnam's 14 million acres of dense forest have been sprayed one or more times and that, as a result, 6.2 billion board feet of merchantable timber have thus far been killed by herbicides. This is the equivalent of South Vietnam's entire domestic timber needs, based on current demand, for the next 31 years. Though Westing acknowledged that not all of this timber would actually have been cut and used, he said that most of the destruction has occurred on prime timber lands close to the Saigon market. The lost timber represents about $500 million in stumpage taxes that would otherwise have accrued to the South Vietnamese government. Westing suggested that it may take decades for some of the damaged forest lands to recover, partly because the invading bamboo and grasses may be difficult to eradicate, and partly because nutrient minerals previously tied up in forest vegetation may have been released and then leached out of sprayed forests by the heavy tropical rains.

Health Effects

Constable, the team's medical expert, found "no definite evidence" of adverse health effects caused by the spraying, but the AAAS team did find deficiencies in a recent study by the U.S. Army and the South Vietnamese Ministry of Health, which tended to exonerate herbicides from causing birth defects. The Army study, based on South Vietnamese hospital records for the past 10 years, reported a downward trend in stillbirths, placental tumors, and malformations, coincident with the peaking of herbicide spraying. However, the AAAS team subtracted the Saigon data from the overall figures and discovered that the Army study actually shows an increase in all three defects for the rest of the country, where the population has been more heavily exposed to herbicides. Still, the AAAS team acknowledged that it would be "totally incorrect" to consider this proof of the effect of herbicides, since many other factors could account for the trends.

Army Study Incomplete

The team evaluated in detail the birth records in Tay Ninh, a very heavily defoliated province, and discovered that the records used for the Army study were grossly deficient. Whereas the Army group had reported 208 stillbirths in the province in 1968 and 1969, the AAAS team, using more complete records, noted 351. The AAAS team found that Tay Ninh City Provincial Hospital showed a stillbirth rate of 64 per thousand, higher than any provincial hospital reported by the Army study and well above the country-wide average of 31.2 per thousand. The AAAS team also discovered that Saigon Childrens Hospital had experienced a "disproportionate rise" in two birth defects—pure cleft palate and spina bifida—in 1967 and 1968. But the team stressed that neither effect could safely be attributed to the impact of herbicides, and it called for further studies to elucidate the cause of the unexplained trends. From interviews with key Vietnamese health officials, the team concluded that there have been no strikingly new deformities (along the lines of the thalidomide baby tragedy) observed in heavily sprayed areas of Vietnam.

Food Chain Contamination

The AAAS team seems to have been the first group of any kind—military or civilian—to collect samples of shrimp, fish, human milk, human hair, human fat, and other materials so that they could be analyzed for the presence of herbicides or their breakdown products. The team is still struggling to develop analytical techniques capable of detecting extremely low concentrations of dioxin, an impurity in Agent Orange that is so toxic that tiny amounts of it concentrated in the food chain could cause health problems. The AAAS team concluded it is "not impossible" that significant amounts of dioxin are entering the Vietnamese diet but Tschirley, of the Agricultural Research Service, reported new experimental results which indicated that dioxin is photodegraded quickly, does not accumulate in the soil, and is picked up only in small amounts by plants. Tschirley said he doesn't believe there is a "very real possibility" that enough dioxin is being concentrated to cause damage, but he acknowledged that further tests must be made to determine whether dioxin accumulates in the fatty tissues.

Military Considerations

The AAAS did not consider the military utility of herbicides, but Gen. Stone, in rebutting the AAAS findings, argued that "the benefits have outweighed the adverse effects" and that "herbicides have been militarily useful and have saved many lives." Stone said that defoliation of thick undergrowth has reduced the incidence of ambushes and surprise attacks and has enabled the Army to keep tabs on enemy movements. He also said that crop destruction has "hurt the enemy's ability to live off the people and the land." This is indicated, he said, by the fact that enemy defectors have complained of food shortages. Meselson countered by arguing that Stone's evidence was essentially anecdotal and that it was not clear just what factors had brought about a decrease in ambushes in a given area. Meselson said he had heard a spectrum of opinion from military officers—ranging from pro to con—concerning the military usefulness of the herbicide program.

Psychological

The AAAS team seems to have been the first nongovernmental group to conduct long interviews with farmers and village officials concerning the herbicide program. Samuel Popkin, assistant professor of government at Harvard, who directed the interviewing, said the spraying has had "a very negative psychological impact" on the farmers. He said many peasants feel the United States is deliberately trying to destroy the rural economy to make the farmers dependent on the United States. Later, Gen. Stone told *Science* he found psychological results reported by Popkin—and by the rest of the AAAS team on the basis of interviews with Montagnards—to be the most dramatic finding of the AAAS study. "They're saying the herbicides have had a negative impact that detracts from our overall program rather than adds to it," he said. "I had frankly never realized there was this psychological impact."

The AAAS team was unable to obtain from the military precise data as to where herbicides had been sprayed, when, and how much herbicide of what type had been used. Meselson said the fact that this information was considered classified greatly hampered his group's efforts to determine, for example, precisely which populations should be examined for possible health effects and precisely which areas of the forest should be examined for possible evidence of laterization (no evidence of laterization was seen by the group). However, the Pentagon has said that it will declassify the information if a full-scale study of the herbicide program is made—as is currently planned—by the National Academy of Sciences (see *Science,* 2 October 1969, p. 43).

The AAAS team's final report will be presented after analysis of the samples is completed, perhaps in a few months time. Meselson stresses that the focus for future action should be shifted away from assessing harm and toward finding ways to repair the damage done, preferably by drawing on the talents of Vietnamese scientists. He suggested that one possible way to get rid of the invading bamboo, for example, might be to plant long north-south lines of shaded trees in the devastated forests in hopes that the shadows would force the bamboo to recede on both sides. If these and other techniques can be found to restore the devastated areas, then the AAAS study might well merit the praise lavished on it by one member of the convention audience who stood up and exclaimed that the herbicide study is "the greatest service the AAAS has ever performed for the human race."

PHILIP M. BOFFEY

Appendix **XI**

Resolution on Chemical Defoliants Adopted by the Council of the AAAS at Its 1970 Annual Meeting in Chicago

RESOLUTION INTRODUCED BY E. W. PFEIFFER
ON BEHALF OF THE SCIENTISTS' COMMITTEE
ON CHEMICAL—BIOLOGICAL WARFARE*

WHEREAS the AAAS has previously expressed its concern to the United States Government regarding the health-related and ecological consequences of the use of defoliants in Vietnam, and

WHEREAS there is now strong evidence that antiplant chemicals used for defoliation and crop destruction in Vietnam have seriously damaged the ecology of that country and may be a serious threat to the health of the Vietnamese people and particularly to the health, livelihood, and social structure of Vietnam's hill tribes (Montagnards), and

WHEREAS the Department of Defense last April 15, 1970, issued an order to end the spraying of agent Orange because of its proven toxicity to experimental animals, and

WHEREAS the consequences of the use of agents Blue and White, still authorized and in massive use in Indochina, are not known,

THEREFORE BE IT RESOLVED: That the Council of the AAAS commends the United States Government for its intention announced on December 26, 1970, rapidly to phase out the use of all herbicides in Vietnam and recommends their immediate discontmuation in Indochina.

* Amended slightly from the original version.

285

Glossary

Abbreviations, Definitions, Scientific Names, and Terminology

AAAS. American Association for the Advancement of Science.

Abscission Layer. A layer of large, thin-walled cells located near the base of the petiole of a leaf; the zone of separation when a leaf falls.

Aedes aegypti. A mosquito, carrier of the causative agent of dengue fever and impulse transmission.

Acrostichum aureum. A tropical salt water fern often found in mangrove forests; family Polypodiaceae.

Adamsite. Trivial name for agents DM, diphenylaminochloroarsine, a war gas and riot control agent with powerful emetic properties.

Aedes aegypti. A mosquito, carrier of the causative agent of dengue fever and other diseases.

AID. U.S. Agency for International Development.

Alkylating Agent. In biological systems, a chemical reagent that binds through a carbon atom to the oxygen, nitrogen, or sulfur atom of a natural substance.

Alluvial. Referring to soil deposits made by flowing water.

Alveoli. Air cells of a lung.

Aminophylline. A smooth-muscle relaxant, myocardial stimulant, and diuretic.

Annamite. Relating to the Annamese, a Mongolian people inhabiting Annam, the central portion of South Vietnam.

Anoxic. Referring to deficient aeration of the blood.

Arboreal. Pertaining to trees.

ARPA. Advanced Research Projects Agency, a division of the U.S. Department of Defense.

Arsenical. A compound or preparation containing arsenic.

Atelectasis. Pulmonary collapse.

Atrial Fibrilation. Fibrilation of the auricular portion of the heart.

Atropine. A pharmaceutical with anticholinergic properties.

Auxin. A plant hormone that may be natural (e.g. indoleacetic acid) or synthetic (e.g., phenoxyacetic acid derivatives).

286

Avicennia. A genus of tropical trees and shrubs found in mangrove forests; family Rhizophoraceae, class Dicotyledoneae.

Bamboos. *Bambusa* spp., *Dendrocalamus* spp., *Thyrsostachys* spp., ect.; family Gramineae, class Monocotyledoneae.

Bambusa. A genus of bamboos; family Gramineae, class Monocotyledoneae.

Bambusa arundinacea. A species of bamboo; family Gramineae, class Monocotyledoneae.

Bananas. *Musa sapientum,* etc.; family Musaceae, class Monocotyledoneae.

Banteng. A wild ox found in Indochina and the Malayan peninsula, *Bos banteng* (= *B. sondaicus*); family Bovidae.

Beans. *Phaseolus vulgaris, Glycine max, Vigna sesquipedalis,* etc.; family Leguminosae, class Dicotyledoneae.

Beriberi. A vitamin B_1 deficiency disease, at one time common in the Orient.

Betel-nut Palm. *Areca catechu;* family Palmae, class Monocotyledoneae.

Biota. Living organisms—plant, animal and microbial.

"Blue." A 6:1 mixture of sodium dimethyl arsenate and dimethyl arsenic (or cacodylic) acid in water. A very similar mixture is known domestically as "Phytar-560." Active ingredients are present at 3.1 pounds per gallon. The agent is applied undiluted at 3 gallons per acre (and thus at 9.3 pounds of active ingredients per acre). Its major use is to destroy rice and other food crops.

Botulinal Toxin. The toxin(s), protein in nature, elaborated by the bacterium *Clostridium botulinum.*

Bovines. Family Bovidae.

Bronchia. The bronchial tubes.

Bronchiectasis. Dilation of one or more of the large bronchial tubes.

Bronchitis. Inflammation of the bronchial tubes.

Bronchospasm. Spasm of the bronchia.

Bruguiera. A genus of trees found in mangrove forests; family Rhizophoraceae, class Dicotyledoneae.

Bullae. Large blisters or vesicles.

BZ. Department of Defense designation for a hallucinogenic chemical warfare agent, a phenylglycollate ester of 3-quinuclidinol.

Cacodylic Acid. Dimethylarsenic acid, a chemical containing 54.29 percent arsenic, the active ingredient of herbicidal preparation "blue."

Carnivorous. Meat-eating.

Cauliflower. *Brassica oleracea botrytis;* family Cruciferae, class Dicotyledoneae.

CBD. Commerce Business Daily.

CBW. Chemical and Biological Warfare.

Cheyne Stokes. An abnormal form of breathing observed especially in coma and in cardiac and cerebral affections.

Chicken. *Gallus gallus*; family Phasianidae.

Chloracne. A dermatitis reported in factory workers preparing industrial chemicals such as the chlorinated phenoxyacetic acid herbicides, particularly 2,4,5-trichlorophenoxy acetic acid.

Chloroacetophenone. Agent CN, a chemical substance used for many decades as a tear gas.

o-**Chlorobenzalmalononitrile** (*o*-**Chlorobenzylidenemalononitrile**). Agent CS, a substance now widely used as a riot control chemical and as an antipersonnel gas in Indochina; sometimes referred to as "super tear gas."

Cholinesterase. The enzyme that cleaves acetylcholine into choline and acetic acid.

Ciliary. Pertaining to the cilia, as of the eye.

Cirrhosis. A degenerative disease of the liver.

Clostridium botulinum. A bacterial species that elaborates the botulinal toxin(s).

CN. Department of Defense designation for chloroacetophenone, a riot-control tear gas.

Coconut Palm. *Cocus nucifera*; family Palmae, class Monocotyledoneae.

Coffee. *Coffee arabica*; family Rabiaceae, class Dicotyledoneae.

Comatose. The condition of dying persona; profoundly lethargic.

Conifers. Cone-bearing trees or shrubs; the major order of gymnosperms.

Corn. *Zea mays*; family Gramineae, class Monocotyledoneae.

Cow (zebu). *Bos indicus;* family Bovidae.

Crustacean. A large class of shellfish including lobster, shrimp and crabs.

CS. Department of Defense designation for *o*-Chlorobenzalmalononitrile, a riot control and antipersonnel gas, referred to as "super tear gas."

CS1. Micropulverized CS.

CS2. Micropulverized, silicone-treated (weatherproofed) CS.

Curare. A plant alkaloid highly poisonous to the motor nerves.

Custard Apple. *Annona diversifolia (?), A. reticulata (?) ;* family Annonaceae, class Dicotyledoneae.

CW. Chemical Warfare.

Cycad. A plant of the family *Cyadaceae,* such as the sago palm, a gymnosperm.

2,4-D. 2,4-Dichlorophenoxyacetic acid, an herbicide for dicotyledenous plants; a component of agents "orange" and "white."

DBH. Diameter at breast height ($4\frac{1}{2}$ feet, a dimension used by foresters for measuring the size of trees.

DDT. Dichlorodiphenyltrichloroethane, a persistent insecticide.

Deciduous. Referring to the seasonal shedding of plant leaves.

Deers. *Cervus aristotelis*, etc.; family Cervidae.

Dendrocalamus strictus. A species of large bamboo; family Gramineae, class Monocotyledoneae.

Dengue. A hemorrhagic fever with a high incidence of mortality in children.

Dessicating. Dehydrating or causing the loss of water.

2,4-Dichlorophenoxyacetic Acid. See 2,4-D.

Dicotyledenous. Referring to broad-leafed plants in the class Dicotyledoneae, a major group of angiosperms or flowering plants (cf. Monocotyledonous).

Dioxin. An extremely toxic impurity found in commercial preparations of chlorinated phenoxyacetic acid herbicides, particularly in 2,4,5-trichloro-phenoxy acetic acid.

Diphenylaminochlorarsine. See adamsite.

Dipterocarps. Family Dipterocarpaceae; class Dicotyledoneae; a major component of the upland forests of Indochina.

DM. Department of Defense designation for adamsite.

DOD. U.S. Department of Defense (formerly the War Department).

Douc langur. A leaf eating monkey of Indochina remarkable for its variegated colors; *Pygathrix nemaeus;* family Cercopithecidae.

DRV. Democratic Republic of [North] Vietnam.

Ducks. Family Anatidae.

Durian. *Durio zebethinus;* family Bombacaceae, class Dicotyledoneae.

Dyspnea. Difficult or painful breathing.

Edaphic. Pertaining to the soil.

Edema. Accumulation of fluid in cells, tissues or cavities; swelling.

Elephant. *Elephas maximus,* family Elephantidae.

Emphysema. A disease of the lungs characterized by the presence of distended air cells.

Erythema. Redness of the skin associated with congestion of capillaries.

Fauna. Aggregate of the animal species of a region.

Fibrosis. Increase in fibrous tissue.

Flaccid Paralysis. Non-rigid paralysis.

Ganglionic. Pertaining to ganglia, a mass of nerve tissues and cells.

Gaur. *Bos gaurus;* family Bovidae; a species of wild cattle found in Indochina.

GB. Department of Defense designation for isopropyl methylphosphono-fluoridate or sarin, a nerve gas.

GCD. Government Contracts Directory.

Gibbon, Indochinese. A species of ape found in Indochina; *Hylobates* sp., family Pongidae.

Ginger. *Zingiber officinale;* family Zingiberaceae, class Dicotyledoneae.

Grasses. Family Gramineae, class Monocotyledoneae.

Guava. *Psidium guajava;* family Myrtaceae, class Dicotyledoneae.

GVN. Government of [South] Vietnam.

HD. Department of Defense designation for mustard gas, a chemical warfare agent causing vesication.

Herbicide. A chemical agent causing the death of plants.

Heterotrophic. Saprophytic and other species deriving nourishment without photosynthesis.

Hevea brasiliensis. Rubber tree; family Euphorbiaceae, class Dicotyledoneae.

Humus. Decaying vegetable or animal matter in or on the soil; the organic fraction of the soil

Hygrometry. Pertaining to the determination of humidity.

Imperata. A genus of tropical grasses; e.g., *Imperata cylindrica* (Cogon or elephant grass); family Gramineae, class Monocotyledoneae.

Incontinence. Involuntary discharges from body openings.

Inspiratory Stridor. A harsh, whistling sound on inhalation.

IRCC. Institut des Recherches sur le Caoutchouc au Cambodge.

Jackfruit. *Artocarpus heterophyllus* (= *A. integra*); family Moraceae; class Dicotyledoneae.

Jute. *Corchorus* spp; family Tiliaceae, class Dicotyledoneae.

Kapok. *Ceiba pentandra*; family Bombacaceae, class Dicotyledoneae.

Kouprey. *Bos sauveli*; family Bovidae; a nearly extinct bovine species found only in Indochina.

Kwashiorkor. A disease caused by a deficiency of protein in the diet.

Lachrymator. An agent that provokes the flow of tears.

Lagerstroemia. A genus of trees common in the upland forests of Indochina; family Lythraceae, class Dicotyledoneae.

Laterite. A rock-like soil formation containing a high quantity of the oxides or iron and aluminum; indurated soil.

Latex. A milky white fluid obtained from *Hevea brasiliensis* from which rubber is manufactured.

Leguminosae. A large family of dicotyledenous plants distinguished by characteristic fruit in the form of a pod.

Longan. *Nephelium longana*; family Sapindaceae, class Dicotyledoneae.

Lumbor. *Shorea hypochra*; family Dipterocarpaceae, class Dicotyledoneae.

Lychee. *Litchi chinensis*; family Sapindaceae; class Dicotyledoneae.

Lycopodium. A large genus of erect or creeping plants with evergreen leaves, the club mosses.

Macaca. A genus of ape; family Cercopithecidae.

Mace[R]. Patented name of a liquid riot-control spray used in police work, the active ingredient of which is agent CN.

Mango. *Mangifera indica*; family Anacardiaceae; class Dicotyledoneae.

Mangrove. A tropical tidal swamp shrub or tree of the family Rhizophoraceae. (class Dicotyledoneae) or containing a high proportion of these plants.

Manioc. *Manihot esculenta.* (*M. utilissima*); family Euphorbiaceae, class Dicotyledoneae.

Marasmus. Emaciation.

Mity Mite. An Army-adapted version of an agricultural blower used for dispersing antipersonnel gas or for pumping it underground.

Mollusk. A large phylum of the animal kingdom that, with the exception of the crustaceans, contains most of the shellfish.

Monkeys. Family Cercopithecidae; a group of old-world species common in Indochina.

Monocotyledenous. Referring to narrow-leafed plants in the class Monocotyledoneae, a major group of angiosperms or flowering plants. (cf. Dicotyledenous.)

Monsoon. Season of alternating winds in Southern Asia and the Indian Ocean, accompanied by heavy rains.

Montane. Pertaining to the flora and fauna of mountainous regions.

Moribund. The condition of a dying person.

MRI. Midwest Research Institute, a private consulting firm in Kansas City, Missouri.

Muntjac. *Muntiacus muntjak*; family Cervidae.

Mustard Gas. See HD.

Napalm. A generic term used for jellied gasoline used as an incendiary munition.

Napalm B. A type of napalm consisting of 50 per cent polystyrene, 25 per cent benzene and 25 per cent gasoline.

NARMIC. National Action / Research on the Military Industrial Complex, a Committee of the American Friends Service Committee in Philadelphia.

NAS. U.S. National Academy of Sciences.

Necrosis. The death or decay of a piece of tissue.

Nerve Gas. An agent that interferes with nerve transmission through poisoning of the enzyme acetylcholinesterase.

Nipa Palm. *Nipa fruticans*; family Palmae, class Monocotyledoneae; a species of salt water palm often found in association with mangroves.

NLF. National Liberation Front of [South] Vietnam.

NSIA. National Security Industrial Association.

Operation Ranch Hand. Department of Defense designation for the defoliation project in Vietnam.

Orange. *Citrus sinensis*; family Rutaceae, class Dicotyledoneae.

"Orange." A 1:1 mixture of the normal-butyl esters of 2,4-dichlorophenoxy-acetic acid and 2,4,5-trichlorophenoxyacetic acid. A mixture very similar to this is known domestically as "Brush Killer." Active ingredients are present at 4.1 and 4.4 pounds per gallon, respectively. The agent is applied undiluted at 3 gallons per acre (and thus at 25.5 pounds of active ingredients per acre). Its major use is to defoliate forest vegetation.

Palms. Family Palmae, class Monocotyledoneae.

Papaya. *Carica papaya*; family Caricaceae; class Dicotyledoneae.

Papilloma. A tumor of the skin or mucous membrane.

Parasitosis. The condition of being infested with parasites.

Pasteurella pestis. A bacterium, the causative agent of bubonic plague.

Petiole. The narrow stalk of a plant leaf which connects it to the stem.

Phdiec. *Anisoptera cochinchinensis*; family Dipterocarpaceae, class Dicotyledoneae.

Phenobarbital. A pharmaceutical with sedative, hypnotic, and anticonvulsant properties.

Phloem. Plant tissue found in the stems and consisting of sieve tubes and associated structures; functions in the translocation of synthesized foods.

Photophobia. An abnormal sensitivity to light.

Phytotoxic. Toxic to plants.

Picloram. The trivial name for a herbicidal preparation, 4-amino-3,5,6-trichloro picolinic acid; equivalent to Dow Co. Tordon; a component of agent "white."

Pig (domestic). *Sus scrofa*; family Suidae.

Pigs (wild). *Sus* spp., family Suidae.

Pineapple. *Ananas comosus*; family Bromeliaceae, class Monocotyledoneae.

Pinnate. A form of plant leaves in which the veins are arranged along the midrib like the barbs on a feather.

Pneumonia. Inflammation of the lungs.

Plasmodium falciparum. A malaria parasite.

Pleural Cavities. Sides of the thorax.

Podzol. A relatively infertile grey colored soil type typically found in northern forests.

Pruritic Eruption. Intense itching of the skin with eruption.

Pseudomonas pseudomallei. A bacterium, the causative agent of Melioidosis.

Pterocarpus. A genus of hardwood trees growing in the tropics; family Leguminosae, class Dicotyledoneae.

Purpura. Purple skin patches caused by subcutaneous escape of blood.

Quartzite. Rock containing quartz.

Rai. A slash-and-burn shifting agricultural practice common in the tropics.

Rales. A rattling or bubbling sound from the lungs during breathing.

Rambutan. *Nephelium lappaceum*; family Sapindaceae, class Dicotyledoneae; a fruit tree found in Southeast Asia and Malaya.

Rhizome. A root-like underground plant stem.

Rhizophora. A genus of tropical trees and shrubs found in mangrove forests; family Rhizophoraceae, class Dicotyledoneae.

Rhonchii. A whistling or snoring sound accompanying breathing in persons with partially obstructed air channels.

Rice. *Oryza sativa*; family Gramineae, class Monocotyledoneae.

Rubber (tree). *Hevea brasiliensis*; family Euphorbiaceae, class Dicotyledoneae.

Rung Sat. Delta of the Nha River; a large swampy region of mangrove forest extending southeast from Saigon to the China Sea.

Salmonids. Belonging to the salmon family of fishes.

Sapodilla. *Achras zapota*; family Sapotaceae, class Dicotyledoneae, a large tropical fruit tree.

Sarin. See GB.

Savanna. A tropical grassland, often with scattered trees.

Schizostachyum sollingeri. A species of small bamboo; family Gramineae, class Monocotyledoneae.

Sensorium. Portion of the cerebral cortex.

Serosanguinous. Referring to bloody serum.

Sheep. *Ovis aries*; family Bovidae.

Somatic. Pertaining to the body as a whole.

Sternutator. A sneeze-producing agent.

Sugar Palm. *Borassus flabellifera*; family Palmae, class Monocotyledoneae.

2,4,5-T. 2,4,5-Trichlorophenoxyacetic acid, an herbicide for woody, dicotyledenous plants; a component of agent "orange."

Taro. *Colocasia esculenta*; family Araceae, class Dicotyledoneae.

Teak. *Tectona grandis*; family Verbenaceae, class Dicotyledoneae.

Typhoon. A violent wind that occurs from time to time, typically in the China Sea.

Tomato. *Lycopersicon esculentum*; family Solanaceae, class Dicotyledoneae.

Tonic and Clonic Convulsions. Continuous and irregular muscle contractions.

Tordon 101. Trade name for a Dow Chemical Company herbicide containing picloram and 2,4-D; equivalent to agent "white".

Trachea. Windpipe.

Translocation. Movement of fluids and solution within plant tissue (either xylem or phloem).

2,4,5-Trichlorophenoxyacetic Acid. See 2,4,5-T.

Ungulate. Pertaining to group of mammals distinguished by the presence of the hoof.

Vagal. Pertaining to the pneumogastric nerve.

Valium. A pharmaceutical with tranquilizing and skeletal muscle relaxant properties.

Vascular. Pertaining to vessels for the conveyance of fluid.

Vasodilator. A substance causing dilation of the blood vessels.

Vasopressor. A substance causing constriction of the blood vessels.

Venosection. Opening of a vein by incision.

Vesicant. A blistering agent.

Viverrid. A weasel-like rodent predator; family Viverridae.

VX. Department of Defense designation for a nerve gas the precise structure of which is secret.

Water Buffalo. *Bubalus bubalis*; family Bovidae.

"White." A 4:1 mixture of the tri-iso-propanolamine salts of 2,4-dichloro-phenoxyacetic acid and 4-amino-3,5,6-trichloropicolinic acid in water (picloram). This mixture is known domestically as "Tordon-101." Active ingredients are present at 2.0 and 0.54 pounds per gallon, respectively. The agent is applied undiluted at 3 gallons per acre (and thus at 7.6 pounds of active ingredients per acre). Its major use is the same as for agent "orange."

Xenopsylla cheopis. A flea, carrier of the bacterium *Pasteurella pestis*, the causative agent of bubonic plague.

Bibliography

ALEXANDER, A. S. *et al. Control of Chemical and Biological Weapons.* New York: Carnegie Endowment for International Peace, 1971.

CLARKE, ROBIN. *Silent Weapons.* New York: David McKay, 1968.

COOKSON, JOHN and JUDITH NOTTINGHAM. *Survey of Chemical and Biological Warfare.* London: Sheed and Ward, 1969.

DUFFETT, JOHN, ed. *Against the Crime of Silence; Proceedings of the Russell International War Crimes Tribunal.* Flanders, New Jersey: O'Hare Books, 1968. (Also available as a Simon & Schuster–Clarion PB.)

Field Manuel 3–10, "Employment of Chemical and Biological Agents." U. S. Dept. of the Army, Navy and Air Force, March, 1966.

Field Manuel 3–8, "Chemical Reference Handbook." U.S. Department of the Army, January, 1967.

HERSH, SEYMOUR M. *Chemical and Biological Warfare: America's Hidden Arsenal.* Indianapolis: Bobbs-Merrill, 1968.

HOUSE, W. B. *et al. Assessment of Ecological Effects of Extensive or Repeated Use of —Herbicides.* Kansas City, Mo.: Midwest Research Institute, 1967.

HUDDLE, F. P. Technology Assessment of the Vietnam Defoliant Matter; a case History. U. S. House of Representatives, Committee on Science and Astronautics, 1969.

HUTCHISON, F. W. "Defoliation of *Hevea brasiliensis* by aerial spraying." *J. Rubber Research Institute of Malaya* 15 (1958): 241–74.

LANGER, ELINOR. "Chemical and Biological Warfare: I, The Research Program and II, The Weapons and the Policies." *Science,* 155 (1967): 174–79, 299–303.

MCCARTHY, RICHARD D. *The Ultimate Folly: War by Pestilence, Asphyxiation and Defoliation.* New York: Knopf (hb) and Vintage (pb), 1969.

MESELSON, M. "Chemical and Biological Weapons." *Scientific American* 222 (5) (1970): 15–25.

MOORMANN, F. R. *The Soils of the Republic of Vietnam.* Saigon: Ministry of Agriculture of the Republic of Vietnam, 1961.

MRAK, E. M. *et al. Report of the Secretary's Commission on Pesticides and Their Relationship to Environmental Health.* U. S. Department of Health, Education and Welfare, 1969.

ORIANS, G. H. and E. W. PFEIFFER "Ecological Effects of the War in Vietnam." *Science,* 168 (1970): 544–54.

ROSE, S., ed. *CBW, Chemical and Biological Warfare.* London: Harrap, 1968; Boston: Beacon, 1969.

294

Scientist and Citizen, Special Issue on Chemical and Biological Warfare, *9* (No. 7), August–September, 1967.

Stanford Biology Study Group. *The Destruction of Indochina: A Legacy of our Presence.* Stanford, Cal.: Stanford Biology Study Group, 1970.

THANT, U. Chemical and bacteriological (biological) weapons and the effects of their possible use. New York, United Nations (1969).

Training Circular 3–16, "Employment of Riot Control Agents, Flame, Smoke, Antiplant agents, and Personnel Detectors in Counterguerrilla Operations." U.S. Department of the Army, April 1969.

TSCHIRLEY, F. H. "Defoliation in Vietnam." *Science,* 163 (1969): 779–86.

WHITESIDE, THOMAS. *Defoliation.* New York: Ballantine Books, 1970.

WILLIAMS, L. *Forests of South East Asia, Puerto Rico and Texas.* U. S. Agricultural Research Service, Publication No. CR-12–67, 1967.

World Health Organization. *Health Aspects of Chemical and Biological Weapons.* Geneva: W.H.O., 1970.

ZABLOCKI, CLEMENT J., ed. "Chemical-Biological Warfare: U. S. Policies and International Effects." Part I, Hearings, Part II, Report. U. S. House of Representatives, Committee on Foreign Affairs, 1970.

Index

Abrams, Creighton, 17
abscission layer, 120
acetylcholine esterase, 55
Achrosticum aureum, 154
Adams, Roger, 21
adamsite, 21, 43
adrenals, hemorrhage, 55
Advanced Research Project Agency (ARPA),
    121, 123, 125
Aedes aegypti, 13
aerosol, 24, 26
Against the Crime of Silence (Duffett, John,
    editor), 29
Agency for International Development (AID),
    108, 130, 141, 155, 164
Agricultural Research Service, 123
Agriculture, Department of, 121, 123, 141, 170,
    172, 173
Air America, 128
Airborne Brigade, 173rd, 33, 34, 37
Air Force (U.S.), 28
Air War—Vietnam (Harvey, Frank), 16
alkylating agents, 52
aluminum naphthenate, 14
aluminum palmitate, 14
alveoli, 25
American Anthropological Association, 181
American Association for the Advancement of
    Science (AAAS), 87, 117, 131, 132,
    135-137, 139-143, 181, 182
    Council, 133
    Pacific Division, 118, 132
American Association of Scientific Workers,
    181
American Bar Association, 70
American Chemical Society, 33, 68, 69
American Friends Service Committee, 87
animal life, destruction in Cambodia, 196
An Lao, 44
Annamite, 148
An Nighiep, 161
An Nhon, 44
Ansul Chemical Company, 128
anthropologists, 11
antibiotics, 11
antiguerrilla, 15
antipersonnel agent, 18
antipersonnel gas, 1
Applegate, Rex, 21, 26, 47, 65
Arms Control and Disarmament Agency, 39,
    75, 88
arms limitation, 4
Army Biological Center, 122, 123
Army Field Manual, 20, 21, 23, 28, 74
Army Munitions Command, 50
arrythmias, 107
arsenic, 21
arsenicals, 139, 140
arsenic trichloride, 21
asphyxiation, 17
atelectasis, 112
Atlantic City, 52
atrial fibrillation, 107, 111
auxin, 120, 121
Avicennia, 147

B-52s, 45
bacillus, plague, 12
bacterial genetics, 11
Ba Den, 38
Ba Gia, 107
Baker, B. R., 59

Ba Leong An, 38
Ba Long An, 37, 44
Baily, Ned, 173
Baltimore, David, 88
bamboo, 146-151, 156, 185, 196
Bambusa arundinacea, 148, 150
banana, 131, 160, 184, 185, 194, 195, 199
Bangkok, 13
Bang Son, 37
Bantong, 163, 164, 197
Barcelona, 17
Barrientos, René, 15
Bau Trai, 37
Beal, Thaddeus, 86
beans, 194
Behar, Abraham, 31
Belfast, 23
Ben Cat, 37
Ben Cui, 159
Ben Mei Thuot, 163
Bennett, Ivan, 81
Ben Tre, 31, 35
benzalkonium chloride, 25
benzene, 15
Benzer, S., 56
benzilates, 10
beri-beri, 105
Berkeley, chemical warfare in, 58
Bertrand Russell War Crimes Tribunal, 30, 38
betel nut palm, 185, 194
Bien Hoa (Bienhoa), 124, 151, 152, 157, 160,
    166, 169
Binh Dinh, 31, 35-37, 44
Binh Duong, 157
Binh Long, 155, 157
Binh Nam, 38, 44
Binhtri, 169
biological agents, 11
Bionetics Research Laboratory, 172
birth defects:
    from 2,4,5-T, 171
    in Cambodia, 197
bis(2-chloroethyl)sulfide, 10
Black Panther Party, 58
Black Paper, 35
blistering agent, 10
Blue, Agent, 119, 120, 166, 167, 184
boar, 162
Bogside, 24
Bohlen, Charles E., 140
Bolivia, 15
Bolivian Army, 15
Bong-san, 18
Bongson, 34
Bonnet, Henri, 174, 175
Borah, William, 73
Bosquet, Charles, 197
bovine species, 163
Bowtell, Robert, 37, 43
bromacil, 151
bronchi, 113
bronchiectasis, 105, 113
bronchioles, 113
bronchitis, 105, 111
bronchoconstriction, 55
Brown, F. J., 47
Bruguiera, 147
bubonic plague, 11
Buckley, Kevin, 18
Buddhist, 30
bullae, 24
Bunker, Ellsworth, 141

297

Bunn, George, 57, 67
Buoy San, 197
burns, 17
Business and Defense Services
    Administration, 128
British Government, development of CS
    gas by, 22
British Society for Social Responsibility
    in Science, 63
Byerly, T. C., 173
BZ(Agent), 18

C-123 aircraft, 125, 126, 169
cacodylic acid, 119, 120, 123, 128, 166, 169
Ca Mau, 31, 35, 125, 147
Cambodia:
    defoliation of, 177
    nerve gas use in, 17
    reference to in Training Circular 3-16, 25
Cambodian Rubber Research Institute, 187
Camp Drum, 122
Canadian news report on 1969 Hanoi
    epidemic, 13
Can Tho, 31, 35, 161
Canton, 11
carbon monoxide, 43, 46
carcinogenesis, 52
Carroll, Lewis, 184
Carson, Rachel, 85
cauliflower, 194
CBW (Chemical-Biological Warfare), 25, 38,
    47, 85
Central Office for South Vietnam (COSVN),
    187
Centre International pour le Denunciation
    des Crimes de Guerre, 178
Centre National de la Recherche Scientifique,
    178
Chai Kim Chun, 190
Chalang (Chalong), 189
chemical agents, 8
Chemical Defense Experimental
    Establishment, 22
chemical industry, 6
Chemical Mace®, 20
Chemical Operations Division, U.S. Army,
    159, 160
Chemical Reference Handbook, 26
Chemical Warfare Service, 19
Chesneaux, Jean, 69
Chessin, Meyer, 88
Cheyne Stokes respirations, 109
Children's Medical Relief International, 197
China, chemical warfare in, 6
Chinese gas masks, 47
Chipeang, 189, 197
Chipes, 189
chloracne, 173
chlorine, 19, 45
chloroacetophenone (Agent CN), 19, 53
o-chlorobenzalmalononitrile (Agent CS),
    22, 34, 43
chlorobenzene, 24
cholera, 105
cholinesterase, 107
Cho Lon, 37
Chu Chi, 37
Chup, 187, 188
Chu Pong, 37
CIA (Central Intelligence Agency), 108,
    128, 187
cirrhosis, 105
Citizen's Commission of Inquiry on U.S. War
    Crimes in Vietnam, 17

Clergy and Laymen Concerned about Vietnam,
    11
Clostridium botulinum, 77
cluster bomb units, 152
CN, Agent (chloroacetophenone):
    first use in Vietnam, 32, 33
    formula, 19
    implicated in death of Robert Bowtell, 37
    in Chemical Mace®, 20, 54
    in grenades, 27
    properties, 18
    toxicity, 53
Co Cong, 31
coconut:
    oil, 14
    trees, 131, 185, 194
coffee, 185, 187, 195, 199
Colombo Plan, 104
Commission on the Consequences of
    Environmental Alteration, 133
Committee for the Denunciation of War
    Crimes, 43
Committee on Chemical and Biological
    Warfare, 181
Committee on Science and Astronautics, 131
Commoner, Barry, 136
Compagnie du Cambodge, 188
COMUSMACV, 29, 41
Condon, E. U., 88
conjunctive, 55
contact dermatitis, 53
convulsions, 110, 111
corn, 187, 194
Corson, Roger, 22
crabs, 163
crimes:
    against humanity, 69, 70
    against peace, 70
    of war, 70
crocodile, 165
crop destruction in Vietnam, 129, 159, 160
crop losses, claims for in Cambodia, 129
crop losses, claims in Vietnam, 162
CS, Agent (o-chlorobenzalmalononitrile):
    and Geneva Protocol, 72
    decontamination, 25
    development of, by Britain, 22, 38
    evolution of use in Vietnam, 33
    first use in Vietnam, 33
    forms, 24
    formula, 22
    grenades, 27
    legal status, 67
    lethality, 66
    lull in use of in Vietnam, 32
    procurement costs, 34
    procurement volume, 40
    properties, 22, 23
    reaction to use of in Vietnam, 31
    suppliers, 47, 48, 49
    toxicity, 55
    use:
        in Berkeley, 58
        consequences of, 42
        in Londonderry, 63
        by "other side," 47
Cucinell, S., 56
custard apple, 163, 184, 194
cuttle fish, 163
cyanide, 23, 55
cycads, 147
cysteine, 56

2,4-D (2,4-dichlorophenoxyacetic acid),
    119, 121-125, 128, 158, 165, 166,
    169, 170-173, 183, 184, 195, 196
Daddario, Emilio Q., 131
Dalton, Hugh, 64
D'Amato, A. A., 73
D'Arcourt, Pierre, 18
darter, 164
Darwin, Charles, 121
Dau Mot, 37
Davidon, William C., 88
DDT, 171
Deconinck, Gilbert, 188
deer, 162, 197
    brow-antler, 163
Defense, Department of:
    assessment of herbicide damage, 141
    assurances on herbicides, 142, 143, 167
    conspiracy to justify herbicides, 138
    contractors, 50
    cooperation in Pfeiffer-Orians mission, 151
    data on defoliation area, 120
    Directorate for News Service, 42
    exchange with R. D. McCarthy, 76
    experiments of Picloram durability, 121
    on gas shipment to Alaska, 86
    on Geneva Protocol, 91, 92
    Midwest Research Institute Report,
        sponsorship, 125
    motivation for gas use in Vietnam, 34, 66
    named in Pfeiffer resolution to AAAS Pacific
        Division, 118, 132
    on napalm usage, 15
    non-participation in funding AAAS herbicide
        commission, 117
    regarding Geneva Protocol at United
        Nations, 174
    restriction of 2,4,5-T, 172
    search for information on herbicides, 123
    statement of Admiral William E. Lemos, 29
    statement on use of tear gas in Mekong
        Delta, 39
    statement regarding overseas storage of
        biological agents, 13
Defense Industry Bulletin, 47
Defense Research and Engineering, 135
Defense Science Board, 134
defoliants, procurement of, 128
defoliation:
    acres, 120
    of Cambodia, 177
    leaflets, 160
    mission, 151, 152
Delacour, Jean, 162
DeLeon, Benjamin, 89
Dellenback, John, 82, 90
Delta, Mekong, 15
Democratic Republic of Vietnam (DRV),
    30, 31, 38, 47
Dendrocalamus strictus, 150
dengue, 13
dermatitis, 53
Detrick, Fort, 51, 85, 122, 123
Diamond Alkali Chemical Company, 128
diarrhea, 24
dicambra, 151
dihydrolipoic acid, 56
Dinh Tuong, 197
dioxin, 173, 197
diphenylamine, 21
diphenylaminochlorarsine (Agent DM), 21
diphenylchlorarsine, 21
dipterocarp, 146, 147, 150
Dipterocarpus, 148

disease, 105
Dispatch News Service, 17
dispenser, Mity Mite, 26
diuron, 151
DM, Agent (diphenylaminochlorarsine):
    formula, 21
    grenades, 27
    non-use in Vietnam, 41
    properties, 55
    use in Vietnam, 30, 32
DNA, 52
doctors, 103
dogs, 170
Don That Trinh, 168
Dooley, Thomas, 103
"Doomsday Bug," 11
Douc Langur, 162
Douglas fir, 148
Dow Chemical Company, 128, 173
Drum, Camp, 122
Dubos, René, 133, 136
DuBridge, Lee A., 79, 168, 172
Duc Hiep, 37
Dugway Proving Ground, 85
durian, 194, 199
dysentery, 105
dyspneic, 110

ecological effects of defoliation, 150
ecology of Vietnam, 144
eczematous reaction to CS, 57
edema, pulmonary, 25, 55, 109, 110, 113
Edgewood Arsenal, 19, 21, 23, 45, 54, 55
Edsall, John T., 77, 87, 88, 89, 118
Education-Action Conference on U.S. Crimes
    of War in Vietnam, 72
egrets, 152, 164
Egypt, 15
Eisenhower, Dwight D., 78
Elder, Joseph, 200
elephants, 162, 197
Elliott, Osborne, 18
emphysema, 105, 112, 113
encephalitis, 105
enucleations (eye), 65
Environmental Defense Fund, 86
epidemics, 13
epiphytes, 196
erythema, 24
Ethiopia, 72
ethylbromacetate, 43, 44
ethyl-S-dimethylaminoethylmethylphosphono-
    thiolate, 9
"exotic" diseases, 13
eye injuries, 53

F-100 aircraft, 152
Faas, Horst, 30
Fairhurst, Isabelle, 16
Falk, Richard A., 72
Fascell, Dante, 90
fauna, South Vietnam, 160, 162
Federal Hazardous Substances Labelling Act,
    65
Federal Laboratories. 36
Federal Outlays, 51
Federated American Societies for
    Experimental Biology, 52, 87, 88
Federation of American Scientists, 47, 118, 181
fever, 13
fibrosis, 113
Field Hospital, First Army, Republic of
    Vietnam, 103
Field Manual, 70

Fieser, Louis, 14
Finch, Robert, 56
First Cavalry (Airmobile) Division, 18
fish, 187
Fisher Chemical Company, 42
Fishhook area, Cambodia, 177, 180
flamethrowers, 15
Flamm, Barry R., 155, 156
fleas, 12
floods, 13
Food and Drug Administration, 65, 121
food chains, 164
food crops, destruction in Cambodia, 194
food staples, 125
Foreign Military Sales Act, 86
Forest Commission, 170
Forest Fire Laboratory, 123
Forest Service, 123, 167
forest succession, 149
Forrestal, James, 50
Fort Detrick, 51, 85, 122, 123
Foster, John S., 135, 137, 140, 168, 174
Fraser, Donald, 41, 45, 81, 90
French Army, 19
fruit trees, 129
Fryklund, R., 113
Fulbright, J. William, 32, 76, 80, 90

Galston, A. W., 88, 89, 120, 121, 160, 172
Gamma Chemical Company, 42
Gases, asphyxiating, 5
gasoline, 15, 16
gas poisoning, 107
gastroenteritis, 13
gaur, 163, 164, 197
GB, Agent, 73, 80, 85
gels, 14
General Ordnance Equipment Corporation,
    20, 61
Geneva Protocol, 32, 33, 47, 64, 68, 70, 74,
    81, 85, 88, 91, 92, 174
Genocide Convention, 69, 70
Gia Dinh, 37, 157
Gia Rai, 37
ginger, 194
Globe, Arizona, 170
glutathione, 56
goblet cells, 55
Go Cong, 35
Goddard, David R., 136
Goldblatt, J., 79
Goodell, Charles, 90
Grand Jury, Alameda County, California, 63
Green Berets, 17
grenades, 27
Grotius, 67
guava, 184, 185, 194
Guillain, Robert, 16
Gulf of Siam, 16

Hague Conventions, 67
Hague Gas Declaration, 5
Hai Mua, 169
Hai Nuc, 169
Hallstrom, Asa, 3
hallucinogenic agents, 18
hamlets, 16
Hanoi, 31, 33
harassing gases, 18
Harding, Warren, 5
Hartman, Philip, 8
Harvey, Frank, 16
Hau Nghia, 43, 157
Havana, 17

HD, Agent, 10
heavy suppression mission, 152
Heffer, Eric, 31
helicopters, CS dispersal, 59
hemorrhagic, 13
Herbert, Edward, 88
Herbicide Assessment Commission (AAAS), 89
herbicides, 117
Hercules Chemical Company, 128
Hermiston, Oregon, 86
herons, 152, 164
Hersh, Seymour, 18, 33
Hevea brasiliensis, 151
Hiep Ninh, 44
Himsworth Committee, 63, 64
Hing Un, 194
Hitler, Adolph, 73
Hoai An, 44
Hoai Nhon, 44
Ho Bo woods, 35
Hodgkin, Dorothy Crowfoot, 72
Holden, A. V., 165
Home, Alec Douglas, 31
Ho Nai, 160
Hong Kong, 11
hootches, 16
Hornig, Donald, 87, 134
Horton, Frank, 32
Hotta, Susumi, 13
House of Commons, 31
Hudson, E. E. A., 88
Hughes, Charles Evans, 5
hydrogen cyanide, 23

immunity, 11
Imperata, 149
imperialism, 3
incapacitating agents, 18
incendiary, 14
Indochinese gibbon, 162
industrial exposure to CS, 57
infectious agents, 11
insecticides, 9
inspiratory stridor, 107
Institut des Recherches sur le Caoutchouc
    au Cambodge, 187, 189
Institute of Fisheries, 165
Interior, Department of, 172
International Association of Chiefs of Police,
    66
international law, 74
International Red Cross, 138
International Rescue Committee, 104
International Union for the Conservation
    of Nature, 162
International War Crimes Tribunal, 70
International War Tribunal for the Far East, 69
In the Name of America, 29
investigating commission, to Hanoi, 4
irritant agent, 18
Isle of Wight, 170
isopropylmethylphosphonofluoridate, 9
Israel, 15
Isthmus of Kra, 128
Italian campaign, in Ethiopia, 72
Iwo Jima, 74

jack fruit, 185, 194, 199
Japan, 7
Japanese, 6, 7
"Japs," 7
Javits, Jacob, 174
jellied gasoline, 15
Johnson Administration, 57, 81

Johnson, Lyndon B., 28, 30, 32, 118, 129
Johnston Island, 86
Jordan, 15
jute, 187

Kahn, M. Francis, 42
Kalman, Sumner, 52
Kambuja, 179
Kantroy (Kantrauy), 189
kapok trees, 185, 187, 194
Kastenmeier, Robert W., 29, 74, 81, 90
Katum, 155, 156
Kellogg-Briand Pact, 68
Kellogg, Frank B., 6
keloid scars, 17
Kennedy, John F., 78
Kent State University, 58
Kiem Tan, 129, 130
Kim Tai, 37
kingfisher, white breasted, 165
Kirk, Claude R. Jr., 86
kite, black winged, 164
Koch, Edward, 90
Kodiak, Alaska, 86
Kompong Cham, 177, 187, 188, 199
Kontume, 163
Korean war, 15
kouprey, 163, 164, 197
Kraus, E. J., 122
Krek, 189
Krock, Arthur, 31
Kruckeberg, A. R., 88
kwashiorkor, 105
Ky An, 38
Ky Anh, 37
Ky Phuoc, 38

Labor Party, 31
lachrymator, 18, 19, 23, 24, 55
lactic dehydrogenase, 56
Lagerstroemia, 148, 156
Lake Erie Chemical Company, 61
La Paz, 15
Lapland, 171
laterite, 145, 196
latex, 189
lauric acid, 15
Lavorel, Jean, 178
Law of Land Warfare, 70
League of Nations, 6
Le Baron Russell Briggs, ship, 80
Lederberg, Joshua, 87
Leguminosae, 150
Leitenberg, Milton, 87
Lemos, William E., 29, 41, 45, 82
leprosy, 13
lethal concentrations, 10
lethal dose, 10
lethal gas, 9
Le Van Hai, 197
Lidman, Sara, 3
Lieberman, E. James, 88
Lindsay, John, 32
Liverpool, 31
livestock, 196
Lo Go, 37
London Conference of CBW, 39, 43
Londonderry, 63
Long An, 194
Long Khanh, 129, 130, 157
Luce, Don, 131
lung gas, 25, 41
lychee trees, 194

M-5 dispenser/disperser, 42
M-3 dispenser/disperser, 42
M-7 canister, 46
M-25 grenade, 42
M-55 rockets, 86
M-106 Mity Mite, 46
MacArthur, Donald, 134
Mace®, 20, 53, 54, 61
Mackworth, J., 56
Macomber, William B., 74, 84
malaria, 13
malononitrile, 23, 55
mango, 184, 185, 194
mangrove, 125, 144, 147, 152, 154, 165
Manila, 13
manioc, 125, 194
Mansfield, Mike, 76, 200
marasmus, 105
Marlowe, Tom, 17
mask, 34
Matarasso, Leo, 178
Mathias, Charles Jr., 32
Mayer, Jean, 133, 159
McCarthy, Richard D., 25, 28, 73, 75-77, 85, 88, 90
McClintock, M., 88
McIndoe, K. G., 188
McNamara, Robert, 30, 32, 36, 134
McWhorter, J., 52
Mead, Margaret, 136
medical facilities, South Vietnam, 103
Medicin(e)-Chef, 102, 103
"Medico Team" (Medical International Cooperative), 103
Mekong Delta, 34, 126, 144, 157, 160, 187
melioidosis, 13
Menon, Krishna, 72
Merck, George R., 7
Merck Index, 22
Meselson, M. S., 25, 39, 46, 89, 117
Michelin Company, 156, 157
Midwest Research Institute Report, 125, 135, 139, 140, 167
Miller, Franklin, 88
MILPHAP (Military Public Health Assistance Program), 104
Mimot, (Mémot), 187, 189, 197
Minarik, C. F., 51, 122, 184
Mink, Patsy, 90
Missionary Alliance, 103
Mity Mite (dispenser/disperser), 46
Mo Duc, 108
mollusks, 163
monkey, 197
Monsanto Chemical Company, 128
monsoon, 105, 144
Montana, 167
Moore, D., 24, 52
Morse, F. Bradford, 32
Moscow, 31
mosquitoes, 165
mustard gas, 52, 85
mutagenesis, 52
mutant organisms, 11
My Lai, 76
My Tho, 197
Myrdal, Gunnar, 72

napalm, 14
National Academy of Science, 118, 122, 132, 134, 136, 137
National Academy of Science—National Research Council fellowships in CBW, 134

National Broadcasting Company, First
    Tuesday Program, 76
National Committee for a Citizen's
    Commission of Inquiry on U.S. War
    Crimes in Vietnam, 72
National Guard, 58
National Institutes of Environmental Health
    Sciences, 172
National Institutes of Health, 172
National Liberation Front (NLF), 30, 36, 38,
    42, 47, 154
National Press Club, 31
National Research Council, 134
National Security Council, 76, 184
National Security Industrial Association, 50
Nature Conservancy, 142
nausea, 24
nausea gas, 32, 33
necrosis, 55
Neilands, J. B., 88, 89
nerve gas, 18, 55
neuropathy, 173
New Delhi, 13
Nga Cay, 37
Ngo Vinh Long, 88
Nguyen Nam, 109, 113
Nguyen Son Cao, 169
Nguyen Thi Hai, 169
Nguyen Thi Luong, 109, 113
Nguyen Van Nhap, 169
Nha Be, 152
Nhu N Duc, 37
Nichols, Rodney W., 134
Niemoller, Martin, 72
Nimitz, Chester, 74
Ninh Khe, 44
Ninh Than, 44
Nipa fructicans, 147
nipa palms, 125, 146, 152
nitrates, 166
Nixon Administration, 38, 43
Nixon, Richard M., 76, 77, 168
Noel-Baker, Philip, 78, 174
non-lethal agents, 18
North Atlantic Treaty Organization (NATO), 73
Northern Ireland, 24
North Vietnamese, 17
Novick, Richard, 88
Norwegian, 17
Nui Dat, 139
Nuremberg, 68

Ochs, Phil, 3
Office of Economic Opportunity, 51
Office of Naval Research, 12
Office of Science and Technology, 134
Okinawa, 85, 86
Omori, Minoru, 71
Operation Ranch Hand, 89, 125, 151
Orange, Agent, 119, 167, 170, 173, 183,
    185, 186
orange (fruit), 194, 195, 199
Orear, Jay, 79, 87
Orians, Gordon, 87, 88
ortho-chlorobenzaldehyde, 23, 55
ortho-chlorobenzalmalononitrile
    (ortho-chlorobenzylidenemalononitrile,
    Agent CS), 22
ortho-chlorohippuric acid, 55
osprey, 164

Pacific theatre, 122
Packard, David, 173
palmitic acid, 15

papaya, 131, 184, 194
papillomas, 54
parasites, 13
parasitosis, 111
Paris, 19
Pasadena, California, 50, 51
Pasteurella pestis, 12
patrol boats, 152
Peers, William R., 72, 76
Peking, 31, 33
Pellegrin, E., 193
Penneys, N., 52, 54
Pentagon, 28-30, 33, 39, 41, 45, 57, 83, 86
People Against Nerve Gas (PANG), 86
People's Park, Berkeley, 58
Pershing, John J., 73
petition on herbicides, 181
Pfeiffer, E. W., 87, 88, 131-133, 137, 138, 177
Phantom 11F4 aircraft, 15
phdiec, 195
phenoxyacetic acids, 122
Philadelphia, Pennsylvania, police
    department, 19
Phnom Penh, 178-180, 188
Phong Phu, 161
phosgene, 5
phosphorus bombs, 14-17
Phu Cat, 44
Phuce Thoi, 161
Phu Lac, 35
Phu My, 37, 44
Phu My Hung, 37
Phuoc Tuy, 157
Phu Yen, 30, 31, 35
Physicians for Social Responsibility, 138, 181
Picloram, 119, 121, 124, 128, 151, 169,
    184
Pieime, 37
pigs, 165, 196, 197
pineapple, 184, 194, 195, 199
plague, 105, 166
Plantation de Dautieng, 157
Plantations Michelin, 151
Plasmodium falciparum, 166
pneumonia, 105, 109, 112
poisons, 4
police, 19, 20
Poliniere, Jean-Paul, 151, 190
polystyrene, 15
Pond, Elizabeth, 129
Porton Down, 22
Prek Chhlong, 189
Prentiss, Augustin M., 19, 21, 23
Price, Don K., 132, 134, 135, 139
primates, 162
procurement costs, riot control agents, 34
Project Vietnam, 104
prometone, 151
proteins, 52
Protocol, Geneva, 5, 72
provinces, 12
Pseudomonas pseudomallei, 13
psychosocial warfare, 4
Pterocarous, 148
public health, 11
Puerto Rico, 122
Pugwash Conferences, 87
pulmonary edema, 55, 111-113
punji sticks, 13
Punte, C. L., 24

Quang Nam, 31, 35, 37, 38, 44
Quang Ngai, 37, 38, 44, 102-105, 107, 113
Quan Loi, 35

Qui Nhon, 33
3-quinuclidinol, 10

rai (slash-and-burn), 146, 149
rales, 110
rambutan, 199
rats, 166
Rector, James, 58
Redcap, Operation, 17
Red Cross, 67, 138
Reedy, George, 28, 30
reindeer, 171
Resing, W. L., 189
Resor, Stanley R., 76
Reston, James, 30
restraints, 7
rhinoceros, 162, 163
Rhodes, G., 52, 56
rhonci, 110
Rhizophora, 147
ribonucleic acid (RNA), 52
rice, 187, 194
riot control agents:
    civilian casualties, 42
    deployment techniques, 25
    domestic use, 57
    evolution, 33
    fatalities, 106
    first use in Vietnam, 29
    grenades, 27
    legal status in war, 67
    lethality, 46
    lull in use, 32
    manufacturers, 47
    procurement costs, 34
    procurement volumes, 40
    properties, 18
    reaction to introduction, 31
    terminology, 18
    toxicology, 51
    use by "other side," 47
Rivers, L. Mendel, 83, 84
RNA, 52
Robert, James, 170
Rocky Mountain Arsenal, 85
Rogers, William P., 80
Rolz-Bennett, Jose, 140
Roosevelt, F. D., 73, 78, 91
Rose, Steven, 173
Rosenthal, Benjamin, 75, 90
Ross, James H., 142
Rottman, Larry, 17
Royal Ulster Constabulary, 24, 63
Roybal, Edward, 90
rubber, 157, 185, 187, 188, 190, 191, 199
Rubber Research Institute of Vietnam, 151,
    156, 159
Rubin, Harry, 88
Rung Sat, 152, 154, 164
Rural Health Department, 103
Rusk, Dean, 30-32, 36, 41, 75
Rusk, H. A., 16
Russell, Bertrand, 70
Rutman, Robert, 88

safety factor, 51
Saigon, 18, 30, 33, 35, 38, 39, 71
St. Petersburg, Declaration, 67
Salmonella typhimurium, 55
salmonids, 165
Santa Rita, California, 59
sapodilla, 194
Sarim, M. Min, 178
sarin, 9

savannas, 163
Schelling, T., 73
Schizostachyum sollingeri, 150
Schoenman, Ralph, 71
Schwartz, Charles, 89
Science Advisory Committee, Presidents', 135
Scientists' Committee on Chemical and
    Biological Warfare, 56, 88, 89, 181
Scientists Institute for Public Information, 138
Secretary General, United Nations, 140
Secretary of Defense, 135, 140
Secretary of State, 140
Secretary of the Army, 29
Seitz, Frederick, 134, 137
Selassie, Haile, 6
Senate Foreign Relations Committee, 32, 73
Senate, U.S., 5, 6
sensitization to Mace®, 54
serosanguinous exudate, 113
sheep, 196
Shoecraft, Mrs. Willard, 170
shrimp, 163
Siekevitz, P., 88, 89
Sihanouk, N., 178, 187
silicona, 24
silvex, 170
Singapore, 13
Smith, Gerard C., 75
smokes, irritant, 5
Society for Social Responsibility in Science,
    65, 87, 143, 181
sodium bicarbonate, 25
sodium bisulfite, 25
sodium carbonate, 25
sodium dimethyl arsenate, 184
Sommer, John, 131
Song Dong Nai, 130
Son Kim, 108
Son My, 38
Son Tinh, 108
Sor Thay Seng, 196
Southeast Asia, 25
South Korean Marines, 105
South Vietnamese Army, 30, 105
Soviet Union, 31
Spanish, 17
spears, 13
Special Forces Camps, 164, 187
Special Forces missions, 187
Special Forces Mobile Strike Force, 16
Special Operations Squadron, 186
Spilhaus, Athelstan F., 136
Spock, Benjamin, 3
spray drift, 127
Sproul Plaza, Berkeley campus, 58
Srekak, 189
stability, of agents, 10
standardized agents, 18
State, Department of, 29, 30, 140-143, 186
steel pellet bombs, 4
sternutators, 23
Stetler, R., 23
Stewart, Michael, 31, 54, 64
Stewart, William H., 54
Stockholm, 38
Stockholm Conferences on Vietnam, 25, 38
Stone, I. F., 3
storks, 152, 164
Stoughton, Roger, 22
Strauss, John S., 88, 89
Subcommittee on National Security Policy and
    Scientific Developments, 41, 76
submarines, 5
sugar palm, 185, 194

super tear gas, 22
Svahnstrom, Bertil, 72
Sweden, 22
Swedish Vietnam Day Committee, 3
sweet potatoes, 125
Swyter, Hans, 82
syrup, 14

2,4,5-T (2,4,5-trichlorophenoxyacetic acid),
    119, 121-125, 128, 151, 158, 159, 165, 168,
    170-173, 183, 196, 197
Takman, John, 17
Tam Ky, 37, 38
Tam Ten, 169
Tan Hiep (Tanhiep), 160, 168, 169
Tan Son Nhut, 125, 166, 173
taro, 194
Task Force Eagle, 85
Tay Ninh, 30, 37, 38, 44, 155, 157, 178, 184
Teach-In, Berkeley, 3
teak, 185, 195, 199
tear gas, 18
teratogenesis, 52, 171, 197
tern, 165
Thailand, 123, 128
Thang Binh, 44
Thanh Binh, 44, 197
Thien Ngon, 155, 156
thiocyanate, 55
Thoi Andong, 161
Thomas, Norman, 3
Thompson Chemical Company, 128
Thompson Hayward Chemical Company, 128
tigers, 162
timber, 142
Tokyo, 16
Tokyo Tribunal, 69
tomato, 194
Tong Le Chon, 155, 156
Tong Thi An, 169
Tordon, 169
toxins, 77
Tra Bong, 108
trachea, 113
Truman, Harry S., 78
Training Circular 3-16, 25, 26, 28, 43, 45, 46
Tran Thi Tien, 169
Tran Van Dong, 169
1,1,1-trichloroethane, 53
1,1,2-trichloro-1,2,2-trifluoroethane, 53
Tschirley, Fred, 124, 128, 141, 150, 154, 164
tuberculosis, 105, 108
Tu Du, 168
tumors, 17
tunnels, gassing, 35
Tupper, Stanley, 32
Tuyen, 161
Tuy Phuoc, 36, 44
typhoid fever, 13

U-19 helicopter, 61
Uniroyal Chemical Company, 128
United Nations, 28, 31, 80, 84, 141-143, 174,
    179
United States:
    Air Force, 28
    Army, 18, 28
    Constitution, 70
    forces, 26
    Infantry Division (25th), 17
    Marines, 28, 105
    Navy, 28
University of Saigon, 151
Utah, 10

U Thant, 75, 81
Utter, L. N., 33, 36, 41

Vandenberg, Arthur H., 6
venereal disease, 13
Vennema, Alje, 23, 42, 45
venosection, 112
Verrett, Jacqueline, 173
Versailles (German) Peace Treaty, 5
vesicant, 24
veterans groups, 6
Viet Cong, 30, 34, 35, 39, 47, 126
Viet Minh, 104
Vietnam, South:
    climate, 144
    forests, 146
    physiography, 146
    population, 144
    size, 144
    vegetation, 146
Vietnam Christian Services, 109, 110
Viet Tri, 4
Vinh Thanh, 44
Vinh Quang, 31, 36
viverrids, 166
vomiting gas, 18, 21
Vung Tau, 124, 147
Vu Van Cua, 38
VX, 80, 85

Wald, George, 17
War Crimes Tribunal, Russell, 30
war gases, 8
Warsaw Pact, 73
Washington, D. C., 18, 28, 30, 42
Washington (State), 167
Washington Arms Conference, 68
Washington Treaty, 5
water buffalo, 166, 196
Waterfall, Project, 17
Watertown, Massachusetts, 17
Weapons Committee, Hanoi, 36
Weigand, D. A., 25
West Germany, 86
Westing, A. H., 89
Westmoreland, William C., 28, 33, 37, 76
Wharton, C. H., 163
whimbrel, 165
White, Agent, 119, 120, 167, 173, 184, 185
White House, 29, 30
white phosphorus, 14
wildlife, 197
Wilhelm, John, 130
Williams, Maslyn, 200
Williamson, Ellis, 33
"Willie Peter" (white phosphorus), 16
Wilson, Harold, 31
Wolff, Lester, 90
Wolfle, Dale, 134, 140
Women's International League for Peace and
    Freedom, 77, 86
World Court, 179
World Health Organization, 52, 138
World War I, 18, 19, 21
World War II, 19, 52, 90

Xenopsylla cheopis, 12
Xu Yen, 30

Yamashita, Tomoyuki, 69

Zablocki, Clement, 20, 29, 80, 88
zebus, 196
zephiran chloride, 25
Zolla, Susan, 88

O wisdom and money
How can you requite
The honey of honey
That flies in that flight?
The useless delight?

So, with his back against a tree, he stared
At the pure, golden feathers in the West
Until the sunset flowed into his heart
Like a slow wave of honey-dropping dew
Murmuring from the other side of Sleep.
There was a fairy hush
Everywhere. Even the setter at his feet
Lay there as if the twilight had bewitched
His russet paws into two russet leaves,
A dog of russet leaves who did not stir a hair.

Then something broke the peace.
Like wind it was, the flutter of rising wind,
But then it grew until it was the rushing
Of winged stallions, distant and terrible,
Trampling beyond the sky.
                    The hissing charge
Of lightless armies of angelic horse
Galloping down the stars.
                    There were no words
In that implacable and feathery thunder,
And yet there must have been, or Ellyat's mind
Caught them like broken arrows out of the air.

Thirteen sisters beside the sea,
(Have a care, my son.)
Builded a house called Liberty
And locked the doors with a stately key.
None should enter it but the free.
(Have a care, my son.)

The walls are solid as Plymouth Rock.
(Rock can crumble, my son.)
The door of seasoned New England stock.

Oh Lordy Je-sus
It's a long time comin'
It's a long time co-o-min'
That Jubilee time.
We'll wait and we'll pray, Lord,
We'll wait and we'll pray, Lord,
But it's a long time, Lord,
Yes, it's a long time.

The dark sobbing ebbed away.
The captain was still talking. "Yes," he said,
"And yet we treat 'em well enough. There's no one
From Salem to the Guinea Coast can say
They lose as few as I do." He stopped.
                    "Well, Mister?"
The mate arose. "Good night sir and—"
                    "Good night."

The mate went up on deck. The breeze was fresh.
There were the stars, steady. He shook himself
Like a dog coming out of water and felt better.
Six weeks, with luck, and they'd be back in port
And he could draw his pay and see his girl.
Meanwhile, it wasn't his watch, so he could sleep.
The captain still below, reading that Bible. . . .
Forget it—and the noises, still half-heard—
He'd have to go below to sleep, this time,
But after, if the weather held like this,
He'd have them sling a hammock up on deck.
You couldn't smell the black so much on deck
And so you didn't dream it when you slept.

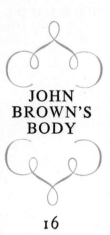

BOOK ONE

Jack Ellyat had been out all day alone,
    Except for his new gun and Ned, the setter,
The old wise dog with Autumn in his eyes,
Who stepped the fallen leaves so delicately
They barely rustled. Ellyat trampled them down
Crackling, like cast-off skins of fairy snakes.
He'd meant to hunt, but he had let the gun
Rest on his shoulder.
                    It was enough to feel
The cool air of the last of Indian summer
Blowing continually across his cheek
And watch the light distill its water of gold
As the sun dropped.
                    Here was October, here
Was ruddy October, the old harvester,

Wrapped like a beggared sachem in a coat
Of tattered tanager and partridge feathers,
Scattering jack-o-lanterns everywhere
To give the field-mice pumpkin-colored moons.
His red clay pipe had trailed across the land
Staining the trees with colors of the sumach:
East, West, South, North, the ceremonial fume
Blue and enchanted as the soul of air
Drifted its incense.
                    Incense of the wild,
Incense of earth fulfilled, ready to sleep
The stupefied dark slumber of the bear
All winter, underneath a frozen star.

Jack Ellyat felt that turning of the year
Stir in his blood like drowsy fiddle-music
And knew he was glad to be Connecticut-born
And young enough to find Connecticut winter
Was a black pond to cut with silver skates
And not a scalping-knife against the throat.
He thought the thoughts of youth, idle and proud.

            Since I was begotten
            My father's grown wise
            But he has forgotten
            The wind in the skies.
            I shall not grow wise.

            Since I have been growing
            My uncle's got rich.
            He spends his time sowing
            A bottomless ditch.
            I will not grow rich.

            For money is sullen
            And wisdom is sly,
            But youth is the pollen
            That blows through the sky
            And does not ask why.

Before it a Yankee fighting-cock
Pecks redcoat kings away from the lock.
(Fighters can die, my son.)

The hearth is a corner where sages sit.
(Sages pass, my son.)
Washington's heart lies under it.
And the long roof-beams are chiseled and split
From hickory tough as Jackson's wit.
(Bones in the dust, my son.)

The trees in the garden are fair and fine.
(Trees blow down, my son.)
Connecticut elm and Georgia pine.
The warehouse groans with cotton and swine.
The cellar is full of scuppernong-wine.
(Wine turns sour, my son.)

Surely a house so strong and bold,
(The wind is rising, my son,)
Will last till Time is a pinch of mould!
There is a ghost, when the night is old.
There is a ghost who walks in the cold.
(The trees are shaking, my son.)

The sisters sleep on Liberty's breast,
(The thunder thunders, my son,)
Like thirteen swans in a single nest.
But the ghost is naked and will not rest
Until the sun rise out of the West.
(The lightning lightens, my son.)

All night long like a moving stain,
(The trees are breaking, my son,)
The black ghost wanders his house of pain.
There is blood where his hand has lain.
It is wrong he should wear a chain.
(The sky is falling, my son.)

The warning beat at his mind like a bird and passed.
Ellyat roused. He thought: they are going South.

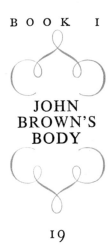

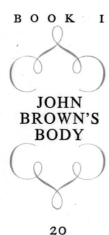
He stared at the sky, confused. It was empty and bleak.
But still he felt the shock of the hooves on his heart.
—The riderless horses never bridled or tamed—
He heard them screaming like eagles loosed from a cloud
As they drove South to trample the indolent sun,
And darkness sat in his mind like a shadow enthroned.
He could not read the riddle their flight had set
But he felt wretched, and glad for the dog's cold nose
That now came nuzzling his hand.
                              Who has set you free?
Who has driven you out in the sky with an iron whip
Like blind, old thunders stubbornly marching abreast
To carry a portent high on shoulders of stone
The length and breadth of the Union?
The North and South are at peace and the East and West,
The tomahawk is buried in prairie-sod.
The great frontier rolls westward with the sun,
And the new States are crowding at the door,
The buckskin-States, the buffalo-horned, the wild
Mustangs with coats the color of crude gold.
Their bodies, naked as the hunter's moon,
Smell of new grass and the sweet milk of the corn.
Defiant virgins, fiercely unpossessed
As the bird-stars that walk the night untrodden.
They drag their skies and sunsets after them
Like calico ponies on a rawhide rope,
And who would ride them must have iron thighs
And a lean heart, bright as a bowie-knife.
Were they not foaled with treasure in their eyes
Between the rattlesnake and the painted rock?
Are they not matches for vaquero gods?
Are they not occupation for the strength
Of a whole ruffian world of pioneers?
And must they wait like spayed mares in the rain,
While Carolina and Connecticut
Fight an old quarrel out before a ghost?

So Ellyat talked to his young indignation,
Walking back home with the October moon.
But, even as he mused, he tried to picture

The South, that languorous land where Uncle Toms
Groaned Biblically underneath the lash,
And grinning Topsies mopped and mowed behind
Each honeysuckle vine.
                              They called them niggers
And cut their ears off when they ran away,
But then they loved their mammies—there was that—
Although they sometimes sold them down the river—
And when the niggers were not getting licked
Or quoting Scripture, they sang funny songs,
By the Swanee river, on the old plantation.

The girls were always beautiful. The men
Wore varnished boots, raced horses and played cards
And drank mint-juleps till the time came round
For fighting duels with their second cousins
Or tar-and-feathering some God-damn Yankee. . . .
The South . . . the honeysuckle . . . the hot sun . . .
The taste of ripe persimmons and sugar-cane . . .
The cloyed and waxy sweetness of magnolias . . .
White cotton, blowing like a fallen cloud,
And foxhounds belling the Virginia hills . . .

And then the fugitive slave he'd seen in Boston,
The black man with the eyes of a tortured horse. . . .

He whistled Ned. What do you think of it, Ned?
We're abolitionists, I suppose, and Father
Talks about Wendell Phillips and John Brown
But, even so, that doesn't have to mean
We'll break the Union up for abolition,
And they can't want to break it up for slavery—
It won't come to real fighting, will it, Ned?
But Ned was busy with a rabbit-track.
There was the town—the yellow window of home.

Meanwhile, in Concord, Emerson and Thoreau
Talked of an ideal state, so purely framed
It never could exist.

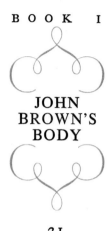

Meanwhile, in Boston
Minister Higginson and Dr. Howe
Waited for news about a certain project
That had to do with pikes and Harper's Ferry.

Meanwhile, in Georgia, Clay Wingate dreamed.

———————

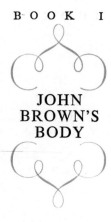
Settled more than a hundred year
By the river and county of St. Savier,
The Wingates held their ancestry
As high as Taliaferro or Huger,
Maryland Carroll, Virginia Lee.
They had ill-spelt letters of Albemarle's
And their first grant ran from the second Charles,
Clerkly inscribed upon parchmentries
"To our well-beloved John Wingate, these,"
Though envy hinted the royal mood
Held more of humor than gratitude
And the well-beloved had less applied
To honest John than his tall young bride,
At least their eldest to John's surprise,
Was very like Monmouth about the eyes,
Till his father wondered if every loyalty
Was always so richly repaid by royalty,
But, having long found that the principal question
In a happy life is a good digestion
And the worst stomachic of all is jealousy
He gave up the riddle, and settled zealously
To farming his acres, begetting daughters,
And making a study of cordial waters
Till he died at ninety of pure senility
And was greatly mourned by the local gentility.

John the Second was different cloth.
He had wings—but the wings of the moth.
Courtly, unlucky, clever and wise,
There was a Stuart in his eyes,
A gambler that played against loaded dice.
He could harrow the water and plough the sand,

But he could not do the thing at hand.
A fencing-foil too supple for use,
A racing colt that must run at loose.
And the Wingate acres had slipped away
If it had not been for Elspeth Mackay.
She was his wife, and her heart was bold
As a broad, bright guinea of Border gold.
Her wit was a tartan of colored weather.
Her walk was gallant as Highland heather.
And whatever she had, she held together.

It was she who established on Georgia soil
Wingate honor and Wingate toil
When John and his father's neighbors stood
At swords' points over a county feud
And only ill-fortune and he were friends.
—They prophesied her a dozen ends,
Seeking new ground for a broken man
Where only the deer and the rabbit ran
And the Indian arrow harried both,
But she held her word and she kept her troth,
Cleared the forest and tamed the wild
And gave the breast to the new-born child
While the painted Death went whooping by
—To die at last as she wished to die
In the fief built out of her blood and bone
With her heart for the Hall's foundation-stone.

Deep in her sons, and the Wingate blood,
She stamped her sigil of fortitude.
Thrift and love for the house and the chief
And a scone on the hob for the son of grief.
But a knife in the ribs for the pleasant thief.
And deep in her sons, when she was gone,
Her words took root, and her ghost lived on.
The slow voice haunting the ocean-shell
To counsel the sons of her sons as well.
And it was well for the Wingate line
To have that stiffening set in its spine.
For once in each breeding of Wingate kin

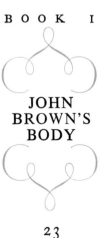

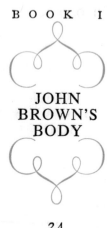

There came a child with an olive skin
And the mouth of Charles, the merry and sad,
And the bright, spoilt charm that Monmouth had.
Luckily seldom the oldest born
To sow the nettle in Wingate corn
And let the cotton blight on its stalk
While he wasted his time in witty talk,
Or worse, in love with no minister handy,
Or feeding a spaniel on nuts and brandy
And taking a melancholy pride
In never choosing the winning side.

Clay Wingate was the last to feel
The prick of that spur of tarnished steel,
Gilt, but crossed with the dubious bar
Of arms won under the bastard's star,
Rowel his mind, at that time or this,
With thoughts and visions that were not his.
A sorrow of laughter, a mournful glamor
And the ghostly stroke of an airy hammer
Shaking his heart with pity and pride
That had nothing to do with the things he eyed.
He was happy and young, he was strong and stout,
His body was hard to weary out.
When he thought of life, he thought of a shout.
But—there was a sword in a blackened sheath,
There was a shape with a mourning wreath:
And a place in his mind was a wrestling-ring
Where the crownless form of an outlawed king
Fought with a shadow too like his own,
And, late or early, was overthrown.

It is not lucky to dream such stuff—
Dreaming men are haunted men.
Though Wingate's face looked lucky enough
To any eye that had seen him then,
Riding back through the Georgia Fall
To the white-pillared porch of Wingate Hall.
Fall of the possum, fall of the 'coon,
And the lop-eared hound-dog baying the moon.

Fall that is neither bitter nor swift
But a brown girl bearing an idle gift,
A brown seed-kernel that splits apart
And shows the Summer yet in its heart,
A smokiness so vague in the air
You feel it rather than see it there,
A brief, white rime on the red clay road
And slow mules creaking a lazy load
Through endless acres of afternoon,
A pine-cone fire and a banjo-tune,
And a julep mixed with a silver spoon.

Your noons are hot, your nights deep-starred,
There is honeysuckle still in the yard,
Fall of the quail and the firefly-glows
And the pot-pourri of the rambler-rose,
Fall that brings no promise of snows . . .

Wingate checked on his horse's rein
With a hand as light as a butterfly
And drank content in body and brain
As he gazed for a moment at the sky.
This was his Georgia, this his share
Of pine and river and sleepy air,
Of summer thunder and winter rain
That spills bright tears on the window-pane
With the slight, fierce passion of young men's grief,
Of the mockingbird and the mulberry-leaf.
For, wherever the winds of Georgia run,
It smells of peaches long in the sun,
And the white wolf-winter, hungry and frore,
Can prowl the North by a frozen door
But here we have fed him on bacon-fat
And he sleeps by the stove like a lazy cat.
Here Christmas stops at everyone's house
With a jug of molasses and green, young boughs,
And the little New Year, the weakling one,
Can lie outdoors in the noonday sun,
Blowing the fluff from a turkey-wing
At skies already haunted with Spring—

Oh, Georgia . . . Georgia . . . the careless yield!
The watermelons ripe in the field!
The mist in the bottoms that tastes of fever
And the yellow river rolling forever . . . !

So Wingate saw it, vision or truth,
Through the colored window of his own youth,
Building an image out of his mind
To live or die for, as Fate inclined.

He drank his fill of the air, and then,
Was just about to ride on again
When—what was that noise beyond the sky,
That harry of unseen cavalry
Riding the wind?
                              His own horse stirred,
Neighing. He listened. There was a word.
He could not hear it—and yet he heard.
It was an arrow from ambush flung,
It was a bell with a leaden tongue
Striking an hour.
                              He was young
No longer. He and his horse were old,
And both were bound with an iron band.
He slipped from the saddle and tried to stand.
He struck one hand with the other hand.
But both were cold.

The horses, burning-hooved, drove on toward the sea,
But, where they had passed, the air was troubled and sick
Like earth that the shoulder of earthquake heavily stirs.
There was a whisper moving that air all night,
A whisper that cried and whimpered about the house
Where John Brown prayed to his God, by his narrow bed.

JOHN BROWN'S PRAYER

Omnipotent and steadfast God,
Who, in Thy mercy, hath

Upheaved in me Jehovah's rod
And his chastising wrath,

For fifty-nine unsparing years
Thy Grace hath worked apart
To mould a man of iron tears
With a bullet for a heart.

Yet, since this body may be weak
With all it has to bear,
Once more, before Thy thunders speak,
Almighty, hear my prayer.

I saw Thee when Thou did display
The black man and his lord
To bid me free the one, and slay
The other with the sword.

I heard Thee when Thou bade me spurn
Destruction from my hand
And, though all Kansas bleed and burn,
It was at Thy command.

I hear the rolling of the wheels,
The chariots of war!
I hear the breaking of the seals
And the opening of the door!

The glorious beasts with many eyes
Exult before the Crowned.
The buried saints arise, arise
Like incense from the ground!

Before them march the martyr-kings,
In bloody sunsets drest,
Oh, Kansas, bleeding Kansas,
You will not let me rest!

I hear your sighing corn again,
I smell your prairie-sky.

And I remember five dead men
Py Pottawattomie.

Lord God it was a work of Thine,
And how might I refrain?
But Kansas, bleeding Kansas,
I hear her in her pain.

Her corn is rustling in the ground,
An arrow in my flesh.
And all night long I staunch a wound
That ever bleeds afresh.

Get up, get up, my hardy sons,
From this time forth we are
No longer men, but pikes and guns
In God's advancing war.

And if we live, we free the slave,
And if we die, we die.
But God has digged His saints a grave
Beyond the western sky.

Oh, fairer than the bugle-call
Its walls of jasper shine!
And Joshua's sword is on the wall
With space beside for mine.

And should the Philistine defend
His strength against our blows,
The God who doth not spare His friend,
Will not forget His foes.

———————

They reached the Maryland bridge of Harper's Ferry
That Sunday night. There were twenty-two in all,
Nineteen were under thirty, three not twenty-one,
Kagi, the self-taught scholar, quiet and cool,
Stevens, the cashiered soldier, Puritan-fathered,
A singing giant, gunpowder-tempered and rash.

Dauphin Thompson, the pippin-cheeked country-boy,
More like a girl than a warrior; Oliver Brown,
Married last year when he was barely nineteen;
Dangerfield Newby, colored and born a slave,
Freeman now, but married to one not free
Who, with their seven children, waited him South,
The youngest baby just beginning to crawl;
Watson Brown, the steady lieutenant, who wrote
Back to his wife,

        "Oh, Bell, I want to see you
And the little fellow very much but must wait.
There was a slave near here whose wife was sold South.
They found him hanging in Kennedy's orchard next morning.
I cannot come home as long as such things are done here.
I sometimes think that we shall not meet again."

These were some of the band. For better or worse
They were all strong men.

        The bearded faces look strange
In the old daguerreotypes: they should be the faces
Of prosperous, small-town people, good sons and fathers,
Good horse-shoe pitchers, good at plowing a field,
Good at swapping stories and good at praying,
American wheat, firm-rooted, good in the ear.
There is only one whose air seems out of the common,
Oliver Brown. That face has a masculine beauty
Somewhat like the face of Keats.

        They were all strong men.

They tied up the watchman and took the rifleworks.
Then John Brown sent a raiding party away
To fetch in Colonel Washington from his farm.
The Colonel was George Washington's great-grand-nephew,
Slave-owner, gentleman-farmer, but, more than these,
Possessor of a certain fabulous sword
Given to Washington by Frederick the Great.
They captured him and his sword and brought them along
Processionally.

        The act has a touch of drama,
Half costume-romance, half unmerited farce.

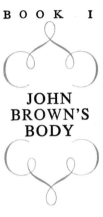

On the way, they told the Washington slaves they were free,
Or free to fight for their freedom.

The slaves heard the news

With the dazed, scared eyes of cattle before a storm.
A few came back with the band and were given pikes,
And, when John Brown was watching, pretended to mount
A slipshod guard over the prisoners.
But, when he had walked away, they put down their pikes
And huddled together, talking in mourning voices.
It didn't seem right to play at guarding the Colonel
But they were afraid of the bearded patriarch
With the Old Testament eyes.

A little later

It was Patrick Higgins' turn. He was the night-watchman
Of the Maryland bridge, a tough little Irishman
With a canny, humorous face, and a twist in his speech.
He came humming his way to his job.

"Halt!" ordered a voice.

He stopped a minute, perplexed. As he told men later,
"Now I didn't know what 'Halt!' mint, any more
Than a hog knows about a holiday."

There was a scuffle.

He got away with a bullet-crease in his scalp
And warned the incoming train. It was half-past-one.
A moment later, a man named Shepherd Heyward,
Free negro, baggage-master of the small station,
Well-known in the town, hardworking, thrifty and fated,
Came looking for Higgins.

"Halt!" called the voice again,

But he kept on, not hearing or understanding,
Whichever it may have been.

A rifle cracked.

He fell by the station-platform, gripping his belly,
And lay for twelve hours of torment, asking for water
Until he was able to die.

There is no stone,

No image of bronze or marble green with the rain
To Shepherd Heyward, free negro of Harper's Ferry,
And even the books, the careful, ponderous histories,
That turn live men into dummies with smiles of wax

JOHN
BROWN'S
BODY

Thoughtfully posed against a photographer's background
In the act of signing a treaty or drawing a sword,
Tell little of what he was.
                                    And yet his face
Grey with pain and puzzled at sudden death
Stares out at us through the bookworm-dust of the years
With an uncomprehending wonder, a blind surprise.
"I was getting along," it says, "I was doing well.
I had six thousand dollars saved in the bank.
It was a good town, a nice town, I liked the folks
And they liked me. I had a good job there, too.
On Sundays I used to dress myself up slick enough
To pass the plate in church, but I wasn't proud
Not even when trashy niggers called me Mister,
Though I could hear the old grannies over their snuff
Mumbling along, 'Look, chile, there goes Shepherd Heyward.
Ain't him fine in he Sunday clo'es—ain't him sassy and fine?
You grow up decent and don't play ball in the street,
And maybe you'll get like him, with a gold watch and chain.'
And then, suddenly—and what was it all about?
Why should anyone want to kill me? Why was it done?"

So the grey lips. And so the hurt in the eyes.
A hurt like a child's, at punishment unexplained
That makes the whole child-universe fall to pieces.
At the time of death, most men turn back toward the child.

Brown did not know at first that the first man dead
By the sword he thought of so often as Gideon's sword
Was one of the race he had drawn that sword to free.
It had been dark on the bridge. A man had come
And had not halted when ordered. Then the shot
And the scrape of the hurt man dragging himself away.
That was all. The next man ordered to halt would halt.
His mind was too full of the burning judgments of God
To wonder who it had been. He was cool and at peace.
He dreamt of a lamb, lying down by a rushing stream.

So the night wore away, indecisive and strange.
The raiders stuck by the arsenal, waiting perhaps

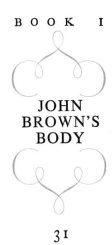

For a great bell of jubilation to toll in the sky,
And the slaves to rush from the hills with pikes in their hands,
A host redeemed, black rescue-armies of God.
It did not happen.

                          Meanwhile, there was casual firing.
A townsman named Boerley was killed. Meanwhile, the train
Passed over the bridge to carry its wild news
Of abolition-devils sprung from the ground
A hundred and fifty, three hundred, a thousand strong
To pillage Harper's Ferry, with fire and sword.
Meanwhile the whole countryside was springing to arms.
The alarm-bell in Charlestown clanged "Nat Turner has come.
Nat Turner has come again, all smoky from Hell,
Setting the slave to murder and massacre!"
The Jefferson Guards fell in. There were boys and men.
They had no uniforms but they had weapons.
Old squirrel-rifles, taken down from the wall,
Shot guns loaded with spikes and scraps of iron.
A boy dragged a blunderbuss as big as himself.
They started for the Ferry.
                                  In a dozen
A score of other sleepy, neighboring towns
The same bell clanged, the same militia assembled.

The Ferry itself was roused and stirring with dawn.
And the firing began again.
                          A queer, harsh sound
In the ordinary streets of that clean, small town,
A desultory, vapid, meaningless sound.

God knows why John Brown lingered! Kagi, the scholar,
Who, with two others, held the rifle-works,
All morning sent him messages urging retreat.
They had the inexorable weight of common sense
Behind them, but John Brown neither replied
Nor heeded, brooding in the patriarch-calm
Of a lean, solitary pine that hangs
On the cliff's edge, and sees the world below
A tiny pattern of toy fields and trees,
And only feels its roots gripping the rock

And the almighty wind that shakes its boughs,
Blowing from eagle-heaven to eagle-heaven.

Of course they were cut off. The whole attempt
Was fated from the first.
                              Just about noon
The Jefferson Guards took the Potomac Bridge
And drove away the men Brown posted there.

There were three doors of possible escape
Open to Brown. With this the first slammed shut.
The second followed it a little later ˌ
With the recapture of the other bridge
That cut Brown off from Kagi and the arsenal
And penned the larger body of the raiders
In the armory.
                  Again the firing rolled,
And now the first of the raiders fell and died,
Dangerfield Newby, the freed Scotch-mulatto
Whose wife and seven children, slaves in Virginia,
Waited for him to bring them incredible freedom.
They were sold South instead, after the raid.
His body lay where the townspeople could reach it.
They cut off his ears for trophies.
                                        If there are souls,
As many think that there are or wish that there might be,
Crystalline things that rise on light wings exulting
Out of the spoilt and broken cocoon of the body,
Knowing no sorrow or pain but only deliverance,
And yet with the flame of speech, the patterns of memory,
One wonders what the soul of Dangerfield Newby
Said, in what terms, to the soul of Shepherd Heyward,
Both born slave, both freed, both dead the same day.
What do the souls that bleed from the corpse of battle
Say to the tattered night?
                              Perhaps it is better
We have no power to visage what they might say.

The firing now was constant, like the heavy
And drumming rains of summer. Twice Brown sent

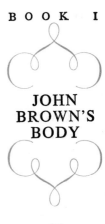

Asking a truce. The second time there went
Stevens and Watson Brown with a white flag.
But things had gone beyond the symbol of flags.
Stevens, shot from a window, fell in the gutter
Horribly wounded. Watson Brown crawled back
To the engine house that was the final fort
Of Brown's last stand, torn through and through with slugs.

A Mr. Brua, one of Brown's prisoners,
Strolled out from the unguarded prison-room
Into the bullets, lifted Stevens up,
Carried him over to the old hotel
They called the Wager House, got a doctor for him,
And then strolled back to take his prisoner's place
With Colonel Washington and the scared rest.
I know no more than this of Mr. Brua
But he seems curiously American,
And I imagine him a tall, stooped man
A little yellow with the Southern sun,
With slow, brown eyes and a slow way of talking,
Shifting the quid of tobacco in his cheek
Mechanically, as he lifted up
The dirty, bloody body of the man
Who stood for everything he most detested
And slowly carrying him through casual wasps
Of death to the flyspecked but sunny room
In the old hotel, wiping the blood and grime
Mechanically from his Sunday coat,
Settling his black string-tie with big, tanned hands,
And, then, incredibly, going back to jail.
He did not think much about what he'd done
But sat himself as comfortably as might be
On the cold bricks of that dejected guard-room
And slowly started cutting another quid
With a worn knife that had a brown bone-handle.

He lived all through the war and died long after,
This Mr. Brua I see. His last advice
To numerous nephews was "Keep out of trouble,
But if you're in it, chew and don't be hasty,
Just do whatever's likeliest at hand."

I like your way of talking, Mr. Brua,
And if there still are people interested
In cutting literary clothes for heroes
They might do worse than mention your string-tie.

There were other killings that day. On the one side, this,
Leeman, a boy of eighteen and the youngest raider,
Trying to flee from the death-trap of the engine-house
And caught and killed on an islet in the Potomac.
The body lay on a tiny shelf of rock
For hours, a sack of clothes still strung by bullets.

On the other side—Fontaine Beckham, mayor of the town,
Went to look at Heyward's body with Patrick Higgins.
The slow tears crept to his eyes. He was getting old.
He had thought a lot of Heyward. He had no gun
But he had been mayor of the town for a dozen years,
A peaceful, orderly place full of decent people,
And now they were killing people, here in his town,
He had to do something to stop it, somehow or other.
He wandered out on the railroad, half-distraught
And peeped from behind a water-tank at the raiders.
"Squire, don't go any farther," said Higgins, "It ain't safe."
He hardly heard him, he had to look out again.
Who were these devils with horns who were shooting his people?
They didn't look like devils. One was a boy
Smooth-cheeked, with a bright half-dreamy face, a little
Like Sally's eldest.
                    Suddenly, the air struck him
A stiff, breath-taking blow. "Oh," he said, astonished.
Took a step and fell on his face, shot through the heart.
Higgins watched him for twenty minutes, wanting to lift him
But not quite daring. Then he turned away
And went back to the town.
                    The bars had been open all day,
Never to better business.
When the news of Beckham's death spread from bar to bar,
It was like putting loco-weed in the whiskey,
The mob came together at once, the American mob,
They mightn't be able to take Brown's last little fort

JOHN
BROWN'S
BODY

35

But there were two prisoners penned in the Wager House.
One was hurt already, Stevens, no fun killing him.
But the other was William Thompson, whole and unwounded,
Caught when Brown tried to send his first flag of truce.

They stormed the hotel and dragged him out to the bridge,
Where two men shot him, unarmed, then threw the body
Over the trestle. It splashed in the shallow water,
But the slayers kept on firing at the dead face.
The carcass was there for days, a riven target,
Barbarously misused.

Meanwhile the armory yard

Was taken by a new band of Beckham's avengers,
The most of Brown's prisoners freed and his last escape cut off.

What need to tell of the killing of Kagi the scholar,
The wounding of Oliver Brown and the other deaths?
Only this remains to be told. When the drunken day
Reeled into night, there were left in the engine-house
Five men, alive and unwounded, of all the raiders.
Watson and Oliver Brown
Both of them hurt to the death, were stretched on the floor
Beside the corpse of Taylor, the young Canadian.
There was no light, there. It was bitterly cold.
A cold chain of lightless hours that slowly fell
In leaden beads between two fingers of stone.
Outside, the fools and the drunkards yelled in the streets,
And, now and then, there were shots. The prisoners talked
And tried to sleep.

John Brown did not try to sleep,

The live coals of his eyes severed the darkness;
Now and then he heard his young son Oliver calling
In the thirsty agony of his wounds, "Oh, kill me!
Kill me and put me out of this suffering!"
John Brown's jaw tightened. "If you must die," he said,
"Die like a man." Toward morning the crying ceased.
John Brown called out to the boy but he did not answer.
"I guess he's dead," said John Brown.

If his soul wept

They were the incredible tears of the squeezed stone.

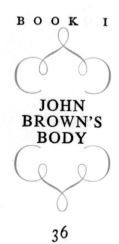

B O O K   I

JOHN
BROWN'S
BODY

36

He had not slept for two days, but he would not sleep.
The night was a chained, black leopard that he stared down,
Erect, on his feet. One wonders what sights he saw
In the cloudy mirror of his most cloudy heart,
Perhaps God clothed in a glory, perhaps himself
The little boy who had stolen three brass pins
And been well whipped for it.

When he was six years old
An Indian boy had given him a great wonder,
A yellow marble, the first he had ever seen.
He treasured it for months but lost it at last,
Boylike. The hurt of the loss took years to heal.
He never quite forgot.

He could see it now,
Smooth, hard and lovely, a yellow, glistening ball,
But it kept rolling away through cracks of darkness
Whenever he tried to catch it and hold it fast.
If he could only touch it, he would be safe,
But it trickled away and away, just out of reach,
There by the wall . . .

Outside the blackened East
Began to tarnish with a faint, grey stain
That caught on the fixed bayonets of the marines.
Lee of Virginia, Light Horse Harry's son,
Observed it broaden, thinking of many things,
But chiefly wanting to get his business done,
A curious, wry, distasteful piece of work
For regular soldiers.

Therefore to be finished
As swiftly and summarily as possible
Before this yelling mob of drunk civilians
And green militia once got out of hand.
His mouth set. Once already he had offered
The honor of the attack to the militia,
Such honor as it was.

Their Colonel had
Declined with a bright nervousness of haste.
"Your men are paid for doing this kind of work.
Mine have their wives and children." Lee smiled briefly,
Remembering that. The smile had a sharp edge.

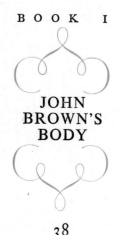

Well, it was time.
                        The whooping crowd fell silent
And scattered, as a single man walked out
Toward the engine-house, a letter in his hand.
Lee watched him musingly. A good man, Stuart.
Now he was by the door and calling out.
The door opened a crack.
                            Brown's eyes were there
Over the cold muzzle of a cocked carbine.
The parleying began, went on and on,
While the crowd shivered and Lee watched it all
With the strict commonsense of a Greek sword
And with the same sure readiness.
                                Unperceived,
The dawn ran down the valleys of the wind,
Coral-footed dove, tracking the sky with coral . . .
Then, sudden as powder flashing in a pan,
The parleying was done.
                        The door slammed shut.
The little figure of Stuart jumped aside
Waving its cap.
                    And the marines came on.

Brown watched them come. One hand was on his carbine.
The other felt the pulse of his dying son.
"Sell your lives dear," he said. The rifle-shots
Rattled within the bricked-in engine-room
Like firecrackers set off in a stone jug,
And there was a harsh stink of sweat and powder.
There was a moment when the door held firm.
Then it was cracked with sun.
                                Brown fired and missed.
A shadow with a sword leaped through the sun.
"That's Ossawattomie," said the tired voice
Of Colonel Washington.
                        The shadow lunged
And Brown fell to his knees.
                            The sword bent double,
A light sword, better for parades than fighting,
The shadow had to take it in both hands

JOHN BROWN

He was a stone,
A stone eroded to a cutting edge.

And fairly rain his blows with it on Brown
Before he sank.

                    Now two marines were down,
The rest rushed in over their comrades' bodies,
Pinning one man of Brown's against the wall
With bayonets, another to the floor.

Lee, on his rise of ground, shut up his watch.
It had been just a quarter of an hour
Since Stuart gave the signal for the storm,
And now it was over.

                    All but the long dying.

————

Cudjo, the negro, watched from the pantry
The smooth glissades of the dancing gentry,
His splay-feet tapping in time to the tune
While his broad face beamed like a drunken moon
At candles weeping in crystal sconces,
Waxed floors glowing like polished bronzes,
Sparkles glinting on Royal Worcester
And all the stir and color and luster
Where Miss Louisa and Miss Amanda,
Proud dolls scissored from silver paper,
With hoopskirts wide as the front veranda
And the gypsy eyes of a caged frivolity,
Pointed their toes in a satin caper
To the nonchalant glory of the Quality.
And there were the gentlemen, one and all,
Friends and neighbors of Wingate Hall—
Old Judge Brooke from Little Vermilion
With the rusty voice of a cracked horse-pistol
And manners as stiff as a French cotillion.
Huger Shepley and Wainscott Bristol,
Hawky arrogant sons of anger
Who rode like devils and fought like cocks
And watched, with an ineffable languor
Their spoilt youth tarnish a dicing-box.
The Cazenove boys and the Cotter brothers,
Pepperalls from Pepperall Ride.

Cummings and Crowls and a dozen others,
Every one with a name and a pride.
Sallow young dandies in shirts with ruffles,
Each could dance like a blowing feather,
And each had the voice that Georgia muffles
In the lazy honey of her May weather.

Cudjo watched and measured and knew them,
Seeing behind and around and through them
With the shrewd, dispassionate, smiling eye
Of the old-time servant in days gone by.
He couldn't read and he couldn't write,
But he knew Quality, black or white,
And even his master could not find
The secret place in the back of his mind
Where witch-bones talked to a scarlet rag
And a child's voice spoke from a conjur-bag.
For he belonged to the hidden nation,
The mute, enormous confederation
Of the planted earth and the burden borne
And the horse that is ridden and given corn.
The wind from the brier-patch brought him news
That never went walking in white men's shoes
And the grapevine whispered its message faster
Than a horse could gallop across a grave,
Till, long ere the letter could tell the master,
The doomsday rabbits had told the slave.

He was faithful as bread or salt,
A flawless servant without a fault,
Major-domo of Wingate Hall,
Proud of his white folks, proud of it all.
They might scold him, they might let him scold them,
And he might know things that he never told them,
But there was a bond, and the bond would hold,
On either side until both were cold.

So he didn't judge, though he knew, he knew,
How the yellow babies down by the Slough,
Had a fourth of their blood from old Judge Brooke,

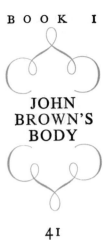

JOHN
BROWN'S
BODY

And where Sue Crowl got her Wingate look,
And the whole, mad business of Shepley's Wager,
And why Miss Harriet married the Major.
And he could trace with unerring ease
A hundred devious pedigrees
Of man and horse, from the Squire's Rapscallion
Back to the stock of the Arab stallion,
And the Bristol line through its baffling dozens
Of doubly-removed half-second-cousins,
And found a creed and a whole theology
On the accidents of human geology.

He looked for Clay in the dancing whirl,
There he was, coming down the line,
Hand in hand with a dark, slim girl
Whose dress was the color of light in wine
Sally Dupré from Appleton
Where the blackshawled ladies rock in the sun
And young things labor and old things rule,
A proud girl, taught in a humbling school
That the only daughters of misalliance
Must harden their hearts against defiance
Of all the uncles and all the aunts
Who succour such offspring of mischance
And wash them clean from each sinful intention
With the kindliest sort of incomprehension.

She had the Appleton mouth, it seemed,
And the Appleton way of riding,
But when she sorrowed and if she dreamed,
Something came out from hiding.
She could sew all day on an Appleton hem
And look like a saint in plaster,
But when the fiddles began to play
And her feet beat fast but her heart beat faster
An alien grace inhabited them
And she looked like her father, the dancing-master,
The scapegrace elegant, "French" Dupré,
Come to the South on a luckless day,
With bright paste buckles sewn on his pumps.

A habit of holding the ace of trumps,
And a manner of kissing a lady's hand
Which the county failed to understand.
He stole Sue Appleton's heart away
With eyes that were neither black nor grey,
And broke the heart of the Brookes' best mare
To marry her safely with time to spare
While the horsewhip uncles toiled behind—
He knew his need and she knew her mind.
And the love they had was as bright and brief
As the dance of the gilded maple-leaf,
Till she died in Charleston of childbed fever
Before her looks or his heart could leave her.
It took the flavor out of his drinking
And left him thoughts he didn't like thinking,
So he wrapped his child in the dead girl's shawl
And sent her politely to Uncle Paul
With a black-edged note full of grief and scruples
And half the money he owed his pupils,
Saw that Sue had the finest hearse
That I. O. U.'s could possibly drape her
And elegized her in vile French verse
While his hot tears spotted the borrowed paper.

He still had manners, he tried to recover,
But something went when he buried his lover.
No women with eyes could ever scold him
But he would make places too hot to hold him,
He shrugged his shoulders and kept descending—
Life was a farce, but it needed ending.
The tag-line found him too tired to dread it
And he died as he lived, with an air, on credit,
In his host's best shirt and a Richmond garret,
Talking to shadows and drinking claret.
He passed when Sally was barely four
And the Appleton kindred breathed once more
And, with some fervor, began to try
To bury the bone of his memory
And strictly expunge from his daughter's semblance
All possible traces of a resemblance.

Which system succeeded, to outward view,
As well as most of such systems do
And resulted in mixing a martyr's potions
For "French" Dupré in his daughter's notions.

And slander is sinful and gossip wrong,
But country memories are long,
The Appleton clan is a worthy clan
But we remember the dancing-man.
The girl is pretty, the girl seems wise,
The girl was born with her father's eyes.
She will play with our daughters and know our sons,
We cannot offend the Appletons.
Bristols and Wingates, Shepleys and Crowls,
We wouldn't hurt her to save our souls.
But after all—and nevertheless—
For one has to think—and one must confess—
And one should admit—but one never knows—
So it has gone, and so it goes,
Through the sun and the wind and the rainy weather
Whenever ladies are gathered together,
Till, little by little and stitch by stitch,
The girl is put in her proper niche
With all the virtues that we can draw
For someone else's daughter-in-law,
A girl to be kind to, a girl we're lucky in,
A girl to marry some nice Kentuckian,
Some Alabaman, some Carolinian—
In fact, if you ask me for my opinion,
There are lots of boys in the Northern sections
And some of them have quite good connections—
She looks charming this evening, doesn't she?
If she danced just a little less *dashingly!*

Cudjo watched her as she went by,
"She's got a light foot," thought Cudgo, "Hi!
A light, swif' foot and a talkin' eye!
But you'll need more'n dat, Miss Sally Dupré
Before you proposals with young Marse Clay.
And as soon as de fiddles finish slewin'

Dey's sixteen things I ought to be doin'.
The Major's sure to be wantin' his dram,
We'll have to be cuttin' a second ham,
And dat trashy high-yaller, Parker's Guinea,
Was sayin' some Yankee name Old John Brown
Has raised de Debil back in Virginny
And freed de niggers all over town,
He's friends with de ha'nts and steel won't touch him
But the paterollers is sure to cotch him.
How come he want to kick up such a dizziness!
Nigger-business ain't white-folks' business."

————

There was no real moon in all the soft, clouded night,
The rats of night had eaten the silver cheese,
Though here and there a forgotten crumb of old brightness
Gleamed and was blotted.
                  But there was no real moon,
No bowl of nacre, dripping an old delusive
Stain on the changed, strange grass, making faces strange;
There was only a taste of warm rain not yet fallen,
A wine-colored dress, turned black because of no moon,
—It would have been spangled in moon—and a broadcloth coat,
And two voices talking together, quite softly, quite calmly.
The dance. Such a lovely dance. But you dance so lightly.
Amanda dances so well. But you dance so lightly.
Louisa looks so pretty in pink, don't you think?
Are you fond of Scott? Yes, I'm very fond of Scott.
Elegant extracts from gilt-edged volumes called Keepsakes
And Godey's Lady's Book words.
                  If I were a girl,
A girl in a Godey's Lady's Book steel-engraving,
I would have no body or legs, no aches or delusions.
I would know what to do. I would marry a man called Mister.
We would live in a steel-engraving, in various costumes
Designed in the more respectable Paris modes,
With two little boys in little plush hats like muffins,
And two little girls with pantalettes to their chins.
I must do that, I think.

But now my light feet know
That they will be tired and burning with all my dancing
Before I cool them in the exquisite coolness
Of water or the cool virginal sheets of virgins,
And a face comes swimming toward me out of black broadcloth
And my heart knocks.
                    Who are you, why are you here?
Why should you trouble my eyes?
                              No, Mr. Wingate,
I cannot agree with you on the beauties of Byron.
But why should something melt in the stuff of my hand,
And my voice sound thin in my ears?
                              This face is a face
Like any other face. Did my mother once
Hear thin blood sing in her ears at a voice called Mister?
And wish for—and not wish for—and when the strange thing
Was consummate, then, and she lay in a coil of darkness,
Did she feel so much changed? What is it to be
A woman?
              No, I must live in a steel-engraving.

His voice said. But there was other than his voice.
Something that heard warm rain on unopened flowers
And spoke or tried to speak across swimming blackness
To the slight profile and the wine-colored dress.
Her hair was black. Her eyes might be black or grey.
He could not remember, it irked him not to remember.
But she was just Sally Dupré from Appleton
Only she was not. Only she was a shadow
And a white face—a terrible, white shut face
That looked through windows of inflexible glass
Disdainfully upon the beauties of Byron
And every puppy that ever howled for the moon
To brush warm raindrops across the unopened flower
And so quiet the heart with—what?
                              But you speak to her aunts.
You are Wingate of Wingate Hall. You are not caught
Like a bee drunk with the smell of honey, the smell of sleep,
In a slight flower of glass whose every petal
Shows eyes one cannot remember as black or grey.

You converse easily on elegant subjects
Suitable for young ladies.
                            You do not feel
The inexorable stairs of the flesh ascended
By an armed enemy with a naked torch.
This has been felt before, this has been quenched
With fitting casualness in flesh that has
A secret stain of the sun.
                            It is not a subject
Suitable for the converse of young ladies.

"My God, My God, why will she not answer the aching?
My God, My God, to lie at her side through the darkness!"

And yet——is it real——do I really——
                            The wine-colored dress
Rose. Broadcloth rose and took her back to the dance.

———————

The nickeled lamp threw a wide yellow disk
On the red tablecloth with the tasseled fringes.
Jack Ellyat put his book down with a slight
Impatient gesture.
                            There was mother, knitting
The same grey end of scarf while Father read
The same unaltered paper through the same
Old-fashioned spectacles with the worn bows.

Jane with one apple-cheek and one enshadowed,
Soundlessly conjugated Latin verbs,
"Amo, amas, amat," through sober lips,
"Amamus, amatis, amant," and still no sound.
He glanced at the clock. On top of it was Phaëton
Driving bronze, snarling horses down the sharp,
Quicksilver, void, careening gulfs of air.
Until they smashed upon a black-marble sea.
The round spiked trophy of the brazen sun
Weighed down his chariot with its heavy load
Of ponderous fire.

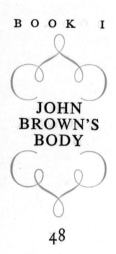
To be like Phaëton
And drive the trophy-sun!
                    But he and his horses
Were frozen in their attitude of snarling,
Frozen forever to the tick of a clock.
Not all the broomstick witches of New England
Could break that congealed motion and cast down
The huge sun thundering on the black marble
Of the mantelpiece, streaked with white veins of foam.
If once such things could happen, all could happen,
The snug, safe world crack up like broken candy
And the young rivers, roaring, rush to the sea;
White bulls that caught the morning on their horns
And shook the secure earth until they found

Some better recompense for life than life,
The untamed ghost, the undiminished star.

But it would not happen. Nothing would ever happen.
He had been here, like this, ten thousand times,
He would be here, like this, ten thousand more,
Until at last the little ticks of the clock
Had cooled what had been hot, and changed the thin,
Blue, forking veins across the back of his hand
Into the big, soft veins on Father's hand.
And the world would be snug.
                              And he would sit
Reading the same newspaper, after dinner,
Through spectacles whose bows were getting worn
While a wife knitted on an endless scarf
And a child slowly formed with quiet lips
"Amo, amas, amat," and still no sound.
And it would be over. Over without having been.

His father turned a creaking page of paper
And cleared his throat. "The *Tribune* calls," he said,
"Brown's raid the work of a madman. Well, they're right,
But—"
            Mrs. Ellyat put her knitting down.
"Are they going to hang him, Will?"

                              "It looks that way."
"But, Father, when—"
                        "They have the right, my son,
He broke the law."
                        "But, Will! You don't believe—"
A little spark lit Mr. Ellyat's eyes.
"I didn't say I thought that he was wrong.
I said they had the right to hang the man,
But they'll hang slavery with him."
                                        A quick pulse
Beat in Jack Ellyat's wrist. Behind his eyes
A bearded puppet creaked upon a rope
And the sky darkened because he was there.
Now it was Mother talking in a strange
Iron-bound voice he'd never heard before.
"I prayed for him in church last Sunday, Will.
I pray for him at home here every night.
I don't know—I don't care—what laws he broke.
I know that he was right. I pray to God
To show the world somehow that he was right
And break these Southern people into knowing!
And I know this—in every house and church,
All through the North—women are praying for him,
Praying for him. And God will hear those prayers."

"He will, my dear," said Mr. Ellyat gently,
"But what will be His answer?"
                                He took her hand,
Smoothing it for a moment. Then she sighed
And turned back to the interminable scarf.
Jack Ellyat's pulse beat faster.
                                Women praying,
Praying at night, in every house in the North,
Praying for old John Brown until their knees
Ached with stiff cold.
                        Innumerable prayers
Inexorably rising, till the dark
Vault of the midnight was so thronged and packed
The wild geese could not arrow through the storm
Of terrible, ascendant, women's prayers. . . .

The clock struck nine, and Phaëton still stood
Frozenly urging on his frozen horses,
But, for a moment, to Jack Ellyat's eyes,
The congealed hoofs had seemed to paw the air
And the bronze car roll forward.

———————

On Saturday, in Southern market towns,
When I was a boy with twenty cents to spend,
The carts began to drift in with the morning,
And, by the afternoon, the slipshod Square
And all broad Center Street were lined with them;
Moth-eaten mules that whickered at each other
Between the mended shafts of rattletrap wagons,
Mud-spattered buggies, mouldy phaetons,
And, here and there, an ox-cart from the hills
Whose solemn team had shoulders of rough, white rock,
Innocent noses, black and wet as snailshells,
And that inordinate patience in their eyes.

There always was a Courthouse in the Square,
A cupolaed Courthouse, drowsing Time away
Behind the grey-white pillars of its porch
Like an old sleepy judge in a spotted gown;
And, down the Square, always a languid jail
Of worn, uneven brick with moss in the cracks
Or stone weathered the grey of weathered pine.
The plump jail-master wore a linen duster
In summer, and you used to see him sit
Tilted against the wall in a pine-chair,
Spitting reflectively in the warm dust
While endless afternoons slowly dissolved
Into the longer shadow, the dust-blue twilight.
Higgledy-piggledy days—days that are gone—
The trotters are dead, all the yellow-painted sulkies
Broken for firewood—the old Courthouse grins
Through new false-teeth of Alabama limestone—
The haircloth lap-robe weeps on a Ford radiator—

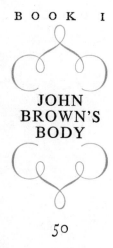

But I have seen the old Courthouse. I have seen
The flyspecked windows and the faded flag
Over the judge's chair, touched the scuffed walls,
Spat in the monumental brass spittoons
And smelt the smell that never could be aired,
Although one opened windows for a year,
The unforgettable, intangible
Mixture of cheap cigars, worm-eaten books,
Sweat, poverty, negro hair-oil, grief and law.
I have seen the long room packed with quiet men,
Fit to turn mob, if need were, in a flash—
Cocked-pistol men, so lazily attentive
Their easy languor knocked against your ribs
As, hour by hour, the lawyers droned along,
And minute on creeping minute, your cold necknape
Waited the bursting of the firecracker,
The flare of fury.
   And yet, that composed fury
Burnt itself out, unflaring—was held down
By a dry, droning voice, a faded flag.
The kettle never boiled, the pistol stayed
At cock but the snake-head hammer never fell. . . .
The little boys climbed down beyond the windows. . . .

So, in the cupolaed Courthouse there in Charlestown,
When the jail-guards had carried in the cot
Where Brown lay like a hawk with a broken back,
I hear the rustle of the moving crowd,
The buzz outside, taste the dull, heavy air,
Smell the stale smell and see the country carts
Hitched in the streets.
   For a long, dragging week
Of market-Saturdays the trial went on.
The droning voices rise and fall and rise.
Stevens lies quiet on his mattress, breathing
The harsh and difficult breath of a dying man,
Although not dying then.
   Beyond the Square
The trees are dry, but all the dry leaves not fallen—

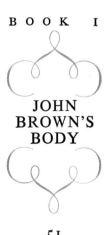

Yellow leaves falling through a grey-blue dusk,
The first winds of November whirl and scatter them. . . .

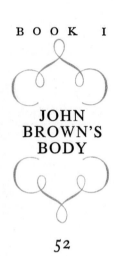

Read as you will in any of the books,
The details of the thing, the questions and answers,
How sometimes Brown would walk, sometimes was carried,
At first would hardly plead, half-refused counsel,
Accepted later, made up witness-lists,
Grew fitfully absorbed in his defense,
Only to flare in temper at his first lawyers
And drive them from the case.
                              Questions and answers,
Wheels creaking in a void.
                              Sometimes he lay
Quiet upon his cot, the hawk-eyes staring.
Sometimes his fingers moved mechanically
As if at their old task of sorting wool,
Fingertips that could tell him in the dark
Whether the wood they touched was from Ohio
Or from Vermont. They had the shepherd's gift.
It was his one sure talent.
                              Questions creaking
Uselessly back and forth.
                              No one can say
That the trial was not fair. The trial was fair,
Painfully fair by every rule of law,
And that it was made not the slightest difference.
The law's our yardstick, and it measures well
Or well enough when there are yards to measure.
Measure a wave with it, measure a fire,
Cut sorrow up in inches, weigh content.
You can weigh John Brown's body well enough,
But how and in what balance weigh John Brown?

He had the shepherd's gift, but that was all.
He had no other single gift for life.
Some men are pasture Death turns back to pasture,
Some are fire-opals on that iron wrist,
Some the deep roots of wisdoms not yet born.

John Brown was none of these,
He was a stone,
A stone eroded to a cutting edge
By obstinacy, failure and cold prayers.
Discredited farmer, dubiously involved
In lawsuit after lawsuit, Shubel Morgan
Fantastic bandit of the Kansas border,
Red-handed murderer at Pottawattomie,
Cloudy apostle, whooped along to death
By those who do no violence themselves
But only buy the guns to have it done,
Sincere of course, as all fanatics are,
And with a certain minor-prophet air,
That fooled the world to thinking him half-great
When all he did consistently was fail.
So far one advocate.
                    But there is this.

Sometimes there comes a crack in Time itself.
Sometimes the earth is torn by something blind.
Sometimes an image that has stood so long
It seems implanted as the polar star
Is moved against an unfathomed force
That suddenly will not have it any more.
Call it the *mores,* call it God or Fate,
Call it Mansoul or economic law,
That force exists and moves.
                    And when it moves
It will employ a hard and actual stone
To batter into bits an actual wall
And change the actual scheme of things.
                    John Brown
Was such a stone—unreasoning as the stone,
Destructive as the stone, and, if you like,
Heroic and devoted as such a stone.
He had no gift for life, no gift to bring
Life but his body and a cutting edge,
But he knew how to die.
                    And yardstick law
Gave him six weeks to burn that hoarded knowledge

In one swift fire whose sparks fell like live coals
On every State in the Union.
                                    Listen now,
Listen, the bearded lips are speaking now,
There are no more guerilla-raids to plan,
There are no more hard questions to be solved
Of right and wrong, no need to beg for peace,
Here is the peace unbegged, here is the end,
Here is the insolence of the sun cast off,
Here is the voice already fixed with night.

JOHN BROWN'S SPEECH

I have, may it please the Court, a few words to say.

In the first place I deny everything but what I have all along admitted: of a design on my part to free slaves. . . .

Had I interfered in the matter which I admit, and which I admit has been fairly proved . . . had I so interfered in behalf of the rich, the powerful, the intelligent, or the so-called great . . . and suffered and sacrificed, what I have in this interference, it would have been all right. Every man in this Court would have deemed it an act worthy of reward rather than punishment.

I see a book kissed which I suppose to be the Bible, or at least the New Testament, which teaches me that all things whatsoever I would that men should do unto me, I should do even so to them. It teaches me further to remember them that are in bonds as bound with them. I endeavored to act up to that instruction. I say I am yet too young to understand that God is any respecter of persons. I believe that to have interfered as I have done, as I have always freely admitted I have done in behalf of His despised poor, I did no wrong, but right. Now, if it is deemed necessary that I should forfeit my life for the furtherance of the ends of justice and mingle my blood further with the blood of my children and with the blood of millions in this slave country whose rights are disregarded by wicked, cruel and unjust enactments, I say, let it be done.

Let me say one word further. I feel entirely satisfied with the treatment I have received on my trial. Considering all the circumstances, it has been more generous than I expected. But I feel no consciousness of guilt. I have stated from the first what was my intention and what was not. I never had any design against the liberty of any person, nor any disposition to commit treason or incite slaves to rebel or make any general insurrection. I never encouraged any man to do so but always discouraged any idea of that kind.

Let me say also, in regard to the statements made by some of those connected with me, I hear it has been stated by some of them that I have induced them to join with me. But the contrary is true. I do not say this to injure them, but as regretting their weakness. Not one but joined me of his own accord, and the greater part at their own expense. A number of them I never saw, and never had a word of conversation with, till the day they came to me, and that was for the purpose I have stated.

Now I have done.

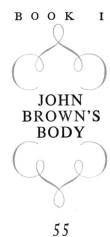
———————

The voice ceased. There was a deep, brief pause.
The judge pronounced the formal words of death.
One man, a stranger, tried to clap his hands.
The foolish sound was stopped.
There was nothing but silence then.
                      No cries in the court,
No roar, no slightest murmur from the thronged street,
As Brown went back to jail between his guards.
The heavy door shut behind them.
There was a noise of chairs scraped back in the court-room,
And that huge sigh of a crowd turning back into men.

———————

A month between the sentence and the hanging.
A month of endless visitors, endless letters.
A Mrs. Russell came to clean his coat.
A sculptor sketched him.
              In the anxious North,
The anxious Dr. Howe most anxiously
Denied all godly connection with the raid,
And Gerrit Smith conveniently went mad
For long enough to sponge his mind of all
Memory of such an unsuccessful deed.

Only the tough, swart-minded Higginson
Kept a grim decency, would not deny.
Pity the portly men, pity the pious,
Pity the fool who lights the powder-mine,
They need your counterfeit penny, they will live long.

In Charlestown meanwhile, there were whispers of rescue.
Brown told them,
"I am worth now infinitely more to die than to live."
And lived his month so, busily.
A month of trifles building up a legend
And letters in a pinched, firm handwriting
Courageous, scriptural, misspelt and terse,
Sowing a fable everywhere they fell
While the town filled with troops.
                          The Governor came,
Enemies, friends, militia-cavaliers,
Old Border Foes.
                    The month ebbed into days,
The wife and husband met for the last time,
The last letter was written:

"To be inscribed on the old family Monument at North Elba,
Oliver Brown born 1839 was killed at Harpers Ferry, Va. Nov.
     17th 1859
Watson Brown born 1835 was wounded at Harpers Ferry Nov.
     17th and died Nov. 19th 1859
(My Wife can) supply *blank* dates to above
John Brown born May 9th 1800 was executed at Charlestown
     Va. December 2nd 1859."

At last the clear warm day, so slow to come.

The North that had already now begun
To mold his body into crucified Christ's,
Hung fables about those hours—saw him move
Symbolically, kiss a negro child,
Do this and that, say things he never said,
To swell the sparse, hard outlines of the event
With sentimental omen.

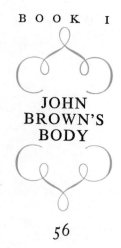

It was not so.
He stood on the jail-porch in carpet-slippers,
Clad in a loose ill-fitting suit of black,
Tired farmer waiting for his team to come.
He left one last written message:

"I, John Brown, am now quite *certain* that the crimes of this
guilty land: will never be purged *away:* but with Blood. I had
as I now think: vainly flattered myself that without *very much*
bloodshed; it might be done."

They did not hang him in the jail or the Square.
The two white horses dragged the rattling cart
Out of the town. Brown sat upon his coffin.
Beyond the soldiers lay the open fields
Earth-colored, sleepy with unfallen frost.
The farmer's eye took in the bountiful land.
"This *is* a beautiful country," said John Brown.

The gallows-stairs were climbed, the death-cap fitted.
Behind the gallows,
Before a line of red-and-grey cadets,
A certain odd Professor T. J. Jackson
Watched disapprovingly the ragged militia
Deploy for twelve long minutes ere they reached
Their destined places.
The Presbyterian sabre of his soul
Was moved by a fey breath.
                              He saw John Brown,
A tiny blackened scrap of paper-soul
Fluttering above the Pit that Calvin barred
With bolts of iron on the unelect;
He heard the just, implacable Voice speak out
"Depart ye wicked to eternal fire."
And sternly prayed that God might yet be moved
To save the predestined cinder from the flame.

Brown did not hear the prayer. The rough black cloth
Of the death-cap hid his eyes now. He had seen
The Blue Ridge Mountains couched in their blue haze.

Perhaps he saw them still, behind his eyes—
Perhaps just cloth, perhaps nothing any more.
"I shall look unto the hills from whence cometh my help."

The hatchet cut the cord. The greased trap fell.

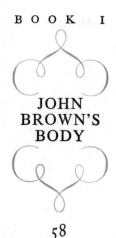

BOOK I

JOHN
BROWN'S
BODY

58

Colonel Preston:

"So perish all such enemies of Virginia,
All such enemies of the Union,
All such foes of the human race."

————

John Brown's body lies a-mouldering in the grave.
He will not come again with foolish pikes
And a pack of desperate boys to shadow the sun.
He has gone back North. The slaves have forgotten his eyes.
John Brown's body lies a-mouldering in the grave.
John Brown's body lies a-mouldering in the grave.
Already the corpse is changed, under the stone,
The strong flesh rotten, the bones dropping away.
Cotton will grow next year, in spite of the skull.
Slaves will be slaves next year, in spite of the bones.
Nothing is changed, John Brown, nothing is changed.

*"There is a song in my bones. There is a song
In my white bones."*
I hear no song. I hear
Only the blunt seeds growing secretly
In the dark entrails of the preparate earth,
The rustle of the cricket under the leaf,
The creaking of the cold wheel of the stars.

*"Bind my white bones together—hollow them
To skeleton pipes of music. When the wind
Blows from the budded Spring, the song will blow."*

I hear no song. I only hear the roar
Of the Spring freshes, and the gushing voice
Of mountain-brooks that overflow their banks,
Swollen with melting ice and crumbled earth.

"That is my song.
It is made of water and wind. It marches on."

No, John Brown's body lies a-mouldering,
A-mouldering.

"My bones have been washed clean
And God blows through them with a hollow sound,
And God has shut his wildfire in my dead heart."

I hear it now,
Faint, faint as the first droning flies of March,
Faint as the multitudinous, tiny sigh
   Of grasses underneath a windy scythe.

"It will grow stronger."

It has grown stronger. It is marching on.
It is a throbbing pulse, a pouring surf,
It is the rainy gong of the Spring sky
Echoing,
John Brown's body,
John Brown's body.
But still it is not fierce. I find it still
More sorrowful than fierce.

"You have not heard it yet. You have not heard
The ghosts that walk in it, the shaking sound."
Strong medicine,
Bitter medicine of the dead,
I drink you now. I hear the unloosed thing,
The anger of the ripe wheat—the ripened earth
Sullenly quaking like a beaten drum
From Kansas to Vermont. I hear the stamp
Of the ghost-feet. I hear the ascending sea.

   "Glory, Glory, Hallelujah,
   Glory, Glory, Hallelujah,
   Glory, Glory, Hallelujah!"

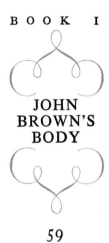

What is this agony of the marching dust?
What are these years ground into hatchet blades?

"Ask the tide why it rises with the moon,
My bones and I have risen like that tide
And an immortal anguish plucks us up
And will not hide us till our song is done."

The phantom drum diminishes—the year
Rolls back. It is only winter still, not spring,
The snow still flings its white on the new grave,
Nothing is changed, John Brown, nothing is changed
John . . . Brown . . .

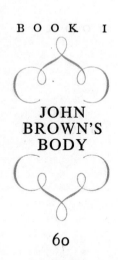

BOOK I

JOHN
BROWN'S
BODY

60

BOOK TWO

A smoke-stained Stars-and-Stripes droops from a broken
toothpick and ninety tired men march out of fallen Sumter
to their ships, drums rattling and colors flying.

Their faces are worn and angry, their bellies empty and cold,
but the stubborn salute of a gun, fifty times repeated, keeps their
backs straight as they march out, and answers something stubborn
and mute in their flesh.

Beauregard, *beau sabreur,* hussar-sword with the gilded hilt,
the gilded metal of the guard twisted into lovelocks and roses,
vain as Murat, dashing as Murat, Pierre Gustave Toutant Beauregard is a pose of conquering courtesy under a palmetto-banner.
The lugubrious little march goes grimly by his courtesy, he
watches it unsmiling, a light half-real, half that of invisible foot-
lights on his French, dark, handsome face.

JOHN
BROWN'S
BODY

The stone falls in the pool, the ripples spread.
The colt in the Long Meadow kicked up his heels.
"That was a fly," he thought, "It's early for flies."
But being alive, in April, was too fine
For flies or anything else to bother a colt.
He kicked up his heels again, this time in pure joy,
And started to run a race with the wind and his shadow.
After the stable stuffiness, the sun.
After the straw-littered boards, the squelch of the turf.
His little hoofs felt lighter than dancing-shoes,
He scared himself with a blue-jay, his heart was a leaf.
He was pure joy in action, he was the unvexed
Delight of all moving lightness and swift-footed pace,
The pride of the flesh, the young Spring neighing and rearing.
Sally Dupré called to him from the fence.
He came like a charge in a spatter of clean-cut clods,
Ears back, eyes wide and wild with folly and youth.
He drew up snorting.
                        She laughed and brushed at her skirt
Where the mud had splashed it.
                                "There, Star—there, silly boy!
Why won't you ever learn sense?"
                                But her eyes were hot,
Her hands were shaking as she offered the sugar
—Long-fingered, appleblossom-shadow hands—
Star blew at the sugar once, then mumbled it up.
She patted the pink nose. "There, silly Star!
That's for Fort Sumter, Star!" How hot her eyes were!
"Star, do you know you're a Confederate horse?
Do you know I'm going to call you Beauregard?"

Star whinnied, and asked for more sugar. She put her hand
On his neck for a moment that matched the new green leaves
And sticky buds of April.
                                You would have said
They were grace in quietness, seen so, woman and horse. . . .
The widened ripple breaks against a stone
The heavy noon walks over Chancellorsville
On brazen shoes, but where the squadron rode

Into the ambush, the blue flies are coming
To blow on the dead meat.

Carter, the telegraph-operator, sighed
And propped his eyes awake again.
                                   He was tired.
Dog-tired, stone-tired, body and mind burnt up
With too much poker last night and too little sleep.
He hated the Sunday trick. It was Riley's turn
To take it, but Riley's wife was having a child.
He cursed the child and the wife and Sunday and Riley.
Nothing ever happened at Stroudsburg Siding
And yet he had to be here and keep awake
With the flat, stale taste of too little sleep in his mouth
And wait for nothing to happen.
                                   His bulky body
Lusted for sleep with every muscle and nerve.
He'd rather have sleep than a woman or whiskey or money.
He'd give up the next three women that might occur
For ten minutes' sleep, he'd never play poker again,
He'd—battered face beginning to droop on his hands—
Sleep—women—whiskey—eyelids too heavy to lift—
"Yes, Ma, I said, 'Now I lay me.'"—
                                   The sounder chattered
And his head snapped back with a sharp, neck-breaking jerk.
By God, he'd nearly—*chat*—*chitter-chatter-chat-chat*—
For a moment he took it in without understanding
And then the vein in his forehead began to swell
And his eyes bulged wide awake.
                                   "By Jesus!" he said,
And stared at the sounder as if it had turned to a snake.
"By Jesus!" he said, "By Jesus, they've done it!" he said.

The cruelty of cold trumpets wounds the air.
The ponderous princes draw their gauntlets on.
The captains fit their coal-black armor on.

Judah P. Benjamin, the dapper Jew.
Seal-sleek, black-eyed, lawyer and epicure,

Able, well-hated, face alive with life,
Looked round the council-chamber with the slight
Perpetual smile he held before himself
Continually like a silk-ribbed fan.
Behind the fan, his quick, shrewd, fluid mind
Weighed Gentiles in an old balance.

                              There they were.
Toombs, the tall, laughing, restless Georgian,
As fine to look at as a yearling bull,
As hard to manage.

                 Stephens, sickly and pale,
Sweet-voiced, weak-bodied, ailingly austere,
The mind's thin steel wearing the body out,
The racked intelligence, the crippled charm.
Mallory—Reagan—Walker—at the head
Davis.

        The mind behind the silk-ribbed fan
Was a dark prince, clothed in an Eastern stuff,
Whose brown hands cupped about a crystal egg
That filmed with colored cloud. The eyes stared, searching.

"I am the Jew. What am I doing here?
The Jew is in my blood and in my hands,
The lonely, bitter and quicksilver drop,
The stain of myrrh that dyes no Gentile mind
With tinctures out of the East and the sad blare
Of the curled ramshorn on Atonement Day.
A river runs between these men and me,
A river of blood and time and liquid gold,
—Oh white rivers of Canaan, running the night!—
And we are colleagues. And we speak to each other
Across the roar of that river, but no more.
I hide myself behind a smiling fan.
They hide themselves behind a Gentile mask
And, if they fall, they will be lifted up,
Being the people, but if I once fall
I fall forever, like the rejected stone.
That is the Jew of it, my Gentile friends,
To see too far ahead and yet go on
And I can smile at it behind my fan

With a drowned mirth that you would find uncouth
For here we are, the makeshift Cabinet
Of a new nation, gravely setting down
Rules, precedents and cautions, never once
Admitting aloud the cold, plain Franklin sense
That if we do not hang together now
We shall undoubtedly hang separately.
It is the Jew, to see too far ahead—

I wonder what they're doing in the North,
And how their Cabinet shapes, and how they take
Their railsplitter, and if they waste their time
As we waste ours and Mr. Davis's.

Jefferson Davis, pride of Mississippi,
First President of the Confederate States,
What are you thinking now?
                    Your eyes look tired.
Your face looks more and more like John Calhoun.
And that is just, because you are his son
In everything but blood, the austere child
Of his ideas, the flower of states-rights.
I will not gird against you, Jefferson Davis.
I sent you a challenge once, but that's forgotten,
And though your blood runs differently from mine,
The Jew salutes you from behind his fan,
Because you are the South he fell in love with
When that young black-haired girl with the Gentile-eyes,
Proud, and a Catholic, and with honey-lips,
First dinted her French heels upon his heart. . . .
We have changed since, but the remembered Spring
Can change no more, even in the Autumn smokes.
We cannot help that havoc of the heart
But my changed mind remembers half the spring
And shall till winter falls.
                    No, Jefferson Davis,
You are not she—you are not the warm night
On the bayou, or the New Orleans lamps,
The white-wine bubbles in the crystal cup,
The almond blossoms, sleepy with the sun:

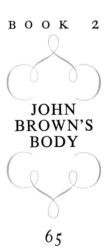

But, nevertheless, you are the South in word,
Deed, thought and temper, the cut cameo
Brittle but durable, refined but fine,
The hands well-shaped, not subtle, but not weak,
The mind set in tradition but not unjust,
The generous slaveholder, the gentleman
Who neither forces his gentility
Nor lets it be held lightly—

                                    and yet, and yet
I think you look too much like John Calhoun,
I think your temper is too brittly-poised,
I think your hands too scholar-sensitive,
And though they say you mingle in your voice
The trumpet and the harp, I think it lacks
That gift of warming men which coarser voices
Draw from the common dirt you tread upon
But do not take in your hands. I think you are
All things except success, all honesty
Except the ultimate honesty of the earth,
All talents but the genius of the sun.
And yet I would not have you otherwise,
Although I see too clearly what you are.

Except—except—oh honeydropping Spring,
Oh black-haired woman with the Gentile eyes!
Tell me, you Gentiles, when your Gentile wives
Pray in the church for you and for the South,
How do they pray?—not in that lulling voice
Where some drowned bell of France makes undertones
To the warm river washing the levee.
You do not have so good a prayer as mine.
You cannot have so good a prayer as mine."

———————

Lincoln, six feet one in his stocking feet,
The lank man, knotty and tough as a hickory rail,
Whose hands were always too big for white-kid gloves,
Whose wit was a coonskin sack of dry, tall tales,
Whose weathered face was homely as a plowed field—

Abraham Lincoln, who padded up and down
The sacred White House in nightshirt and carpet-slippers,
And yet could strike young hero-worshipping Hay
As dignified past any neat, balanced, fine
Plutarchan sentences carved in a Latin bronze;
The low clown out of the prairies, the ape-buffoon,
The small-town lawyer, the crude small-time politician,
State-character but comparative failure at forty
In spite of ambition enough for twenty Caesars,
Honesty rare as a man without self-pity,
Kindness as large and plain as a prairie wind,
And a self-confidence like an iron bar:
This Lincoln, President now by the grace of luck,
Disunion, politics, Douglas and a few speeches
Which make the monumental booming of Webster
Sound empty as the belly of a burst drum,
Lincoln shambled in to the Cabinet meeting
And sat, ungainly and awkward. Seated so
He did not seem so tall nor quite so strange
Though he was strange enough. His new broadcloth suit
Felt tight and formal across his big shoulders still
And his new shiny top-hat was not yet battered
To the bulging shape of the old familiar hat
He'd worn at Springfield, stuffed with its hoard of papers.
He was pretty tired. All week the office-seekers
Had plagued him as the flies in fly-time plague
A gaunt-headed, patient horse. The children weren't well
And Mollie was worried about them so sharp with her tongue.
But he knew Mollie and tried to let it go by.
Men tracked dirt in the house and women liked carpets.
Each had a piece of the right, that was all most people could
    stand.

Look at his Cabinet here. There were Seward and Chase,
Both of them good men, couldn't afford to lose them,
But Chase hates Seward like poison and Seward hates Chase
And both of 'em think they ought to be President
Instead of me. When Seward wrote me that letter
The other day, he practically told me so.
I suppose a man who was touchy about his pride

Would send them both to the dickens when he found out,
But I can't do that as long as they do their work.
The Union's too big a horse to keep changing the saddle
Each time it pinches you. As long as you're sure
The saddle fits, you're bound to put up with the pinches
And not keep fussing the horse.

                        When I was a boy
I remember figuring out when I went to town
That if I had just one pumpkin to bump in a sack
It was hard to carry, but once you could get two pumpkins,
One in each end of the sack, it balanced things up.
Seward and Chase'll do for my pair of pumpkins.
And as for me—if anyone else comes by
Who shows me that he can manage this job of mine
Better than I can—well, he can have the job.
It's harder sweating than driving six cross mules,
But I haven't run into that other fellow yet
And till or supposing I meet him, the job's my job
And nobody else's.

                    Seward and Chase don't know that.
They'll learn it, in time.

                        Wonder how Jefferson Davis
Feels, down there in Montgomery, about Sumter.
He must be thinking pretty hard and fast,
For he's an able man, no doubt of that.
We were born less than forty miles apart,
Less than a year apart—he got the start
Of me in age, and raising too, I guess,
In fact, from all you hear about the man,
If you set out to pick one of us two
For President, by birth and folks and schooling,
General raising, training up in office,
I guess you'd pick him, nine times out of ten
And yet, somehow, I've got to last him out.

These thoughts passed through the mind in a moment's flash.
Then that mind turned to business.

                        It was the calling
Of seventy-five thousand volunteers.

———————

Shake out the long line of verse like a lanyard of woven steel
And let us praise while we can what things no praise can deface,
The corn that hurried so fast to be ground in an iron wheel
The obdurate, bloody dream that slept before it grew base.

Not the silk flag and the shouts, the catchword patrioteers,
The screaming noise of the press, the preachers who howled for
    blood,
But a certain and stubborn pith in the hearts of the cannoneers
Who hardly knew their guns before they died in the mud.

They came like a run of salmon where the ice-fed Kennebec flings
Its death at the arrow-silver of the packed and mounting host,
They came like the young deer trooping to the ford by Eutaw
    Springs,
Their new horns fuzzy with velvet, their coats still rough with
    the frost.

North and South they assembled, one cry and the other cry,
And both are ghosts to us now, old drums hung up on a wall,
But they were the first hot wave of youth too-ready to die,
And they went to war with an air, as if they went to a ball.

Dress-uniform boys who rubbed their buttons brighter than gold,
And gave them to girls for flowers and raspberry-lemonade,
Unused to the sick fatigue, the route-march made in the cold,
The stink of the fever camps, the tarnish rotting the blade.

We in our time have seen that impulse going to war
And how that impulse is dealt with. We have seen the circle
    complete.
The ripe wheat wasted like trash between the fool and the whore.
We cannot praise again that anger of the ripe wheat.

This we have seen as well, distorted and half-forgotten
In what came before and after, where the blind went leading
    the blind,
The first swift rising of youth before the symbols were rotten,
The price too much to pay, the payment haughty in kind.

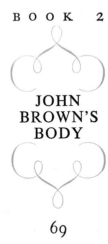

So with these men and then. They were much like the men you
    know,
Under the beards and the strangeness of clothes with a different
    fit.
They wrote mush-notes to their girls and wondered how it would
    go,
Half-scared, half-fierce at the thought, but none yet ready to
    quit.

Georgia, New York, Virginia, Rhode Island, Florida, Maine,
Piney-woods squirrel-hunter and clerk with the brand-new gun,
Thus they were marshalled and drilled, while Spring turned
    Summer again,
Until they could stumble toward death at gartersnake-crooked
    Bull Run.

———————

Wingate sat in his room at night
Between the moon and the candle-light,
Reading his Byron with knitted brows,
While his mind drank in the peace of his house,
It was long past twelve, and the night was deep
With moonlight and silence and wind and sleep,
And the small, dim noises, thousand-fold,
That all old houses and forests hold.
The boards that creak for nothing at all,
The leaf that rustles, the bough that sighs,
The nibble of mice in the wainscot-wall,
And the slow clock ticking the time that dies
All distilled in a single sound
Like a giant breathing underground,
A sound more sleepy than sleep itself.
Wingate put his book on the shelf
And went to the window. It was good
To walk in the ghost through a silver wood
And set one's mettle against the far
Bayonet-point of the fixed North Star.
He stood there a moment, wondering.
North Star, wasp with the silver sting
Blue-nosed star on the Yankee banners,

We are coming against you to teach you manners!
With crumbs of thunder and wreaths of myrtle
And cannon that dance to a Dixie chorus,
With a song that bites like a snapping-turtle
And the tiger-lily of Summer before us,
To pull you down like a torn bandanna,
And drown you deeper than the Savannah!

And still, while his arrogance made its cry,
He shivered a little, wondering why.

There was his uniform, grey as ash,
The boots that shone like a well-rubbed table,
The tassels of silk on the colored sash
And sleek Black Whistle down in the stable,
The housewife, stitched from a beauty's fan,
The pocket-Bible with Mother's writing,
The sabre never yet fleshed in man,
And all the crisp new toys of fighting.
He gloated at them with a boyish pride,
But still he wondered, Monmouth-eyed.
The Black Horse Troop was a cavalier
And gallant name for a lady's ear.
He liked the sound and the ringing brag
And the girls who stitched on the county flag,
The smell of horses and saddle-leather
And the feel of the squadron riding together,
From the loose-reined canter of colts at large,
To the crammed, tense second before the charge:
He liked it all with the young, keen zest
Of a hound unleashed and a hawk unjessed.

And yet—what happened to men in war?
Why were they all going out to war?

He brooded a moment. It wasn't slavery,
That stale red-herring of Yankee knavery
Not even states-rights, at least not solely,
But something so dim that it must be holy.

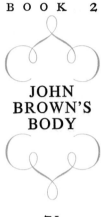

A voice, a fragrance, a taste of wine,
A face half-seen in old candleshine,
A yellow river, a blowing dust,
Something beyond you that you must trust,
Something so shrouded it must be great,
The dead men building the living State
From 'simmon-seed on a sandy bottom,
The woman South in her rivers laving
That body whiter than new-blown cotton
And savage and sweet as wild-orange-blossom,
The dark hair streams on the barbarous bosom,
If there ever has been a land worth saving—
In Dixie land, I'll take my stand,
And live and die for Dixie! . . .

And yet—and yet—in some cold Northern room,
Does anyone else stare out the obdurate moon
With doubtful passion, seeing his toys of fighting
Scribbled all over with such silver writing
From such a heart of peace, they seem the stale
Cast properties of a dead and childish tale?
And does he see, too soon,
Over the horse, over the horse and rider,
The grey, soft swathing shadowness of the spider,
Spinning his quiet loom?
No—no other man is cursed
With such doubleness of eye,
They can hunger, they can thirst,
But they know for what and why.

I can drink the midnight out,
And rise empty, having dined.
For my courage and my doubt
Are a double strand of mind,
And too subtly intertwined.
They are my flesh, they are my bone,
My shame and my foundation-stone.
I was born alone, to live alone.

Sally Dupré, Sally Dupré,
Eyes that are neither black nor grey,
Why do you haunt me, night and day?

Sea-changing eyes, with the deep, drowned glimmer
Of bar-gold crumbling from sunken ships,
Where the sea-dwarfs creep through the streaked, green shim-
    mer
To press the gold to their glass-cold lips.
They sculpture the gold for a precious ring,
In the caverns under the under-skies,
They would marry the sea to a sailor-king!
You have taken my heart from me, sea-born eyes.
You have taken it, yes, but I do not know.
There are too many roads where I must go.
There are too many beds where I have slept
For a night unweeping, to quit unwept,
And it needs a king to marry the sea.

Why have you taken my heart from me?
I am not justice nor loyalty.
I am the shape of the weathercock,
That all winds come to and all winds mock.
You are the image of sea-carved stone,
The silent thing that can suffer alone,
The little women are easier,
The easy women make lighter love,
I will not take your face to the war,
I will not carry your cast-off glove.

Sally Dupré, Sally Dupré,
Heart and body like sea-blown spray,
I cannot forget you, night or day.

So Wingate pondered in Wingate Hall,
And hated and loved in a single breath,
As he tried to unriddle the doubtful scrawl
Of war and courage and love and death,
And then was suddenly nothing but sleep—

And tomorrow they marched—to a two-months chasing
Of Yankees running away like sheep
And peace in time for the Macon racing.

He got in his bed. Where the moonlight poured,
It lay like frost on a sleeping sword.

———————

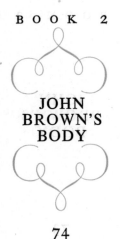

It was stuffy at night in the cabins, stuffy but warm.
And smells are a matter of habit. So, if the air
Was thick as black butter with the commingled smells
Of greens and fried fat and field-sweat and heavy sleep,
The walls were well-chinked, the low roof kept out the rain.
Not like the tumble-down cabins at Zachary's place
Where the field-hands lived all year on hominy-grits
And a piece of spoiled pork at Christmas.
                                    But Zachary
Was a mean man out of the Bottoms, no quality to him.
Wingate was quality. Wingate cared for its own.
A Wingate cabin was better than most such cabins,
You might have called it a sty, had they set you there;
A Middle Age serf might have envied the well-chinked walls.
While as for its tenants then, being folk unversed
In any law but the law of the Wingate name,
They were glad to have it, glad for fire on the hearth,
A roof from the dark-veined wind.
                                Their bellies were warm
And full of food. They were heavy in love with each other.
They liked their cabin and lying next to each other,
Long nights of winter when the slow-burning pine-knots
Danced ghosts and witches over the low, near ceiling,
Short nights of summer, after the work of the fields,
When the hot body aches with the ripened sweetness
And the children and the new tunes are begotten together.

"What you so wakeful for, black boy?"
                                "Thinkin', woman."
"You got no call to be thinkin', little black boy,

Thinkin's a trouble, a h'ant lookin' over de shoulder,
Set yo' head on my breas' and forget about thinkin'."

"I got my head on yo' breas', and it's sof' dere, woman,
Sof' and sweet as a mournin' out of de Scriptures,
Sof' as two Solomon doves. But I can't help thinkin'."

"Ain't I good enough for you no more, black boy?
Don' you love me no more dat you mus' keep thinkin'?"

"You's better'n good to me and I loves you, woman,
Till I feels like Meshuck down in de fiery furnace,
Till I feels like God's own chile. But I keeps on thinkin',
Wonderin' what I'd feel like if I was free."

"Hush, black boy, hush for de Lord's sake!"
                                    "But listen, woman—"

"Hush yo'self, black boy, lean yo'self on my breas',
Talk like that and paterollers'll git you,
Swinge you all to bits with a blacksnake whip,
Squinch-owl carry yo' talk to de paterollers,
It ain't safe to talk like that."
                              "I got to, woman,
I got a feelin' in my heart."
                              "Den you sot on dat feelin'!
Never heard you talk so in all my born days!
Ain't we got a good cabin here?"
                              "Sho', we got a good cabin."
"Ain't we got good vittles, ain't old Mistis kind to us?"

"Sho' we got good vittles, and ole Mistis she's kind.
I'se mighty fond of ole Mistis."
                              "Den what you talkin',
You brash fool-nigger?"
                              "I just got a feelin', woman.
Ole Marse Billy, he's goin' away tomorrow,
Marse Clay, he's goin' with him to fight de Yankees,
All of 'em goin', yes suh."
                              "And what if dey is?"

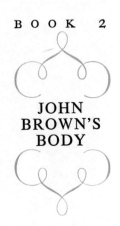
"Well, sposin' de Yankees beats?"

        "Ain't you got *no* sense,
  nigger?
Like to see any ole Yankees lick ole Marse Billy
And young Marse Clay!"

        "Hi, woman, ain't dat de trufe!"
"Well, den——"

        "But I sees 'em all, jus' goin' and goin',
Goin' to war like Joshua, goin' like David,
And it makes me want to be free. Ain't you never thought
At all about bein' free?"

        "Sho', co'se I thought of it.
I always reckoned when ole Marse Billy died,
Ole Mistis mebbe gwine to set some of us free,
Mebbe she will."

        "But we-uns gwine to be old den,
We won't be young and have the use of our hands,
We won't see our young 'uns growin' up free around us,
We won't have the strength to hoe our own co'n ourselves,
I want to be free, like me, while I got my strength."

"You might be a lot worse off and not be free,
What'd you do if ole man Zachary owned us?"

"Kill him, I reckon."

        "Hush, black boy, for God's sake hush!"

"I can't help it, woman. Dey ain't so many like him
But what dey is is too pizen-mean to live.
Can't you hear dat feelin' I got, woman? I ain't scared
Of talk and de paterollers, and I ain't mean.
I'se mighty fond of ole Mistis and ole Marse Billy,
I'se mighty fond of 'em all at de Big House,
I wouldn't be nobody else's nigger for nothin'.
But I hears 'em goin' away, all goin' away,
With horses and guns and things, all stompin' and wavin',
And I hears de chariot-wheels and de Jordan River,
Rollin' and rollin' and rollin' thu' my sleep,
And I wants to be free. I wants to see my chillun
Growin' up free, and all bust out of Egypt!

I wants to be free like an eagle in de air,
Like an eagle in de air."

———————

Iron-filings scattered over a dusty
Map of crook-cornered States in yellow and blue.
Little, grouped male and female iron-filings,
Scattered over a patchwork-quilt whose patches
Are the red-earth stuff of Georgia, the pine-bough green of Ver-
    mont.
Here you are clustered as thick as a clump of bees
In swarming time. The clumps make cities and towns.
Here you are strewn at random, like single seeds
Lost out of the wind's pocket.
                    But now, but now,
The thunderstone has fallen on your map
And all the iron-filings shiver and move
Under the grippings of that blinded force,
The cold pull of the ash-and-cinder star.

The map is vexed with the long battle-worms
Of filings, clustered and moving.
                 If it is
An enemy of the sun who has so stolen
Power from a burnt star to do this work,
Let the bleak essence of the utter cold
Beyond the last gleam of the most outpost light
Freeze in his veins forever.
                But if it is
A fault in the very metal of the heart,
We and our children must acquit that fault
With the old bloody wastage, or give up
Playing the father to it.
              O vexed and strange,
Salt-bitter, apple-sweet, strong-handed life!
Your million lovers cast themselves like sea
Against your mountainy breast, with a clashing noise
And a proud clamor—and like sea recoil,
Sucked down beneath the forefoot of the new
Advancing surf. They feed the battle-worms,

Not only War's, but in the second's pause
Between the assaulting and the broken wave,
The voices of the lovers can be heard,
The sea-gull cry.

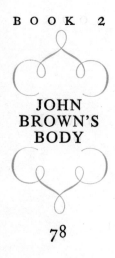

———————

Jake Diefer, the barrel-chested Pennsylvanian,
Hand like a ham and arms that could wrestle a bull,
A roast of a man, all solid meat and good fat,
A slow-thought-chewing Clydesdale horse of a man,
Roused out of his wife's arms. The dawn outside
Was ruddy as his big cheeks. He yawned and stretched
Gigantically, hawking and clearing his throat.
His wife, hair tousled around her like tousled corn,
Stared at him with sleep-blind eyes.

                                           "Jake, it ain't come morning,
Already yet?"
                He nodded and started to dress.
She burrowed deeper into the bed for a minute
And then threw off the covers.
                      They didn't say much
Then, or at breakfast. Eating was something serious.
But he looked around the big kitchen once or twice
In a puzzled way, as if trying hard to remember it.
She too, when she was busy with the first batch
Of pancakes, burnt one or two, because she was staring
At the "SALT" on the salt-box, for no particular reason.
The boy ate with them and didn't say a word,
Being too sleepy.
                 Afterwards, when the team
Was hitched up and waiting, with the boy on the seat,
Holding the reins till Jake was ready to take them,
Jake didn't take them at once.
                   The sun was up now,
The spilt-milk-mist of first morning lay on the farm,
Jake looked at it all with those same mildly-puzzled eyes,
The red barn, the fat rich fields just done with the winter,
Just beginning the work of another year.
The boy would have to do the rest of the planting.

He blew on his hands and stared at his wife dumbly.
He cleared his throat.

> "Well, good-by, Minnie," he said,
"Don't you hire any feller for harvest without you write me,
And if any more of those lightning-rodders come around,
We don't want no more dum lightning-rods."

> He tried
To think if there was anything else, but there wasn't.
She suddenly threw her big, red arms around his neck,
He kissed her with clumsy force.

> Then he got on the wagon
And clucked to the horses as she started to cry.

———————

Up in the mountains where the hogs are thin
And razorbacked, wild Indians of hogs,
The laurel's green in April—and if the nights
Are cold as the cold cloud of watersmoke
Above a mountain-spring, the midday sun
Has heat enough in it to make you sweat.

They are a curious and most native stock,
The lanky men, the lost, forgotten seeds
Spilled from the first great wave-march toward the West
And set to sprout by chance in the deep cracks
Of that hill-billy world of laurel-hells.
They keep the beechwood-fiddle and the salt
Old-fashioned ballad-English of our first
Rowdy, corn-liquor-drinking, ignorant youth;
Also the rifle and the frying-pan,
The old feud-temper and the old feud-way
Of thinking strangers better shot on sight
But treating strangers that one leaves unshot
With border-hospitality.

> The girls
Have the brief-blooming, rhododendron-youth
Of pioneer women, and the black-toothed age.
And if you yearn to meet your pioneers,
You'll find them there, the same men, inbred sons
Of inbred sires perhaps, but still the same;

A pioneer-island in a world that has
No use for pioneers—the unsplit rock
Of Fundamentalism, calomel,
Clan-virtues, clannish vices, fiddle-tunes
And a hard God.
     They are our last frontier.
They shot the railway-train when it first came,
And when the Fords first came, they shot the Fords.
It could not save them. They are dying now
Or being educated, which is the same.
One need not weep romantic tears for them,
But when the last moonshiner buys his radio,
And the last, lost, wild-rabbit of a girl
Is civilized with a mail-order dress,
Something will pass that was American
And all the movies will not bring it back.

They are misfit and strange in our new day,
In Sixty-One they were not quite so strange,
Before the Fords, before the day of the Fords . . .

Luke Breckinridge, his rifle on his shoulder,
Slipped through green forest alleys toward the town,
A gawky boy with smoldering eyes, whose feet
Whispered the crooked paths like moccasins.
He wasn't looking for trouble, going down,
But he was on guard, as always. When he stopped
To scoop some water in the palm of his hand
From a sweet trickle between moss-grown rocks,
You might have thought him careless for a minute,
But when the snapped stick cracked six feet behind him
He was all sudden rifle and hard eyes.
The pause endured a long death-quiet instant,
Then he knew who it was.
     "Hi, Jim," he said,
Lowering his rifle. The green laurel-screen
Hardly had moved, but Jim was there beside him.
The cousins looked at each other. Their rifles seemed
To look as well, with much the same taut silentness.
"Goin' to town, Luke?"

"Uh-huh, goin' to town,
You goin'?"
                    "Looks as if I was goin'."
                                        "Looks
As if you was after squirrels."
                    "I might be.
You goin' after squirrels?" "I might be, too."
"Not so many squirrels near town."
                                        "No, reckon there's not."

Jim hesitated. His gaunt hands caressed
The smooth guard of his rifle. His eyes were sharp.
"Might go along a piece together," he said.
Luke didn't move. Their eyes clashed for a moment,
Then Luke spoke, casually.
                    "I hear the Kelceys
Air goin' to fight in this here war," he said.
Jim nodded slowly, "Yuh, I heerd that too."
He watched Luke's trigger-hand.
                                        "I might be goin'
Myself sometime," he said reflectively
Sliding his own hand down. Luke saw the movement.
"We-uns don't like the Kelceys much," he said
With his eyes down to pinpoints.
                                        Then Jim smiled.
"We-uns neither," he said.
                    His hand slid back.

They went along together after that
But neither of them spoke for half-a-mile,
Then finally, Jim said, half-diffidently,
"You know who we air goin' to fight outside?
I heard it was the British. Air that so?"
"Hell, no," said Luke, with scorn. He puckered his brows.
"Dunno's I rightly know just who they air."
He admitted finally, "But 'tain't the British.
It's some trash-lot of furriners, that's shore.
They call 'em Yankees near as I kin make it,
But they ain't Injuns neither."
                    "Well," said Jim

Soothingly, "Reckon it don't rightly matter
Long as the Kelceys take the other side."

———————

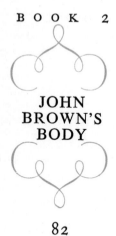

BOOK 2

JOHN
BROWN'S
BODY

82

It was noon when the company marched to the railroad-station.
The town was ready for them. The streets were packed.
There were flags and streamers and pictures of Lincoln and
    Hamlin.
The bad little boys climbed up on the trees and yelled,
The good little boys had clean paper-collars on,
And swung big-eyed on white-painted wicket-gates,
Wanting to yell, and feeling like Fourth of July.
Somebody fastened a tin can full of firecrackers
To a yellow dog's tail and sent him howling and racketing
The length of the street.
    "There goes Jeff Davis!" said somebody,
And everybody laughed, and the little boys
Punched each other and squealed between fits of laughing
"There goes Jeff Davis—lookit ole yellow Jeff Davis!"
And then the laugh died and rose again in a strange
Half-shrill, half-strangled unexpected shout
As they heard the Hillsboro' Silver Cornet Band
Swinging "John Brown's Body" ahead of the soldiers.
I have heard that soul of crowd go out in the queer
Groan between laughter and tears that baffles the wise.
I have heard that whanging band.

"We'll hang Jeff Davis on a sour-apple tree."
Double-roll on the snare-drums, double squeal of the fife,
"We'll hang Jeff Davis on a sour-apple tree!"
Clash of the cymbals zinging, throaty blare of cornets,
"We'll hang Jeff Davis on a sour-apple tree!"
"On to Richmond! On to Richmond! On to Richmond!"
"Yeah! There they come! Yeah! Yeah!"
And they came, the bearskin drum-major leading the band,
Twirling his silver-balled baton with turkey-cock pomp,
The cornet-blowers, the ranks. The drum-major was fine,
But the little boys thought the captain was even finer,
He looked just like a captain out of a book
With his sword and his shoulder-straps and his discipline-face.

He wasn't just Henry Fairfield, he was a captain,
—Henry Fairfield worried about his sword,
Hoping to God that he wouldn't drop his sword,
And wondering hotly whether his discipline-face
Really looked disciplined or only peevish—
"Yeah! There they come! There's Jack! There's Charlie! Yeah!
   Yeah!"
The color-guard with the stiff, new flapping flag,
And the ranks and the ranks and the ranks, the amateur
Blue, wavering ranks, in their ill-fitting tight coats,
Shoulders galled already by their new guns,
—They were three-months' men, they had drilled in civilian
   clothes
Till a week ago—"There's Charlie! There's Hank, yeah,
   yeah!"
"On to Richmond, boys! Three cheers for Abe Lincoln!
Three cheers for the boys! Three groans for old Jeff Davis
And the dirty Rebs!"
"We'll hang Jeff Davis on a sour-apple tree!"

Jack Ellyat, marching, saw between blue shoulders
A blur of faces. They all were faces he knew,
Old Mrs. Cobb with her wart and her Paisley shawl,
Little George Freeman, the slim Tucker girls,
All of them cheering and shouting—and all of them strange
Suddenly, different, faces he'd never seen.
Faces somehow turned into one crowd-face.
His legs went marching along all right but they felt
Like somebody else's legs, his mind was sucked dry.
It was real, they were going away, the town was cheering them.
Henry Fairfield was marching ahead with his sword.
Just as he'd thought about it a thousand times,
These months—but it wasn't the way that he'd thought about it.
"On to Richmond! On to Richmond! On to Richmond!"
There were Mother and Father and Jane and the house.
Jane was waving a flag. He laughed and called to them.
But his voice was stiff in his throat, not like his real voice.
This, everything, it was too quick, too crowded, not Phaëton
Charging his snarling horses at a black sea,
But a numb, hurried minute with legs that marched

Mechanically, feeling nothing at all.
The white crowd-face—the sweat on the red seamed neck
Of the man ahead— "On to Richmond!" —blue shoulders bob-
   bing—
Flags—cheering—somebody kissed him—Ellen Baker—
She was crying—wet mouth of tears—didn't want her to kiss
   him—
Why did she want to—the station—*halt*—Mother and Jane.
The engineer wore a flag in his coat-lapel.
The engine had "On to Richmond!" chalked all over it.
Nothing to say now—Mother looks tired to death—
I wish I weren't going—no, I'm glad that I am—
The damn band's playing "John Brown's Body" again,
I wish they'd stop it!—I wish to God we could start—
There—*close up, men!*—oh my God, they've let Ned out!
I told them for God's sake to lock him up in the cellar,
But they've let him out—maybe he got out by himself—
He's got too much sense— "No, down, Ned! Down, good dog!
Down, I tell you!—"

   *"Good-by, boys! Good-by! We'll hang
   Jeff Davis!"*

The engine squealed, the packed train started to move.
Ned wanted to come, but they wouldn't let him come.
They had to kick him away, he couldn't see why.

———————

In another column, footsore Curly Hatton
Groaned at the thought of marching any more.
His legs weren't built for marching and they knew it,
Butterball-legs under a butterball-body.
The plump good-tempered face with its round eyes
Blue and astonished as a china-doll's,
Stared at the road ahead and hated it
Because there was so much of it ahead
And all of it so dry.
                    He didn't mind
The rest so much. He didn't even mind
Being the one sure necessary joke
Of the whole regiment. He'd always been

SALLY DUPRÉ
Heart and body like sea blown spray

A necessary joke—fat people were.
Fat babies always were supposed to laugh.
Fat little boys had fingers poked at them.
And, even with the road, and being fat,
You had a good time in this funny war,
Considering everything, and one thing most.

His mind slipped back two months. He saw himself
In the cool room at Weatherby's Retreat
Where all the girls were sewing the new star
In the new flag for the first volunteers.
He hadn't thought of fighting much before,
He was too easy-going. If Virginia
Wanted secession, that was her affair.
It seemed too bad to break the Union up
After some seventy years of housekeeping.
But he could understand the way you'd feel
If you were thin and angry at the Yanks.
He knew a lot of Yankees that he liked,
But then he liked most people, on the whole
Although most girls and women made him shy.
He loved the look of them and the way they walked,
He loved their voices and their little sweet mouths,
But something always seemed to hold him back,
When he was near them.
                              He was too fat, too friendly,
Too comfortable for dreams, too easy-shy.
The porcelain dolls stood on the mantelpiece,
Waiting such slim and arrant cavaliers
As porcelain dolls must have to make them proud,
They had no mercy for fat Cupidons,
Not even Lucy, all the years before,
And Lucy was the porcelain belle of the world!
And so when she said.
                              And he couldn't believe
At first.
              But she was silver and fire and steel
That day of the new stars and the new flag,
Fire and bright steel for the invading horde
And silver for the men who drove them off,

And so she sewed him in her flag and heart:
Though even now, he couldn't believe she had
In spite of all the letters and the socks
And kissing him before he went away.
But it was so—the necessary joke
Made into a man at last, a man in love
And loved by the most porcelain belle of the world.
And he was ready to march to the world's end
And fight ten million Yanks to keep it so.

"Oh God, after we're married—the cool night
Over the garden—and Lucy sitting there
In her blue dress while the big stars come out."
His face was funny with love and footsore pride,
The man beside him saw it, gave a laugh,
"Curly's thinking it's time for a julep, boys!
Hot work for fat men, Curly!"

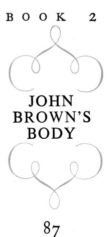
———————

The crows fly over the Henry House, through the red sky of
     evening, cawing,
Judith Henry, bedridden, watches them through the clouded
     glass of old sight.
(July is hot in Virginia—a parched, sun-leathered farmer sawing
Dry sticks with a cicada-saw that creaks all the lukewarm night.)

But Judith Henry's hands are cool in spite of all midsummer's
     burning,
Cool, muted and frail with age like the smoothness of old yellow
     linen, the cool touch of old, dulled rings.
Her years go past her in bed like falling waters and the waters
     of a millwheel turning,
And she is not ill content to lie there, dozing and calm, remem-
     bering youth, to the gushing of those watersprings.

She has known Time like the cock of red dawn and Time like a
     tired clock slowing;
She has seen so many faces and bodies, young and then old, so
     much life, so many patterns of death and birth.

She knows that she must leave them soon. She is not afraid to
   flow with that river's flowing.
But the wrinkled earth still hangs at her sufficed breast like a
   weary child, she is unwilling to go while she still has milk for
   the earth.

She will go in her sleep, most likely, she has the sunk death-sleep
   of the old already,
(War-bugles by the Potomac, you cannot reach her ears with
   your brass lyric, piercing the crowded dark.)
It does not matter, the farm will go on, the farm and the children
   bury her in her best dress, the plow cut its furrow, steady,
(War-horses of the Shenandoah, why should you hurry so fast
   to tramp the last ashy fire from so feeble and retired a spark?)

There is nothing here but a creek and a house called the Henry
   House, a farm and a bedridden woman and people with country faces.
There is nothing for you here. And La Haye Sainte was a quiet
   farm and the mile by it a quiet mile.
And Lexington was a place to work in like any one of a dozen
   dull, little places.
And they raised good crops at Blenheim till the soldiers came
   and spoiled the crops for a while.

The red evening fades into twilight, the crows have gone to
   their trees, the slow, hot stars are emerging.
It is cooler now on the hill—and in the camps it is cooler, where
   the untried soldiers find their bivouac hard.
Where, from North and South, the blind wrestlers of armies
   converge on the forgotten house like the double pincers of an
   iron claw converging.
And Johnston hurries his tired brigades from the Valley, to
   bring them up in time before McDowell can fall on Beauregard.

———

The congressmen came out to see Bull Run,
The congressmen who like free shows and spectacles.
They brought their wives and carriages along,
They brought their speeches and their picnic-lunch,

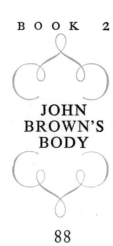

Their black constituent-hats and their devotion:
Some even brought a little whiskey, too,
(A little whiskey is a comforting thing
For congressmen in the sun, in the heat of the sun.)
The bearded congressmen with orator's mouths,
The fine, clean-shaved, Websterian congressmen,
Come out to see the gladiator's show
Like Iliad gods, wrapped in the sacred cloud
Of Florida-water, wisdom and bay-rum,
Of free cigars, democracy and votes,
That lends such portliness to congressmen.
(The gates fly wide, the bronze troop marches out
Into the stripped and deadly circus-ring,
"Ave, Caesar!" the cry goes up, and shakes
The purple awning over Caesar's seat.)
"Ave, Caesar! Ave, O congressmen,
We who are about to die,
Salute you, congressmen!"
Eleven States,
New York, Rhode Island, Maine,
Connecticut, Michigan and the gathered West,
Salute you, congressmen!
The red-fezzed Fire-Zouaves, flamingo-bright,
Salute you, congressmen!
The raw boys still in their civilian clothes,
Salute you, congressmen!
The second Wisconsin in its homespun grey,
Salutes you, congressmen!
The Garibaldi Guards in cocksfeather hats,
Salutes you, congressmen!
The Second Ohio with their Bedouin-caps,
Salutes you, congressmen!
Sherman's brigade, grey-headed Heintzelman,
Ricketts' and Griffin's doomed and valiant guns,
The tough, hard-bitten regulars of Sykes
Who covered the retreat with the Marines,
Burnside and Porter, Willcox and McDowell,
All the vast, unprepared, militia-mass
Of boys in red and yellow Zouave pants,
Who carried peach-preserves inside their kits

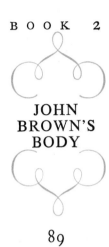

BOOK 2

JOHN
BROWN'S
BODY

89

JOHN
BROWN'S
BODY

And dreamt of being generals overnight;
The straggling companies where every man
Was a sovereign and a voter—the slack regiments
Where every company marched a different step;
The clumsy and unwieldy-new brigades
Not yet distempered into battle-worms;
The whole, huge, innocent army, ready to fight
But only half-taught in the tricks of fighting,
Ready to die like picture-postcard boys
While fighting still had banners and a sword
And just as ready to run in blind mob-panic,
Salutes you with a vast and thunderous cry,
Ave, Caesar, ave, O congressmen,
Ave, O Iliad gods who forced the fight!
You bring your carriages and your picnic-lunch
To cheer us in our need.
                                        You come with speeches,
Your togas smell of heroism and bay-rum.
You are the people and the voice of the people
And, when the fight is done, your carriages
Will bear you safely, through the streaming rout
Of broken troops, throwing their guns away.
You come to see the gladiator's show,
But from a high place, as befits the wise:
You will not see the long windrows of men
Strewn like dead pears before the Henry House
Or the stone-wall of Jackson breathe its parched
Devouring breath upon the failing charge,
Ave, Caesar, ave, O congressmen,
Cigar-smoke wraps you in a godlike cloud,
And if you are not to depart from us
As easily and divinely as you came,
It hardly matters.
                                Fighting Joe Hooker once
Said with that tart, unbridled tongue of his
That made so many needless enemies,
"Who ever saw a dead cavalryman?"
                                                The phrase
Stings with a needle sharpness, just or not,
But even he was never heard to say,

"Who ever saw a dead congressman?"
And yet, he was a man with a sharp tongue.

———————

The day broke, hot and calm. In the little farm-houses
That are scattered here and there in that rolling country
Of oak and rail-fence, crooked creeks and second-growth pine,
The early-risers stand looking out of the door
At the long dawn-shadows for a minute or two
—Shadows are always cool—but the blue-grass sky
Is fusing with heat even now, heat that prickles the hairs
On the back of your hand.
                           They sigh and turn back to the house.
"Looks like a scorcher today, boys!"
                                        They think already
Of the cool jug of vinegar-water down by the hedge.

Judith Henry wakened with the first light,
She had the short sleep of age, and the long patience.
She waited for breakfast in vague, half-drowsy wonderment
At various things. Yesterday some men had gone by
And stopped for a drink of water. She'd heard they were sol-
    diers.
She couldn't be sure. It had seemed to worry the folks
But it took more than soldiers and such to worry her now.
Young people always worried a lot too much.
No soldiers that had any sense would fight around here.
She'd had a good night. Today would be a good day.

———————

A mile and a half away, before the Stone Bridge,
A Union gun opened fire.

———————

Six miles away, McDowell had planned his battle
And planned it well, as far as such things can be planned—
A feint at one point, a flanking march at another
To circle Beauregard's left and crumple it up.
There were Johnston's eight thousand men to be reckoned with
But Patterson should be holding them, miles away,

And even if they slipped loose from Patterson's fingers
The thing might still be done.
                                    If you take a flat map
And move wooden blocks upon it strategically,
The thing looks well, the blocks behave as they should.
The science of war is moving live men like blocks.
And getting the blocks into place at a fixed moment.
But it takes time to mold your men into blocks
And flat maps turn into country where creeks and gullies
Hamper your wooden squares. They stick in the brush,
They are tired and rest, they straggle after ripe blackberries,
And you cannot lift them up in your hand and move them.
—A string of blocks curling smoothly around the left
Of another string of blocks and crunching it up—
It is all so clear in the maps, so clear in the mind,
But the orders are slow, the men in the blocks are slow
To move, when they start they take too long on the way—
The General loses his stars and the block-men die
In unstrategic defiance of martial law
Because still used to just being men, not block-parts.
McDowell was neither a fool nor a fighting fool;
He knew his dice, he knew both armies unready,
But congressmen and nation wanted a battle
And he felt their hands on his shoulders, forcing his play.
He knew well enough when he played that he played for his
    head
As Beauregard and Johnston were playing for theirs,
So he played with the skill he had—and does not lie
Under a cupolaed gloom on Riverside Drive.
Put Grant in his place that day and with those same dice,
Grant might have done little better.
                                    Wherefore, now,
Irvin McDowell, half-forgotten general,
Who tried the game and found no luck in the game
And never got the chance to try it again
But did not backbite the gamblers who found more luck in it
Then or later in double-edged reminiscences;
If any laurel can grow in the sad-colored fields
Between Bull Run and Cub Run and Cat Hairpin Bend
You should have a share of it for your hardworking ghost

Because you played as you could with your cold, forced dice
And neither wasted your men like the fighting fools
Nor posed as an injured Napoleon twenty years later.
Meanwhile, McDowell watched his long flanking column
File by, on the Warrentown pike, in the first dawn-freshness.
"Gentlemen, that's a big force," he said to his staff.

———————

A full rifled battery begins to talk spitefully to Evans' Carolinians. The grey skirmish-line, thrown forward on the other side of Bull Run, ducks its head involuntarily as a locomotive noise goes by in the air above it, and waits for a flicker of blue in the scrub-oaks ahead.

———————

Beauregard, eager *sabreur,* whose heart was a French
Print of a sabretasche-War with "La Gloire" written under it,
Lovable, fiery, bizarre, picturesque as his name,
Galloped toward Mitchell's Ford with bald, quiet Joe Johnston,
The little precise Scotch-dominie of a general,
Stubborn as flint, in advance not always so lucky,
In retreat more dangerous than a running wolf—
Slant shadow, sniffing the traps and the poisoned meat,
And going on to pause and slash at the first
Unwary dogs before the hunters came up.
Grant said of him once,
"I was always anxious with Joe Johnston in front of me,
I was never half so anxious in front of Lee."
He kissed his friends in the Nelson-way we've forgotten,
He could make men cheer him after six-weeks retreating.
Another man said of him, after the war was done,
Still with that puzzled comparison we find
When Lee, the reticent sword, comes into the question,
"Yes, Lee was a great general, a good man;
But I never wanted to put my arms round his neck
As I used to want to with Johnston."
                                    The two sayings
Make a good epitaph for so Scotch a ghost,
Or would if they were all.
                        They are not quite all,

He had to write his reminiscenses, too,
And tell what he would have done if it had not been
For Davis and chance and a dozen turns of the wheel.
That was the thistle in him—the other strain—
But he was older then.
                              I'd like to have seen him
That day as he galloped along beside Beauregard,
Sabreur and dominie planning the battle-lines.
They'd ordered Jackson up to the threatened left
But Beauregard was sure that the main assault
Would come on the right. He'd planned it so—a good plan—
But once the blocks start moving, they keep on moving.

———————

The hands of the scuffed brown clock in the kitchen of the
    Henry House point to nine-forty-five.
Judith Henry does not hear the clock, she hears in the sky a
    vast dim roar like piles of heavy lumber crashingly falling.
They are carrying her in her bed to a ravine below the Sudley
    Road, maybe she will be safe there, maybe the battle will go
    by and leave her alive.
The crows have been scared from their nests by the strange
    crashing, they circle in the sky like a flight of blackened
    leaves, wheeling and calling.

———————

Back at Centerville, there are three-months' men,
A Pennsylvania regiment, a New York Battery.
They hear the spent wave of the roar of the opening guns,
But they are three-months' men, their time is up today.
They would have fought yesterday or a week ago,
But then they were still enlisted—today they are not—
Their time is up, and there can't be much use or sense
In fighting longer than you've promised to fight.
They pack up their things and decide they'd better go home,
And quietly march away from that gathering roar.

———————

Luke Breckinridge, crouched by the Warrentown pike,
Saw stuffed dolls in blue coats and baggy trousers

Go down like squirrels under the rifle-cracks.
His eyes glowed as a bullet ripped his sleeve
And he felt well. Armies weren't such a much,
Too damn many orders, too damn much saluting,
Too many damn officers you weren't allowed
To shoot when they talked mean to you because
They were your officers, which didn't make sense.
But this was something he could understand,
Except for those dirty stinkers of big guns,
It wasn't right to shoot you with big guns
But it was a good scrap except for that—
Carried a little high, then . . . change it . . . good . . .
Though men were hard to miss when you were used
To squirrels. His eyes were narrow. He hardly heard
The officer's voice. The woods in front of him
Were full of Kelceys he was going to kill,
Blue-coated Kelcey dolls in baggy trousers.
It was a beautiful and sufficing sight.

———————

The first blue wave of Burnside is beaten back from the pike to stumble a little way and rally against Porter's fresh brigade.

Bee and Bartow move down from the Henry House plateau—grey and butternut lines trampling the bullet-cut oak-leaves, splashing across Young's Branch.

Tall, black-bearded Bee rides by on his strong horse, his long black hair fluttering.

Imboden's red-shirted gunners unlimber by the Henry House to answer the Parrotts and howitzers of Ricketts and Griffin. The air is a sheet of iron, continually and dully shaken.

———————

Shippy, the little man with the sharp rat-eyes,
Saw someone run in front of them waving a sword;
Then they were going along toward a whining sound
That ran like cold spring-water along his spine.
God, he was in for it now! His sharp rat-eyes
Flickered around and about him hopelessly.
If a fellow could only drop out, if a fellow could only
Pretend he was hurt a little and then drop out

Behind a big, safe oak-tree—no use—no use—
He was in for it, now. He couldn't get away.
*"Come on, boys—come on, men—clean them out with the
     bayonet!"*
He saw a rail-fence ahead, a quiet rail-fence,
But men were back of it—grey lumps—a million bees
Stinging the air—Oh Jesus, the corporal's got it—
He couldn't shoot, even—he was too scared to shoot—
His legs took him on—he couldn't stop his legs
Or the weak urine suddenly trickling down them.

———

Curly Hatton, toiling along the slow
Crest of the Henry Hill, over slippery ground,
Glanced at the still-blue sky that lay so deep
Above the little pines, so pooled, so calm.
He thought, with the slow drowsiness of fatigue,
Of Lucy feeding the white, greedy swans
On the blue pool by Weatherby's Retreat.
They stretched their necks, and clattered with their wings.
There was a fragrance sleeping in her hair.
"Close up, folks—don't straggle—we're going into action!"
His butterball-legs moved faster—Lucy—Lucy—

———

Bee and Bartow's brigades are broken in their turn—it is fight
and run away—fight and run away, all day—the day will go to
whichever of the untried wrestlers can bear the pain of the grips
an instant longer than the other.

Beauregard and Johnston hurry toward the firing—McDowell
has already gone—

The chessplayers have gone back to little pieces on the shaken
board—little pieces that cannot see the board as a whole.

The block-plan is lost—there is no plan any more—only the
bloodstained, fighting blocks, the bloodstained and blackened
men.

———

Jack Ellyat heard the guns with a knock at his heart
When he first heard them. They were going to be in it, soon.

He wondered how it would feel. They would win, of course,
But how would it feel? He'd never killed anything much.
Ducks and rabbits, but ducks and rabbits weren't men.
He'd never even seen a man killed, a man die,
Except Uncle Amos, and Uncle Amos was old.
He saw a red sop spreading across the close
Feathers of a duck's breast—it had been all right,
But now it made him feel sick for a while, somehow.
Then they were down on the ground, and they were firing,
And that was all right—just fire as you fired at drill.
Was anyone firing at them? He couldn't tell.
There was a stone bridge. Were there rebels beyond the
　　bridge?
The shot he was firing now might go and kill rebels
But it didn't feel like it.
　　　　　　　　　A man down the line
Fell and rolled flat, with a minor coughing sound
And then was quiet. Ellyat felt the cough
In the pit of his stomach a minute.
But, after that, it was just like a man falling down.
It was all so calm except for their guns and the distant
Shake in the air of cannon. No more men were hit,
And, after a while, they all got up and marched on.
If Rebels had been by the bridge, the rebels were gone,
And they were going on somewhere, you couldn't say where,
Just marching along the way that they always did.
The only funny thing was, leaving the man
Who had made that cough, back there in the trampled grass
With the red stain sopping through the blue of his coat
Like the stain on a duck's breast. He hardly knew the man
But it felt funny to leave him just lying there.

————

　　The wreckage of Bee, Bartow and Evans' commands streams
back into a shallow ravine below a little wood—broken blocks
hammered into splinters by war—two thousand confused men
reeling past their staggering flags and the hoarse curses and
rallying cries of their officers, like sheep in a narrow run.
　　Bee tries to halt them furiously—he stands up in his stirrups,

tree-tall, while the blue flood of the North trickles over the stream and pours on and on.

He waves his sword—the toyish glitter sparkles—he points to a grey dyke at the top of the ravine—a grey dyke of musket-holding Virginians, silent and ready.

"Look, men, there's Jackson's brigade! It stands there like a stone wall. Rally behind the Virginians!"

They rally behind them—Johnston and Beauregard are there—the Scotch dominie plucks a flag and carries it forward to rally the Fourth Alabama—the French hussar-sword rallies them with bursting rockets of oratory—his horse is shot under him, but he mounts again.

And the grey stone wall holds like a stiff dyke while the tired men get their breath behind it—and the odd, lemon-sucking, ex-professor of tactics who saw John Brown hung in his carpet-slippers and prayed a Presbyterian prayer for his damned soul, has a new name that will last as long as the face they cut for him on Stone Mountain, and has the same clang of rock against the chisel-blade.

———————

Judith Henry, Judith Henry, they have moved you back at last, in doubt and confusion, to the little house where you know every knothole by heart.

It is not safe, but now there is no place safe, you are between the artillery and the artillery, and the incessant noise comes to your dim ears like the sea-roar within a shell where you are lying.

The walls of the house are riddled, the brown clock in the kitchen gouged by a bullet, a jar leaks red preserves on the cupboard shelf where the shell-splinter came and tore the cupboard apart.

The casual guns do not look for you, Judith Henry, they find you in passing merely and touch you only a little, but the touch is enough to give your helpless body five sudden wounds and leave you helplessly dying.

———————

Wingate gentled Black Whistle's pawing
With hand and wisdom and horseman's play

And listened anew to the bulldogs gnawing
Their bone of iron, a mile away.
There was a wood that a bonfire crowned
With thick dark smoke without flame for neighbor,
And the dull, monotonous, heavy sound
Of a hill or a woman in too-long labor,
But that was all for the Black Horse Troop
And had been all since the day's beginning,
That stray boy beating his metal hoop
And the tight-lipped wonder if they were winning.
Wainscott Bristol, behind his eyes,
Was getting in bed with a sweet-toothed wench,
Huger Shepley felt for his dice
And Stuart Cazenove swore in French
"Mille diables and Yankee blood!
How long are we going to stick in the mud?"
While a Cotter hummed with a mocking sigh,
" 'If you want a good time, jine the cavalry!' "
"Stuart's in it, Wade Hampton's in it."
"The Yanks'll quit in another minute!"
"General Beau's just lost us!"
                            "Steady!"
"And he won't find us until he's ready!"
"It must be two—we've been here since six."
"It's Virginia up to her old-time tricks!
They never did trust a Georgia man,
But Georgia'll fight while Virginia can!"

The restless talk was a simmering brew
That made the horses restless too;
They stamped and snuffled and pricked their ears—
There were cheers, off somewhere—but which side's cheers?
Had the Yankees whipped? Were the Yankees breaking?
The whole troop grumbled and wondered, aching
For fighting or fleeing or fornicating
Or anything else except this bored waiting.

An aide rode up on a sweating mare
And they glowered at him with hostile stare.
He had been in it and they had not.

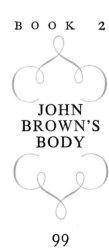

B O O K   2

JOHN
BROWN'S
BODY

99

He had smelt the powder and heard the shot,
And they hated his soul and his martial noise
With the envious hate of little boys.
Then "Yaaih! Yaaih!"

—and Wingate felt

The whole troop lift like a lifted dart
And loosened the saber at his belt,
And felt his chest too small for his heart.

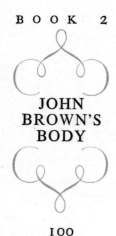

BOOK 2

JOHN
BROWN'S
BODY

100

———

Curly Hatton was nothing any more
But a dry throat and a pair of burnt black hands
That held a hot gun he was always firing
Though he no longer remembered why he fired.
They ran up a cluttered hill and took hacked ground
And held it for a while and fired for a while,
And then the blue men came and they ran away,
To go back, after a while, when the blue men ran.
There was a riddled house and a crow in a tree,
There was uneven ground. It was hard to run.
The gun was heavy and hot. There once had been
A person named Lucy and a flag and a star
And a cane chair beside wistarias
Where a nigger brought you a drink. These had ceased to exist.
There was only very hot sun and being thirsty.
Yells—crashings—screams from black lips—a dead, tattered
 crow
In a tattered tree. There had once been a person named Lucy
Who had had an importance. There was none of her now.

Up the hill again. Damn tired of running up hill.
And then he found he couldn't run any more,
He had to fall down and be sick. Even that was hard,
Because somebody near kept making a squealing noise—
The dolefully nasty noise of a badly-hurt dog.
It got on his nerves and he tried to say something to it,
But it was he who made it, so he couldn't stop it.

———

Jack Ellyat, going toward the battle again,
Saw the other side of the hill where Curly was lying,

Saw, for a little while, the two battered houses,
The stuffed dead stretched in numb, disorderly postures,
And heard for a while again that whining sound
That made you want to duck, and feel queer if you did.

To him it was noise and smoke and the powder-taste
And, once and again, through the smoke, for a moment seen,
Small, monstrous pictures, gone through the brain like light,
And yet forever bitten into the brain;
A marsh, a monstrous arras of live and dead
Still shaking under the thrust of the weaver's hand,
The crowd of a deadly fair.
                              Then, orders again.
And they were going away from the smoke once more.

The books say "Keyes' brigade made a late and weak
Demonstration in front of the Robinson house
And then withdrew to the left, by flank, down Young's Branch,
Taking no further part in the day."
                              To Jack Ellyat
It was a deadly fair in a burning field
Where strange crowds rushed to and fro and strange drunkards
    lay
Sprawled in a stupor deeper than wine or sleep,
A whining noise you shrank from and wanted to duck at,
And one dead cough left behind them in the tall grass
With the slow blood sopping its clothes like the blood on a
    shot duck's breast.

———————

Imboden is wounded, Jackson is shot through the hand, the
guns of Ricketts and Griffin, on the Henry House plateau, are
taken and retaken; the gunners shot down at their guns while
they hold their fire, thinking the advancing Thirty-Third Virginia is one of their own regiments, in the dimness of the battle-
cloud.

It is nearly three o'clock—the South gathers for a final charge
—on the left, Elzey's brigade, new-come from the Shenandoah,
defiles through the oaks near the Sudley Road to reinforce the
grey wrestler—the blue wrestler staggers and goes back, on
unsteady heels.

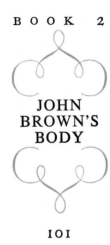

The charge sweeps the plateau—Bartow is killed, black-haired
Bee mortally wounded, but the charge goes on.

For a moment, the Union line is a solid crescent again—a
crescent with porcupine-pricks of steel—and then a crescent of
sand—and then spilt sand, streaming away.

There is no panic at first. There is merely a moment when
men have borne enough and begin to go home. The panic comes
later, when they start to jostle each other.

Jefferson Davis, riding from Manassas, reaches the back-wash
of the battle. A calm grey-bearded stranger tells him calmly that
the battle is lost and the South defeated. But he keeps on, his
weak eyes stung with the dust, a picture, perhaps, of a Plutarch
death on a shield in his schooled mind—and is in time to see the
last blue troops disappear beyond Bull Run, and hear the last
sour grumble of their guns.

———————

Judith Henry, Judith Henry, your body has born its ghost at
last, there are no more pictures of peace or terror left in the
broken machine of the brain that was such a cunning pic-
ture-maker:
Terrified ghost, so rudely dishoused by such casual violence, be
at rest; there are others dishoused in this falling night, the
falling night is a sack of darkness, indifferent as Saturn to
wars or generals, indifferent to shame or victory.
War is a while but peace is a while and soon enough the earth-
colored hands of the earth-workers will scoop the last buried
shells and the last clotted bullet-slag from the racked em-
bittered acre,
And the rustling visitors drive out fair Sundays to look at the
monument near the rebuilt house, buy picture postcards and
wonder dimly what you were like when you lived and what
you thought when you knew you were going to die.

———————

Wingate felt a frog in his throat
As he patted Black Whistle's reeking coat
And reined him in for a minute's breath.
He was hot as the devil and tired to death,
And both were glad for the sun in the West

And a panting second of utter rest,
While Wingate's mind went patching together
Like a cobbler piecing out scraps of leather
The broken glimmers of what they'd done
Since the sun in the West was a rising sun,
The long, bored hours of shiftless waiting
And that single instant of pure, fierce hating
When the charge came down like a cataract
On a long blue beach of broken sand
And Thought was nothing but all was Act
And the sabre seemed to master the hand.
Wainscott Bristol, a raging terrier
Killing the Yankee that shot Phil Ferrier
With a cut that spattered the bloody brains
Over his saddle and bridle-reins,
One Cotter cursing, the other praying,
And both of them slashing like scythes of slaying,
Stuart Cazenove singing "Lord Randall"
And Howard Brooke as white as a candle,
While Father fought like a fiend in satin,
And killed as he quoted tag-ends of Latin,
The prisoners with their sick, dazed wonder
And the mouths of children caught in a blunder
And over it all, the guns, the thunder,
The pace, the being willing to die,
The stinging color of victory.

He remembered it all like a harsh, tense dream.
It had a color. It had a gleam.
But he had outridden and lost the rest
And he was alone with the bloody West
And a trampled road, and a black hill-crest.

The road and the bushes all about
Were cluttered with relics of Yankee rout,
Haversacks spilling their shirts and socks,
A burst canteen and a cartridge-box.
Rifles and cups trampled underfoot,
A woman's locket, a slashed black boot
Stained and oozing along the slash

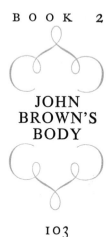

And a ripe pear crushed to a yellow mash.
Who had carried the locket and munched the pear,
And why was a dead cat lying there,
Stark and grinning, a furry sack,
With a red flannel tongue and a broken back?
You didn't fight wars with a tabby-cat. . . .
He found he was telling the Yankees that,
They couldn't hear him of course, but still . . .
He shut his eyes for a minute until
He felt less dizzy. There, that was better,
And the evening wind was chilly and keen—
—He'd have to write Mother some sort of letter—
—He'd promised Amanda a Yank canteen,
But he didn't feel like getting it here,
Where that dead cat snickered from ear to ear—

Back in the pinewoods, clear and far,
A bugle sang like a falling star.
He shivered, turned Black Whistle around
And galloped hastily toward the sound.

————————

Curly Hatton opened his eyes again.
A minute ago he had been marching, marching,
Forever up and down enormous hills
While his throat scratched with thirst and something howled—
But then there was a clear minute—and he was lying
In a long, crowded, strangely-churchly gloom
Where lanterns bobbed like marshlights in a swamp
And there was a perpetual rustling noise
Of dry leaves stirred by a complaining wind.
No, they were only voices of wounded men.
"Water. Water. Water. Water. Water."
He heard the rain on the roof and sucked his lips.
"Water. Water. Water. Water. Water."
Oh, heavy sluices of dark, sweet, Summer rain,
Pour down on me and wash me free again,
Cleanse me of battles, make my flesh smell sweet,
I am so sick of thirst, so tired of pain,
So stale with wounds and the heat!

Somebody went by, a doctor with red sleeves;
He stared at the red sleeves and tried to speak
But when he spoke, he whispered. This was a church.
He could see a dim altar now and a shadow-pulpit.
He was wounded. They had put the wounded men in a church.
Lucy's face came to him a minute and then dissolved,
A drowned face, ebbing away with a smile on its mouth.
He had meant to marry that face in another church.
But he was dying instead. It was strange to die.

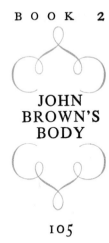
———————

All night from the hour of three, the dead man's hour, the rain
    falls in heavy gusts, in black irresistible streams as if the whole
        sky were falling in one wet huddle.
All night, living and dead sleep under it, without moving, on
    the field; the surgeons work in the church; the wounded moan;
        the dissevered fragments of companies and regiments look
            for each other, trying to come together.
In the morning, when the burial-parties go out, the rain is still
    falling, damping the powder of the three rounds fired over the
        grave; before the grave is well-dug, the bottom of the grave
            is a puddle.
All day long the Southern armies bury their dead to the sodden
    drums of the rain; all day the bugle calls a hoarse-throated
        "Taps"; the bugler lets the water run from his bugle-mouth
            and wipes it clean again and curses the rainy weather.

———————

All night the Union army fled in retreat
Like horses scared by a shadow—a stumbling flood
Of panicky men who had been brave for a while
And might be brave again on another day
But now were merely children chased by the night
And each man tainting his neighbor with the same
Blind fear.
        When men or horses begin to run
Like that, they keep on running till they tire out
Unless a strong hand masters a bridle-rein.
Here there was no hand to master, no rein to clutch,
Where the riderless horses kicked their way through the crowd
And the congressmen's carriages choked Cat Hairpin Bend.

Sykes and the regulars covered the retreat,
And a few brigades were kept in some sort of order,
But the rest—They tried to stop them at Centerville.
McDowell and his tired staff held a haggard conference.
But before the officers could order retreat
The men were walking away.

                        They had fought and lost.
They were going to Washington, they were going back
To their tents and their cooking-fires and their letters from
    Susie,
They were going back home to Maine or Vermont or Ohio,
And they didn't care who knew it, and that was that.

Meanwhile, on the battlefield, Johnston and Beauregard,
Now joined by the dusty Davis, found themselves
As dazed by their victory as their foes by defeat.
They had beaten one armed mob with another armed mob
And Washington was theirs for the simple act
Of stretching a hand to the apple up on the bough,
If they had known. But they could not know it then.
They too saw spectres—unbroken Union reserves
Moving to cut their supply-line near Manassas.
They called back the pursuit, such scattered pursuit as it was.
Their men were tired and disordered. The chance went by
While only the stiff-necked Jackson saw it clear
As a fighting-psalm or a phrase in Napoleon's tactics.
He said to the surgeon who was binding his wound,
With a taciturn snap, "Give me ten thousand fresh troops
And I will be in Washington by tomorrow."
But they could not give him the troops while there yet was time.
He had three days' rations cooked for the Stonewall Brigade
And dourly awaited the order that never came.
He had always been at God's orders, and God had used him
As an instrument in winning a certain fight.
Now, if God saw fit to give him the men and guns,
He would take Washington for the glory of God.
If He didn't, it was God's will and not to be questioned.

Meanwhile he could while the hours of waiting away
By seeing the Stonewall Brigade was properly fed,

Endeavoring, with that rigid kindness of his
To show Imboden his error in using profanity
—In the heat of battle many things might be excused,
But nothing excused profanity, even then—
And writing his Pastor at Lexington a letter
Enclosing that check for the colored Sunday-school
Which he'd promised, and, being busy, had failed to send.
There is not one word of Bull Run in all that letter
Except the mention of "a fatiguing day's service."
It would not have occurred to Jackson there might have been.

————

Walt Whitman, unofficial observer to the cosmos, reads of the
defeat in a Brooklyn room. The scene rises before him, more real
than the paper he stares upon. He sees the defeated army pouring
along Pennsylvania Avenue in the drizzling rain, a few regiments
in good order, marching in silence, with lowering faces—the rest
a drenched, hungry mob that plods along on blistered feet and
falls asleep on the stoops of houses, in vacant lots, in basement-
areas huddled, too tired to remember battle or be ashamed of
flight.

Nothing said—no cries or cheers from the windows, no jeers
from the secessionists in the watching crowd—half the crowd is
secessionist at heart, even now, more than ever now.

Two old women, white-haired, stand all day in the rain, giving
coffee and soup and bread to the passing men. The tears stream
down their faces as they cut the bread and pour out the coffee.

Whitman sees it all in his mind's eye—the tears of the two
women—the strange look on the men's faces, awake or asleep—
the dripping, smoke-colored rain. Perplexed and deep in his heart,
something stirs and moves—he is each one of them in turn—the
beaten men, the tired women, the boy who sleeps there quietly
with his musket still clutched tightly to him. The long lines of a
poem begin to lash themselves against his mind, with the lashing
surge and long thunder of Montauk surf.

————

Horace Greeley has written Lincoln an hysterical letter—he
has not slept for seven nights—in New York, "on every brow
sits sullen, scorching, black despair."

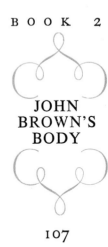

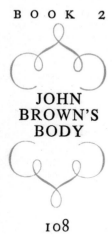
He was trumpeting "On to Richmond!" two weeks ago. But then the war was a thing for an editorial—a triumphal parade of Unionists over rebels. Now there has been a battle and a defeat. He pleads for an armistice—a national convention—anything on almost any terms to end this war.

Many think as he does; many fine words ring hollow as the skull of an orator, the skull of a maker of war. They have raised the Devil with slogans and editorials, but where is the charm that will lay him? Who will bind the Devil aroused?

Only Lincoln, awkwardly enduring, confused by a thousand counsels, is neither overwhelmed nor touched to folly by the madness that runs along the streets like a dog in August scared of itself, scaring everyone who crosses its path.

Defeat is a fact and victory can be a fact. If the idea is good, it will survive defeat, it may even survive the victory.

His huge, patient, laborious hands start kneading the stuff of the Union together again; he gathers up the scraps and puts them together; he sweeps the corners and the cracks and patches together the lost courage and the rags of belief.

The dough didn't rise that time—maybe it will next time. God must have tried and discarded a lot of experiment-worlds before he got one even good enough to whirl for a minute—it is the same with a belief, with a cause.

It is wrong to talk of Lincoln and a star together—that old rubbed image is a scrap of tinsel, a scrap of dead poetry—it dries up and blows away when it touches a man. And yet Lincoln had a star, if you will have it so—and was haunted by a prairie-star.

Down in the South another man, most unlike him but as steadfast, is haunted by another star that has little to do with tinsel, and the man they call "Evacuation" Lee begins to grow taller and to cast a longer shadow.

BOOK THREE

By Pittsburg Landing, the turbid Tennessee
  Sucks against black, soaked spiles with soil-colored waters.
That country is huge and disorderly, even now.
—This is Ellyat's tune, this is no tune but his—
Country of muddy rivers, sombre and swollen,
Country of bronze wild turkeys and catfish-fries
And brushpile landings going back to the brush.
A province of mush and milk, a half-cleared forest,
A speckled guinea-cock that never was cooped
But ran away to grow his spurs by himself.
Neither North nor South, but crunching a root of its own
Between strong teeth—perhaps a wild-onion-root,
Perhaps a white stalk of arbutus, hardier there,
Than any phantom-arbutus of Eastern Springs.
A mudsill man with the river-wash in his ears,

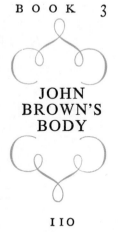
Munching the coarse, good meal of a johnny-cake
Hot from the hob—even now it tastes of the brush,
The wilderness, the big lost star in the pines,
The brown river-dirt, the perpetual river-sound,
In spite of the sidewalks, in spite of the trolley-cars.
No trolley-car-bell can drown that river-sound,
Or take the loneliness out of the lost moon,
The night too big for a man, too lonesome and wide.
The vastness has been netted in railroad tracks
But it is still vast, uneasy.
                              And when the brief
Screech of the railway-whistle stabs at the trees
That grow so thick, so unplanned, so untidily strong
On either side of the two planned ribs of steel,
Ghost-steamboats answer it from the sucking brown water.
In Sixty-two, it was shaggy with wilderness still
For stretches and stretches of close-packed undergrowth,
Wild as a muskrat, ignorant of the axe;
Stretches and stretches where roughly-chinked log-cabins,
Two shouts and a holler away from the nearest neighbors,
Stood in a wisp of open. All night long
The cabin-people heard the chant of the trees,
The forest, hewn away from the painful clearing
For a day or a year, with sweat and back-breaking toil,
But waiting to come back, to crush the crude house
And the planted space with vines and trailers of green,
To quench the fire on the hearth with running green saps,
With a chant of green, with tiny green tendrils curling,
—This is Ellyat's tune, this is no tune but his—
The railway-train goes by with a shrill, proud scream
And the woman comes to the door in a butternut dress
Hair tousled up in a knot on the back of her head,
A barefoot child at her skirt.
                              The train goes by.
They watch it with a slow wonder that is not pathos
Nor heroism but merely a slow wonder.

———————

Jack Ellyat, in camp above Pittsburg Landing,
Speck in Grant's Army of the Tennessee,

Thought of old fences in Connecticut
With a homesick mind.
                    This country was too new,
Too stragglingly-unplanned, too muddy with great,
Uncomfortable floods, too roughly cut
With a broad hatchet out of a hard tree.

It had seemed fine when he was mustered out
After Bull Run, to wear a veteran air,
And tell pink Ellen Baker about war
And how, as soon as he could re-enlist
He'd do it where he got a chance to fight—
Wet mouth of tears—he hadn't wanted to kiss her
At first, but it was easier later on.
Why had he ever gone out to Chicago?
Why had he ever heard that shallow band
Whanging its brass along a Western street
And run to sign the muster-roll again?
Why had he ever talked about Bull Run
To these green, husky boys from Illinois
And Iowa, whose slang was different slang,
Who called suspenders galluses and swore
In the sharp pops of a mule-driver's whip?
Bull Run—it had impressed them for a week
But then they started to call him "Bull Run Jack." . . .

Henry Fairfield marching along with his sword,
All the old company marching after him
Back in McClellan's army, back by the known
Potomac, back in the safe and friendly East;
All the papers telling how brave they were
And how, as soon as the roads dried up in the spring,
"The little Napoleon" would hammer the South to bits
With a blue thunderbolt.
                    And here he was
A lost pea, spilt at random in a lost war;
A Tennessee war that had no *Tribunes* or polish
Where he was the only Easterner in the whole
Strange-swearing regiment of Illinois farmers,
Alien as Rebels, and rough as all outdoors.

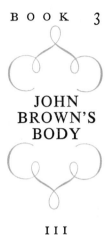

He wanted to get transferred, he wanted to be
Back with the company, back with the Eastern voices,
Back where nobody called him "Bull Run Jack"
And snickered at him for shaving every two days.
He'd written about it and Father knew a congressman
But nothing would happen—he'd never get away,
He'd stay being Bull Run Jack till the end of the war
And march through acres of hostile Tennessee mud
Till his legs dropped off, and never get to be Corporal.
He was sick of the war and the mud and the Western faces.
He hated the sight of his Illinois uniform.
He was sorry for himself. He felt with a vague
Soft blur of self-pity that he was really quite brave,
And if people only knew, they'd do something about it.

This is Ellyat's tune, this is no tune but his.
Nine months have passed since McDowell reddened Bull Run,
Nine strong-hoofed months, but they have meant little to Ellyat.
What means the noise of the wind to the dust in the wind?
But the wind calls strange things out, calls strange men out,
A dozen pictures flash in front of the eyes
And are gone in a flash—

                    rough-bearded Tecumseh Sherman,
Who had tried most things, but being cursed with a taste
For honesty, had found small luck in his stars;
Ex-soldier, banker, lawyer, each in its turn,
Ex-head of a Southern military-school,
Untidy ex-president of a little horse-railroad;
Talkative, nervous, salty, Scotch-Irish fighter,
High-strung, quick-tempered, essentially modern-minded,
Stamping the length of the dusty corridors
Of a Western hotel with a dead cigar in his teeth,
Talking the war to himself, till the word goes round
The new general is crazy—

                    neat, handsome McClellan,
Ex-railroad president too, but a better railroad;
The fortunate youth, the highly-modern boy-wonder,
The snapping-eyed, brisk banner-salesman of war
With all the salesman's gifts and the salesman's ego;
Great organizer, with that magnetic spark

That pulls the heart from the crowd—and all of it spoiled
By the Napoleon-complex that haunts such men.
There never has been a young banner-salesman yet
That did not dream of a certain little cocked-hat
And feel it fit. McClellan felt that it fitted.
—After a year and a day, the auditors come,
Dry auditors, going over the books of the company,
Sad auditors, with groups of red and black figures
That are not moved by a dream of precious cocked hats.
And after the auditors go, the board of directors
Decides, with a sigh, to do without banner-salesmen—
It is safer to dream of a rusty Lincoln stovepipe.
That dream has more patience in it.

And yet, years later,

Meeting the banner-salesman in some cheap street
With the faded clippings of old success in his pocket,
One cannot help feeling sorry for the cocked hat
So briefly worn in a dream of luck and the ego.
One cannot help feeling sorry for George McClellan,
He should have been a hero by every rule.
He looked the part—he could have acted the part
Word perfectly. He looked like an empire-maker.
But so few empire-makers have looked the part.

Fate has a way of picking unlikely material,
Greasy-haired second lieutenants of French artillery,
And bald-headed, dubious, Roman rake-politicians.
Her stiff hands were busy now with an odd piece of wood,
Sometime Westpointer, by accident more than choice,
Sometime brevet-captain in the old Fourth Infantry,
Mentioned in Mexican orders for gallant service
And, six years later, forced to resign from the Army
Without enough money to pay for a stateroom home.
Turned farmer on Hardscrabble Farm, turned bill-collector,
Turned clerk in the country-store that his brothers ran,
The eldest-born of the lot, but the family-failure,
Unloading frozen hides from a farmer's sleigh
With stoop-shouldered strength, whittling beside the stove,
And now and then turning to whiskey to take the sting
From winter and certain memories.

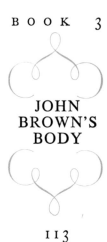

It didn't take much.
A glass or two would thicken the dogged tongue
And flush the fair skin beneath the ragged brown beard.
Poor and shabby—old "Cap" Grant of Galena,
Who should have amounted to something but hadn't so far
Though he worked hard and was honest.

A middle-aged clerk,
A stumpy, mute man in a faded army overcoat,
Who wrote the War Department after Fort Sumter,
Offering them such service as he could give
And saying he thought that he was fit to command
As much as a regiment, but getting no answer.
So many letters come to a War Department,
One can hardly bother the clerks to answer them all—
Then a Volunteer colonel, drilling recruits with a stick,
A red bandanna instead of an officer's sash;
A brigadier-general, one of thirty-seven,
Snubbed by Halleck and slighted by fussy Frémont;
And then the frozen February gale
Over Fort Henry and Fort Donelson,
The gunboats on the cold river—the brief siege—
"Unconditional surrender"—and the newspapers.

Major-General Grant, with his new twin-stars,
Who, oddly, cared so little for reading newspapers,
Though Jesse Grant wrote dozens of letters to them
Pointing out all the wonders his son had done
And writing one dogged letter from that same son
That should have squelched anybody but Jesse Grant.
It did not squelch him. He was a business man,
And now Ulysses had astonished Galena
By turning out to be somebody after all;
Ulysses' old father was going to see him respected
And, incidentally, try to wangle a contract
For army-harness and boom the family tannery.
It was a great surprise when Ulysses refused,
The boy was so stubborn about it.

And everywhere
Were business-people, picking up contraband cotton,
Picking up army-contracts, picking up shoddy,

Picking up shoes and blankets, picking up wagons,
Businesslike robins, picking up juicy earthworms,
Picking up gold all over Tom-Tiddler's Ground,
And Ulysses wouldn't see it.
                              Few people have been
More purely Yankee, in essence, than Jesse Grant.

More pictures—Jefferson Davis, in dripping Spring rain,
Reading a chilly inauguration-address
To an unstirred crowd. He is really President now.
His eyes are more tired, his temper beginning to fray.
A British steamer in the Bahama Channel
Stopped by a Captain Wilkes and a Union cruiser.
They take two men, and let the steamer puff on
—And light a long hissing fuse that for a month
Nearly brings war with England. Lincoln and Seward
Stamp out the fuse, and let the Confederates go—
Wooden frigates at anchor in Hampton Roads
Burning and sinking with tattered banners apeak
Under the strange new, armadillo-bite
Of something plated with iron that yet can float,
The *Merrimac*—and all Washington and the North
In a twenty-four-hours' panic—then, next day—
As Lincoln stares from the window of the White House
For the sooty sign in the sky that means defeat—
The armadillo, smoking back in her pride
To crunch up another meal of weak wooden ships,
Is beaten off by another leaky prodigy
A tin-can cylinder on a floating shingle,
The *Monitor*—the first fight of iron-clads,
The sinking of all the world's old sea-bitten names,
Temeraire, Victory, and *Constellation,*
Serapis, Bon Homme Richard, Golden Hind,
Galleys of Antony, galleys of Carthage,
Galleons with gilded Virgins, galleasses,
Viking long-serpents, siren-haunted galliots,
Argos and argosies and the Achæan pride,
Moving to sea in one long wooden wall
Behind the huge ghost-flagship of the Ark
In such a swelling cloud of phantom sail

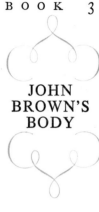

They whitened Ocean—going down by the head,
Green water seeping through the battened ports,
Spreading along the scrubbed and famous decks,
Going down—going down—going down—to mermaid-pools,
To Fiddler's Green—to the dim barnacle-thrones,
Where Davy Jones drinks everlasting rum
With the sea-horses of his sunken dreams.

But this is Ellyat's tune—and if the new
Army of the Potomac stands astrain
To end Secession with its "little Napoleon."
If Lee is just about to find his hour;
If, among many mirrors and gilt chairs,
Under the flare of the gas-chandeliers
A sallow-faced and puffy Emperor
With waxed mustachios and a slick goatee
Gave various Southern accents, talking French,
Evasive answers and no definite help,
Ready enough to recognize the South
If he were sure of profit in the scheme
But not yet finding such a profit sure;
If in the foggy streets of Westminister,
The salty streets of Liverpool and Hull,
The same mole-struggle in the dark went on
Between Confederate and Unionist—
The *Times* raved at the North—Mr. Gladstone thought
England might recognize the South next year,
While Palmerstone played such a tangled game
It is illegible yet—and Henry Adams
Added one more doubt to his education
By writing propaganda for the North,
It is all mist to Ellyat.
                            And when he sleeps,
He does not dream of Grant or Lee or Lincoln
He only dreams that he is back at home
With a heroic wound that does not hurt,
A uniform that never stings with lice,
And a sword like Henry Fairfield's to show Ellen Baker.

———————

As far as the maps and the blocks on the maps have meaning
The situation is this.
                          A wide Western river,
A little lost land, with a steamboat-store,
A post office where the roads from the landings meet,
A plank church three miles inland called Shiloh Chapel,
An undulating and broken table-land
Roughened into a triangle by bordering creeks.
Each side of the triangle runs about four miles long
And, scattered in camps from the tip of the triangle
To the base at the landing, are thirty-three thousand men,
Some fairly seasoned in war, but many green sticks,
Grant's Army of the Tennessee.
                          Down the river
Don Carlos Buell has twenty-five thousand more
In the Army of the Ohio.
                          Opposing these
Are Albert Sidney Johnston and Beauregard
With something like forty thousand butternut fighters,
Including a martial bishop.
                          Johnston plans
To smash Grant's army to bits, before Buell can join it,
And water his wagon-trains in the Tennessee.
He has sneaked his army along through wilderness roads
Till now they are only a mile and a half away
Tonight from the Union lines.
                          He is tall and active.
Light brown hair streaked with grey feathers, blue claymore eyes
That get steel shadows in battle, a face like Hamilton's,
Old Westpointer, old cavalry-colonel, well-schooled in war.
Lincoln offered to make him a major-general
And rumor says that he could have had the command
Of the Union armies, once.
                          But he resigned
And later, went with his State. It is hard to say
What he might have been.
                          They called him the *"preux chevalier"*
At times, as they called and were to call many others
With that Waverly-streak that was so strong in the South.
They also called him one of Davis's pets,

JOHN
BROWN'S
BODY

One of the tin Westpointers that Davis favored
Above good politicians and courtesy colonels.
The Richmond *Enquirer* didn't think so much of him,
His soldiers thought rather more.

                Only this can be said.

He caught Grant napping in some strange flaw of skill
Which happened once and did not happen again.
And drove his unprepared, unwatchful brigades
Back almost into the river.

                And in the heat
Of seeing his lines go forward, he bled to death
From a wound that should not have been mortal.

                    After which,
While the broken Union stragglers under the bluff
Were still howling that they were beaten, Buell came up,
Lew Wallace came up, the knife half-sunk in the wound
Was not thrust home, the night fell, the battle lagged.
The bulldog got the bone in his teeth again
And next day, reinforced, beat Beauregard back
And counted a Union victory.

                In the books
Both sides claim victory on one day or the other
And both claims seem valid enough.

                    It only remains
To take the verdict of the various dead
In this somewhat indecisive meeting of blocks.
There were thirty-five hundred dead when the blocks had met.
But, being dead, their verdict is out of court.
They cannot puzzle the books with their testimony.

Now, though, it is only the evening before the day.
Johnston and Beauregard meet with their corps-commanders
By the wagon-cut Pittsburgh road. The march has been slow.
The marching men have been noisy and hard to manage.
By every rule of war, Grant must have been warned
Long before now, and is planning an ambush for them.
They are being marched into an open Union trap.
So Beauregard thinks and says—and is perfectly right
According to rules. There is only one difficulty.
There is no ambush.

Sherman has just reported
The presence of enemy troops in front of his lines
But says he expects nothing more than some picket-firing
And Grant that evening telegraphs General Halleck,
"I have scarcely the faintest idea of an attack."

So much for the generals. Beauregard makes his point
And is overruled.
                    The April night comes down.
The butternut men try to get some sleep while they can.
They are to be up and fighting by five in the morning.

—————

Jack Ellyat, least of any, expected attack.
He woke about five with a dazzle struck in his eyes
Where a long dawn-ray slid through a crack in the tent.
He cursed at the ray and tried to go back to sleep
But he couldn't do it, although he was tired enough,
Something ate at his mind as soon as he wakened
And kept on eating.
                    This morning was Sunday morning.
The bells would be jangling for church back home, pretty soon,
The girls would be going to church in white Sunday dresses,
No, it was too early for that—they'd be muffled up
In coats and galoshes. Their cheeks would be pink as apples.
He wanted to see a girl who washed her hair,
Not a flat old woman sucking a yellow snuffstick
Or one of the girls in the dirty blue silk wrappers
With flags on their garters. He wanted to see a girl.

He wondered idly about the flags on the garters.
Did they change them to Rebel flags when the Rebels came?
Some poor whore down the river had had herself
Tattooed with a Secesh flag. She was patriotic.
She cried so hard when the Union troops were landed
That the madam had to hide her down in the cellar.
He must be bad to be thinking of things like that
On Sunday morning. He'd better go to church
If they had any kind of church, and make up for it—
O frosty churchbells jangling across the thin

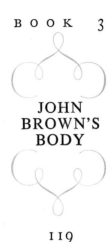

Crust of packed frost, under Connecticut sky,
Put snow on my tongue, and the grey, cool flower of rain—
He had to get up. He couldn't lie here and listen
To Bailey and the rest of them, snoring away.
His throat was dry. He needed a drink of water
But not from a muddy river—put rain on my tongue!
Souse me with chilly, sweet flaws of Puritan rain—
He started to put on his boots, looking over at Bailey.
Bailey was bearded, Bailey was thirty-two,
Bailey had been a teamster and was a corporal.
The walking Bailey looked like a stupid horse,
The sleeping Bailey looked like a dirty sack,
Bailey called him "Colonel" and didn't mean it,
Bailey had had him tossed in a blanket once,
Bailey had told the tale of the tattooed whore,
Somehow he hated Bailey worse than the rest.
He managed to leave the tent without waking Bailey.
It was very early still. The sun was just up.
A fair sky, a very fair day. The air still held
That bloom which is not the bloom on apple or peach
But the bloom on a fruit made up of pure water and light,
The freshness of dawn, still trembling, being new-born.
He sucked at it gratefully.

                The camp was asleep.
All that length of tents still asleep. He could see through the tents.
He could see all those sleeping, rough, lousy, detested men
Laden with sleep as with soft leaden burdens laden,
Movelessly lying between the brown fawns of sleep
Like infants nuzzled against the flanks of a doe,
In quietness slumbering, in a warm quietness,
While sleep looked at them with her fawn's agate eyes
And would not wake them yet.

                      And he was alone,
And for a moment, could see this, and see them so
And, being free, stand alone, and so being free
To love or hate, do neither, but merely stand
Above them like sleep and see them with untouched eyes.
In a while they would wake, and he would hate them again.
But now he was sleep. He was the sun on the coat
Of the halted fawn at the green edge of the wood

Staring at morning.
                  He could not hate them yet.

Somebody near by, in the woods, took a heap of dry sticks,
And began to break them quickly, first one by one,
Then a dozen together, then hard-cracking axe-helves breaking.
Ellyat was running. His mouth felt stiff with loud words
Though he heard no sound from his mouth. He could see the
    white
Fine pine-splinters flying from those invisible axe-helves. . . .

For a minute all of them were tangled together
In the bucking tent like fish in a canvas scoop,
Then they were out of it somehow—falling in line—
Bailey's hair looked angry and sleepy. The officers
Were yelling the usual things that officers yelled.
It was a surprise. They were going to be licked again.
It did not matter yet. It would matter soon.
Bailey had lost his blouse and his pants weren't buttoned.
He meant to tell Bailey about it. There wasn't time.
His eyes felt bald as glass but that was because
He kept looking for flying pine-splinters in the air.
Now they were setting off firecrackers under a boiler
And a man ran past with one hand dripping red paint,
Holding the hand with his other hand and talking
As if the hurt hand were a doll.
                      An officer hit him
With the flat of a sword. It spanked some dust from his coat
And the man's face changed from a badly-fitting mask
Of terror, cut into ridges of sallow wax,
To something pink and annoyed, but he kept on running.
All this happened at once as they were moving.
The dawn had been hit to pieces with a hard mallet.
There were no fawns. There was an increasing noise
Through which he heard the lugubrious voice of Bailey
Singing off-key, like a hymn,
          "When I was a weaver, I lived by myself,
           And I worked at the weaver's tra-a-de—"

The officers were barking like foxes now.

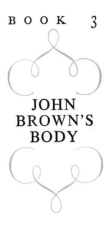

As the last tent dropped behind them, Ellyat saw
A red, puzzled face, looking out from under a tent-flap,
Like a bear from a cave. The face had been drunk last night,
And it stared at the end of the column with a huge and stupid
     wisdom.

———————

"When I was a weaver, I lived by myself,
And I worked at the weaver's trade—"

Jack Ellyat found himself back behind somebody's tent
After a while. He had been out in the woods.
He remembered scrouging against a too-porous tree
For a day or a number of minutes while he jerked
A rattling ramrod up and down in a gun.
But they couldn't stay in the woods—they had to come back.
They had called him "Bull Run Jack" but they had to come
     back,
Bailey and all the rest. He had come back with them,
But that was different—that was all right for him.
This red-colored clang of haste was different for him.
Bailey and all the rest could run where they liked.
He was an old soldier. He would stay here and fight.
Running, he tripped on a rope, and began to fall,
Bailey picked him back on his feet. "Did they get you, Bud?"
"No, they didn't get me."
                              Ellyat's voice was a snarl.
What business had Bailey steadying him like that?
He hadn't been running.
                              Suddenly he saw
Grey shouting strangers bursting into the tents
And his heart shrank up in a pea.
                              "Oh hell," he said,
Hopelessly ramming a cartridge. He was an old soldier.
He wasn't going to run. He was going to act
Vast fictive heroisms in front of Bailey,
If they only gave him time, just a little time.

A huge horse rose above the wall of the tent
And hung there a second like a bad prodigy,

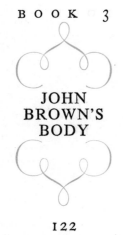

A frozen scream full of hoofs.
                              He struck at its head
And tried to get out from under as it lunged down
But he wasn't quite quick enough.
                              As he slipped and fell
He saw the laughter pasted on Bailey's face
But before he could hear the laugh, the horse had fallen,
Jarring the world.
                    After blunt, sickly time
A fat young man with a little pink moustache
Was bawling "Hey, Yank, surrender!" into his ear
And nervously waving a pistol in front of his eyes.
He nodded weakly. "Hey, boys," called the fat young man,
"I got two Yanks!" His mouth was childish with pleasure.
He was going to tell everybody he had two Yanks.
"Here, Yank, come and pull the horse off the other Yank."

The prisoner's column straggled along the road
All afternoon. Jack Ellyat marched in it numbly.
He was stiff and sore. They were going away from the battle
But they could still hear it, quaking,
The giant stones rolled over the grumbling bridge.

Some of the prisoners tried to joke with the guards,
Some walked in silence, some spoke out now and then,
As if to explain to the world why they were there.
One man said, "I got a sore heel." Another said,
"All the same the Tenth Missouri's a damn good regiment."
Another said, "Listen, boys, don't it beat all hell?
I left my tobacco behind me, back in the tent,
Don't it beat all hell to lose your tobacco like that?"

Bailey kept humming the "Weaver," but now and then
He broke it off, to say, with a queer satisfaction,
"Well, we surely did skedaddle—we surely did."
Jack Ellyat had said nothing for a long time.
This was war, this was Phaëton, this was the bronze chariot
Rolling the sky. If he had a soul any more
It felt scrawny and thin as a sick turkey-poult.
It was not worth the trouble to fatten. He tried to fatten it

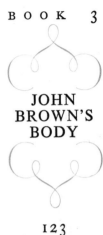

BOOK   3

JOHN
BROWN'S
BODY

123

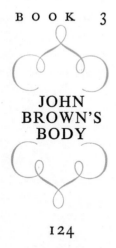
With various thoughts, now and then, but the thoughts were
   spoilt
Corn. They had damn well skedaddled. They damn well had.
That was all. The rest of the army could win or lose
They had surely skedaddled. They had been whipped again.
He had been whipped again.

                    He was no longer
The old soldier—no longer even "Bull Run Jack."
He had lost a piece of himself. It had ragged edges
That piece. He could see it left behind in the tents
Under a dirty coat and a slab of tobacco.

After a while he knocked against Bailey's arm.
"Where are we going?" he said, in a shy voice.
Bailey laughed, not badly, "Well, Colonel, Corinth I guess,
Corinth first—and then some damn prison-camp."
He spat in the road. "It won't be good grub," he said.
"Bacon and hominy-grits. They don't eat right.
They don't eat nothing but bacon and hominy-grits.
God, I'm goin' to get tired of bacon and hominy-grits!"

Ellyat looked. There was something different about him.
He stated a fact. "You've buttoned your pants," he said.
"I remember you didn't have 'em buttoned this morning."

"That's so," said Bailey, impressed, "Now when did I button
   'em?"
They chewed at the question, trying to puzzle it out.
It seemed very important to both for quite a long time.

————

It was night now. The column still marched. But Bailey and
   Ellyat
Had dropped to the rear of the column, planning escape.
There were few guards and the guards were as tired as they.
Two men could fall in a ditch by the side of the road
And get away, perhaps, if they picked a good time.
They talked it over in stupid whispers of weariness.
The next bend—no, the guard was coming along.
The next bend after—no, there was light for a moment

From a brief star, then clouded—the top of the hill—
The bottom of the hill—and they still were marching.
Rain began to fall, a drizzle at first, then faster.
Ellyat's eyes were thick. He walked in a dream,
A heavy dream, cut from leaden foil with blunt shears.
Then Bailey touched him—he felt the tired bones of his skull
Click with a sudden spark—his feet stopped walking—
He held his breath for an instant,
And then wearily slumped in the ditch with enormous noise,
Hunching his shoulders against a phantom bayonet.

But when he could raise his head, the column had gone.
He felt fantastic. They couldn't escape like this.
You had to escape like a drawing in *Harper's Weekly*
With stiff little men on horses like sickle-pears
Firing round frozen cream-puffs into your back.
But they had escaped.
             Life came back to him in a huge
Wave of burnt stars. He wanted to sing and yell.
He crackled out of the ditch and stood beside Bailey.
Had he ever hated Bailey? It could not have been.
He loved Bailey better than anything else in the world.

They moved slyly toward the woods, they were foxes escaped.
Wise foxes sliding away to a hidden earth
To a sandy floor, to the warm fawn-flanks of sweet sleep. . . .
And then an awful molasses-taffy voice
Behind them yelled "Halt!" and "Halt!" and—sudden explosion
Of desultory popcorn in iron poppers—
Wild running at random—a crash among broken boughs—
A fighting sound—Bailey's voice, half-strangled but clear,
"Run like hell, Jack, they'll never catch you!"
                  He ran like hell.

Time passed like the rain. Time passed and was one with the
    rain.

————

Ellyat woke from a nightmare and put out his hand
To touch the wall by his bed, but there was no wall.

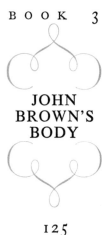

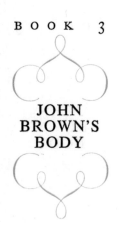

BOOK 3

JOHN
BROWN'S
BODY

126

Then he listened for Bailey's snoring.

                And he heard
The gorged, sweet pouring of water through infinite boughs,
The hiss of the big spilt drop on the beaten leaf,
The bird-voiced and innumerable rain,
A wet quail piping, a thousand soaked black flutes
Building a lonely castle of sliding tears,
Strange and half-cruel as a dryad's bright grief.

Ellyat huddled closer under the tree,
Remembering what he could. He had run for years,
He had slept for years—and yet it was still not dawn.
It seemed cruel to him that it should never be dawn.
It seemed cruel that Bailey was lost. He had meant to show
Some fictive heroisms in front of Bailey.
He had not. Bailey had saved his skin instead,
And Bailey was lost. And in him something was lost,
Something worse than defeat or this rain—some piece of himself.
Some piece of courage.

                Now the slant rain began
To creep through his sodden heart. He thought, with wild awe,
"This is Nibelung Hall. I am lying in Nibelung Hall.
I am long dead. I fell there out of the sky
In a wreck of horses, spilling the ball of the sun,
And they shut my eyes with stone runes and put me to sleep
On a bier where the living stream perpetually flows
Past Ygdrasil and waters the roots of the world.
I can hear the ravens scream from the cloudy roof.
I can hear the bubbles rising in the clear stream.
I can hear the old gods shout in the heathen sky
As the hawk-Valkyrie carry the stiffened lumps
Of corpse-faced heroes shriekingly to Valhalla.
This is Nibelung Hall. I must break the runes from my eyes.
I must escape it or die."

                He slept. The rain fell.

————

Melora Vilas, rising by candlelight,
Looked at herself in the bottom of the tin basin
And wished that she had a mirror.

Now Spring was here,
She could kneel above the well of a forest pool
And see the shadow hidden under the water,
The intent brown eyes, the small face cut like a heart.
She looked at the eyes and the eyes looked back at her,
But just when it seemed they could start to talk to each other—
"What are you like? Who are you?"—
                                                    a ripple flawed
The deep glass and the shadow trembled away.

If she only had a mirror, maybe she'd know
Something, she didn't know what, but something important,
Something like knowing your skin and you were alive
On a good day, something as drenched as sleep,
As wise as sleep, as piercing as the bee's dagger.
But she'd never know it unless she could get a mirror
And they'd never get a mirror while they were hiders.
They were bound to be hiders as long as the war kept on.
Pop was that way. She remembered roads and places.
She was seventeen. She had seen a lot of places,
A lot of roads. Pop was always moving along.
Everybody she'd ever known was moving along.
—Dusty wagons full of chickens and children,
Full of tools and quilts, Rising Sun and Roses of Sharon,
Mahogany dressers out of Grandmother's house,
Tin plates, cracked china, a couple of silver spoons,
Moving from State to State behind tired, scuffed horses
Because the land was always better elsewhere.

Next time they'd quit. Next stop they'd settle right down.
Next year they'd have time to rub up the mahogany dresser.
Next place, Mom could raise the flowers she wanted to raise.
But it never began. They were always moving along.

She liked Kansas best. She wished they'd go back to Kansas.
She liked the smell of the wind there.
But Pop hadn't wanted to join with the Free-Soilers
And then the slavery men had shot up the town
And killed the best horse they had. That had settled Pop.
He said something about a plague on both of your houses

JOHN
BROWN'S
BODY

And moved along. So now they were hiders here
And whenever you wanted to ask Pop about the war
All he said was that same old thing about the plague.
She mustn't call him Pop—that was movers'-talk.
She must call him Father, the way Mom, Mother wanted.
But it was hard to remember. Mom talked a lot
About old times back in the East and Grandmother's house.
She couldn't remember an East. The East wasn't real.
There was only the dusty road and moving along.
Although she knew that Mom had worn a silk dress
And gone to a ball, once. There was a picture of Pop
And Mom, looking Eastern, in queer old Eastern clothes.
They weren't white trash. She knew how to read and figure.
She'd read *Macbeth* and *Beulah* and *Oliver Twist*.
She like *Beulah* best but *Macbeth* would have suited Pop.
Sometimes she wondered what had happened to them,
When Mother used to live in Grandmother's house
And wear silk dresses, and Father used to read Latin—
When had they started to go just moving along,
And how would it feel to live in Grandmother's house?

But it was so long ago, so hard to work out
And she liked it this way—she even liked being hiders.
It was exciting, especially when the guns
Coughed in the sky as they had all yesterday,
When Bent hid out in the woods to keep from recruiters,
And you knew there were armies stumbling all around you,
Big, blundering cows of armies, snuffling and tramping
The whole scuffed world with their muddy, lumbering hoofs,
Except the little lost brushpile where you were safe.
There were guns in the sky again today. Big armies.
An army must be fine to look at.
                                        But Pop
Would never let her do it or understand.
An army or a mirror. She didn't know
Which she'd rather find, but whenever she thought of it
The mirror generally won. You could keep a mirror yourself.
——————

She had to call the hogs that afternoon.
You had to call them once or twice a month

And give them food or else they ran too wild
And never came for butchering in the Fall,
Though they lived well enough without your calling,
Fat in the forest, feeding on beech mast,
Wild muscadines and forest provender
That made their flesh taste sweet as hazelnuts.

She liked the hogs, they weren't tame, sleepy hogs
Grunting in a black wallow, they were proud
Rapid and harsh and savage as Macbeth.
There was a young boar that she called Macbeth,
She'd seen him fight grey-bristled, drowsy Duncan
And drive him from the trough.
                                        Fagin was there,
Bill Sikes was there and Beulah the black sow,
And Lady Macduff whose grunt was half a whine.
You could learn lots about a book from hogs.
She poured the swill and cupped her hands to call.
Sometimes they'd help her with it, Pop or Bent,
But Pop was off with Bent this afternoon
And Mom was always busy.
                                        Slim and straight
She stood before the snake-rail pen that kept
Macbeths on their own proper side of the fence.
"Piggy," she called, "Here, piggy, piggy, piggy!"
It wasn't the proper call, but the hogs knew
That sweet clear loudness with its sleepy silver
Trembling against a chanter of white ash.
"Here, piggy, piggy, piggy, piggy, piggy!
Here, piggy, piggy!" There was a scrambling noise
At the edge of the woods. "Here, piggy!"
                                        It was Banquo.
Greedy, but hesitant.
                        The Artful Dodger
Slim, black and wicked, had two feet in the trough
Before that obese indecision moved.
"Here, piggy! Here, piggy, piggy!"
                                    The gleaming call
Floated the air like a bright glassy bubble,
Far, far, with its clean silver and white ash.

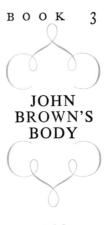

And Ellyat, lost and desperate in the wood,
Heard it, desirous as the elvish blast
Wound on a tiny horn of magic grass
To witch steel riders into a green hill.
He stumbled toward its music.

                                    "Piggy, piggy,
Here, piggy, piggy!"
                        The swine grunted and jostled.
Melora watched them, trying to count them up
With grave eyes, brown as nuts in rainwater.
They were all there, she thought—she must be sure.
She called again. No, something moved in the woods.
She stared past the clearing, puzzled. So Ellyat saw her
Beyond the swine, head lifted like a dark foal
That listens softly for strangeness.

                                    And she saw
An incoherent scarecrow in blue clothes
Stagger on wooden feet from the deep wood.
She called to him to keep away from the hogs,
Half-frightenedly.

                        He did not hear or obey.
He was out of Nibelung Hall.

                                    She put one hand
On the rail of the fence to steady herself and waited.
"You can't come in here," she said, fiercely. "The hogs'll kill
    you."
But he was past the fed hogs and over the fence.
She saw a queer look on his face. "You're hungry," she said.
He grinned, made a noise in his throat, and fell, trying to touch
    her.

                                ——————

                    Now that I am clean again,
                    Now I've slept and fed,
                    How shall I remember when
                    I was someone dead?

                    Now the balm has worked its art
                    And the gashes dry,
                    And the lizard at my heart
                    Has a sleepy eye,

How shall I remember yet
Freezing underground,
With the wakened lizard set
To the living wound?

Do not ponder the offence
Nor reject the sore,
Do not tear the cerements
Flesh may need once more.

Cold comes back and pain comes back
And the lizard, too.
And the burden in the sack
May be meant for you.

Do not play the risen dunce
With unrisen men.
Lazarus was risen once
But earth gaped again.

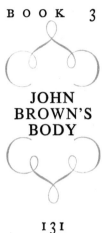

———————

So Ellyat swam back to life, swam back to warmth
And the smell of cooking food. It was night. He heard
Impenetrable rain shake a low roof
And hiss stray, scattering drops on an open fire.
But he was safe. That rain was caged in the sky.
It could not fall on him.
                    He lay in a lax
Idleness, warm and hungry, not wanting to move.
A grub in a close cocoon neither bold nor wise, but content.

A tall woman was cooking mush in an iron pot.
The smell of the mush was beautiful, the shape of the pot
More beautiful than an urn by sea-nymphs carved
From sunken marbles stained with the cold sea-rose.
The woman was a great Norn, in her pot she cooked a new world,
Made of pure vapors and the juices of unspoilt light,
A new globe of sulliless amber and grains of white corn,
An orbed perfection. All life was beautiful now.

A girl came into the room upon light, quick feet.
He stared at her, solemnly. She was young and thin.
The small, just head was set on the slender neck
With a clean sureness. The heavy hair was a helm
Of bronze cooled under a ripple, marked by that flowing.
It was not slight but it could not weight her down.
Her hands and feet were well made and her body had
That effortless ease, that blood that flies with the bird.
She saw his open eyes and came over to him,
Not shyly but not concernedly.

       Their eyes met.
The older woman kept stirring her melted world.
"Well," said the girl, "You look better." He nodded, "Yes."
Their eyes said, "I have seen a new thing. In the deep cells
Below the paltry clockwork of the ticked heart,
I have seen something neither light nor night,
A new thing, a new picture. It may mean
The lifting of a shut latch. It may mean nothing."

She made an escaping gesture with her right hand.
"You didn't say who you were," she said. "You just fell.
You better tell who you are, Pop'll want to know."
A shadow crossed her. "Pop won't want to keep you," she said.
"But I reckon we'll have to keep you here for a piece,
You're not fit to travel yet and that's a fact.
You look a little bit like Young Seward," she said
Reflectively, "But sometimes you look more like Oliver.
I dunno. What's your name?"

       Ellyat put forth his hand
Toward being alive again, slowly, hauling it down.
He remembered. He was Jack Ellyat. He had been lost.
He had lain with hel-shoes on in Nibelung Hall
For twenty years. This was the girl with the swine
Whose loud sweet calling had come to him in the wood
And lifted him back to warmth and a cooking world.
He had lost a piece of himself, a piece of life,
He must find it, but now—

    "What's your name?" he said in a whisper.

————

This is the hidden place that hiders know.
This is where hiders go.
Step softly, the snow that falls here is different snow,
The rain has a different sting.
Step softly, step like a cloud, step softly as the least
Whisper of air against the beating wing,
And let your eyes be sealed
With two blue muscadines
Stolen from secret vines,
Or you will never find in the lost field
The table spread, the signs of the hidden feast.

This is where hiders live.
This is the tentative
And outcast corner where hiders steal away
To bake their hedgehogs in a lump of clay,
To raise their crops and children wild and shy,
And let the world go by
In accidental marches of armed wrath
That stumble blindly past the buried path.
Step softly, step like a whisper, but do not speak
Or you will never see
The furriness curled within the hollow tree,
The shadow-dance upon the wilderness-creek.

This is the hiders' house.
This is the ark of pine-and-willow-boughs.
This is the quiet place.
You may call now, but let your call be sweet
As clover-honey strained through silver sieves
And delicate as the dust upon the moth
Or you will never find your fugitives.
Call once, and call again,
Then, if the lifted strain
Has the true color and substance of the wild,
You may perceive, if you have lucky eyes,
Something that ran away from being wise
And changed silk ribbons for a greener cloth,
Some budding-horned and deer-milk-suckled child

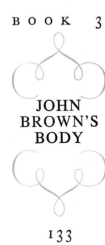

BOOK 3

JOHN
BROWN'S
BODY

133

Some lightness, moving toward you on light feet,
Some girl with indolent passion in her face.

———————

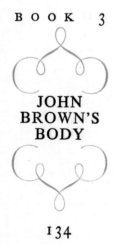

Jack Ellyat wondered about things, six days later.
The world had come back to its shape. He was well and strong.
He had seen the old man with the burnt dreams in his eyes,
Who had fallen from something years ago in his youth
Or risen from something with an effort too stark;
The runaway who had broken the pasture-bars
To test the figments of life on a wild stone.
You could see the ultimate hardness of that strange stone
Cut in his face—but then, there was something else,
That came at moments and went, and answered no questions.
Had the feel of the stone been worth it, after all?
It puzzled Ellyat.
                    He couldn't figure it out.
Going West to get fat acres was common enough,
But, once you got the acres, you settled down,
You sent your children to school. You put up a fence.
When a war came along, you fought on your proper side;
You didn't blast both sides with Mercutio's curse
And hide in a wilderness.
                          The man was all wrong,
And yet the man was not weak. It was very strange.
If the man had been weak, you could understand him all right.

The woman was more easy to understand.
He liked the woman—he liked the rough shaggy boy
Who had lived so much in the woods to keep from the armies
That his ears were sharp as a squirrel's, and all his movements
Had something untamed about them, something leafy and strange.
Of course he ought to be fighting for the North,
He was really a skulk—but things were different here.
You couldn't reason about the difference in words
But you felt it inside your skin.
                                  Things were different here.
Like Nibelung Hall in the rain of his fever-dream,
But with no terror, with an indolent peace.

He'd have to get back to the regiment pretty soon.
He couldn't stay here. They none of them wanted him here.
He'd have to get back. But he didn't know where to go.
They could tell him how to get back to Pittsburg Landing
But how did he know if the army was there or not?
He didn't even know who'd won in the battle,
And, if the Rebs had won, he'd be captured again
As soon as he got on a road.
                              Well, he'd have to chance it.
He couldn't stay here and fall in love with Melora.
Melora came walking down the crooked path
With a long shadow before her. It was the hour
When the heat is out of the gold of afternoon
And the cooled gold has not yet turned into grey,
The hour of the paused tide, neither flow nor ebb,
The flower beginning to close but not yet closed.

He saw her carry her fairy head aloft
Against that descending gold,
He saw the long shadow that her slight body made.

When she came near enough to him, she heard him humming
A tune he had thought forgotten, the weaver's tune.
"And the only harm that I've ever done,
Was to love a pretty maid."

She halted, trying to listen. He stopped the tune.
"What's that you were singing?" she said.
                              "Oh, just trash," he said.
"I liked it. Sing it some more."
                              But he would not sing it.

They regarded each other a foot or so apart.
Their shadows blotted together into one shadow.

She put her hand to both cheeks, and touched them lightly,
As if to cool them from something.
                              A soft, smooth shock
Inexplicable as the birth of a star
And terrible as the last cry of the flesh

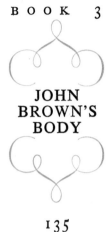

Ran through his cords and struck.

He stared at the shadows.

Then she took her shadow into the house with her
But he still stood looking where the shadows had touched.

———————

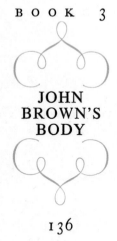
John Vilas watched them go off through the wood
To get the water from the other spring,
The big pail clanking between them.

His hard mouth
Was wry with an old nursery-rhyme, but his eyes
Looked somewhere beyond hardness.

Let them go.

Harriet said and Harriet always said
And Harriet was right, but let them go.
Men who go looking for the wilderness-stone
And find it, should not marry or beget,
But, having done so, they must take the odds
As the odds are.

Faustus and I are old.
We creep about among the hollow trees
Where the bright devils of our youth have gone
Like a dissolving magic, back to earth.
But in our tarnished and our antique wands
And in the rusty metal of our spells
There still remain such stubbornness and pith
As may express elixirs from a rock
Or pick a further quarrel with the gods
Should we find cause enough.

I know this girl,
This boy, this youth, this honey in the blood,
This kingly danger, this immediate fire.
I know what comes of it and how it lies
And how, long afterwards, at the split core
Of the prodigious and self-eaten lie,
A little grain of truth lies undissolved
By all the acids of philosophy.
Therefore, I will not seek a remedy
Against a sword but in the sword itself

Nor medicine life with anything but life.
I am too old to try the peddler's tricks,
Too wise, too foolish, too long strayed in the wood,
The custom of the world is not my custom,
Nor its employments mine.
                    I know this girl
As well as if I never lay with her mother.
I know her heart touched with that wilderness-stone
That turns good money into heaps of leaves
And builds an outcast house of apple-twigs
Beside a stream that never had a name.
She will forget what I cannot forget,
And she may learn what I shall never learn,
But, while the wilderness-stone is strong in her,
I'd have her use it for a touchstone yet
And see the double face called good and bad
With her own eyes. So, if she stares it down,
She is released, and if it conquers her,
She was not weighted with a borrowed shield.

We are no chafferers, my daughter and I.
We give what pleases us and when we choose,
And, having given, we do not take back.
But once we shut our fists upon a star
It will take portents to unloose that grip
And even then the stuff will keep the print.
It is a habit of living.
                    For the boy
I do not know but will not stand between.
He has more toughness in him than he thinks.
—I took my wife out of a pretty house.
—I took my wife out of a pleasant place.
—I stripped my wife of comfortable things.
—I drove my wife to wander with the wind.
—And we are old now, Faustus.
                         Let it be so.
There was one man who might have understood,
Because he was half-oriole and half-fox,
Not Emerson, but the man by Walden Pond.

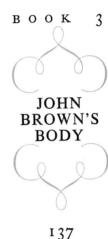

But he was given to the birds in youth
And never had a woman or a daughter.

———————

The filled pail stood on a stone by the lip of the spring,
But they had forgotten the pail.

The spring was a cool
Wavering mirror that showed them their white, blurred faces
And made them wonder to see the faces so like
And yet so silent and distant.

Melora turned.
"We ought to go back," she said in a commonplace voice.
"Not yet, Melora."

Something, as from the spring
Rising, in silver smoke, in arras of silvers,
Drifting around them, pushed by a light, slow wind.
"Not yet Melora."

They sat on a log above.
Melora's eyes were still looking down at the spring.
Her knees were hunched in her arms.

"You'll be going," she said,
Staring at the dimmed glass. "You'll be going soon."
The silver came closer, soaking into his body,
Soaking his flesh with bright, impalpable dust.
He could smell her hair. It smelt of leaves and the wind.
He could smell the untaken whiteness of her clean flesh,
The deep, implacable fragrance, fiercer than sleep,
Sweeter than long sleep in the sun.

He touched her shoulder.
She let the hand stay but still she gazed at the spring.
Then, after a while, she turned.

The mirrored mouths
Fused in one mouth that trembled with the slow waters.

———————

Melora, in the room she had to herself
Because they weren't white-trash and used to be Eastern,
Let the rain of her hair fall down,
In a stream, in a flood, on the white birch of her body.
She was changed, then. She was not a girl any more.
She was the white heart of the birch,

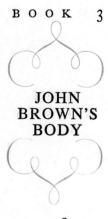

JEFFERSON DAVIS
He is really president now
His eyes are more tired, his temper beginning to fray

Half hidden by a fleece that a South wind spun
Out of bronze air and light, on a wheel of light.
Her sharp clear breasts
Were two young victories in the hollow darkness
And when she stretched her hands above her head
And let the spun fleece ripple to her loins,
Her body glowed like deep springs under the sun.

She had no song to sing herself asleep
Tonight, but she would need no song to sing.
A thousand thoughts ran past her in a brief
Unhurrying minute, on small, quiet feet
But did not change her. Nothing could change her now.
—Black winter night against the windowpane
And she, a child, singing her fear to sleep
With nursery-rhymes and broken scraps of tunes.
How well she could remember those old songs.
But this night she would sleep without a song
Except the song the earth knows in the night
After the huge embrace of the bright day,
And that was better.
                              She thought to herself.
"I don't know. I can't think. I ought to be scared.
I ought to have lots of maybes. I can't find them.
It's funny. It's different. It's a big pair of hands
Pushing you somewhere—but you've got to go.
Maybe you're crazy but you've got to go.
That's why Mom went. I know about Mom now.
I know how she used to be. It's pretty sweet.
It's rhymes, it's hurting, it's feeling a bird's heart
Beat in your hand, it's children growing up,
It's being cut to death with bits of light,
It's wanting silver bullets in your heart,
It's not so happy, but it's pretty sweet,
I've got to go."
                              She passed her narrow hands
Over her body once, half-wonderingly.

"Divide this transitory and temporal flesh
Into twelve ears of red and yellow corn

And plant each ear beside a different stream.
Yet, in the summer, when the harvesters
Come with their carts, the grain shall change again
And turn into a woman's body again
And walk across a heap of sickle-blades
To find the naked body of its love."

She slipped her dress back on and stole downstairs.
The bare feet, whispering, made little sound.
A sleeper breathed, a child turned in its sleep.
She heard the tiny breathings. She shut the door.

The moon rode a high heaven streaked with cloud.
She watched it for a moment. Then she drank
That moon from its high heaven with her mouth
And felt the immaculate burning of that frost
Run from her fingers in such corporal silver
Her whole slight body was a corposant
Of hollow light and the cold sap of the moon.

She knew the dark grass cool beneath her feet.
She knew the opening of the stable door.
It shut behind her. She was in darkness now.

———————

Jack Ellyat, lying in a warm nest of hay,
Stared at the sweet-smelling darkness with troubled eyes.
He was going tomorrow. He couldn't skulk any more.
—Oh, reasonless thirst in the night, what can slake your thirst,
Reasonless heart, why will you not let me rest?
I have seen a woman wrapped in the grace of leaves,
I have kissed her mouth with my mouth, but I must go—
He was going back to find a piece of himself
That he had lost in a tent, in a red loud noise,
Under a sack of tobacco. Until he found it
He could never be whole again
                              —but the hunger creeps
Like a vine about me, crushing my narrow wisdom,
Crushing my thoughts—
                    He couldn't stay with Melora.

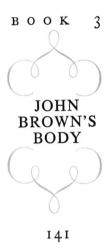

JOHN
BROWN'S
BODY

141

He couldn't take her back home. If he were Bailey
He would know what to do. He would follow the weaver's tune,
He would keep Melora a night from the foggy dew
And then go off with the sunrise to tell the tale
Sometime for a campfire yarn. But he wasn't Bailey.
He saw himself dead without ever having Melora
And he didn't like it.

Maybe, after the war.
Maybe he could come back to the hider's place,
Maybe—it is a long time till after the war
And this is now—you took a girl when you found her—
A girl with flags on her garters or a new girl—
It didn't matter—it made a good campfire yarn—
It was men and women—Bailey—the weaver's tune—

He heard something move and rustle in the close darkness
"What's that?" he said. He got no answering voice
But he knew what it was. He saw a light-footed shadow
Come toward the nest where he lay. For a moment then he felt
  weak, half-sickened almost.

Then his heart began
To pound to a marching rhythm that was not harsh
Nor sweet, but enormous cadence.

"Melora," he said.
His hand went out and touched the cup of her breast.

————

What things shall be said of you,
Terrible beauty in armor?
What things shall be said of you,
Horses riding the sky?
The fleetness, the molten speed,
The rhythm rising like beaten
Drums of barbaric gold
Until fire mixes with fire?

The night is a sparkling pit
Where Time no longer has power
But only vast cadence surging
Toward an instant of tiny death.

Then, with the slow withdrawal
Of seas from a rock of moonlight,
The clasping bodies unlock
And the lovers have little words.

What is this spear, this burnished
Arrow in the deep waters
That is not quenched by them
Until it has found its mark?
What is this beating of wings
In the formless heart of the tempest?
This wakening of a sun
That was not wakened before?

They have dragged you down from the sky
And broken you with an ocean
Because you carried the day,
Phaëton, charioteer.
But still you loose from the cloud
The matched desires of your horses
And sow on the ripened earth
The quickened, the piercing flame.

What things shall be said of you,
Terrible beauty in armor?
Dance that is not a dance,
Brief instant of welded swords.
For a moment we strike the black
Door with a fist of brightness.
And then it is over and spent,
And we sink back into life.

Back to the known, the sure,
The river of sleep and waking,
The dreams floating the river,
The nearness, the conquered peace.
You have come and smitten and passed,
Poniard, poniard of sharpness.
The child sleeps in the planet.
The blood sleeps again.

————

He wasn't going away when he went to the wood.
He told himself that. They had broken the dime together.
They had cut the heart on the tree.

                    The jack-knife cut
Two pinched half-circles of white on the green bark.
The tree-gum bled from the cuts in sticky, clear drops,
And there you were.

               And shortly the bark would dry
Dead on the living wood and leave the white heart
All through the winter, all through the rain and snow,
A phantom-blaze to guide a tall phantom-hunter
Who came in lightness along a leaf-buried path.
All through the snowing winter it would be white.
It would take many springs to cover that white again.
What have I done in idleness, in sweet idleness,
What have I done to the forest?

                   I have marked
A tree to be my own with a jack-knife blade
In idleness, in sweet idleness. I have loosed
A dryad out of the tree to chain me with wild
Grapevines and forest trailers forever and ever
To the hider's place, to the outcast house of the lost,
And now, when I would be free, I am free no more.
He thought of practical matters. There ought to be
A preacher and a gold ring and a wedding-dress,
Only how could there be?

               He rolled hard words
Over his tongue. "A shotgun wedding," he said.
It wasn't like that, it never could be like that,
But there was a deadly likeness.

                He saw the bored
Shamefaced seducer in the clean Sunday collar,
The whining, pregnant slut in the cheesecloth veil.
They weren't like that—but the picture colored his mind.

If he only could go away without going away
And have everything turn out just as it ought to be
Without rings or hiding!

              He told himself "I'm all right.

I'm not like Bailey. I wouldn't sleep with a girl
Who never slept with anybody before
And then just go off and leave her."

                         But it was Melora.
It wasn't seducing a girl. It was all mixed up.
All real where it ought to be something told in a sermon,
And all unreal when you had to do something about it,
His thoughts went round and round like rats in a cage,
But all he knew was—

                    he was sick for a room
And a red tablecloth with tasselled fringes,
Where a wife knitted on an end of a scarf,
A father read his paper through the same
Unchanging spectacles with the worn bows
And a young girl beneath a nickeled lamp
Soundlessly conjugated Latin verbs,
"Amo, amas, amat," and still no sound—

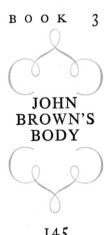
Slight dryad, trailing the green, curled vines of the Spring,
I hate you for this moment, I hate your white breast
And idleness, sweet, hidden idleness—
He started awake. He had been walking through dreams.
How far had he come? He studied the sun and the trees.
Was he lost? No, there was the way.

                    He turned back slowly,
To the dryad, the idleness—to the cheesecloth veil,
The incredible preacher, the falling out of life.
He'd ask her this evening where you could find such preachers.
The old man mustn't know till the thing was done
Or he would turn to a father out of a cheap
Play, a cheap shotgun father with a wool beard
Roaring gilt rhetoric—and loading a musket.
He got the dry grins.

                 If the property-father shot him
Would they carve his name on the soldiers' monument
After the war?

              There should be a special tablet.
"Here lies John Ellyat Junior, shot and killed
By an angry father for the great cause of Union.

'How sleep the brave.' "

He stumbled and looked around him.
"Well, I might go on as far as the road," he said.

A little while later he burst through the screen of brush.
And saw the highroad below him.

He wiped his face.
The road dipped down a hill to a little bridge.
He was safe enough now.

What was it Melora had said?
The highroad was six miles away from the farm,
Due west, and he could tell the west by the sun.
He must have covered a dozen, finding the road,
But getting back would be easy.

The sun was high.
He ought to be starting soon. But he lay down
And stared for a while at the road. It was good to see
A road in the open again, a dust-bitten road
Where people and horses went along to a town.
—Dryad, deep in the woods, your trails are small,
Winding and faint—they run between grass and flowers—
But it is good once more to come on a road
That is not drowsy with your idleness—
He looked down toward the bridge. There were moving blobs of
    dust
Crossing it—men on horses. His heart gave a strange
Throb of desire. What were they? They looked like soldiers.
Blue coats or grey? He could not tell for the dust.
He'd have to get back in the woods before they passed,
He was a hider now. But he kept on staring
A long two minutes, trying to make them out,
Till his eyes stung. One man had a yellow beard
And carried his rifle slung the Missouri way
But there were Missouri troops on either side.
In a minute he could tell—and wriggle away—

A round stick jabbed in his back.

A slow voice said
"Reach for the sky, Yank, or I'll nachully drill yuh."
His hands flew up.

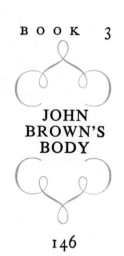

"Yuh're the hell of a scout," said the voice
With drawling scorn. "Yuh h'ain't even got a gun.
I could have picked yuh off ten minutes ago,
Yuh made more noise than a bear, bustin thru' that bresh.
What'd yuh ust to work at—wrappin' up corsets?
Yeah—yuh kin turn around."
                    Jack Ellyat turned
Incredulously.
                "Well, I'll be damned," said the boy
In butternut clothes with the wrinkled face of a leaf.
"Yuh're a young 'un all right—aw, well, don't take it so hard.
Our boys get captured, too. Hey, Billy!" he called,
"Got a Yankee scout."
                    The horse-hoofs stopped in the road.
"Well, bring him along," said a voice.
                              Jack Ellyat slid
Down a little bank and stood in front of the horses.
He was dazed. This was not happening. But the horses
Were there, the butternut men on the horses were there.

A gaunt old man with a sour, dry mouth was talking,
"He's no scout," he said, "He's one of their lousy spies.
Don't he look like a spy? Let's string him up to a tree."
His eye roved, looking for a suitable branch,
His mouth seemed pleased.
                    Ellyat saw two little scooped dishes,
Hung on a balance, wavering in the air.
One was bright tin and carried his life and breath,
The other was black. They were balanced with dreadful evenness.
But now the black dish trembled, starting to fall.

"Hell, no," said the boy with the face like a wrinkled leaf.
"He's a scout all right. What makes yuh so savage, Ben?
Yuh're always hankerin' after a necktie-party.
Who captured the bugger anyhow?"
                            "Oh, well,"
Said the other man. "Oh, well." He spat in the dust.
"Anyhow," he said, with a hungry look at Ellyat,
"He's got good boots."
                    The boy with the wrinkled face

Remarked that, as for the boots, no Arkansaw catfish
Was going to take them away from their lawful captor.

The rest sat their horses loosely and looked at him
With mild curiosity, ruminating tobacco.
Ellyat tried to think. He could not think.
                                        He was free,
These stuffless men on stuffless horses had freed him
From dryads and fathers, from cheesecloth veils and Melora.
He began to talk fast. He didn't hear what he said.
"But I've got to get back," he said. Then he stopped. They
    laughed.
"Oh, yuh'll get over it, Bub," said the wrinkled boy,
"It ain't so bad. You won't have to fight no more.
Maybe yuh'll git exchanged. Git up on that horse.
No, take off them boots first, thanks."
                                        He slung the boots
Around his neck. "Now I got some good boots," he said.
And grinned at the gaunt man with the sour mouth.
"Now, Bub, I'll just tie yuh a little with this yere rope
And then you won't be bustin' loose from the gang.
Grab the pommel as well as yuh kin."
                                        The gaunt man coughed.
"I tell you," he said, in a disappointed voice,
"If we just strung him up it'd make things a hull lot easier.
He's a spy for sure, and everyone strings up spies.
We got a long piece to go yet and he's a nuisance."

"Aw, shut yore face," said Jim Breckinridge in a drawl,
"Yuh kin hang any Yanks yuh ketch on a piece uh dishrag,
Yuh ain't caught no armies yit."
                                        The gaunt man was silent.
Ellyat saw the little tin dish that carried the life
Slowly sink down, to safety, the black dish rise.
"Come on," said Billy. The horses started to move,
Stirring a dust that rose for a little while
In a faint cloud. But after the horses had gone,
The cloud settled, the road went to sleep again.

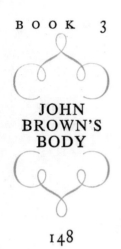

BOOK 3

JOHN
BROWN'S
BODY

148

BOOK FOUR

Strike up, strike up for Wingate's tune,
  Strike up for Sally Dupré!
Strike up, strike up for the April moon,
And the rain on the lilac spray!
For Wingate Hall in its pride once more,
For the branch of myrtle over the door,
Because the men are back from the war;
For the clean bed waiting the dusty rider
And the punchbowl cooling for thirsty throttles,
For the hot cooks boiling the hams in cider
And Cudjo grinning at cobwebbed bottles—
The last of the wine, the last of the wine,
The last of the '12 and the '29!
Three times voyaged around the Cape
Till old Judge Brooke, with an oath oracular,

Pronounced it the living soul of the grape,
And the veriest dregs to be supernacular!

Old Judge Brooke with his double chins
Sighing over his hoarded claret
And sending the last of his cherished bins
To the hospital-doctors with "I can spare it
But if you give it to some damned layman
Who doesn't know brandy from licorice-water
And sports a white ribbon, by fire and slaughter,
I'll hang the lot of you higher than Haman!"

The Wingate cellars are nearly bare
But Miss Louisa is doing her hair
In the latest style of Napoleon's court.
(A blockade-runner brought the report,
A blockade-runner carried the silk,
Heavy as bullion and white as milk,
That makes Amanda a gleaming moth.
For the coasts are staked with a Union net
But the dark fish slip through the meshes yet,
Shadows sliding without a light,
Through the dark of the moon, in the dead of night,
Carrying powder, carrying cloth,
Hoops for the belle and guns for the fighter,
Guncotton, opium, bombs and tea.
Fashionplates, quinine and history.
For Charleston's corked with a Northern fleet
And the Bayou City lies at the feet
Of a damn-the-torpedoes commodore;
The net draws tighter and ever tighter,
But the fish dart past till the end of the war,
From Wilmington to the Rio Grande,
And the sandy Bahamas are Dixie Land
Where the crammed, black shadows start for the trip
That, once clean-run, will pay for the ship.
They are caught, they are sunk with all aboard.
They scrape through safely and praise the Lord,
Ready to start with the next jammed hold
To pull Death's whiskers out in the cold,

The unrecorded skippers and mates
Whom even their legend expurgates,
The tough daredevils from twenty ports
Who thumbed their noses at floating forts
And gnawed through the bars of a giant's cage
For a cause or a laugh or a living-wage,
Who five long years on a sea of night,
Pumped new blood to the vein bled white
—And, incidentally, made the money
For the strangely rich of the after years—
For the flies will come to the open honey,
And, should war and hell have the same dimensions,
Both have been paved with the best intentions
And both are as full of profiteers.)

The slaves in the quarters are buzzing and talking.
—All through the winter the ha'nts went walking,
Ha'nts the size of a horse or bigger,
Ghost-patrollers, scaring a nigger,
But now the winter's over and broken,
And the sun shines out like a lovin' token,
There's goin' to be mixin's and mighty doin's,
Chicken-fixin's and barbecuin's,
Old Marse Billy's a-comin' home!
He's slewn a brigade with a ha'nts's jaw-bone,
He's slewn an army with one long sabre,
He's scared old Linkum 'most to death,
Now he's comin' home to rest from he labor,
Play on he fiddle and catch he breath!

The little black children with velvet eyes
Tell each other tremendous lies.
They play at Manassas with guns of peeled
Willow-stalks from the River Field,
Chasing the Yanks into Kingdom Come
While one of them beats on a catskin drum.
They are happy because they don't know why.
They scare themselves pretending to die,
But all through the scare, and before and after,
Their voices are rich with the ancient laughter,

The negro laughter, the blue-black rose,
The laughter that doesn't end with the lips
But shakes the belly and curls the toes
And prickles the end of the fingertips.

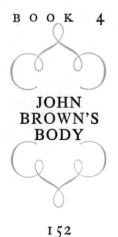

BOOK 4

JOHN
BROWN'S
BODY

152

Up through the garden, in through the door,
That undercurrent of laughter floats,
It mounts like a sea from floor to floor,
A dark sea, covering painted boats,
A warm sea, smelling of earth and grass,
It seeps through the back of the cheval-glass
Where Amanda stares at her stately self
Till her eyes are bright with a different spark,
It sifts like a dye, where Louise's peering
In a shagreen-case for a garnet ear-ring
Till the little jewels shine in the dark,
It spills like a wave in the crowded kitchen
Where the last good sugar of Wingate Hall
Is frosting a cake like a Polar Highland
And fat Aunt Bess in her ice-wool shawl
Spends the hoarded knowledge her heart is rich in
On oceans of trifle and floating-island.

Fat Aunt Bess is older than Time
But her eyes still shine like a bright, new dime,
Though two generations have gone to rest
On the sleepy mountain of her breast.
Wingate children in Wingate Hall,
From the first weak cry in the bearing-bed
She has petted and punished them, one and all,
She has closed their eyes when they lay dead.
She raised Marse Billy when he was puny,
She cared for the Squire when he got loony,
Fed him and washed him and combed his head,
Nobody else would do instead.
The matriarch of the weak and the young,
The lazy crooning, comforting tongue.
She has had children of her own,
But the white-skinned ones are bone of her bone.

They may not be hers, but she is theirs,
And if the shares were unequal shares,
She does not know it, now she is old.
They will keep her out of the rain and cold.
And some were naughty, and some were good,
But she will be warm while they have wood,
Rule them and spoil them and play physician
With the vast, insensate force of tradition,
Half a nuisance and half a mother
And legally neither one nor the other,
Till at last they follow her to her grave,
The family-despot, and the slave.

—Curious blossom from bitter ground,
Master of masters who left you bound,
Who shall unravel the mingled strands
Or read the anomaly of your hands?
They have made you a shrine and a humorous fable,
But they kept you a slave while they were able,
And yet, there was something between the two
That you shared with them and they shared with you,
Brittle and dim, but a streak of gold,
A genuine kindness, unbought, unsold,
Graciousness founded on hopeless wrong
But queerly living and queerly strong. . . .

There were three stout pillars that held up all
The weight and tradition of Wingate Hall.
One was Cudjo and one was you
And the third was the mistress, Mary Lou.
Mary Lou Wingate, as slightly made
And as hard to break as a rapier-blade.
Bristol's daughter and Wingate's bride,
Never well since the last child died
But staring at pain with courteous eyes.
When the pain outwits it, the body dies,
Meanwhile the body bears the pain.
She loved her hands and they made her vain,
The tiny hands of her generation

That gathered the reins of the whole plantation;
The velvet sheathing the steel demurely
In the trained, light grip that holds so surely.

She was at work by candlelight,
She was at work in the dead of night,
Smoothing out troubles and healing schisms
And doctoring phthisics and rheumatisms,
Guiding the cooking and watching the baking,
The sewing, the soap-and-candle-making,
The brewing, the darning, the lady-daughters,
The births and deaths in the negro-quarters,
Seeing that Suke had some new, strong shoes
And Joe got a week in the calaboose,
While Dicey's Jacob escaped a whipping
And the jellybag dripped with its proper dripping,
And the shirts and estrangements were neatly mended,
And all of the tasks that never ended.
Her manner was gracious but hardly fervent
And she seldom raised her voice to a servant.
She was often mistaken, not often blind,
And she knew the whole duty of womankind,
To take the burden and have the power
And seem like the well-protected flower,
To manage a dozen industries
With a casual gesture in scraps of ease,
To hate the sin and to love the sinner
And to see that the gentlemen got their dinner
Ready and plenty and piping-hot
Whether you wanted to eat or not.
And always, always, to have the charm
That makes the gentlemen take your arm
But never the bright, unseemly spell
That makes strange gentlemen love too well,
Once you were married and settled down
With a suitable gentleman of your own.

And when that happened, and you had bred
The requisite children, living and dead,

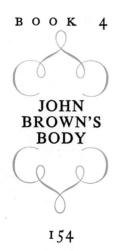

To pity the fool and comfort the weak
And always let the gentlemen speak
To succor your love from deep-struck roots
When gentlemen went to bed in their boots,
And manage a gentleman's whole plantation
In the manner befitting your female station.

This was the creed that her mother taught her
And the creed that she taught to every daughter.
She knew her Bible—and how to flirt
With a swansdown fan and a brocade skirt.
For she trusted in God but she liked formalities
And the world and Heaven were both realities.
—In Heaven, of course, we should all be equal,
But, until we came to that golden sequel,
Gentility must keep to gentility
Where God and breeding had made things stable,
While the rest of the cosmos deserved civility
But dined in its boots at the second-table.
This view may be reckoned a trifle narrow,
But it had the driving force of an arrow,
And it helped Mary Lou to stand up straight,
For she was gentle, but she could hate
And she hated the North with the hate of Jael
When the dry hot hands went seeking the nail,
The terrible hate of women's ire,
The smoky, the long-consuming fire.
The Yankees were devils, and she could pray,
For devils, no doubt, upon Judgment Day,
But now in the world, she would hate them still
And send the gentlemen out to kill.

The gentlemen killed and the gentlemen died,
But she was the South's incarnate pride
That mended the broken gentlemen
And sent them out to the war again,
That kept the house with the men away
And baked the bricks where there was no clay,
Made courage from terror and bread from bran

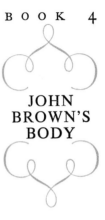

And propped the South on a swansdown fan
Through four long years of ruin and stress,
The pride—and the deadly bitterness.

Let us look at her now, let us see her plain,
She will never be quite like this again.
Her house is rocking under the blast
And she hears it tremble, and still stands fast,
But this is the last, this is the last.
The last of the wine and the white corn meal,
The last high fiddle singing the reel,
The last of the silk with the Paris label,
The last blood-thoroughbred safe in the stable
—Yellow corn meal and a jackass colt,
A door that swings on a broken bolt,
Brittle old letters spotted with tears
And a wound that rankles for fifty years—
This is the last of Wingate Hall,
The last bright August before the Fall,
Death has been near, and Death has passed,
But this is the last, this is the last.
There will be hope, and a scratching pen,
There will be cooking for tired men,
The waiting for news with shut, hard fists,
And the blurred, strange names in the battle-lists,
The April sun and the April rain,
But never this day come back again.

But she is lucky, she does not see
The axe-blade sinking into the tree
Day after day, with a slow, sure stroke
Till it chops the mettle from Wingate oak.
The house is busy, the cups are filling
To welcome the gentlemen back from killing,
The hams are boiled and the chickens basting,
Fat Aunt Bess is smiling and tasting,
Cudjo's napkin is superfine,
He knows how the gentlemen like their wine,
Amanda is ready, Louisa near her,
Glistering girls from a silver mirror,

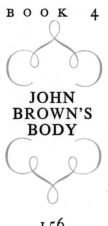

Everyone talking, everyone scurrying,
Upstairs and downstairs, laughing and hurrying,
Everyone giving and none denying,
There is only living, there is no dying.
War is a place but it is not here,
The peace and the victory are too near.
One more battle, and Washington taken,
The Yankees mastered, the South unshaken,
Fiddlers again, and the pairing season,
The old-time rhyme and the old-time reason,
The grandchildren, and the growing older
Till at last you need a gentleman's shoulder,
And the pain can stop, for the frayed threads sever,
But the house and the courtesy last forever.

So Wingate found it, riding at ease,
The cloud-edge lifting over the trees,
A white-sail glimmer beyond the rise,
A sugar-castle that strained the eyes,
Then mounting, mounting, the shining spectre
Risen at last from the drop of nectar,
The cloud expanding, the topsails swelling,
The doll's house grown to a giant's dwelling,
Porches and gardens and ells and wings
Linking together like puzzle-rings,
Till the parts dissolved in a steadfast whole,
And Wingate saw it, body and soul.

Saw it completely, and saw it gleam,
The full-rigged vessel, the sailing dream,
The brick and stone that were somehow quick
With a ghost not native to stone and brick,
The name held high and the gift passed on
From Wingate father to Wingate son,
No longer a house but a conjur-stone
That could hate and sorrow and hold its own
As long as the seed of Elspeth Mackay
Could mix its passion with Wingate clay
And the wind and the river had memories. . . .

Wingate saw it all—but with altered eyes.
He was not yet broken on any wheel,
He had no wound of the flesh to heal,
He had seen one battle, but he was still
The corn unground by the watermill,
He had ridden the rainy winter through
And he and Black Whistle were good as new,
The Black Horse Troop still carried its pride
And rode as the Yankees could not ride,
But, when he remembered a year-old dawn,
Something had come and something gone,
And even now, when he smelt the Spring,
And his heart was hot with his homecoming,
There was a whisper in his ear
That said what he did not wish to hear,
"This is the last, this is the last,
Hurry, hurry, this is the last,
Drink the wine before yours is spilled,
Kiss the sweetheart before you're killed,
She will be loving, and she will grieve,
And wear your heart on her golden sleeve
And marry your friend when he gets his leave.
It does not matter that you are still
The corn unground by the watermill,
The stones grind till they get their will.
Pluck the flower that hands can pluck,
Touch the walls of your house for luck,
Eat of the fat and drink the sweet,
There is little savor in dead men's meat.
It does not matter that you once knew
Future and past and a different you,
That went by when the wind first blew.
There is no future, there is no past,
There is only this hour and it goes fast,
Hurry, hurry, this is the last,
This is the last,
This is the last."

He heard it and faced it and let it talk.
The tired horses dropped to a walk.

And then Black Whistle lunged at the bit
And whinnied because he was alive,
And he saw the porch where the evenings sit
And the tall magnolias shading the drive,
He heard the bell of his father's mirth,
"Tallyho, Yanks—we've gone to earth!
Home, boy, home to Wingate Hall,
Home in spite of them, damn them all!"
He was stabbed by the rays of the setting sun,
He felt Black Whistle break to a run,
And then he was really there again,
Before he had time to think or check,
And a boy was holding his bridle-rein,
And Mary Lou's arms were around his neck.

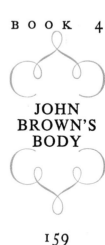
———

Sally Dupré and Wingate talk with the music. . . .

The dance. Such a lovely dance. But you dance so lightly.
Amanda dances so well. But you dance so lightly.
(Do you remember the other dance?)
Phil Ferrier was here, remember, last year.
(He danced with me. He could dance rather well. He is dead.)
We were all so sorry when we heard about Phil.
(How long will you live and be able to dance with me?)
Yes. Phil was a fine fellow. We all liked Phil.
(Do not talk of the dead.
At first we talk of the dead, we write of the dead,
We send their things to their people when we can find them,
We write letters to you about them, we say we liked him,
He fought well, he died bravely, here is his sword,
Here is his pistol, his letters, his photograph case;
You will like to have these things, they will do instead.
But the war goes on too long.
After a while you still want to talk of the dead.
But we are too tired. We will send you the pistol still,
The photograph-case, the knickknacks, if we can find them,
But the war has gone on too long.
We cannot talk to you still, as we used to, about the dead.)
Nancy Huguenot's here tonight. Have you danced with her yet?

She didn't want to come. She was brave to come.
(Phil Ferrier was Nancy's lover.
She sent him off. She cut her hair for a keepsake.
They were going to be married as soon as he came back.
For a long time she dressed in black.
Then one morning she rose, and looked at the sun on the wall,
She put on a dress with red sleeves and a red, striped shawl,
She said "Phil was my beau. He wouldn't have liked me in black."
She used to cry quite a lot but she hasn't cried much since then.
I think she'll get well and marry somebody else.
I think she's right. If I had to wear grief for a lover,
I wouldn't wear black.
I would wear my best green silk and my Empire sacque
And walk in the garden at home and feel the wind
Blow through my rags of honor forever and ever.
And after that, when I married some other beau.
I would make a good wife and raise my children on sweet
Milk, not on poison, though it might have been so.
And my husband would never know
When he turned to me, when I kissed him, when we were kind,
When I cleaned his coat, when we talked about dresses and
    weather,
He had married something that belonged to the wind
And felt the blind
And always stream of that wind on her too-light bones,
Neither fast nor slow, but never checked or resigned,
Blowing through rags of honor forever and ever.)

They are calling for partners again. Shall we dance again?
(Why do we hate each other so well, when we
Are tied together by something that will not free us?
If I see you across a room, I will go to you,
If you see me across a room, you will come to me,
And yet we hate each other.)

Not yet, for a minute. I want to watch for a minute.
(I do not hate you. I love you. But you must take me.
I will not take your leavings nor you my pity.
I must break you first for a while and you must break me.

We are too strong to love the surrendered city.
So we hate each other.)

That's a pretty girl over there. Beautiful hair.
(She is the porcelain you play at being.)
Yes, isn't she. Her name is Lucy Weatherby.
(I hate her hair. I hate her porcelain air.)
She can't be from the county or I'd remember her.
(I know that kind of mouth. Your mouth is not that.
Your mouth is generous and bitter and sweet.
If I kissed your mouth, I would have to be yours forever.
Her mouth is pretty. You could kiss it awhile.)
No, they're kin to the Shepleys. Lucy comes from Virginia.
(I know that kind of mouth. I know that hair.
I know the dolls you like to take in your hands,
The dolls that all men like to take in their hands,
I will not fight with a doll for you or any one.)

We'd better dance now.
(Lucy Weatherby.
When this dance is done, I will leave you and dance with her.
I know that shallow but sufficient mouth.)
As you please.
(Lucy Weatherby.
I will make an image of you, a doll in wax.
I will pierce the little wax palms with silver bodkins.
No, I will not.)
That's good music. It beats in your head.
(It beats in the head, it beats in the head,
It ties the heart with a scarlet thread,
This is the last,
This is the last,
Hurry, hurry, this is the last.
We dance on a floor of polished sleet,
But the little cracks are beginning to meet,
Under the play of our dancing feet.
I do not care. I am Wingate still.
The corn unground by the watermill.
And I am yours while the fiddles spill,

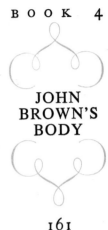

But my will has a knife to cut your will,
My birds will never come to your hill.

You are my foe and my only friend,
You are the steel I cannot bend,
You are the water at the world's end.

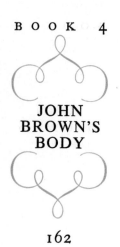

But Wingate Hall must tumble down,
Tumble down, tumble down,
A dream dissolving, a ruined thing,
Before we can melt from the shattered crown
Gold enough for a wedding-ring.
And Wingate Hall must lie in the dust,
And the wood rot and the iron rust
And the vines grow over the broken bust,
Before we meet without hate or pride,
Before we talk as lover and bride,
Before the daggers of our offence
Have the color of innocence,
And nothing is said and all is said,
And we go looking for secret bread,
And lie together in the same bed.)

Yes, it's good music, hear it lift.
(It is too mellow, it is too swift,
I am dancing alone in my naked shift,
I am dancing alone in the snowdrift.
You are my lover and you my life,
My peace and my unending strife
And the edge of the knife against my knife.
I will not make you a porcelain wife.

We are linked together for good and all,
For the still pool and the waterfall,
But you are married to Wingate Hall.
And Wingate Hall must tumble down,
Tumble down, tumble down,
Wingate Hall must tumble down,
An idol broken apart,
Before I sew on a wedding gown

And stitch my name in your heart.
And Wingate Hall must lie in the grass,
And the silk stain and the rabbits pass
And the sparrows wash in the gilded glass,
Before the fire of our anger smothers,
And our sorrows can laugh at their lucky brothers,
Before the knives of our enmity
Are buried under the same green tree
And nothing is vowed and all is vowed
And we have forgotten how to be proud,
And we sleep like cherubs in the same cloud.)

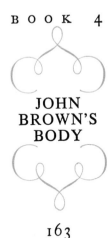
———————

Lucy Weatherby, cuddled up in her bed,
Drifted along toward sleep with a smile on her mouth,
"I was pretty tonight," she thought, "I was pretty tonight.
Blue's my color—blue that matches my eyes.
I always ought to wear blue. I'm sorry for girls
Who can't wear that sort of blue. Her name is Sally
But she's too dark to wear the colors I can,
I'd like to give her my blue dress and see her wear it,
She looked too gawky, poor thing.
                              He danced with her
For a while at first but I hadn't danced with him then,
He danced with me after that. He's rather a dear.
I wonder how long he'll be here. I think I like him.
I think I'm going to be pretty while I am here.

Lucy Weatherby—Lucy Shepley—Lucy Wingate—
Huger's so jealous, nearly as jealous as Curly,
Poor Curly—I ought to answer his mother's letter
But it's so hard answering letters."
                              She cried a little,
Thinking of Curly. The tears were fluent and warm,
They did not sting in her eyes. They made her feel brave.
She could hardly remember Curly any more
But it was right to cry for him, now and then,
Slight tears at night and a long, warm, dreamless sleep
That left you looking pretty.
                    She dried the tears

And thought to herself with a pleasant little awe,
"You really are mighty brave, dear. You really are.
Nobody would think your beau was killed at Manassas."
—She could hardly remember Curly any more—
She tried to make Curly's face come out of the darkness
But it was too hard—the other faces kept coming—
Huger Shepley and all the Virginia boys
And now this new boy's face with the dark, keen eyes.

Boys who were privates, boys who were majors and captains,
Nice old Generals who patted your shoulder,
Darling convalescents who called you an angel—
A whole, great lucky-bag of nice, thrilling boys,
Fighting for you—and the South and the Cause, of course.
You were a flame for the Cause. You sang songs about it.
You sent white feathers to boys who didn't enlist
And bunches of flowers to boys who were suitably wounded.
You wouldn't dream of making peace with the North
While a single boy was left to fight for the Cause
And they called you the Dixie Angel.
                              They fought for the Cause
But you couldn't help feeling, too, that they fought for you,
And when they died for you—and the Cause and the flag—
Your heart was tender enough. You were willing to say
You had been engaged to them, even when you hadn't
And answer their mothers' letters in a sweet way,
Though answering letters was hard.
                              She cuddled closer,
"Pillow, tell me I'm pretty, tell me I'm lovely,
Tell me I'm nicer than anybody you know,
Tell me that nice new boy is thinking about me,
Tell me that Sally girl couldn't wear my blue,
Tell me the war won't end till we've whipped the Yankees,
Tell me I'll never get wrinkles and always have beaus."

————

The slave got away from Zachary's place that night.
He was a big fellow named Spade with one cropped ear.
He had splay feet and sometimes walked with a limp.
His back was scarred. He was black as a pine at night.

He'd tried to run away a couple of times
—That was how he got some of the marks you could tell him
   by—
But he'd been pretty quiet now for a year or so
And they thought he had settled down.

                        When he got away
He meant to kill Zachary first but the signs weren't right.
He talked to the knife but the knife didn't sweat or heat,
So he just got away instead.

                When he reached the woods
And was all alone, he was pretty scared for a while,
But he kept on going all night by the big soft stars,
Loping as fast as he could on his long splay feet
And when morning broke, he knew he was safe for a time.

He came out on a cleared place, then. He saw the red
Sun spill over the trees.

              He threw his pack
Down on the ground and started to laugh and laugh,
"Spade, boy, Spade, you's lucky to git dis far.
You never managed to git dis far before,
De Lawd's sho'ly with you, Spade."

                  He ate and drank.
He drew a circle for Zachary's face in the ground
And spat in the circle. Then he thought of his woman.
"She's sho'ly a grievin' woman dis mawnin', Spade."
The thought made him sad at first, but he soon cheered up.
"She'll do all right as soon as she's thu with grievin'.
Grievin' yaller gals always does all right.
Next time I'se gwine to git me a coal-black gal.
I'se tired of persimmon-skins.

                    I'se gwine to break loose.
De signs is right dis time. I'se gwine to be free,
Free in de Norf."

            He saw himself in the North.
He had a stovepipe hat and a coal-black gal.
He had a white-folks' house and a regular mule.
He worked for money and nobody ever owned him.
He got religion and dollars and lucky dice
And everybody he passed in the white folks' street

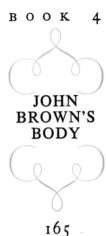

Said "Good mawnin', Mr. Spade—Mr. Spade, good mawnin'."
He chuckled aloud. "Good mawnin', Mistuh Spade,
Gwine to be free, Mistuh Spade—yes, suh, Mistuh Spade!"
For a lazy moment, he was already there—
Then he stiffened, nostrils flaring, at a slight sound.
It couldn't be dogs already.

           "Jesus," he whispered,
"Sweet, lovin' Jesus, don't let 'em git me again,
Burn me up, but don't let 'em git me again,
Dey's gwine to cut me apart."

            The rabbit ran past.
He stared at it for a moment with wild, round eyes,
Started a yell of laughter—and choked it off.
"Dat ain't no nachul rabbit dere, Spade, boy.
Dat's a sign. Yes, suh. You better start makin' tracks.
Take your foot in your hand, Mistuh Spade."

            He swung the bundle
Up on his shoulders and slid along through the trees.
The bundle was light. He was going to be hungry soon
And the big splay feet would soon be bleeding and sore,
But, as he went, he shook with uncanny chuckles.
"Good mawnin', Mr. Spade—glad to see you dis mawnin'
How's Mrs. Spade, Mr. Spade?"

———

Sally Dupré, from the high porch of her house
Stared at the road.

           They would be here soon enough.
She had waved a flag the last time they went away.
This time she would wave her hand or her handkerchief.
That was what women did. The column passed by
And the women waved, and it came back and they waved,
And, in between, if you loved, you lived by a dull
Clock of long minutes that passed like sunbonneted women
Each with the same dry face and the same set hands.
I have read, they have told me that love is a pretty god
With light wings stuck to his shoulders.

           They did not tell me
That love is nursing a hawk with yellow eyes,

That love is feeding your heart to the beak of the hawk
Because an old woman, gossiping, uttered a name.
They were coming now.
She remembered the first time.
They were different now. They rode with a different rein.
They rode all together. They knew where they were going.
They were famous now, but she wondered about the fame.
And yet, as she wondered, she felt the tears in her blood
Because they could ride so easily.

He was there.

She fed her heart to the hawk and watched him ride.

She thought, "But they like this, too. They are like small boys
Going off to cook potatoes over a fire
Deep in the woods, where no women can ever come
To say how blackened and burnt the potatoes are
And how you could cook them better back in a house.
Oh, they like to come home. When they're sick they like to come
    home,
They dream about home—they write you they want to come
    back,
And they come back and live in the house for a while
And raise their sons to hear the same whistle-tune
Under the window, the whistle calling the boys
Out to the burnt potatoes.

O whistler Death,

What have we done to you in a barren month,
In a sterile hour, that our lovers should die before us?"
Then she thought. "No, no, I can't bear it. It cannot be borne."
And knowing this, bore it.

He saw her. He turned his horse.

"If he comes here, I can't keep it back, I can't keep it back,
I can't stand it, don't let him come." He was coming now.
He rides well, she thought, while her hands made each other cold.
I will have to remember how. And his face is sharper.
The moustache quite changes his face. The face that I saw
While he was away was clean-shaven and darker-eyed.
I must change that, now. I will have to remember that.
It is very important.

He swung from Black Whistle's back.

His spurs made a noise on the porch. She twisted her hands.
"If I shut my eyes, I can make him kiss me. I will not."

They were saying good-by, now. She heard polite voices say-
    ing it.
Then the voices ended. "No, no, it is not to be borne,
It is the last twist of the vise."
                            Her will snapped then.
When she looked at him, she knew that the knives were edgeless.
In an instant life would begin, life would be forever.

His eyes wavered. There was a thin noise in her ears,
A noise from the road.
                        The instant fell and lay dead
Between them like something broken.

She turned to see what had killed it.

Lucy Weatherby, reining a bright bay mare,
Played with the braided lash of a riding-whip
And talked to Wingate's father with smiling eyes,
While Huger Shepley tried to put in a word
And the whole troop clustered about her.
                                Her habit was black
But she had a knot of bright ribbons pinned at her breast,
Red and blue—the Confederate colors.
                            They had cheered her.
They had cheered her, riding along with her colored ribbons.
It was that which had killed the instant.
                                Sally looked
At the face with the new moustache she had to remember.
"Good-by," she said. The face bent over her hand
And kissed it acceptably.
                        Then the face had gone.
He was back with the others now. She watched for a minute.
Lucy was unpinning her knot of ribbons.
She saw a dozen hands go up for the knot
And Lucy laugh her sweet laugh and shake her bright head,
Glance once at Huger Shepley and once at Clay,
And then toss the colored knot to the guidon-bearer

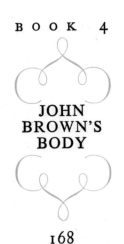

Who grinned and tied the ribbons around the staff
While some of them cheered again.
                            Then the horses moved.
They went by Lucy. Lucy was waving her hand.
She had tears in her eyes and was saying brave words to the
    soldiers.
Sally watched a back and a horse go out of sight.
She was tired, then.
When the troop had quite disappeared
Lucy rode up to the house.
                        The two women kissed
And talked for a while about riding-habits and war.
"I just naturally love every boy in the Black Horse Troop,
Don't you, Sally darling? They're all so nice and polite,
Quite like our Virginia boys, and the Major's a dear,
And that nice little one with the guidon is perfectly sweet.
You ought to have heard what he said when I gave him the knot.
Though, of course, I can tell why you didn't come down to the
    road,
War's terrible, isn't it? All those nice boys going off—
I feel just the way you do, darling—we just have to show them
Whenever we can that we know they are fighting for us,
Fighting for God and the South and the cause of the right—
'Law, Chile, don't you fret about whether you's pretty or plain,
You just do what you kin, and the good Lawd'll brighten your
    tracks.'
That's what my old mammy would tell me when I was knee-high
And I always remember and just try to do what I can
For the boys and the wounded and—well, that's it, isn't it, dear?
We've all got to do what we can in this horrible war."
Sally agreed that we had, and drank from a cup.
She thought. "Lucy Weatherby. Yes. I must look for a doll.
I must make a doll with your face, an image of wax.
I must call that doll by your name."

———————

Now the scene expands, we must look at the scene as a whole.
How are the gameboards chalked and the pieces set?
There is an Eastern game and a Western game.
In the West, blue armies try to strangle the long

Snake of the Mississippi with iron claws;
Buell and Grant against Bragg and Beauregard.
They have hold of the head of the snake where it touches the
    Gulf,
New Orleans is taken, the fangs of the forts drawn out,
The ambiguous Butler wins ambiguous fame
By issuing orders stating that any lady
Who insults a Union soldier in uniform
Shall be treated as a streetwalker plying her trade.
The orders are read and hated. The insults stop
But the ladies remember Butler for fifty years
And make a fabulous devil with pasteboard horns
—"Beast" Butler, the fiend who pilfered the silver spoons—
From a slightly-tarnished, crude-minded, vain politician
Who loved his wife and ached to be a great man.
You were not wise with the ladies, Benjamin Butler,
It has been disproved that you stole New Orleans spoons
But the story will chime at the ribs of your name and stain it,
Ghost-silver, clinking against the ribs of a ghost,
As long as the ladies have tongues.
                                    Napoleon was wiser
But he could not silence one ugly, clever De Staël.
Make war on the men—the ladies have too-long memories.

The head of the snake is captured—the tail gripped fast—
But the body in between still writhes and resists,
Vicksburg is still unfallen—Grant not yet master—
Sheridan, Sherman, Thomas still in the shadow.
The eyes of the captains are fixed on the Eastern game,
The presidents—and the watchers oversea—
For there are the two defended kings of the board,
Muddy Washington, with its still-unfinished Capitol,
Sprawling, badly-paved, beset with sharp hogs
That come to the very doorsteps and grunt for crumbs,
Full of soldiers and clerks, full of all the baggage of war,
"Bombproof" officers, veterans back on leave,
Recruits, spies, spies on the spies, politicians, contractors,
Reporters, slackers, ambassadors, bands and harlots,
Negro-boys who organize butting-matches
To please the recruits, tattooers and fortune-tellers,

Rich man, poor man, soldier, beggarman, thief,
And one most lonely man in a drafty White House
Whose everlasting melancholy runs
Like a deep stream under the funny stories,
The parable-maker, humble in many things
But seldom humble with his fortitude,
The sorrowful man who cracked the sure-fire jokes,
Roared over Artemus Ward and Orpheus C. Kerr
And drove his six cross mules with a stubborn hand.
He has lost a son, but he has no time to grieve for him.
He studies tactics now till late in the night
With the same painful, hewing industry
He put on studying law.
                    McClellan comes,
McClellan goes, McClellan bustles and argues,
McClellan is too busy to see the President,
McClellan complains of this, complains of that,
The Government is not supporting him,
The Government cannot understand grand strategy,
The Government—
                    McClellan feels abused.
McClellan is quite sincere and sometimes right.
They come to the lonely man about McClellan
With various tales.
                    McClellan lacks respect,
McClellan dreams about a dictatorship,
McClellan does that and this.
                         The lonely man
Listens to all the stories and remarks,
"If McClellan wins, I will gladly hold his horse."

A hundred miles away in an arrow-line
Lies the other defended king of the giant chess,
Broad-streeted Richmond.
                    All the baggage of war
Is here as well, the politicians, the troops,
The editors who scream at the government,
The slackers, the good and the bad, but the flavor is different:
There is something older here, and smaller and courtlier,
The trees in the streets are old trees used to living with people,

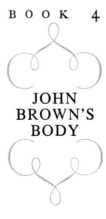

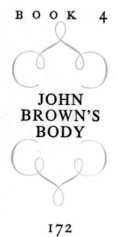
Family-trees that remember your grandfather's name.
It is still a clan-city, a family-city, a city
That thinks of the war, on the whole, as a family-matter,
A woman city, devoted and fiercely jealous
As any of the swan-women who ruled it then—
Ready to give their lives and hearts for the South,
But already a little galled by Jefferson Davis
And finding him rather too much of a doctrinaire
With a certain comparative touch of the parvenu.
He is not from Virginia, we never knew his grandfather.

The South is its husband, the South is not quite its master.
It has a soul while Washington is a symbol,
Beautiful, witty, feminine, narrow and valiant,
Unwisely-chosen, perhaps, for a king of the game,
But playing the part with a definite air of royalty
Until, in the end, it stands for the South completely
And when it falls, the sword of the South snaps short.

At present, the war has not yet touched it home.
McClellan has landed, on the Peninsula,
But his guns are still far away.
                              The ladies go
To Mrs. Davis's parties in last year's dresses.
Soon they are to cut the green and white chintz curtains
That shade their long drawing-rooms from the lazy sun
To bandage the stricken wounded of Seven Pines.

The lonely man with the chin like John Calhoun's
Works hard and is ill at ease in his Richmond White House.
His health was never too strong—it is tiring now
Under a mass of detail, under the strain
Of needless quarrels with secretaries and chiefs
And a Congress already beginning to criticize him.
He puts his trust in God with a charmed devotion
And his faith, too often, in men who can feed his vanity.
They mock him for it. He cannot understand mocking.
There is something in him that prickles the pride of men
Whom Lincoln could have used, and makes them his foes.
Joe Johnston and he have been at odds from the first.

Beauregard and he are at odds and will be at odds,
One could go through a list—
                    He is quite as stubborn as Lincoln
In supporting the people he trusts through thick and thin,
But—except for Lee—the people he trusts so far
Seldom do the work that alone can repay the trust.
They fail in the end and his shoulders carry the failure,
And leave him, in spite of his wife, in spite of his God,
Lonely, beginning and end, with that other's loneliness.
The other man could have understood him and used him.
He could never have used or comprehended the other.
It is their measure.
                    And yet, a deep loneliness,
A deep devotion, a deep self-sacrifice,
Binds the strange two together.
                    He, too, is to lose
A child in his White House, ere his term is accomplished.
He, too, is to be the scapegoat for all defeat.
And he is to know the ultimate bitterness,
The cause lost after every expense of mind,
And bear himself with decent fortitude
In the prison where the other would not have kept him.
One cannot balance tragedy in the scales
Unless one weighs it with the tragic heart.
The other man's tragedy was the greater one
Since the blind fury tore the huger heart,
But this man's tragedy is the more pitiful.
Thus the Eastern board and the two defended kings.
But why is the game so ordered, what crowns the kings?
They are cities of streets and houses like other cities.
Baltimore might be taken, and war go on,
Atlanta will be taken and war go on,
Why should these two near cities be otherwise?
We do not fight for the real but for shadows we make.
A flag is a piece of cloth and a word is a sound,
But we make them something neither cloth nor a sound,
Totems of love and hate, black sorcery-stones,
So with these cities.
                    And so the third game is played,
The intricate game of the watchers oversea,

JOHN
BROWN'S
BODY

The shadow that falls like the shadow of a hawk's wing
Over the double-chessboard until the end—
The shadow of Europe, the shadows of England and France,
The war of the cotton against the iron and wheat.
The shadows ponder and mutter, biding their time;
If the knights and bishops that play for the cotton-king
Can take the capital-city of wheat and iron,
The shadow-hands will turn into hands of steel
And intervene for the cotton that feeds the mills.
But if the fable throned on a cotton-bale
Is checkmated by the pawns of iron and wheat,
The shadows will pause, and cleave to iron and wheat,
They will go their ways and lift their eyes from the game,
For iron and wheat are not to be lightly held.
So the watchers, searching the board.

        And so the game.
The blockade grips, the blockade-runners break through,
There are duels and valors, the Western game goes on
And the snake of the Mississippi is tamed at last,
But the fight in the East is the fight between the two kings.
If Richmond is threatened, we threaten Washington,
You check our king with McClellan or Hooker or Grant,
We will check your king with Jackson or Early or Lee
And you must draw back strong pieces to shield your king,
For we hold the chord of the circle and you the arc
And we can shift our pieces better than you.

So it runs for years until Jubal Early, riding,
A long twelve months after Gettysburg's high tide,
Sees the steeples of Washington prick the blue June sky
And the Northern king is threatened for the last time.
But, by then, the end is too near, the cotton is withered.
Now the game still hangs in the balance—the cotton in bloom—
The shadows of the watchers long on the board.
McClellan has moved his men from their camps at last
In a great sally.

      There are many gates he can try.
The Valley gate and the old Manassas way,
But he has chosen to ferry his men by sea,
To the ragged half-island between the York and the James

And thrust up a long, slant arm from Fortress Monroe
Northwest toward Richmond.

                The roads are sticky and soft,
There are forts at Yorktown and unmapped rivers to cross.
He has many more men than Johnston or John Magruder
But the country hinders him, and he hinders himself
By always thinking the odds on the other side
And that witches of ruin haunt each move he makes.
But even so—he has boarded that jutting deck
That is the Peninsula, and his forces creep
Slowly toward Richmond, slowly up to the high
Defended captain's cabin of the great ship.
—There was another force that came from its ships
To take a city set on a deck of land,
The cause unlike, but the fighting no more stark,
The doom no fiercer, the fame no harder to win.
There are no gods to come with a golden smoke
Here in the mud between the York and the James
And wrap some high-chinned hero away from death.
There are only Bibles and buckles and cartridge belts
That sometimes stop a bullet before it kills
But oftener let it pass.

              And when Sarpedon
Falls and the heavy darkness stiffens his limbs
They will let him lie where he fell, they will not wash him
In the running streams of Scamander, the half-divine,
They will bury him at a shallow and cumbered pit.
But, if you would sing of fighters, sing of these men,
Sing of Fair Oaks and the battered Seven Days,
Not of the raging of Ajax, the cry of Hector,
These men were not gods nor shielded by any gods,
They were men of our shape: they fought as such men may fight
With a mortal skill: when they died it was as men die.

Army of the Potomac, advancing army,
Alloy of a dozen disparate, alien States,
City-boy, farm-hand, bounty-man, first volunteer,
Old regular, drafted recruit, paid substitute,
Men who fought through the war from First Bull Run,
And other men, nowise different in look or purpose,

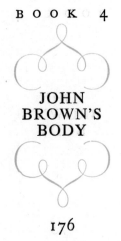
Whom the first men greeted at first with a ribald cry
"Here they come! Two hundred dollars and a ka-ow!"
Rocks from New England and hickory-chunks from the West,
Bowery boy and clogging Irish adventurer,
Germans who learnt their English under the shells
Or didn't have time to learn it before they died.
Confused, huge weapon, forged from such different metals,
Misused by unlucky swordsmen till you were blunt
And then reforged with anguish and bloody sweat
To be blunted again by one more unlucky captain
Against the millstone of Lee.
       Good stallion,
Ridden and ridden against a hurdle of thorns
By uncertain rider after uncertain rider.
The rider fails and you shiver and catch your breath,
They plaster your wounds and patch up your broken knees,
And then, just as you know the grip of your rider's hands
And begin to feel at home with his horseman's tricks,
Another rider comes with a different seat,
And lunges you at the bitter hurdle again,
And it beats you again—and it all begins from the first,
The patching of wounds, the freezing in winter camps,
The vain mud-marches, the diarrhea, the wastage,
The grand reviews, the talk in the newspapers,
The sour knowledge that you were wasted again,
Not as Napoleons waste for a victory
But blindly, unluckily—
        until at last
After long years, at fish-hook Gettysburg,
The blade and the millstone meet and the blade holds fast.
And, after that, the chunky man from the West,
Stranger to you, not one of the men you loved
As you loved McClellan, a rider with a hard bit,
Takes you and uses you as you could be used,
Wasting you grimly but breaking the hurdle down.
You are never to worship him as you did McClellan,
But at the last you can trust him. He slaughters you
But he sees that you are fed. After sullen Cold Harbor
They call him a butcher and want him out of the saddle,
But you have had other butchers who did not win

ROBERT E. LEE
　　This man who murmured "It is well that war
　　Should be so terrible, if it were not
　　We might become too fond of it—"

And this man wins in the end.

You see him standing,
Reading a map, unperturbed, under heavy fire.
You do not cheer him as the recruits might cheer
But you say "Ulysses doesn't scare worth a darn.
Ulysses is all right. He can finish the job."
And at last your long lines go past in the Grand Review
And your legend and his begins and are mixed forever.

Now, though, he is still just one of the Western leaders,
And Little Mac is your darling.

You are unshaken
By the ruin of Fredericksburg, the wounds of Antietam.
Chancellorsville is a name in the Wilderness,
Your pickets, posted in front of the Chickahominy,
Hear the churchbells of Richmond, ringing;
Listen well to those bells, they are very near tonight,
But you will not hear them again for three harsh years.

Black months of war, hard-featured, defeated months
Between Fair Oaks and Gettysburg,
What is your tale for this army?
What do the men,
So differently gathered for your word to devour,
Say to your ears, deaf with cannon? What do they bring
In powder-pocked hands to the heart of the burst shell?
Let us read old letters awhile,
Let us try to hear
The thin, forgotten voices of men forgotten
Crying out of torn scraps of paper, notes scribbled and smudged
On aces, on envelope-backs, on gilt-edged cards stolen out of a
dead man's haversack.

—Two brothers lay on the field of Fredericksburg
After the assault had failed.
They were unwounded but they could not move,
The sharpshooters covered that patch of ground too well.
They had a breastwork to hide them from the bullets,
A shelter of two dead men. One had lost his back,
Scooped out from waist to neck with a solid shot.

The other's legs were gone. They made a good breastwork.
The brothers lay behind them, flat in the mud,
All Sunday till night came down and they could creep off.
They did not dare move their hands for fourteen hours.
—A middle-aged person named Fletcher from Winchester
Enlisted in the Massachusetts Sharpshooters.
He was a crack-duckshooter, skilful and patient.
They gave him the wrong sort of rifle and twenty rounds
And told him to join his company.
It took him days to find it. He had no rations,
He begged bread and green corn and peaches and shot a hog;
So got there at last. He joined just before Antietam.
He'd never been drilled but he knew how to shoot,
Though at first his hands kept shaking.
"It was different kind of gunning from what I was used to,
I was mad with myself that I acted so like a coward."
But as soon as they let him lie down and fight on his own,
He felt all right. He had nineteen cartridges now.
The first five each killed a man—he was a good shot—
Then the rifle fouled. He began to get up and fix it,
Mechanically. A bullet went through his lung.
He lay on the field all day. At the end of the day
He was captured, sent to prison, paroled after weeks,
Died later, because of the wound.
That was his war—
Other voices, rising out of the scraps of paper,
Till they mix in a single voice that says over and over
"It is cold. It is wet. We marched till we couldn't stand up.
It is muddy here. I wish you could see us here.
I wish everybody at home could see us here.
They would know what war is like. We are still patriotic.
We are going to fight. We hope this general's good.
We hope he can make us win. We'll do all we can.
But I wish we could show everybody who stays at home
What this is like."
Voices of tired men,
Sick, convalescent, afraid of being sick.
"The diarrhea is bad. I hope I don't get it
But everybody seems to get it sometime.
I felt sick last night. I thought I was going to die.

But Jim rubbed me and I feel better. There's just one thing,
I hope I never get sent to the hospital,
You don't get well when you go to the hospital.
I'd rather be shot and killed quick."
(Nurses and doctors, savagely, tenderly working,
Trying to beat off death without enough knowledge,
Trying and failing.
Clara Barton, Old Mother Bickerdyke,
Overworked evangels of common sense,
Nursing, tending, clearing a ruthless path
Through the cant and red tape, through the petty jealousies
To the bitter front, bringing up the precious supplies
In spite of hell and high water and pompous fools,
To the deadly place where the surgeons' hands grew stiff
Under the load of anguish they had to deal,
Where they bound men's wounds and swabbed them with green
        corn leaves,
There being no other lint.
Whitman, with his sack of tobacco and comfits,
Passing along the terrible, crowded wards,
Listening, writing letters, trying to breathe
Strong life into lead-colored lips.
He does what he can. The doctors do what they can.
The nurses save a life here and another there,
But the sick men die like flies in the hospitals.)
Voices of boys and men,
Homesick, stubborn, talking of little things,
"We get better food. I'm getting to be a good cook.
The food's bad. The whole company yelled 'Hard Bread!' today.
There are only three professed Christians in my whole regiment,
I feel sad about that.
I wish you could see the way we have to live here,
I wish everybody at home could see what it's like.
It's muddy. It's cold. My shoes gave out on the march.
We lost the battle. The general was drunk.
This is the roughest life that you ever saw.
If I ever get back home—"
And, over and over, in stiff, patriotic phrases,
"I am resigned to die for the Union, mother.
If we die in this battle, we will have died for the right,

We will have died bravely—you can trust us for that.
It is only right to die for our noble Union.
We will save it or die for it. There's just one thing.
I hope I die quick. I hope I don't have to die
In the hospital.
There is one thought that to me is worse than death.
(This, they say over and over) it is the thought
Of being buried as they bury us here
After a battle. Sometimes they barely cover us.
I feel sick when I think of getting buried like that,
Though if nothing except our death will rescue our Union,
You can trust us to die for it."
And, through it all, the deep diapason swelling,
"It is cold. We are hungry. We marched all day in the mud.
We could barely stand when we got back into camp.
Don't believe a thing the newspapers say about us.
It's all damn lies.
                    We are willing to die for our Union,
But I wish you could all of you see what this is like,
Nobody at home can imagine what it is like.
We are ready to fight. We know we can fight and win.
But why will they waste us in fights that cannot be won?
When will we get a man that can really lead us?"
These are the articulate that write the letters.
The inarticulate merely undergo.
There are times of good food and times of campfire jokes,
Times of good weather, times of partial success
In those two years.
                    "The mail came. Thanks for the papers.
We had a good feed at Mrs. Wilson's place.
I feel fine today. We put on a show last night.
You ought to have seen Jim Wheeler in 'Box and Cox.'
Our little band of Christians meets often now
And the spirit moves in us strongly, praise be to God.
The President reviewed us two days ago.
You should have seen it, father, it was majestic.
I have never seen a more magnificent sight.
It makes me proud to be part of such an army.
We got the tobacco. The socks came. I'm feeling fine."
All that—but still the deep diapason throbs

Under the rest.
        The cold. The mud. The bleak wonder.
The weakening sickness—the weevils tainting the bread—
We were beaten again in spite of all we could do.
We don't know what went wrong but something went wrong.
When will we find a man who can really lead us?
When will we not be wasted without success?

Army of the Potomac, army of brave men,
Beaten again and again but never quite broken,
You are to have the victory in the end
But these bleak months are your anguish.
                Your voice dies out.
Let us hear the voice of your steadfast enemy.

Army of Northern Virginia, fabulous army,
Strange army of ragged individualists,
The hunters, the riders, the walkers, the savage pastorals,
The unmachined, the men come out of the ground,
Still for the most part, living close to the ground
As the roots of the cow-pea, the roots of the jessamine,
The lazy scorners, the rebels against the wheels,
The rebels against the steel combustion-chamber
Of the half-born new age of engines and metal hands.
The fighters who fought for themselves in the old clan-fashion.
Army of planters' sons and rusty poor-whites,
Where one man came to war with a haircloth trunk
Full of fine shirts and a body-servant to mend them,
And another came with a rifle used at King's Mountain
And nothing else but his pants and his sun-cracked hands,
Aristo-democracy armed with a forlorn hope,
Where a scholar turned the leaves of an Arabic grammar
By the campfire-glow, and a drawling mountaineer
Told dirty stories old as the bawdy world,
Where one of Lee's sons worked a gun with the Rockbridge
    Battery
And two were cavalry generals.
                Praying army,
Full of revivals, as full of salty jests,
Who debated on God and Darwin and Victor Hugo,

Decided that evolution might do for Yankees
But that Lee never came from anything with a tail,
And called yourselves "Lee's miserables faintin' "
When the book came out that tickled your sense of romance,
Army of improvisators of peanut-coffee
Who baked your bread on a ramrod stuck through the dough,
Swore and laughed and despaired and sang "Lorena,"
Suffered, died, deserted, fought to the end.
Sentimental army, touched by "Lorena,"
Touched by all lace-paper-valentines of sentiment,
Who wept for the mocking-bird on Hallie's grave
When you had better cause to weep for more private griefs,
Touched by women and your tradition-idea of them,
The old, book-fed, half-queen, half-servant idea,
False and true and expiring.
                    Starving army,
Who, after your best was spent and your Spring lay dead,
Yet held the intolerable lines of Petersburg
With deadly courage.
                    You too are a legend now
And the legend has made your fame and has dimmed that fame,
—The victor strikes and the beaten man goes down
But the years pass and the legend covers them both,
The beaten cause turns into the magic cause,
The victor has his victory for his pains—
So with you—and the legend has made a stainless host
Out of the dusty columns of footsore men
Who found life sweet and didn't want to be killed,
Grumbled at officers, grumbled at Governments.
That stainless host you were not. You had your cowards,
Your bullies, your fakers, your sneaks, your savages.
You got tired of marching. You cursed the cold and the rain.
You cursed the war and the food—and went on till the end.
And yet, there was something in you that matched your fable.
What was it? What do your dim, faint voices say?
"Will we ever get home? Will we ever lick them for good?
We've got to go on and fight till we lick them for good.
They've got the guns and the money and lots more men
But we've got to lick them now.
We're not fighting for slaves.

Most of us never owned slaves and never expect to,
It takes money to buy a slave and we're most of us poor,
But we won't lie down and let the North walk over us
About slaves or anything else.

                           We don't know how it started
But they've invaded us now and we're bound to fight
Till every last damn Yankee goes home and quits.
We used to think we could lick them in one hand's turn.
We don't think that any more.

                        They keep coming and coming.
We haven't got guns that shoot as well as their guns,
We can't get clothes that wear as well as their clothes,
But we've got to keep on till they're licked and we're independent,
It's the only thing we can do.

                      Though some of us wonder—
Some of us try and puzzle the whole thing through,
Some of us hear about Richmond profiteers,
The bombproofs who get exempted and eat good dinners,
And the rest of it, and say, with a bitter tongue,
'This is the rich man's war and the poor man's fight.'
And more of us, maybe, say that, after a while,
But most of us just keep on till we're plumb worn out,
We just keep on.

                  We've got the right men to lead us,
It doesn't matter how many the Yankees are,
Marse Robert and Old Jack will take care of that,
We'll have to march like Moses and fight like hell
But we're bound to win unless the two of them die
And God wouldn't be so mean as to take them both,
So we just keep on—and keep on—"

                         To the Wilderness,
To Appomattox, to the end of the dream.
Army of Northern Virginia, army of legend,
Who were your captains that you could trust them so surely?
Who were your battle-flags?

                     Call the shapes from the mist,
Call the dead men out of the mist and watch them ride.
Tall the first rider, tall with a laughing mouth,
His long black beard is combed like a beauty's hair,
His slouch hat plumed with a curled black ostrich-feather,

He wears gold spurs and sits his horse with the seat
Of a horseman born.
                    It is Stuart of Laurel Hill,
"Beauty" Stuart, the genius of cavalry,
Reckless, merry, religious, theatrical,
Lover of gesture, lover of panache,
With all the actor's grace and the quick, light charm
That makes the women adore him—a wild cavalier
Who worships as sober a God as Stonewall Jackson,
A Rupert who seldom drinks, very often prays,
Loves his children, singing, fighting, spurs, and his wife.
Sweeney his banjo-player follows him.
And after them troop the young Virginia counties,
Horses and men, Botetort, Halifax,
Dinwiddie, Prince Edward, Cumberland, Nottoway,
Mecklenburg, Berkeley, Augusta, the Marylanders,
The horsemen never matched till Sheridan came.
Now the phantom guns creak by. They are Pelham's guns.
That quiet boy with the veteran mouth is Pelham.
He is twenty-two. He is to fight sixty battles
And never lose a gun.
                    The cannon roll past,
The endless lines of the infantry begin.
A.P. Hill leads the van. He is small and spare,
His short, clipped beard is red as his battleshirt,
Jackson and Lee are to call him in their death-hours.
Dutch Longstreet follows, slow, pugnacious and stubborn,
Hard to beat and just as hard to convince,
Fine corps commander, good bulldog for holding on,
But dangerous when he tries to think for himself,
He thinks for himself too much at Gettysburg,
But before and after he grips with tenacious jaws.
There is D. H. Hill—there is Early and Fitzhugh Lee—
Yellow-haired Hood with his wounds and his empty sleeve,
Leading his Texans, a Viking shape of a man,
With the thrust and lack of craft of a berserk sword,
All lion, none of the fox.
                    When he supersedes
Joe Johnston, he is lost, and his army with him,
But he could lead forlorn hopes with the ghost of Ney.

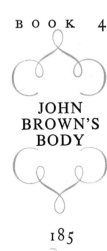

His bigboned Texans follow him into the mist.
Who follows them?
                                   These are the Virginia faces,
The Virginia speech. It is Jackson's foot-cavalry,
The Army of the Valley,
It is the Stonewall Brigade, it is the streams
Of the Shenandoah, marching.
                                        Ewell goes by,
The little woodpecker, bald and quaint of speech,
With his wooden leg stuck stiffly out from his saddle,
He is muttering, "Sir, I'm a nervous Major-General,
And whenever an aide rides up from General Jackson
I fully expect an order to storm the North Pole."
He chuckles and passes, full of crotchets and courage,
Living on frumenty for imagined dyspepsia,
And ready to storm the North Pole at a Jackson phrase.
Then the staff—then little Sorrel—and the plain
Presbyterian figure in the flat cap,
Throwing his left hand out in the awkward gesture
That caught the bullet out of the air at Bull Run,
Awkward, rugged and dour, the belated Ironside
With the curious, brilliant streak of the cavalier
That made him quote Mercutio in staff instructions,
Love lancet windows, the color of passion-flowers,
Mexican sun and all fierce, taut-looking fine creatures;
Stonewall Jackson, wrapped in his beard and his silence,
Cromwell-eyed and ready with Cromwell's short
Bleak remedy for doubters and fools and enemies,
Hard on his followers, harder on his foes,
An iron sabre vowed to an iron Lord,
And yet the only man of those men who pass
With a strange, secretive grain of harsh poetry
Hidden so deep in the stony sides of his heart
That it shines by flashes only and then is gone.
It glitters in his last words.
                                    He is deeply ambitious,
The skilled man, utterly sure of his own skill
And taking no nonsense about it from the unskilled,
But God is the giver of victory and defeat,
And Lee, on earth, vicegerent under the Lord.

Sometimes he differs about the mortal plans
But once the order is given, it is obeyed.
We know what he thought about God. One would like to know
What he thought of the two together, if he so mingled them.
He said two things about Lee it is well to recall.
When he first beheld the man that he served so well,
"I have never seen such a fine-looking human creature."
Then, afterwards, at the height of his own fame,
The skilled man talking of skill, and something more.
"General Lee is a phenomenon,
He is the only man I would follow blindfold."
Think of those two remarks and the man who made them
When you picture Lee as the rigid image in marble.
No man ever knew his own skill better than Jackson
Or was more ready to shatter an empty fame.
He passes now in his dusty uniform.
The Bible jostles a book of Napoleon's Maxims
And a magic lemon deep in his saddlebags.

And now at last,
Comes Traveller and his master. Look at them well.
The horse is an iron-grey, sixteen hands high,
Short back, deep chest, strong haunch, flat legs, small head,
Delicate ear, quick eye, black mane and tail,
Wise brain, obedient mouth.
                              Such horses are
The jewels of the horseman's hands and thighs,
They go by the word and hardly need the rein.
They bred such horses in Virginia then,
Horses that were remembered after death
And buried not so far from Christian ground
That if their sleeping riders should arise
They could not witch them from the earth again
And ride a printless course along the grass
With the old manage and light ease of hand.
The rider, now.
                 He too, is iron-grey,
Though the thick hair and thick, blunt-pointed beard
Have frost in them.
                    Broad-foreheaded, deep-eyed,

Straight-nosed, sweet-mouthed, firm-lipped, head cleanly set,
He and his horse are matches for the strong
Grace of proportion that inhabits both.
They carry nothing that is in excess
And nothing that is less than symmetry,
The strength of Jackson is a hammered strength,
Bearing the tool marks still. This strength was shaped
By as hard arts but does not show the toil
Except as justness, though the toil was there.
—And so we get the marble man again,
The head on the Greek coin, the idol-image,
The shape who stands at Washington's left hand,
Worshipped, uncomprehended and aloof,
A figure lost to flesh and blood and bones,
Frozen into a legend out of life,
A blank-verse statue—
                                    How to humanize
That solitary gentleness and strength
Hidden behind the deadly oratory
Of twenty thousand Lee Memorial days,
How show, in spite of all the rhetoric,
All the sick honey of the speechifiers,
Proportion, not as something calm congealed
From lack of fire, but ruling such a fire
As only such proportion could contain?

The man was loved, the man was idolized,
The man had every just and noble gift.
He took great burdens and he bore them well,
Believed in God but did not preach too much,
Believed and followed duty first and last
With marvellous consistency and force,
Was a great victor, in defeat as great,
No more, no less, always himself in both,
Could make men die for him but saved his men
Whenever he could save them—was most kind
But was not disobeyed—was a good father,
A loving husband, a considerate friend:
Had little humor, but enough to play
Mild jokes that never wounded, but had charm,

Did not seek intimates, yet drew men to him,
Did not seek fame, did not protest against it,
Knew his own value without pomp or jealousy
And died as he preferred to live—sans phrase,
With commonsense, tenacity and courage,
A Greek proportion—and a riddle unread.
And everything that we have said is true
And nothing helps us yet to read the man,
Nor will he help us while he has the strength
To keep his heart his own.

            For he will smile
And give you, with unflinching courtesy,
Prayers, trappings, letters, uniforms and orders,
Photographs, kindness, valor and advice,
And do it with such grace and gentleness
That you will know you have the whole of him
Pinned down, mapped out, easy to understand—
And so you have.

            All things except the heart.
The heart he kept himself, that answers all.
For here was someone who lived all his life
In the most fierce and open light of the sun,
Wrote letters freely, did not guard his speech,
Listened and talked with every sort of man,
And kept his heart a secret to the end
From all the picklocks of biographers.

He was a man, and as a man he knew
Love, separation, sorrow, joy and death.
He was a master of the tricks of war,
He gave great strokes and warded strokes as great.
He was the prop and pillar of a State,
The incarnation of a national dream,
And when the State fell and the dream dissolved
He must have lived with bitterness itself—
But what his sorrow was and what his joy,
And how he felt in the expense of strength,
And how his heart contained its bitterness,
He will not tell us.

            We can lie about him,

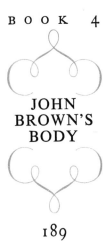

BOOK 4

JOHN
BROWN'S
BODY

189

JOHN
BROWN'S
BODY

Dress up a dummy in his uniform
And put our words into the dummy's mouth,
Say "Here Lee must have thought," and "There, no doubt.
By what we know of him, we may suppose
He felt—this pang or that—" but he remains
Beyond our stagecraft, reticent as ice,
Reticent as the fire within the stone.

Yet—look at the face again—look at it well—
This man was not repose, this man was act.
This man who murmured "It is well that war
Should be so terrible, if it were not
We might become too fond of it—" and showed
Himself, for once, completely as he lived
In the laconic balance of that phrase;
This man could reason, but he was a fighter,
Skilful in every weapon of defence
But never defending when he could assault,
Taking enormous risks again and again,
Never retreating while he still could strike,
Dividing a weak force on dangerous ground
And joining it again to beat a strong,
Mocking at chance and all the odds of war
With acts that looked like hairbreadth recklessness
—We do not call them reckless, since they won.
We do not see him reckless for the calm
Proportion that controlled the recklessness—
But that attacking quality was there.
He was not mild with life or drugged with justice,
He gripped life like a wrestler with a bull,
Impetuously. It did not come to him
While he stood waiting in a famous cloud,
He went to it and took it by both horns
And threw it down.
                              Oh, he could bear the shifts
Of time and play the bitter loser's game,
The slow, unflinching chess of fortitude,
But while he had an opening for attack
He would attack with every ounce of strength.
His heart was not a stone but trumpet-shaped

And a long challenge blew an anger through it
That was more dread for being musical
First, last, and to the end.
                                    Again he said
A curious thing to life.
"I'm always wanting something."
                                    The brief phrase
Slides past us, hardly grasped in the smooth flow
Of the well-balanced, mildly-humorous prose
That goes along to talk of cats and duties,
Maxims of conduct, farming and poor bachelors,
But for a second there, the marble cracked
And a strange man we never saw before
Showed us the face he never showed the world
And wanted something—not the general
Who wanted shoes and food for ragged men,
Not the good father wanting for his children,
The patriot wanting victory—all the Lees
Whom all the world could see and recognize
And hang with gilded laurels—but the man
Who had, you'd say, all things that life can give
Except the last success—and had, for that,
Such glamor as can wear sheer triumph out,
Proportion's son and Duty's eldest sword
And the calm mask who—wanted something still,
Somewhere, somehow and always.
                                    Picklock biographers,
What could he want that he had never had?

He only said it once—the marble closed—
There was a man enclosed within that image.
There was a force that tried Proportion's rule
And died without a legend or a cue
To bring it back. The shadow-Lees still live.
But the first-person and the singular Lee?

The ant finds kingdoms in a foot of ground
But earth's too small for something in our earth,
We'll make a new earth from the summer's cloud,
From the pure summer's cloud.

It was not that,
It was not God or love or mortal fame.
It was not anything he left undone.
—What does Proportion want that it can lack?
—What does the ultimate hunger of the flesh
Want from the sky more than a sky of air?
He wanted something. That must be enough.

Now he rides Traveller back into the mist.

———

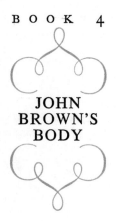

BOOK 4

JOHN
BROWN'S
BODY

Continual guns, be silent for a moment,
Be silent, now.
We know your thirst. We hear the roll of your wheels
Crushing down tangled June,
Virginia June,
With tires of iron, with heavy caissons creaking,
Crushing down maidenhair and wilderness-seal,
Scaring the rabbit and the possum-children,
Scaring the redbird and the mockingbird
As McClellan's army moves forward.
We know your bloody thirst so soon to be slaked
With the red burst-grape juices.
But now, we would have you silent, a little moment,
We would have you hold your peace and point at the moon
For when you speak, we can hear no sound but your sound,
And we would hear the voices of men and women
For a little while.

Jake Diefer, the barrel-chested Pennsylvanian,
Shippy, the little man with the sharp rat-eyes,
Luke Breckinridge, the gawky boy from the hills,
Clay Wingate, Melora Vilas, Sally Dupré,
The slaves in the cabins, ragged Spade in the woods,
We have lost these creatures under a falling hammer.
We must look for them now, again.

Jake Diefer is with the assault that comes from the ships,
He has marched, he has fought at Fair Oaks, but he looks the
    same:

A slow-thought-chewing Clydesdale horse of a man
Who doesn't think much of the way that they farm down here.
The sun may be good, if you like that sort of sun,
But the barns and the fields are different, they don't look right,
They don't look like Pennsylvania.

He spits and wonders.

Whenever he can, he reads a short, crumpled letter
And tries to puzzle out from the round, stiff writing
How things are back on the farm.

The boy's a good boy

But the boy can't do it all, or the woman either.
He knows too much about weather and harvest-hands
—It's all right fighting the Rebels to save the Union
But they ought to get through with it quicker, now they've begun,
They don't take the way the crops are into account,
You can't go off and leave a farm like a store,
And you can't expect a boy to know everything,
Or a hired man. No, sir.

He walks along like an ox.

—He'd like to see the boy and the woman again,
Eat pancakes and sleep in a bed and look at the hay—
This business comes first but after it's finished up—
He can't say he's bothered exactly most of the time.
The weather bothers him more than anything.
He knows it's not the same sort of weather down here,
But every day when he wakes, he looks at the sky
And tries to figure out what it's like back home.

Shippy, the little man with the sharp rat-eyes,
Creeps into an old house in beleaguered Richmond
And meets a woman dressed in severe black silk
With a gentle voice, soft delicate useless hands,
A calm, smooth, faded, handsome mask of a face
And an incredible secret under her brooches.
You would picture her with ivory crochet-needles
Demurely tatting, demurely singing mild hymns
To an old melodeon before a blurred mirror.
She is to live in Richmond throughout the war,
A Union spy, never caught, never once suspected,
And when she dies, she dies with a shut prim mouth

Locked on her mystery.
                    Shippy is afraid.
She gives him instructions, he tries to remember them.
But his hands are sweating, his eyes creep around the floor.
He is afraid of the rustle of the black silk.
He wishes he were back in Pollet's Hotel
With Sophy, the chambermaid.
                              The woman talks
And he listens, while the woman looks through and through him.

Melora Vilas, rising by crack of dawn,
Looked at herself in the bottom of her tin basin
And wished that she had a mirror.
                              She thought dully,
"He's been gone two months. I can't get used to it yet.
I've got to get used to it. Maybe I'll die instead.
No, I'd know if he'd died."

Sally Dupré was tired of scraping lint
But her hands kept on. The hours, sunbonneted women,
Passed and passed. "If he ever comes back to me!"
She finished her scraping and wondered how to make coffee
Out of willow-bark and life from a barren stick. . . .
Spade the fugitive stared at the bleak North Star. . . .
Luke Breckinridge, on picket out in the woods,
Remembered a chambermaid at Pollet's Hotel.
And wanted a fight. He hadn't been lucky, of late.
Jim, his cousin, was lucky, out in the West,
Riding a horse and capturing Yankee scouts.
But his winter here had been nothing but work and mud,
He'd nearly got courtmartialed a dozen times,
Though they knew how he could shoot.
                              The chambermaid's name
Was Sophy. She was little and scared and thin,
But he liked her looks and he liked the size of her eyes,
He'd like to feed her up and see how she looked,
If they ever got through with fighting the Yankees here.
The Yankees weren't all Kelceys. He knew that now,
But he always looked for Kelceys whenever he fought. . . .
Clay Wingate slept in his cloak and dreamed of a girl

With Sally's face and Lucy Weatherby's mouth
And waked again
To know today there would be continual guns.
Continual guns, silent so brief a moment,
Speak again, now,
For now your ignorance
Drowns out the little voices of human creatures.
Jackson slips from the Valley where he has played
A dazzling game against Banks and Shield and Frémont
And threatened the chess-game-king of Washington
Till strong pieces meant to join in McClellan's game
Are held to defend that king.

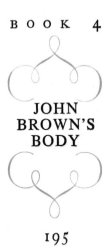
                            And now the two,
Jackson and Lee, strike hard for Seven Days
At the host come up from its ships, come up from the sea
To take the city set on a deck of land,
Till the deck is soaked and red with a bloody juice.
And the host goes back.
                    You can read in the histories
How the issue wavered, the fog of tiny events,
How here, at one dot, McClellan might have wrung
A victory, perhaps, with his larger force,
And there, on the other hand, played canny and well;
How Jackson, for once, moved slowly, how Porter held,
And the bitter, exhausted wrestling of Malvern Hill.
What we know is this.
                        The host from the ships went back,
Hurt but not broken, hammered but undestroyed,
To find a new base far up the crook of the James
And rest there, panting.
                        Lincoln and Halleck come.
The gaunt, plain face is deeper furrowed than ever,
The eyes are strained with looking at books of tactics
And trying to understand.
                            There is so much
For one man to understand, so many lies,
So much half-truth, so many counselling voices,
So much death to be sown and reaped and still no end.
The dead of the Seven Days. The four months dead
Boy who used to play with a doll named Jack,

Was a bright boy as boys are reckoned and now is dead.
The doll named Jack was sometimes a Union soldier,
Sometimes a spy.

         The boy and his brother held
A funeral in the White House flower-beds
After suitably executing the doll named Jack
But then they thought of a different twist to the game.
The gaunt man signed a paper.

            "The doll named Jack
Is pardoned. By order of the President.
A. Lincoln."

        So Jack was held in honor awhile
But next day the boy and his brother forgot the pardon
And the doll named Jack was shot and buried once more.
So much death to be sown and reaped.

            So much death to be sown
By one no sower of deaths.

        And still no end.

The council is held. The chiefs and captains debate.
McClellan clings to his plan of storming the deck
From the water ways. He is cool now. He argues well.
He has written Lincoln "From the brink of eternity"
—A strained, high-flown, remarkable speech of a letter
Of the sort so many have written and still will write—
Telling how well he has done in saving his army,
No thanks to the Government, or to anything else
But the pith of his fighting-men and his own craft.
Lincoln reads and pockets the speech and thanks him.
There had been craft and courage in that retreat
And much was due to McClellan.

            The others speak.
Some corps commanders agree and some demur,
The Peninsula-stroke has failed and will fail again.
Elbow-rubbing Halleck, newly-made chief of staff,
Called "Old Brains," for reasons that history
Still tries to fathom, demurs. He urges withdrawal.
Washington must be defended first and last—
Withdraw the army and put it in front of Washington.
Lincoln listens to all as he tries to sift

The mustardseed from the twenty barrels of chaff
With patient hands.

         There has been a growth in the man,
A tempering of will in these trotting months
Whose strong hoofs striking have scarred him again and again.
He still rules more by the rein than by whip or spur
But the reins are fast in his hands and the horses know it.
He no longer says "I think," but "I have decided."
And takes the strength and the burden of such decision
For good or bad on himself.

         He will bear all things
But lack of faith in the Union and that not once.
Now at last he decides to recall McClellan's army
For right or wrong.

         We see the completed thing,
Long afterward, knowing all that was still to come,
And say "He was wrong."

         He saw the incomplete,
The difficult chance that might turn a dozen ways
And so decided.

         Be it so. He was wrong.

So the deck is cleared and the host goes back to its ships.
The bells in the Richmond churches, clanging for Sunday,
Clang as if silver were mixed in their sweet bell-metal,
The dark cloud lifts, the girls wear flowers again.
Virginia June,
Crushed under cannon, under the cannon ruts,
The trampled grass lifts up its little green guidons,
The honeysuckle and the eglantine
Blow on their tiny trumpets,
Blow out "Dixie,"
Blow out "Lorena," blow the "Bonnie Blue Flag"
—There are many dead, there are many too many dead,
The hospitals are crowded with broken dolls—
But cotton has won again, cotton is haughty,
Cotton is mounting again to a sleepy throne,
Wheat and iron recoil from the fields of cotton,
The sweet grass grows over them, the cotton blows over them,
One more battle and free, free, free forever.

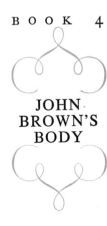

Cotton moves North in a wave, in a white-crested
Wave of puff-blossoms—in a long grey coil
Of marching men with tongues as dry as cotton.
Cotton and honeysuckle and eglantine
Move North in a drenching wave of blossom and guns
To wash out wheat and iron forever and ever.
There will be other waves that set toward the North,
There will be a high tide,
But this is the high hour.
Jackson has still three hammerstrokes to strike,
Lee is still master of the attacking sword,
Stuart still carries his black feather high.
Put silver in your bell-metal, Richmond bells,
The wave of the cotton goes North to your sweet ringing,
The first great raiding wave of the Southern dream.

———————

Jack Ellyat, in prison deep in the South,
Gaunt, bearded, dirty old man with the captive eyes,
Lay on his back and stared at the flies on the wall
And tried to remember, through an indifferent mist,
A green place lost in the woods and a herd of black swine.
They came and went and the mist moved round them again.
The mist was not death. He was used to death by now,
But the mist still puzzled him, sometimes.
It was curious—being so weak and yet used to death.
When you were strong, you thought of death as a strong
Rider on a black horse, perhaps, or at least
As some strong creature, dreadful because so strong.
But when you were weak and lived in a place like this,
Things changed. There was nothing strong about death any
        more.
He was only the gnawed rat-bone on the dirty floor,
That you stumbled across and hardly bothered to curse.
That was all.
                    The two Michigan men had died last night.
The Ohio brothers were going to die this week,
You got pretty soon so you knew when people would die,
It passed the time as well as carving bone-rings,
Playing checkers with straws or learning Italian nouns
From the lanky schoolteacher-sergeant from Vermont.

Somewhere, sometime, in a tent, by a red loud noise,
Under a dirty coat and a slab of tobacco,
He had lost a piece of himself, a piece of life.
He couldn't die till he got that piece of him back
And felt its ragged edges fit in his heart.
Or so he thought. Sometimes, when he slept, he felt
As if he were getting it back—but most of the time
It was only the mist and counting the flies that bothered him.
He heard a footstep near him and turned his head.
"Hello, Charley," he said, "Where you been?"
 Bailey's face looked strange,
The red, hot face of a hurt and angry boy,
"Out hearing the Rebs," he said. He spat on the floor
And broke into long, blue curses. When he was through,
"Did you hear them?" he asked. Jack Ellyat tried to remember
A gnat-noise buzzing the mist. "I guess so," he said.
"What was it? Two-bottle Ed on another tear?"
"Hell," said Bailey. "They cheered. They've licked us again.
The news just come. It happened back at Bull Run."
"You're crazy," said Ellyat. "That was the start of the war.
"I was in that one."
                "Oh, don't be a fool," said Bailey,
"They licked us again, I tell you, the same old place.
Pope's army's ruined."
                "Who's he?" said Ellyat wearily.
"Aw, we had him out West—he's God Almighty's pet horse,
He came East and told all the papers how good he was,
'Headquarters in the saddle'!" Bailey snickered.
"Well, they snaffled his saddle and blame near snaffled him,
Jackson and Lee—anyhow they licked us again."

"What about Little Mac?"
                "Well, Gawd knows what's happened to *him*,"
Said Bailey, flatly, "Maybe he's captured, too,
Maybe they captured Old Abe and everyone else.
I don't know—you can't tell from those lyin' Rebs."

There was a silence. Ellyat lay on his back
And watched the flies on the wall for quite a long time.
"I wish I had a real newspaper," said Bailey,

"Not one of your Richmond wipers. By God, you know, Jack,
When we get back home, I'll read a newspaper, sometimes.
I never was much at readin' the newspaper
But I'd like to read one now, say once in a while."
Ellyat laughed.
           "You know, Charley," he said at last.
"We've got to get out of this place."
               Bailey joined in the laugh.
Then he stopped and stared at the other with anxious eyes.
"You don't look crazy," he said, "Stop countin' those flies."
Ellyat raised himself on one arm.
           "No, honest, Charley,
I mean it, damn it. We've got to get out of here.
I know we can't but we've got to. . . ."
             He swallowed dryly.
"Look here—" he said, "It just came over me then.
I've got a girl and she doesn't know where I am.
I left her back in a tent—no, that wasn't a girl—
And you say we got licked again. But that's just it, Charley.
We get licked too much. We've got to get out of here."

He sank back to the floor and shut his ghost-ridden eyes.
Bailey regarded him for a long, numb moment.
"You couldn't walk a mile and a half," he muttered,
"And, by God, I couldn't carry you twenty feet,
And, by God, if we could, there ain't no way to get out,
But all the same—"
          "If there was any use tryin',"
He said, half-pleadingly, half-defiantly,
"I tell you, Jack, if there was any use tryin'—"
He stopped. Ellyat's eyes were shut. He rose with great care.
"I'll get you some water," he muttered. "No, let you sleep."
He sat down again and stared at the sleeping face.
"He looks bad," he thought. "I guess I look bad myself.
I guess the kid's goin' to die if we don't get out.
I guess we're both goin' to die. I don't see why not."
He looked up at the flies on the ceiling and shook his fist.
"Listen, you dirty Rebs," he said, under his breath,
"Flap your goddam wings—we're goin' to get out of here!"

————

John Brown lies dead in his grave and does not stir,
It is nearly three years since he died and he does not stir,
There is no sound in his bones but the sound of armies
And that is an old sound.

He walks, you will say, he walks in front of the armies,
A straggler met him, going along to Manassas,
With his gun on his shoulder, his phantom-sons at heel,
His eyes like misty coals.

A dead man saw him striding at Seven Pines,
The bullets whistling through him like a torn flag,
A madman saw him whetting a sword on a Bible,
A cloud above Malvern Hill.

But these are all lies. He slumbers. He does not stir.
The spring rains and the winter snows on his slumber
And the bones of his flesh breed armies and yet more armies
But he himself does not stir.

It will take more than cannon to shake his fortress,
His song is alive and throbs in the tramp of the columns,
His song is smoke blown out of the mouth of a cannon,
But his song and he are two.
The South goes ever forward, the slave is not free,
The great stone gate of the Union crumbles and totters,
The cotton-blossoms are pushing the blocks apart,
The roots of cotton grow in the crevices,
(John Brown's body lies a-mouldering in the grave.)
Soon the fight will be over, the slaves will be slaves forever.
(John Brown's body lies a-mouldering in the grave.)
You did not fight for the Union or wish it well,
You fought for the single dream of a man unchained
And God's great chariot rolling. You fought like the thrown
Stone, but the fighters have forgotten your dream.
(John Brown's body lies a-mouldering in the grave.)
You fought for a people you did not comprehend,
For a symbol chained by a symbol in your own mind,
But, unless you arise, that people will not be free.
Are there no seeds of thunder left in your bones

JOHN
BROWN'S
BODY

Except to breed useless armies?
(John Brown's body lies a-mouldering in the grave.)
Arise, John Brown,
Call up your sons from the ground,
In smoky wreaths, call up your sons to heel,
Call up the clumsy country boys you armed
With crazy pikes and a fantastic mind.
Call up the American names,
Kagi, the self-taught scholar, quiet and cool,
Stevens, the cashiered soldier, bawling his song,
Dangerfield Newby, the freed Scotch-mulatto,
Watson and Oliver Brown and all the hard-dying.
Call up the slug-riddled dead of Harper's Ferry
And cast them down the wind on a raid again.
This is the dark hour,
This is the ebb-tide,
This is the sunset, this is the defeat.
The cotton-blossoms are growing up to the sky,
The great stone gate of the Union sinks beneath them,
And under the giant blossoms lies Egypt's land,
The dark river,
The ground of bondage,
The chained men.
If the great gate falls, the cotton grows over your dream.
Find your heart, John Brown,
(A-mouldering in the grave.)
Call your sons and get your pikes,
(A-mouldering in the grave.)
Your song goes on, but the slave is still a slave,
And all Egypt's land rides Northward while you moulder in the
    grave!
Rise up, John Brown,
(A-mouldering in the grave.)
Go down, John Brown,
(Against all Egypt's land)
Go down, John Brown,
Go down, John Brown,
Go down, John Brown, and set that people free!

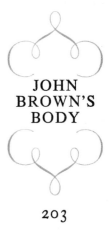

BOOK FIVE

It was still hot in Washington, that September,
  Hot in the city, hot in the White House rooms,
Desiccate heat, dry as a palm-leaf fan,
That makes hot men tuck cotton handkerchiefs
Between their collars and their sweaty necks,
And Northern girls look limp at half-past-four,
Waiting the first cool breath that will not come
For hours yet.
                    The sentinel on post
Clicks back and forth, stuffed in his sweltering coat,
And dreams about brown bottles of cold beer
Deep in a cellar.
                    In the crowded Bureaus
The pens move slow, the damp clerks watch the clock.
Women in houses take their corsets off

And stifle in loose gowns.
                              They could lie down
But when they touch the bed, the bed feels hot,
And there are things to do.
                              The men will want
Hot food when they come back from work.
                                    They sigh
And turn, with dragging feet, to the hot kitchens.

Sometimes they pause, and push a window up
To feel the blunt, dry buffet of the heat
Strike in the face and hear the locust-cry
Of shrilling newsboy-voices down the street,
"News from the army—extra—ter-ble battle—
Terr-r-ble vic'try—ter-r-ble defeat—
Lee's army trapped invading Maryland—
McClellan—Sharpsburg—fightin'—news from the front—"
The women at the windows sigh and wonder
"I ought to buy a paper—No, I'll wait
Till Tom gets home—I wonder if it's true—
Terrible victory—terrible defeat—
They're always saying that—when Tom gets home
He'll have some news—I wonder if the army—
No, it's too hot to buy a paper now—"

A hot, spare day of waiting languidly
For contradictory bits of dubious news.

It was a little cooler, three miles out,
Where the tall trees shaded the Soldiers' Home.
The lank man, Abraham Lincoln, found it so,
Glad for it, doubtless, though his cavernous eyes
Had stared all day into a distant fog
Trying to pierce it.
                        "General McClellan
Is now in touch with Lee in front of Sharpsburg
And will attack as soon as the fog clears."

It's cleared by now. They must be fighting now.

We can't expect much from the first reports.
Stanton and Halleck think they're pretty good
But you can't tell. Nobody here can tell.
We're all too far away.
                              You get sometimes
Feeling as if you heard the guns yourself
Here in the room and felt them shake the house
When you keep waiting for the news all day.
I wish we'd get some news.
                              Bull Run was first.
We got the news of Bull Run soon enough.
First that we'd won, hands down, which was a lie,
And then the truth.
                              It may be that to-day.
I told McClellan not to let them go,
Destroy them if he could—but you can't tell.
He's a good man in lots of different ways,
But he can't seem to finish what he starts
And then, he's jealous, like the rest of them,
Lets Pope get beaten, wanted him to fail,
Because he don't like Pope.
                              I put him back
Into command. What else was there to do?
Nobody else could lick those troops in shape.
But, if he wins, and lets Lee get away,
I'm done with him.
                              Bull Run—the Seven Days—
Bull Run again—and eighteen months of war—
And still no end to it.
                              What is God's will?

They come to me and talk about God's will
In righteous deputations and platoons,
Day after day, laymen and ministers.
They write me Prayers From Twenty Million Souls
Defining me God's will and Horace Greeley's.
God's will is General This and Senator That,
God's will is those poor colored fellows' will,
It is the will of the Chicago churches,
It is this man's and his worst enemy's.

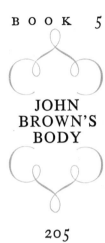

BOOK 5

JOHN
BROWN'S
BODY

205

But all of them are sure they know God's will.
I am the only man who does not know it.

And, yet, if it is probable that God
Should, and so very clearly, state His will
To others, on a point of my own duty,
It might be thought He would reveal it me
Directly, more especially as I
So earnestly desire to know His will.

The will of God prevails. No doubt, no doubt—
Yet, in great contests, each side claims to act
In strict accordance with the will of God.
Both may, one must be wrong.
                              God could have saved
This Union or destroyed it without war
If He so wished. And yet this war began,
And, once begun, goes on, though He could give
Victory, at any time, to either side.
It is unfathomable. Yet I know
This, and this only. While I live and breathe,
I mean to save the Union if I can,
And by whatever means my hands can find
Under the Constitution.
                        If God reads
The hearts of men as clearly as He must
To be Himself, then He can read in mine
And has, for twenty years, the old, scarred wish
That the last slave should be forever free
Here, in this country.
                       I do not go back
From that scarred wish and have not.
                                      But I put
The Union, first and last, before the slave.
If freeing slaves will bring the Union back
Then I will free them; if by freeing some
And leaving some enslaved I help my cause,
I will do that—but should such freedom mean
The wreckage of the Union that I serve
I would not free a slave.

O Will of God,
I am a patient man, and I can wait
Like an old gunflint buried in the ground
While the slow years pile up like moldering leaves
Above me, underneath the rake of Time,
And turn, in time, to the dark, fruitful mold
That smells of Sangamon apples, till at last
There's no sleep left there, and the steel event
Descends to strike the live coal out of me
And light the powder that was always there.

That is my only virtue as I see it,
Ability to wait and hold my own
And keep my own resolves once they are made
In spite of what the smarter people say.
I can't be smart the way that they are smart.
I've known that since I was an ugly child.
It teaches you—to be an ugly child.
It teaches you—to lose a thing you love.
It sticks your roots down into Sangamon ground
And makes you grow when you don't want to grow
And makes you tough enough to wait life out,
Wait like the fields, under the rain and snow.

I have not thought for years of that lost grave
That was my first hard lesson in the queer
Thing between men and women we call love.
But when I think of it, and when I hear
The rain and snow fall on it, as they must,
It fills me with unutterable grief.

We've come a good long way, my hat and I,
Since then, a pretty lengthy piece of road,
Uphill and down but mostly with a pack.
Years of law-business, years of cracking jokes,
And watching Billy Herndon do his best
To make me out, which seemed to be a job;
Years trying how to learn to handle men,
Which can be done, if you've got heart enough,
And how to deal with women or a woman

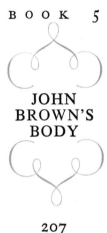

BOOK 5

JOHN
BROWN'S
BODY

207

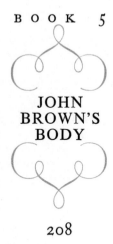
And that's about the hardest task I know.
For, when you get a man, you've got the man
Like a good big axehandle in your fist,
But you can't catch a woman like an axe.
She'll run like mercury between your hands
And leave you wondering which road she went,
The minute when you thought you knew her ways.

I understand the uses of the earth,
And I have burned my hands at certain fires
Often enough to know a use for fire,
But when the genius of the water moves,
And that's the woman's genius, I'm at sea
In every sense and meaning of the word,
With nothing but old patience for my chart,
And patience doesn't always please a woman.

Bright streams of water, watering the world,
Deep seas of water that all men must sail
Or rest half-men and fill the narrow graves,
When will I understand or comprehend
Your salt, sweet taste, so different from the taste
Of Sangamon russets, weighing down the bough?
You can live with the water twenty years
And never understand it like the earth
But that's the lesson I can't seem to learn.

"Abraham Lincoln, his hand and pen,
He will be good, but God knows when."
He will be wise, but God knows when.

It doesn't matter. If I had some news—
News from that fog—

                 I'll get the hypo, sure,
Unless I watch myself, waiting for news.
I can't afford to get the hypo now,
I've got too much to do.

                    Political years,
Housekeeping years of marrying and begetting
And losing, too, the children and the town,

The wife, the house, the life, the joy and grief,
The profound wonder still behind it all.

I had a friend who married and was happy.
But something haunted him that haunted me
Before he did, till he could hardly tell
What his own mind was, for the brooding veil
And immaterial horror of the soul
Which colors the whole world for men like that.

I do not know from whence that horror comes
Or why it hangs between us and the sun
For some few men, at certain times and days,
But I have known it closer than my flesh,
Got up with it, lain down and walked with it,
Scotched it awhile, but never killed it quite,
And yet lived on.
            I wrote him good advice,
The way you do, and told him this, for part,
"Again you fear that that Elysium
Of which you've dreamed so much is not to be.
Well, I dare swear it will not be the fault
Of that same black-eyed Fanny, now your wife.
And I have now no doubt that you and I,
To our particular misfortune, dream
Dreams of Elysium far exceeding all
That any earthly thing can realize."

I wrote that more than twenty years ago,
At thirty-three, and now I'm fifty-three,
And the slow days have brought me up at last
Through water, earth and fire, to where I stand,
To where I stand—and no Elysiums still.

No, no Elysiums—for that personal dream
I dreamt of for myself and in my youth
Has been abolished by the falling sledge
Of chance and an ambition so fulfilled
That the fulfillment killed its personal part.

My old ambition was an iron ring
Loose-hooped around the live trunk of a tree.
If the tree grows till bark and iron touch
And then stops growing, ring and tree are matched
And the fulfillment fits.
                But, if by some
Unlikely chance, the growing still keeps on,
The tree must burst the binding-ring or die.

I have not once controlled the circumstances.
They have controlled me. But with that control
They made me grow or die. And I have grown.
The iron ring is burst.
              Three elements,
Earth, water and fire. I have passed through them all,
Still to find no Elysium for my hands,
Still to find no Elysium but growth,
And the slow will to grow to match my task.

Three elements. I have not sought the fourth
Deeply, till now—the element of air,
The everlasting element of God,
Who must be there in spite of all we see,
Who must be there in spite of all we bear,
Who must exist where all Elysiums
Are less than shadows of a hunter's fire
Lighted at night to scare a wolf away.

I know that wolf—his scars are in my hide
And no Elysiums can rub them out.
Therefore at last, I lift my hands to You
Who Were and Are and Must Be, if our world
Is anything but a lost ironclad
Shipped with a crew of fools and mutineers
To drift between the cold forts of the stars.

I've never found a church that I could join
Although I've prayed in churches in my time
And listened to all sorts of ministers
Well, they were good men, most of them, and yet—

The thing behind the words—it's hard to find.
I used to think it wasn't there at all
Couldn't be there. I cannot say that, now.
And now I pray to You and You alone.
Teach me to know Your will. Teach me to read
Your difficult purpose here, which must be plain
If I had eyes to see it. Make me just.

There was a man I knew near Pigeon Creek
Who kept a kennel full of hunting dogs,
Young dogs and old, smart hounds and silly hounds.
He'd sell the young ones every now and then,
Smart as they were and slick as they could run.
But the one dog he'd never sell or lend
Was an old half-deaf foolish-looking hound
You wouldn't think had sense to scratch a flea
Unless the flea were old and sickly too.
Most days he used to lie beside the stove
Or sleeping in a piece of sun outside.
Folks used to plague the man about that dog
And he'd agree to everything they said,
"No—he ain't much on looks—much on speed—
A young dog can outrun him any time,
Outlook him and outeat him and outleap him,
But, Mister, that dog's hell on a cold scent
And, once he gets his teeth in what he's after,
He don't let go until he knows he's dead."
I am that old, deaf hunting-dog, O Lord,
And the world's kennel holds ten thousand hounds
Smarter and faster and with finer coats
To hunt your hidden purpose up the wind
And bell upon the trace you leave behind.
But, when even they fail and lose the scent,
I will keep on because I must keep on
Until You utterly reveal Yourself
And sink my teeth in justice soon or late.
There is no more to ask of earth or fire
And water only runs between my hands,
But in the air, I'll look, in the blue air,
The old dog, muzzle down to the cold scent,

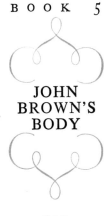

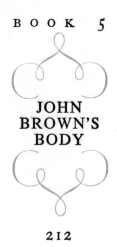

Day after day, until the tired years
Crackle beneath his feet like broken sticks
And the last barren bush consumes with peace.

I should have tried the course with younger legs,
This hunting-ground is stiff enough to pull
The metal heart out of a dog of steel;
I should have started back at Pigeon Creek
From scratch, not forty years behind the mark.
But you can't change yourself, and, if you could,
You might fetch the wrong jack-knife in the swap.
It's up to you to whittle what you can
With what you've got—and what I am, I am
For what it's worth, hypo and legs and all.
I can't complain. I'm ready to admit
You could have made a better-looking dog
From the same raw material, no doubt,
But, since You didn't, this'll have to do.

Therefore I utterly lift up my hands
To You, and here and now beseech Your aid.
I have held back when others tugged me on,
I have gone on when others pulled me back
Striving to read Your will, striving to find
The justice and expedience of this case,
Hunting an arrow down the chilly airs
Until my eyes are blind with the great wind
And my heart sick with running after peace.
And now, I stand and tremble on the last
Edge of the last blue cliff, a hound beat out,
Tail down and belly flattened to the ground,
My lungs are breathless and my legs are whipped,
Everything in me's whipped except my will.
I can't go on. And yet, I must go on.

I will say this. Two months ago I read
My proclamation setting these men free
To Seward and the rest. I told them then
I was not calling on them for advice
But to hear something that I meant to do.

We talked about it. Most of them approved
The thing, if not the time. Then Seward said
Something I hadn't thought of, "I approve
The proclamation—but, if issued now
With our defeats in everybody's mouth
It may be viewed as a last shriek for help
From an exhausted, beaten government.
Put it aside until a victory comes,
Then issue it with victory."

                                    He was right.
I put the thing aside—and ever since
There has been nothing for us but defeat,
Up to this battle now—and still no news.

If I had eyes to look to Maryland!
If I could move that battle with my hands!
No, it don't work. I'm not a general.
All I can do is trust the men who are.

I'm not a general, but I promise this,
Here at the end of every ounce of strength
That I can muster, here in the dark pit
Of ignorance that is not quite despair
And doubt that does but must not break the mind!
The pit I have inhabited so long
At various times and seasons, that my soul
Has taken color in its very grains
From the blind darkness, from the lonely cave
That never hears a footstep but my own
Nor ever will, while I'm a man alive
To keep my prison locked from visitors.
What if I heard another footstep there,
What if, some day—there is no one but God,
No one but God who could descend that stair
And ring his heavy footfalls on the stone.
And if He came, what would we say to Him?

That prison is ourselves that we have built,
And, being so, its loneliness is just,
And, being so, its loneliness endures.

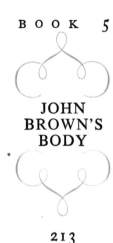

But, if another came,

                What would we say?

What can the blind say, given back their eyes?

No, it must be as it has always been.
We are all prisoners in that degree
And will remain so, but I think I know
This—God is not a jailor. . . .

                        And I make

A promise now to You and to myself.
If this last battle is a victory
And they can drive the Rebel army back
From Maryland, back over the Potomac,
My proclamation shall go out at last
To set those other prisoners and slaves
From this next year, then and forever free.

So much for my will. Show me what is Yours!

That must be news, those footsteps in the hall,
Good news, or else they wouldn't come so fast.

What is it, now? Yes, yes, I'm glad of that.
I'm very glad. There's no mistake this time?
We have the best of them? They're in retreat?
This is a great day, Stanton. . . . .
. . . . If McClellan
Can only follow up the victory now!

Lord, I will keep my promise and go on,
Your will, in much, still being dark to me,
But, in this one thing, as I see it, plain.
And yet—if Lee slips from our hands again
As he well may from all those last reports
And the war still goes on—and still no end—
Even after this Antietam—not for years—

I cannot read it but I will go on,
Old dog, old dog, but settled to the scent
And with fresh breath now from this breathing space,

Almighty God.
                    At best we never seem
To know You wholly, but there's something left,
A strange, last courage.
                    We can fail and fail,
But, deep against the failure, something wars,
Something goes forward, something lights a match,
Something gets up from Sangamon County ground
Armed with a bitten and a blunted axe
And after twenty thousand wasted strokes
Brings the tall hemlock crashing to the ground.

————————

Spade saw the yellow river rolling ahead
His sore, cracked lips curled back in a death's head grin
And his empty belly ceased to stick to his sides.
He sat on the bank a minute to rest his legs
And catch his breath. He had lived for the last three days
On a yam, two ears of horse-corn and the lame rabbit
That couldn't run away when he threw the stick.

He was still a big man but the ribs stuck into his skin
And the hard, dry muscles were wasted to leather thongs.
"Boy, I wisht we had a good meal," he thought with a dull
Fatigue. "Dat's Freedom's lan' ovah dere fer sho',
But how we gwine to swim it without a good meal?
I wisht we had even a spoonful of good hot pot-licker
Or a smidgin' of barbecued shote.
                    Dat river's cold.
Colder'n Jordan. I wisht we had a good meal."

He went down to the river and tested it with his hand.
The cold jumped up his arm and into his heart,
Sharp as the toothache. His mouth wried up in a queer
Grimace. He felt like crying. "I'se tired," he said.
"Flow easy, river," he said.
                    Then he tumbled in.
The hard shock of the plunge took his breath away.
So stinging at first that his arms and legs moved fast,
But then the cold crept into his creaking bones

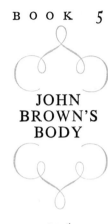

And he rolled wild eyes.

                 "Oh, God," he thought as he struggled,
"I'se weak as a cat. I ust to be a strong man."

The yellow flood sucked round him, pulling him down,
The yellow foam had a taste like death in his mouth,
"We ought to of had a good meal," he thought with a weak
Wonder, as he fought weakly. "A good hot meal.
Dis current, she's too strong for a hungry mouth.
We'se done our best, but she fights like a angel would
Like wrestlin' with a death-angel."

                        He choked and sank
To come up gasping and staring with bloodshot eyes.
His brain had a last, clear flash. "You're drowned," said the brain.
Then it stopped working.

                    But the black, thrashing hands
Caught hold of something solid and hard and rough
And hung to it with a last exhausted grip.
—He had been fighting an angel for seven nights
And now he hung by his hands to the angel's neck,
Lost in an iron darkness of beating wings.
If he once let go, the angel would push him off
And touch him across the loins with a stony hand
In the last death-trick of the wrestle.

                       He moaned a little.
The blackness began to lighten. He saw the river
Rolling and rolling. He was clutched to a log
Like a treetoad set afloat on a chip of wood,
And the log and he were rushing downstream together,
But the current pulled them both toward the freedom side.

He hunched up a little higher. An eddy took
The log and him and spun them both like a top
While he prayed and sickened.

                  Then they were out of the eddy
And drifting along more slowly, straight for the shore.
He hauled himself up the bank with enormous care,
Vomited and lay down.

                  When he could arise
He looked at his hands. They were still hooked into a curve.

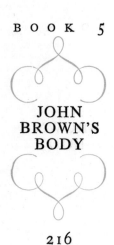

BOOK 5

JOHN
BROWN'S
BODY

216

It took quite a time to straighten them back again.

He said a prayer as he tried to dry his clothes,
Then he looked for a stone and threw it into the river.
"You'se a mean and hungry river," he said. "You is.
Heah's a present for you. I hope it busts up your teef.
Heah's a present fum Mistah Spade."
                                        He felt better then,
But his belly started to ache. "Act patient," he said,
Rubbing it gently, "We'se loose in Freedom's land,
Crossed old Jordan—bound to get vittles now."

He started out for the town. The town wasn't far
But he had to go slow. Sometimes he fell on the way.
The last time he fell was in front of a little yard
With a white, well-painted fence. A woman came out.
"Get along," she said. "You can't get sick around here.
I'm tired of you nigger tramps. You're all of you thieves."
Spade rose and said something vague about swimming rivers
And vittles. She stamped her foot. "Get along!" she said,
"Get along or I'll call the dog and———"
                                        Spade got along.

The next house, the dog was barking out in the yard,
He went by as fast as he could, but when he looked back
A man had come out with a hostile stick in his hand.
Spade shook his head. "Freedom's land," he thought to himself,
"They's some mighty quick-actin' people in Freedom's land,
Some mighty rash-tempered dogs."
                                        He swayed as he walked.
Here was another house. He looked for the dog
With fright in his eyes. Then a swimming qualm came over him,
A deathly faintness. His hands went out to the fence.
He gripped two palings, hung, and stared at his shoes.
Somebody was talking to him. He tried to move on
But his legs wouldn't walk. The voice was a woman's voice.

She'd be calling the dog in a minute. He shivered hard.
"Excuse me ma'am, but I'se feelin' poorly," he said.
"I just crossed over—I'll go as soon as I kin."

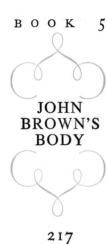

A man's voice now. They were taking him under the arms.
He didn't care what they did. He let himself walk.

Then he was sitting up in a bentwood chair
In a tidy kitchen that smelt of frying and ham;
The thick, good smell made him strangely sick at first
But it soon passed off. They fed him little by little
Till at last he could tell his tale and ask about them.

They were churchgoing people and kind to runaway slaves.
She wore a blue dress. They had two sons in the war.
That was all that he knew and all that he ever knew.
But they let him sleep in the garret and gave him some shoes
And fifty cents when he left.
                              He wanted to stay
But times were bad and they couldn't afford to keep him.
The town was tired of runaway negroes now.

All the same, when he left, he walked with a different step.
He went down town. He was free. He was Mister Spade.
The President had written a letter about it
And the mule and the coal-black gal might come any day.

He hummed a tuneless whistle between his teeth
And fished a piece of paper out of his pants,
They'd written him down a boss's name and address
But he'd have to get somebody to read it again.
He approached a group of three white men on a corner
Holding the paper.
                    " 'Scuse me, boss, can you tell me——"
The white men looked at him with hard, vacant eyes.
At last one of them took the paper. "Oh, Hell," he said,
Spitting, and gave Spade a stare. Then he seemed to think
Of something funny. He nudged the other two men.
"Listen, nigger," he said. "You want Mr. Braid.
You'll find him two blocks down at the Marshal's office,
Tell him Mr. Clarke sent you there—Mr. William Clarke—
He'll fix you up all right."
                            The other men grinned,
Adding directions. Spade thanked them and went away.

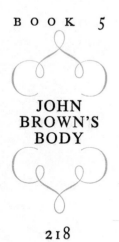

He heard them laugh as he went.

                    Another man took him
To a red-faced person who sat in a tilted chair,
Reading a paper, his feet cocked up on his desk.
He looked at Spade and his feet came down with a slam.
"Take that God damn smile off," he said. "Who let you come in?
You contraband niggers think that you own this town
And that all you've got to do is cross over here
For people to feed you free the rest of your lives.
Well it don't go down with me—just understand that."

Spade brought out his paper, dumbly. The man looked at it.
"Hell, this ain't for me," he said.

                    Spade started to go.

"Come back here, nigger," ordered the red-faced man.
"Hey, Mike!" he yelled, "Here's another of Lincoln's pets.
Send him out with the rest of the gang."

                    "But, boss——" said Spade.
"Don't get lippy with me," said the man, "Mike, take him along."
The pimply boy named Mike jerked a sallow thumb.
"Come on, black beauty," he said. "We got you a job."
Spade followed him, dazed.

                When they were out in the street
The boy turned to him. "Now, nigger, watch out," he said,
Patting a heavy pistol swung at his belt,
With puppy-fierceness, "You don't get away from me.
I'm a special deputy, see?"

                  "All right, boss," said Spade.
"I ain't aimin' to get away from nobody now,
I just aims to work till I gets myself a good mule."
The boy laughed briefly. The conversation dropped.
They walked out of the town till they came to a torn-up road
Where a gang of negroes was working.

                    "Say, boss——" said Spade.
The boy cut him off. "Hey, Jerry," he called to the foreman,
"Here's another one."

              The foreman looked up and spat.
"Judas!" he said, "Can't they keep the bastards at home?
I'd put a gun on that river if I was Braid.

Well, come along, nig, get a move on and find a shovel.
Don't stand lookin' at me all day."

                            The boy went away.
Spade found a shovel and started work on the road.
The foreman watched him awhile with sarcastic eyes,
Spade saw that he, too, wore a pistol.

                            "Christ," said the foreman,
Disgustedly, "Try and put some guts in it there.
You're big enough. That shovel'll cost five dollars.
Remember that—it comes out of your first week's pay.
You're a free nigger now."

                            He chuckled. Spade didn't answer
And, after a while, the foreman moved away.

Spade turned to the gingerskinned negro who worked beside him.
"You fum de Souf?" he mouthed at him.

                            Ginger nodded.
"I been here a month now. They fotched me here the first day.
Got any money?"

                 "Nuthin' but fifty cents."
"You better give it to him," said Ginger, stealing
A glance at the foreman. "He'll treat you bad if you don't.
He's a cranky man."

                      Spade's heart sank into his boots.
"Don't we uns get paid? We ain't none of us slaves no more,
The President said so. Why we wuhkin' like dis?"
Ginger snickered. "Sho' we uns get paid," he said,
"But we got to buy our stuff at de company sto'
And he sells his old shovels a dozen times what dey's wuth.
I only been here a month but I owes twelve dollars.
Dey ain't no way to pay it except by wuhk,
And de more you wuhk de more you owe at the sto.'
I kain't figure it out exactly but it's dat way."
Spade worked for a while, revolving these things in his mind.
"I reckoned I sho' was gwine to be sassy and free
When I swum dat river," he said.

                            Ginger grinned like a monkey,
"Swing your shubbel, boy, and forget what you ain't.
You mought be out on de chain-gang, bustin' up rocks,
Or agin, you mought be enlisted."

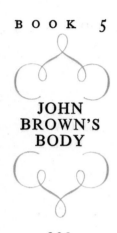

BOOK 5

JOHN
BROWN'S
BODY

220

ABRAHAM LINCOLN
O Will of God,
I am a patient man, and I can wait
Like an old gunflint buried in the ground

"Huh?" said Spade.

"Sho', dey's gwine to enlist us all when we finish dis road.
All excep' me. I got bad sight in my eyes
And dey knows about it."

                              "Dey kain't enlist me," said Spade.
"I ain't honin' to go an' fight in no white-folks war,
I ain't bust loose into Freedom's land fer dat,
All I want is a chance to get me a gal and a mule.
If I'se free, how kin dey enlist me, lessen I want?"

"You watch 'em," said Ginger. They worked on for a time.
The foreman stood on the bank and watched them work,
Now and then he drank from a bottle.

                              Spade felt hungry.

Autumn is filling his harvest-bins
    With red and yellow grain,
Fire begins and frost begins
    And the floors are cold again.

Summer went when the crop was sold,
    Summer is piled away,
Dry as a faded marigold
    In the dry, long-gathered hay.

It is time to walk to the cider-mill
    Through air like apple wine
And watch the moon rise over the hill,
    Stinging and hard and fine.

It is time to cover your seed-pods deep
    And let them wait and be warm,
It is time to sleep the heavy sleep
    That does not wake for the storm.

Winter walks from the green, streaked West
    With a bag of Northern Spies,

The skins are red as a robin's breast,
The honey chill as the skies.

Melora Vilas walked in the woods that autumn
And heard the dry leaves crackle under her feet,
Feeling, below the leaves, the blunt heavy earth.
"It's getting-in time," she thought. "It's getting-in time,
Time to put things in barns and sit by the stove,
Time to watch the long snow and remember your lover.

He isn't dead. I know he isn't dead.
Maybe they've changed his body into a tree,
Maybe they've changed his body into a cloud
Or something that sleeps through the Winter.
                                        But I'll remember.
I'll sleep through the Winter, too. We all sleep then
And when the Spring freshet drums in the narrow brooks
And fills them with a fresh water, they'll let him come
Out of the cloud and the tree and the Winter-sleep.

The Winter falls and we lie like beleaguered stones
In the black, cramped ground.
                        And then you wake in the morning
And the air's got soft and you plant the narrow-edged seeds,
They grow all Summer and now we've put them in barns
To sleep again for a while.
I am the seed and the husk. I have sown and reaped.
My heart is a barn full of grain that my work has harvested.
My body holds the ripe grain. I can wait my time."

She walked on farther and came to the lip of the spring,
The brown leaves drifted the water. She watched them drift.

"I am satisfied," she thought, "I am satisfied.
I can wait my time in spite of Mom being sad
And Pop looking fierce and sad when he sees me walk
So heavy and knows I'll have to walk heavier still
Before my time comes. I'm sorry to make them sad,
I'm sorry I did a bad thing if it was a bad thing;

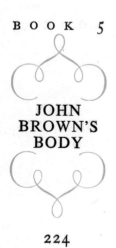
But I'm satisfied.
                    We cut the heart on the tree.
I've got my half of the dime and he's got his,
He'll come back when Winter's over or else I'll find him,
When you can push up the windows, when the new colts
Come out in the Spring, when the snake sheds his winter coat,
When the old, shed coat of Winter lies on the ground
Grey as wasp-paper under the green, slow rain,
When the big barn door rolls open.
I was worried to death at first and I couldn't tell.
But as soon as I knew what it was—it was different then—
It made things all right.
                        I can't tell why it did that."

She awkwardly stooped and put her hand on the ground,
Under the brittle leaves the soil was alive,
Torn with its harvest, turned on its side toward sleep,
But stripped for battle, too, for the unending
Battle with Winters till the Spring is born
Like a tight green leaf uncurling, so slightly, so gently,
Out of the husk of ice and the blank, white snows.

The wind moved over it, blowing the leaves away,
Leaving the bare, indomitable breast.
She felt a wind move over her heavy body,
Stripping it clean for war.
                        She felt the blind-featured
Mystery move, the harmonics of the quick grain,
The battle and the awakening for battle,
And the salt taste of peace.

A flight of geese passed by in a narrow V,
Honking their cry.
                    That cry was stuck in her heart
Like a bright knife.
                    She could have laughed or wept
Because of that cry flung down from a moving wing,
But she stood silent.
                    She had touched the life in the ground.
————————————————

Love came by from the riversmoke,
    When the leaves were fresh on the tree,
But I cut my heart on the blackjack oak
    Before they fell on me.

The leaves are green in the early Spring,
    They are brown as linsey now,
I did not ask for a wedding-ring
    From the wind in the bending bough.

Fall lightly, lightly, leaves of the wild,
    Fall lightly on my care,
I am not the first to go with child
    Because of the blowing air.

I am not the first nor yet the last
    To watch a goosefeather sky,
And wonder what will come of the blast
    And the name to call it by.

Snow down, snow down, you whitefeather bird,
    Snow down, you winter storm,
Where the good girls sleep with a gospel word
    To keep their honor warm.

The good girls sleep in their modesty,
    The bad girls sleep in their shame,
But I must sleep in the hollow tree
    Till my child can have a name.

I will not ask for the wheel and thread
    To spin the labor plain,
Or the scissors hidden under the bed
    To cut the bearing-pain.

I will not ask for the prayer in church
    Or the preacher saying the prayer,
But I will ask the shivering birch
    To hold its arms in the air.

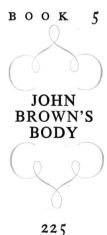

Cold and cold and cold again,
  Cold in the blackjack limb
The winds of the sky for his sponsor-men
  And a bird to christen him.

Now listen to me, you Tennessee corn,
  And listen to my word,
This is the first child ever born
  That was christened by a bird.

He's going to act like a hound let loose
  When he comes from the blackjack tree,
And he's going to walk in proud shoes
  All over Tennessee.

I'll feed him milk out of my own breast
  And call him Whistling Jack.
And his dad'll bring him a patridge nest,
  As soon as his dad comes back.

———————

John Brown's raid has gone forward, the definite thing is done,
Not as we see it done when we read the books,
A clear light burning suddenly in the sky,
But dimly, obscurely, a flame half-strangled by smoke,
A thing come to pass from a victory not a victory,
A dubious doctrine dubiously received.
The papers praise, but the recruiting is slow,
The bonds sell badly, the grind of the war goes on—
There is no sudden casting off of a chain,
Only a slow thought working its way through the ground,
A slow root growing, touching a hundred soils,
A thousand minds—no blossom or flower yet

It takes a long time to bring a thought into act
And when it blossoms at last, the gardeners wonder—
There have been so many to labor this patch of ground,
Garrison, Beecher, a dozen New England names,
Courageous, insulting Sumner, narrow and strong,
With his tongue of silver and venom and his wrecked body,

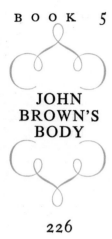

Wendell Phillips, Antinous of Harvard—
But now that the thought has arisen, they are not sure
It was their thought after all—it is good enough—
The best one could expect from a man like Lincoln,
But this and that are wrong, are unshrewdly planned,
We could have ordered it better, we knew the ground,
It should have been done before, in a different way,
And our praise is grudging.
                              Pity the gardeners,
Pity Boston, pity the pure in heart,
Pity the men whom Time goes past in the night,
Without their knowledge. They worked through the heat of the
     day.
Let us even pity
Wendell Phillips, Antinous of Harvard,
For he was a model man and such men deserve
A definite pity at times.
                              He too did his best.
Secure in his own impenetrable self-knowledge,
He seldom agreed with Lincoln or thought him wise;
He sometimes thought that a stunning defeat would give
A needed lesson to the soul of the nation,
And, before, would have broken the Union as blithely as Yancey
For his own side of abolition, speaking about it
In many public meetings where he was heckled
But usually silenced the hecklers sooner or later
With his mellifluous, masculine, well-trained accents.
War could hardly come too soon for a man like that
And when it came, he was busy. He did his part,
Being strong and active, blessed with a ready mind,
And the cause being one to which he professed devotion,
He spoke. He spoke well, with conviction, and frequently.

So much for the banner-bearers of abolition,
The men who carried the lonely flag for years
And could bear defeat with the strength of the pure in heart
But could not understand the face of success.

The other dissenters are simpler to understand.
They are ready to fight for the Union but not for niggers,

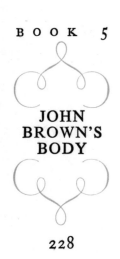

They don't give a damn for niggers and say so now
With a grievous cry.
                    And yet the slow root-thought works
Gradually through men's minds.
                              The Lancashire spinners,
Thrown out of work because no cotton can come
To feed their mills through the choking Union blockade,
Yet hold starvation meetings and praise the Union.
The tide has begun to turn in some English minds,
The watchers overseas feel their hands grow numb,
Slidell and Mason and Huse still burrow and argue,
But a cold breath blows through the rooms with the chandeliers.
A door is beginning to close.
                        Few men perceive
The turn of the tide, the closing of the door.
Lincoln does not perceive it. He sees alone
The grind of the war, the lagging of the recruits,
Election after election going against him,
And Lee back safe in Virginia after Antietam
While McClellan sticks for five weeks and will not move.
He loses patience at last and removes McClellan.
Burnside succeeds him—
                        and the grimly bewildered
Army of the Potomac has a new rider,
Affable, portly, whiskered and self-distrusting,
Who did not wish the command and tried to decline it,
Took it at last and almost wept when he did.
A worried man who passes like a sad ghost
Across November, looking for confidence,
And beats his army at last against stone walls
At Fredericksburg in the expected defeat
With frightful slaughter.
                        The news of the thing comes back.
There are tears in his eyes. He never wanted command.
"Those men over there," he groans, "Those men over there"
—They are piled like cordwood in front of the stone wall—

He wants to lead a last desperate charge himself,
But he is restrained.
                    The sullen army draws back,

Licking its wounds. The night falls. The newspapers rave.
There are sixty-three hundred dead in that doomed attack
That never should have been made.
                              His shoulders are bowed.
He tries a vain march in the mud and resigns at last
The weapon he could not wield.
                              Joe Hooker succeeds him.
The winter clamps down, cold winter of doubt and grief.

———————

        The sun shines, the wind goes by,
        The prisoners and captives lie
        In a cell without an eye.

        Winter will not touch them more
        Than the cold upon a sore
        That was frozen long before.

        Summer will not make them sweet
        Nor the rainy Springs refresh
        That extremity of heat
        In the self-corrupting flesh.

        The band blares, the bugles snort,
        They lose the fort or take the fort,
        Someone writes a wise report.

        Someone's name is Victory.
        The prisoners and captives lie
        Too long dead before they die.

———————

For all prisoners and captives now,
For the dark legion,
The Andersonvillers, the Castle Thunder men,
The men who froze at Camp Morton and came from the dun-
    geons
With blood burst out on their faces.
The men who died at Salisbury and Belle Isle,
Elmira, St. Louis, Camp Douglas—the Libby tunnellers—
The men in the fetid air.

There are charges back and forth upon either side,
Some true, some false.

                    You can read the official reports,
The dozen thick black-bound volumes of oaths and statements,
A desert of type, a dozen black mummy-cases
Embalming the long-forgotten, building again
The cumbrous machine of guards and reports and orders,
"Respectfully submitted" . . . "I beg to state" . . .
"State of kitchen—good." . . . "Food, quality of—quite
    good." . . .
"Police of hospital—good except Ward 7" . . .
"Remarks—we have ninety-five cases of smallpox now." . . .
"Remarks—as to general health of prisoners, fair." . . .
"Remarks" . . . "Remarks" . . . "Respectfully submitted" . . .
Under this type are men who used to have hands
But the creaking wheels have respectfully submitted them
Into a void, embalmed them in mummy-cases,
With their chills and fever, their looks and plans of escape.
They called one "Shorty," they called another "The Judge,"
One man wore the Virgin's medal around his neck,
One had a broken nose and one was a liar,
"Respectfully submitted—"

                    But, now and then,
A man or a scene escapes from the mummy-cases,
Like smoke escaping, blue smoke coiling into pictures,
Stare at those coils—

                    and see in the hardened smoke,
The triple stockade of Andersonville the damned,
Where men corrupted like flies in their own dung
And the gangrened sick were black with smoke and their filth.
There were thirty thousand Federal soldiers there
Before the end of the war.

                    A man called Wirtz,
A Swiss, half brute, half fool, and wholly a clod,
Commanded that camp of spectres.

                            One reads what he did
And longs to hang him higher than Haman hung,
And then one reads what he said when he was tried
After the war—and sees the long, heavy face,
The dull fly buzzing stupidly in the trap,

The ignorant lead of the voice, saying and saying,
"Why, I did what I could, I was ordered to keep the jail.
Yes, I set up deadlines, sometimes chased men with dogs,
Put men in torturing stocks, killed this one and that,
Let the camp corrupt till it tainted the very guards
Who came there with mortal sickness.
But they were prisoners, they were dangerous men,
If a hundred died a day—how was it my fault?
I did my duty. I always reported the deaths.
I don't see what I did different from other people.
I fought well at Seven Pines and was badly wounded.
I have witnesses here to tell you I'm a good man
And that I was really kind. I don't understand.
I'm old. I'm sick. You're going to hang me. Why?"

Crush out the fly with your thumb and wipe your hand,
You cannot crush the leaden, creaking machine,
The first endorsement, the paper on the desk
Referred by Adjutant Feeble to Captain Dull
For further information and his report.
Some men wish evil and accomplish it
But most men, when they work in that machine,
Just let it happen somewhere in the wheels.
The fault is no decisive, villainous knife
But the dull saw that is the routine mind.

Why, if a man lay dying on their desk
They'd do their best to help him, friend or foe,
But this is merely a respectfully
Submitted paper, properly endorsed
To be sent on and on, and gather blood.

Stare at the smoke again for a moment's space
And see another live man in another prison.

A colored trooper named Woodson was on guard
In the prison at Newport News, one night around nine.
There was a gallery there, where the privy was,
But prisoners weren't allowed in it after dark.

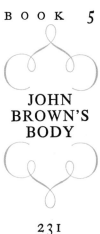

BOOK 5

JOHN
BROWN'S
BODY

231

The colored soldier talked with the prisoners
At first, in a casual, more or less friendly way;
They tried to sell him breastpins and rings they had
And bothered him by wanting to go to the privy.

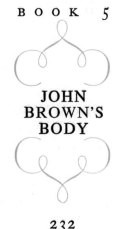
At last, he fired on a man
Who went in the gallery, but happened to miss him.
A lieutenant came down to ask the cause of the shot.
Woodson told him.
                              A second prisoner went
On the same errand, a shadow slipping through shadows.
Woodson halted him twice but he kept on moving.
"There's a man in the gallery now," said the young lieutenant.
"Well, I reckon it's one of the men makin' water again,"
Said Woodson, uneasily. The lieutenant stiffened.
He was officer of the guard and orders were orders.
"Why don't you use the bayonet on him?" he said.
Woodson jumped forward. The bayonet hunched and struck.
The man ran into the privy and fell like a log. . . .
A prisoner said "You've killed him dead," in a voice.
"Yes, by God!" said Woodson, cleaning his bayonet,
"They buried us alive at Fort Pillow."
                                        The court
Found the sentry a trifle hasty, but on the whole
Within his instructions, the officer's orders lawful;
One cannot dispute the court.
                              And yet the man
Who went to the privy is inconveniently dead.
It seems an excessive judgment for going there.

The little pictures wreathe into smoke again.
The mummy-cases close upon the dark legion.
The papers are filed away.
                              If they once were sent
To another court for some last word of review,
They are back again. It seems strange that such tidy files
Of correspondence respectfully submitted
Should be returned from God with no final endorsement.

———————

The slow carts hitched along toward the place of exchange
Through a bleak wind.

     It was not a long wagon train,
Wagons and horses were too important to waste
On prisoners for exchange, if the men could march.
Many did march and some few died on the way
But more died up in the wagons, which was not odd.
If a man was too sick to walk, he was pretty sick.

They had been two days on the road.

       Jack Ellyat lay
Between a perishing giant from Illinois
Who raved that he was bailing a leaky boat
Out on the Lakes, and a slight, tubercular Jew
Who muttered like a sick duck when the wagon jounced.
Bailey marched. He still was able to march
But his skin hung on him. He hummed to the Weaver's tune.

They got to the river at last.

      Jack Ellyat saw
A yellow stream and slow boats crossing the stream.
Bailey had helped him out. He was walking now
With his arm around Bailey's neck. Their course was a crab's.
The Jew was up and staring with shoe-button eyes
While his cough took him. The giant lay on a plank,
Some men were trying to lift him.

       The wind blew
Over a knife of frost and shook their rags.
The air was a thawing ice of most pure, clear gold.
They stared across the river and saw the flag
And the tall, blue soldiers walking in thick, warm coats
Like strong, big men who fed well. And then they cheered,
A dry thin cheer, pumped up from exhausted lungs
And yet with a metal vibrance.

       The bright flag flapped.
"I can smell 'em frying meat," said the coughing Jew
He sniffed, "Oh God, I hope it ain't ham," he said
With his mouth puckered. A number of scarecrows laughed.
And then they heard the echo of their own cheer
Flung back at them, it seemed, in a high, shrill wail

With that tongue of metal pulsing its feebleness.
But it did not end like an echo, it gathered and rose,
It was the Confederate sick on the other side,
Cheering their own.

                                    The two weak crowd-voices met
In one piping, gull-like cry.

                            Then the boats began
To take the weak men on board.

                                    Jack Ellyat walked
To his boat on stuffless legs. "Keep quiet," he thought,
"You're not through yet—you won't be through till you land.
They can jerk you back, even now, if you look too pleased.
Look like a soldier, damn you, and show them how."
The thought was childish but it stiffened his back
And got him into the boat.

                            In the midst of the stream
They passed a boat with Confederate prisoners
So near they could yell at each other.

                                        "Hello there, Yank."
"Hello Reb" . . . "You look pretty sick—don't we feed you
    good?" . . .
"You don't look so damn pretty, yourself" . . . "My, ain't
    that a shame!" . . .
"You'll look a lot sicker when Hooker gets after you." . . .
"Hell, old Jack'll take Hooker apart like a coffee-pot" . . .
"Well, good-by, Yank" . . . "Good-by, Reb" . . . "Get fat
    if you kin."

So might meet and pass, perhaps, on a weedier stream
Other boats, no more heavily charged, to a wet, black oar.
Bailey watched the boat move away with its sick grey men
Still yelling stingless insults through tired lips.
He cupped his hands to his mouth. "Oh——" he roared,
Then he sank back, coughing.

                            "They look pretty bad," he said,
"They look glad to get back. They ain't such bad Rebs at that."

The boat's nose touched the wharf. It swung and was held.
They got out. They didn't move toward the camp at first.
They looked back at the river first and the other side,

BOOK 5

JOHN
BROWN'S
BODY

234

Without saying words. They stood there thus for a space
Like a row of tattered cranes at the edge of a stream,
Blinking at something.

"All right, you men," said an officer. "Come along."
Jack Ellyat's heart made a sudden lump in his chest.
It was a blue officer. They were back in their lines,
Back out of prison.
                    Bailey whirled out his arm
In a great wheel gesture. "Hell," he said in a low,
Moved voice, thumbed his nose across at the Stars and Bars
And burst into horrible tears. Jack Ellyat held him.
"Captain, when do we eat?" said the Jew in a wail.

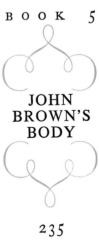

BOOK 5

JOHN
BROWN'S
BODY

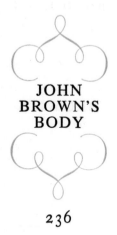

BOOK SIX

Cudjo breathed on the silver urn
    And rubbed till his hand began to burn,
With his hoarded scrap of chamois-skin.
The metal glittered like bright new tin
And yet, as he labored, his mouth was sad—
"Times is gettin' almighty bad.
Christmas a-comin', sure and swif',
But no use hollerin' 'Christmas Gif'!'
No use keepin' the silver fittin',
No use doin' nothin' but sittin'.
Old Marse Billy stayin' away,
Yankees shootin' at Young Marse Clay,
Grey hairs in Miss Mary's brush,
And a-whooin' wind in de berry-bush,
Dat young red setter done eat her pups,

We was washin' de tea set an' bust two cups,
Just come apart in Liza's han'—
Christmas, where has you gwine to, man?
Won't you never come back again?
I feels like a cat in de outdoors rain."
Christmas used to come without fail,
A big old man with a raccoon tail,
So fine and bushy it brushed the ground
And made folks sneeze when he waltzed around.
He was rolling river and lucky sun
And a laugh like a double-barrelled gun,
And the chip-straw hat on his round, bald head
Was full of money and gingerbread.
"Come in, Christmas, and have a cheer!
But, if he's comin', he won't stop here,
He likes folks cheerful and dinners smokin'
And famblies shootin' off caps and jokin',
But he won't find nothin' on dis plantation,
But a lot of grievin' conversation.

Dey's tooken de carpets and window-weights
To go and shoot at de Yankee States,
Dey's tooken Nelly, de cross-eye mule,
And whoever took her was one big fool;
Dey's tooken dis an' dey's tooken dat,
Till I kain't make out what dey's drivin' at.
But if Ole Marse Billy could see dis place
He'd cuss all Georgia blue in de face.
To see me wuhkin with dis ole shammy
Like a field-hand-nigger fum Alabammy,
And Ole Miss wearin' a corn-husk hat,
Dippin' ole close in de dyein' vat,
Scrapin' her petticoats up for lint
An' bilin' her tea out of julep-mint.

Young Marse Clay he'd feel mighty sad
If he'd seed de weddin' his sisters had.
De grooms was tall and de brides was fine,
But dey drunk de health in blackberry wine,
And supper was thu at half-past-nine.

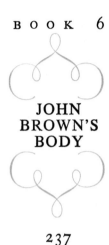

Weddin's ust to last for a week,
But now we's rowin' up Hard Times Creek.
Somethin's conjured dis white-folks' South.
Somethin' big with a hongry mouth,
Eatin' an' eatin'—I done my bes',
Scattered de fedders and burnt de nes',
Filled de bottle an' made de hand
An' buried de trick in Baptis' land,
An' dat trick's so strong, I was skeered all night,
But, somehow or udder, it don' wuhk right.
Ef I got me a piece of squinch-owl's tail
An' some dead-folks' yearth fum de county jail,
It mout wuhk better—but I ain't sho',
And de wind keeps scrabblin' under de do',
Scratchin' and scratchin' his buzzard-claws,
Won't nuthin' feed you, hongry jaws?

Field hands keeps on hoein' de corn,
Stupidest niggers ever born,
All dey's good for is gravy-lickin',
Ram-buttin' and cotton-pickin';
Dey don't hear de wind in de slew,
But dat wind's blowin' over 'em too,
An' dat wind's res-less an' dat wind's wile,
An' dat wind aches like a motherless chile,
Won't nuthin' feed you, achin' wind?"

The hand stopped rubbing. The spoons were shined.
He put them back in the flannel bag
And stared at his scrap of chamois-rag.
War was a throat that swallowed things
And you couldn't cure it with conjurings.

————

Sally Dupré watched over her dyeing-pots,
Evening was setting in with a light slow rain
That marched like a fairy army—there being nothing
From the white fog on the hill to the soaked door-stone
But a moving grey and silver hurry of lances,
Distinct yet crowded, thin as the edge of the moon,

Carried in no fleshed hand.

She thought to herself,

"I have stained my arms with new colors, doing this work,
The red is pokeberry-juice, the grey is green myrtle,
The deep black is queen's delight.

If he saw me now

With my hands so parti-colored he would not know them.
He likes girls' hands that nothing has stained but lotions,
This is too fast a dye.

I will dye my heart

In a pot of queen's delight, in the pokeberry sap,
I will dye it red and black in the fool's old colors
And send it to him, wrapped in a calico rag,
To keep him warm through the rain.

It will keep him warm

And women in love do better without a heart.
What fools we are to wait the wheel of the year,
The year will not help our trouble.

What fools we are

To give our parti-colored hearts to the rain.

I am tired of the slogans now and tired of the saving,
I want to dance all night in a brand-new dress
And forget about wars and love and the South and courage.

The South is an old high house full of charming ladies,
The war is a righteous war full of gallant actions,
And love is a white camellia worn in the hair.

But I am tired of talking to charming ladies
And the smell of the white camellia, I will dye
My hands twice as black as ink in the working waters
And wait like a fool for bitter love to come home.

He was wounded this year. They hurt him. They hurt you,
    darling.
I have no doubt she came with a bunch of flowers
And talked to your wound and you like a charming lady.
I have no doubt that she came.
Her heart is not parti-colored. She'll not go steeping

Her gentle hands in the pulp and the dead black waters
Till the crooked blot lies there like a devil's shadow,
And the heart is stained with the stain.

If I came to the bed where you lay sick and in fever,
I would not come with little tight-fisted flowers
But with the white heron's plume that lay in the forest
Till it was cooler than sleep.

The living balm would touch on your wound less gently,
The Georgia sun less fierce than my arms to hold you,
The steel bow less stubborn than my curved body
Strung against august death.

They hurt you, darling, they hurt you and I not with you,
I nowhere there to slit the cloth from your burning,
To find the head of the man who fired the bullet
And give his eyes to the crows.

House, house, house, it is not that my friend was wounded,
But that you kept him from me while he had freedom,
You and the girl whose heart is a snuffed white candle—
Now I will curse you both.

Comely house, high-courteous house of the gentle,
You must win your war for my friend is mixed in your quarrel,
But then you must fall, you must fall, for your walls divide us,
Your worn stones keep us apart.

I am sick of the bland camellias in your old gardens,
Your pride and passion are not my pride and my passion,
I am strangling to death in your cables of honeysuckle,
Your delicate lady-words.

I would rather dig in the earth than learn your patience,
I have need of a sky that never was cut for dresses
And a rough ground to tear my hands on like lion's clothing,
And a hard wheel to move.

The low roof by the marches of rainy weather,
The sharp love that carries the fool's old colors,

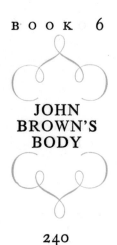

The bare bed that is not a saint's or a lady's,
The strong death at the end.

They hurt you, darling, they hurt you, and I not with you,
I nowhere by to see you, to touch my darling,
To take your fever upon me if I could take it
And burn my hands at your wound.

If I had been there—oh, how surely I would have found you,
How surely killed your foe—and sat by your bedside
All night long, like a mouse, like a stone unstirring,
Only to hear your slow breath moving the darkness,
Only to hear, more precious than childish beauty,
The slow tired beat of your heart."

———————

Wingate sat by a smoky fire
Mending a stirrup with rusty wire.
His brows were clenched in the workman's frown,
In a day or a week they'd be back in town,
He thought of it with a brittle smile
That mocked at guile for its lack of guile
And mocked at ease for its lack of ease.
It was better riding through rainy trees
And playing tag with the Union spies
Than telling ladies the pleasant lies,
And yet, what else could you do, on leave?

He touched a rent in his dirty sleeve,
That was the place that the bullet tore
From the blue-chinned picket whose belt he wore,
The man who hadn't been quick enough,
And the powder-burn on the other cuff
Belonged to the fight with the Yankee scout
Who died in Irish when he went out.
He thought of these things as a man might think
Of certain trees by a river-brink,
Seen in a flash from a passing train,
And, before you could look at them, gone again.
It was more important to eat and drink

Than give the pain or suffer the pain
And life was too rapid for memory.
"There are certain things that will cling to me,
But not the things that I thought would cling,
And the wound in my body cannot sting
Like the tame black crow with the bandaged wing,
The nervous eye and the hungry craw
That picked at the dressing-station straw
Till I was afraid it would pick my eyes
And couldn't lift hand to beat it off.
I can tell the ladies the usual lies
Of the wild night-duels when two scouts clash
And your only light is his pistol-flash;
But I remember a watering-trough
Lost in a little brushwood town
And the feel of Black Whistle slumping down
Under my knees in the yellow air,
Hit by a bullet from God knows where . . .
Not the long, mad ride round the Union lines
But the smell of the swamp at Seven Pines,
The smell of the swamp by Gaines's Mill,
And Lee in the dusk before Malvern Hill,
Riding along with his shoulders straight
Like a sending out of the Scæan Gate,
The cold intaglio of war.
'This is Virginia's *Iliad,*'
But Troy was taken nevertheless—
I remember the eyes my father had
When we saw our dead in the Wilderness—
I cannot remember any more—

Lucy will wear her English gown
When the Black Horse Troop comes back to town,
Pin her dress with a silver star
And tell our shadows how brave we are.
Lucy I like your white-and-gold—"

He blew on his hands for the day was cold,
And the damp, green wood gave little heat:
There was something in him that matched the sleet

And washed its hands in a rainy dream,
Till the stirrup-strap and the horses' steam
And Shepley and Bristol behind his back,
Playing piquet with a dog-eared pack
And the hiss of the sap in the smoky wood
Mixed for a moment in something good,
Something outside of peace or war
Or a fair girl wearing a silver star,
Something hardly as vain as pride
And gaunt as the men he rode beside.
It made no comments but it was there,
Real as the color of Lucy's hair
Or the taste of Henry Weatherby's wine.
He thought "These people are friends of mine.
And we certainly fooled the Yanks last week,
When we caught those wagons at Boiling Creek,
I guess we're not such a bad patrol
If we never get straight with the muster-roll,
I guess, next Spring, we can do it again—"

Bristol threw down the flyspecked ten,
"Theah," he said, in the soft, sweet drawl
That could turn as hard as a Minie-ball,
"This heah day is my lucky day,
And Shepley nevah could play piquet."
He stretched his arms in a giant yawn,
"Gentlemen, when are we movin' on?
I have no desire for a soldier's end,
While I still have winnin's that I can spend
And they's certain appointments with certain ladies
Which I'd miss right smart if I went to Hades,
Especially one little black-eyed charmer
Whose virtue, one hopes, is her only armor,
So if Sergeant Wingate's mended his saddle
I suggest that we all of us now skedaddle,
To employ a term that the Yankees favor—"
He tasted his words, for he liked the flavor.
"And yet, one dreads to be back," said he,
"One knows how tippled one well may be
If one meets with the oppor-tun-ity.

And even the charmers can likewise raise
Unpleasant doubts that may last for days—
And as one," he sighed, "of our martial lads,
I'd rather be chargin' Columbiads,
Than actin' sweet to some old smooth-bore
When he tells me how he could win the War
By burnin' the next Yank crossroads-store.
The Yanks aren't always too blame polite,
But they fight like sin when they've got to fight,
And after they've almost nailed your hide
To your stinkin' saddle in some ole ride,
It makes you mad when some nice home-guard
Tells you they nevah could combat hard.
I have no desire to complain or trouble
But I'd find this conflict as comfortable
As a big green pond for a duck to swim in,
If it wasn't for leave, and the lovin' women."

———

The snow lay hard on the hills. You could burn your eyes
By too-long-looking into the cold ice-lens
Of infinite, pure, glittering, winter air.
It was as cold as that, as sparkling as that,
Where the crystal trees stood up like strange, brittle toys
After the sleet storm passed, till the setting sun
Hung the glass boughs with rainbows frozen to gems
And the long blue shadows pooled in the still hill-hollows.

The white and the purple lilacs of New England
Are frozen long, they will not bloom till the rains,
But when you look from the window, you see them there,
A great field of white lilacs.
                              A gathered sheaf
Of palest blossoms of lilac, stained with the purple evening.

Jack Ellyat turned away from the window now,
The frosty sleighbell of winter was in his ears,
He saw the new year, a child in a buffalo-robe,
Dragged in a sleigh whose runners were polished steel
Up the long hill of February, into chill light.

The child slept in the robe like a reindeer-colt,
Nuzzled under the winter. The bright bells rang.

He warmed his hands at the stove and shivered a little
Hearing that ice-sweet chime.

                 He was better now,
But his blood felt thin when he thought of skating along
Over black agate floors in the bonfire light
Or beating a girl's red mittens free of the snow,
And he slept badly at times, when his flesh recalled
Certain smells and sights that were prison.

He stared at the clock where Phaëton's horses lunged
With a queer nod of recognition. The rest had altered
People and winter and nightmares and Ellen Baker,
Or stayed in a good dimension that he had lost,
But Phaëton was the same. He said to himself,
"I have met you twice, old, drunken charioteer,
Once in the woods, and once in a dirty shack
Where Death was a coin of spittle left on the floor.
I suppose we will meet again before there's an end,
Well, let it happen.

               It must have been cold last year
At Fredericksburg. I'm glad I wasn't in that.
Melora, what's happened to you?"

                   He saw Melora
Walking down from the woods in the low spring light.
His body hurt for a minute, but then it stopped.
He was getting well. He'd have to go back pretty soon.
He grinned, a little dryly, thinking of chance,
Father had seen the congressman after all,
Just before Shiloh. So now, nearly ten months later,
The curious wheels that are moved by such congressmen
Were sending him back to the Army of the Potomac,
Back with the old company, back with the Eastern voices,
Henry Fairfield limping along with his sticks,
Shot through both hips at Antietam.

                      He didn't care,
Except for losing Bailey, which made it tough.
He tried to puzzle out the change in his world

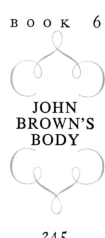

But gave it up. Things and people looked just the same,
You could love or like or detest them just the same way,
But whenever you tried to talk of your new dimension
It didn't sound right, except to creatures like Bailey.
"I have met you twice, old, drunken charioteer,
The third time you may teach me how to be cool."

Ned, asleep by the stove, woke up and yawned,
"Hello Ned," said his master, with a half-smile,
"I told a girl about you, back in a wood,
You'd like that girl. She'd rub the back of your ears.
And Bailey'd like you too. I wish Bailey was here.
Want to go to war, Ned?" Ned yawned largely again.
Ellyat laughed. "You're right, old fella," he said,
"You get too mixed up in a war. You better stay here.
God, I'd like to sleep by a stove for a million years,
Turn into a dog and remember how to stand cold."
The clock struck five. Jack Ellyat jumped at the sound
Then he sank back. "No, fooled you that time," he said,
As if the strokes had been bullets.
                              Then he turned
To see his mother, coming in with a lamp,
And taste the strange tastes of supper and quietness.

———————

John Vilas heard the beating of another
Sleet at another and a rougher wall
While his hands knotted together and then unknotted.
Each time she had to moan, his hands shut down,
And now the moans were coming close together,
Close as bright streaks of hail.
                              The younger children
Slept the uneasy sleep of innocent dogs
Who know there's something strange about the house,
Stranger than storms, and yet they have to sleep,
And someone has to watch them sleeping now.

"Harriet's right and Harriet's upstairs,
And Harriet cried like this when she gave birth,
Eighteen years back, in that chintz-curtained room,

And her long cry ran like an icicle
Into my veins. I can remember yet
The terrible old woman with the shawl
Who sat beside me, like deserted Fate,
Cursing me with those eyes each time she cried,
Although she must, one time, have cried like that
And been the object of as wild a cry,
And so far back,—and on—and always that,
The linked, the agonizing chain of cries
Brighter than steel, because earth will be earth
And the sun strike it, and the seed have force.
And yet no cry has touched me like this cry.

Harriet's right and Harriet's upstairs
And Harriet would have kept her from today,
And now today has come, I look at it,
Under the icicle, and wish it gone,
Because it hurts me to be sitting here,
Biting my fingers at my daughter's cry
And knowing Harriet has the harder task
As she has had for nearly twenty years.
And yet, what I have sought that I have sought
And cannot disavouch for my own pang,
Or be another father to the girl
Than he who let her run the woods alone
Looking for stones that have no business there.
For Harriet sees a dozen kinds of pain.
And some are blessed, being legitimate,
And some are cursed, being outside a law:
But she and I see only pain itself
And are hard-hearted with our epitaphs,
And yet I wish I could not hear that cry.
I know that it will pass because all things
Pass but the search that only ends with breath,
And, even after that, my daughter and I
May still get up from bondage, being such
Smoke as no chain of steel-bright cries can chain
To walk like Indian Summer through the woods
And be the solitaries of the wind
Till we are sleepy as old clouds at last.

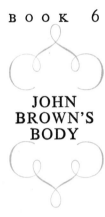

She has a lover and will have a child
And I'm alone. I had forgotten that,
Though you'd not think it easy to forget.
No, we'll not go together.

                The cries beat
Like hail upon the cold panes of my heart
Faster and faster, till they crack the glass
And I can know at last how old I am.

That is my punishment and my defence,
My ecstasy and my deep-seated bane.
I prayed to life for life once, in my youth,
Between the rain and a long stroke of cloud
Till my soaked limbs felt common with the sky
And the black stone of heaven swung aside,
With a last clap of water, to reveal
Lonely and timid, after all that wrath,
The small, cold, perfect flower of the new moon
And now, perhaps, I'll pray again tonight,
Still to the life that used me as a man
Uses and wears a strong and riotous horse,
Still to the vagrants of no fortunate word.

Men who go looking for the wilderness-stone,
Eaters of life who run away from bread
And are not satisfied with lucky days!
Robbers of airy gold, skin-changing men
Who find odd brothers when the moon is full,
Stray alchemics who entertain an imp
And feed it plums within a hollow tree
Until its little belly is sufficed,
Men who have seen the bronze male-partridge beat
His drum of feathers not ten feet away,
Men who have listened to wild geese at night
Until your hearts were hollowed with that sound,
Moth-light and owl-light and first-dayspring men,
Seekers and seldom-finders of the woods,
But always seekers till your eyes are shut;
I have an elder daughter that I love
And, having loved from childhood, would not tame

Because I once was tamed.
                    If you're my friends,
Then she's your friend.
                    I do not ask for her
Refusal or compunction or the safe
Road between little houses and old gates
Where Death lies sleepy as a dog in the sun
And the slow cows come home with evening bells
Into the tired peace that's good for pain.
Those who are never tired of eating life
Must immolate themselves against a star
Sooner or late, as she turns crucified
Now, on that flagellating wheel of light
Which will not miss one revolution's turn
For any anguish we can bring to it,
Because it is our master and our stone,
Body of pain, body of sharpened fire,
Body of quenchless life, itself, itself,
That safety cannot buy or peddlers sell
Or the rich cowards leave their silly sons.
But, oh,
She's tired out, she's broken, she's athirst.
Wrap her in twilights now, she is so torn,
And mask again the cold, sweat-runnelled mask
With the deep silence of a leafy wood
So cool and dim its birds are all asleep
And will not fret her. Wipe her straining hands
With the soft, gleaming cobwebs April spins
Out of bright silver tears and spider silk
Till they are finer than the handkerchiefs
Of a young, wild, spear-bearing fairy-queen.
Soothe her and comfort her and let her hear
No harshness but the mumbling peaceful sound
The fed bee grumbles to his honey-bags
In the red foxglove's throat.
                    Oh, if you are
Anything but lost shadows, go to her!"

Melora did not make such words for herself,
Being unable, and too much in pain.

If wood-things were beside her, she did not see them,
But only a lamp, and hands.

                          The pains came hard now,
A fist that hardly opened before it shut,
A red stair mounting into an ultimate
Flurry of misty conflict, when it seemed
As if she fought against the earth itself
For mere breath and something other than mere breath.
She heard the roar of the tunnel, drowned in earth.
Earth and its expulsive waters, tearing her, being born.
Then it was yellow silence and a weak crying.

After the child was washed, they showed her the child,
Breakable, crumpled, breathing, swathed and indignant,
With all its nails and hands that moved of themselves—
A queer thing to come out of that, but then it was there.
"Looks healthy enough," said her mother in a tired voice.
Melora stared. "He's got blue eyes," she said finally.
Her mother sniffed. "A lot of 'em start out blue."
She looked at the child as if she wanted to tell it,
"You aren't respectable. What are you doing here?"
But the child began wailing. She rocked it mechanically.
The rain kept on through the night but nobody listened.
The parents talked for a while, then they fell asleep.
Even the new child slept with its fists tight shut.
Melora heard the rain for a single moment
And then deep, beautiful nothing. "Over," she thought.
She slept, handfasted to the wilderness-stone.

————————

Now the earth begins to roll its wheel toward the sun,
The deep mud-gullies are drying.

                          The sluggish armies
That have slept the bear-months through in their winter-camps
Begin to stir and be restless.

                          They're tired enough
Of leaky huts and the rain and punishment-drill.
They haven't forgotten what it was like last time,
But next time we'll lick 'em, next time it won't be so bad,
Somehow we won't get killed, we won't march so hard.

"These huts looked pretty good when we first hit camp
But they look sort of lousy now—we might as well git—
Fight the Rebs—and the Yanks—and finish it up."
So they think in the bored, skin-itching months
While the roads are drying. "We're sick of this crummy place,
We might as well git, it doesn't much matter where."
But when they git, they are cross at leaving the huts,
"We fixed up ours first rate. We had regular lamps.
We knew the girls at the Depot. It wasn't so bad.
Why the hell do we have to git when we just got fixed?
Oh, well, we might as well travel."
                                        So they go on,
The huts drop behind, the dry road opens ahead. . . .

Fighting Joe Hooker feels good when he looks at his men.
A blue-eyed, uncomplex man with a gift for phrase.
"The finest army on the planet," he says.
The phrase is to turn against him with other phrases
When he is beaten—but now he is confident.
Tall, sandy, active, sentimental and tart,
His horseman's shoulder is not yet bowed by the weight
Of knowing the dice are his and the cast of them,
The weight of command, the weight of Lee's ghostly name.
He rides, preparing his fate.
                              In the other camps,
Lee writes letters, is glad to get buttermilk,
Wrings food and shoes and clothes from his commissariat,
Trusts in God and whets a knife on a stone.
Jackson plays with his new-born daughter, waiting for Spring,
His rare laugh clangs as he talks to his wife and child.
He is looking well. War always agrees with him,
And this, perhaps, is the happiest time of his life.
He has three months of it left.
                                By the swollen flood
Of the Mississippi, stumpy Grant is a mole
Gnawing at Vicksburg. He has been blocked four times
But he will carry that beaver-dam at last.
There is no brilliant lamp in that dogged mind
And no conceit of brilliance to shake the hand,
But hand and mind can use the tools that they get

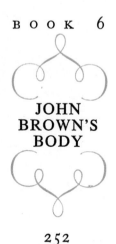
This long way out of Galena.

        Sherman is there
And Sherman loves him and finds him hard to make out,
In Sherman's impatient fashion—the quick, sharp man
Seeing ten thousand things where the slow sees one
And yet with a sort of younger brother awe
At the infinite persistence of that slow will
—They make a good pair of hunting dogs, Grant and Sherman,
The nervous, explosive, passionate, slashing hound
And the quiet, equable, deadly holder-on,
Faded-brown as a cinnamon-bear in Spring—
See them like that, the brown dog and the white dog,
Calling them back and forth through the scrubby woods
After the little white scut of Victory,
Or see them as elder brother and younger brother,
But remember this. In their time they were famous men
And yet they were not jealous, one of the other.
When the gold has peeled from the man on the gilded horse,
Riding Fifth Avenue, and the palm-girl's blind;
When the big round tomb gapes empty under the sky,
Vacant with summer air, when it's all forgotten,
When nobody reads the books, when the flags are moth-dust,
Write up that. You won't have to write it so often.
It will do as well as the railway-station tombs.

So with the troops and the leaders of the bear-armies,
The front-page-newspaper-things.

        Tall Lincoln reviews
Endless columns crunching across new snow.
They pass uncheering at the marching-salute.
Lincoln sits on his horse with his farmer's seat,
Watching the eyes go by and the eyes come on.
The gaunt, long body is dressed in its Sunday black,
The gaunt face, strange as an omen, sad and foreboding.
The eyes look at him, he looks back at the eyes;
They pass and pass. They go back to their camps at last.
"So that was him," they say. "So that's the old man.
I'm glad we saw him. He isn't so much on looks
But he looks like people you know. He looks sad all right,
I never saw nobody look quite as sad as that

STONEWALL JACKSON

"Let us cross the River," he said,
"and rest under the shade of the trees."

Without it made you feel foolish. He don't do that.
He makes you feel—I dunno—I'm glad we could see him.
He was glad to see us but you could tell all the same
This war's plumb killin' him. You can tell by his face.
I never saw such a look on any man's face.
I guess it's tough for him. Well, we saw him, for once."

That day in Richmond, a mob of angry women
Swarm in the streets and riot for bread or peace.
They loot some shops, a few for the bread they need,
A few for thieving, most because they are moved
By discontent and hunger to do as the rest.
The troops are called out. The troops are about to fire,
But Davis gets on a wagon and calms the crowd
Before the tumbled bodies clutter the street.
He never did a better thing with his voice
And it should be told. Next day they riot again,
But this time the fire is weaker. They are dispersed,
A few arrested. Bread grows dearer than ever.
The housewives still go out with their market-baskets,
But coffee's four dollars a pound and tea eleven.
They come back with a scraping of this and a scrap of that
And try to remember old lazy, lagnappe days,
The slew-foot negro chanting his devilled crabs
Along the street, and the market-women piling
The wicker baskets with everything good and fresh;
Topping it off with a great green fist of parsley
That you used to pretty the sides of the serving-dish
And never bothered to eat.
                    They improvise dishes,
"Blockade pudding" . . . "Confederate fricassee,"
Serve hominy grits on the Royal Derby china
And laugh or weep in their cups of willow-bark tea.

Davis goes back from the riot, his shoulders stooped,
The glow of speech has left him and he feels cold.
He eats a scant meal quickly and turns to the endless
Papers piled on his desk, the squabbles and plans.
A haggard dictator, fretting the men he rules
And being fretted by them.

He dreams, perhaps,
Of old days, riding wild horses beside his wife
Back in his youth, on a Mississippi road.
That was a good time. It is past. He drowns in his papers.

The curtain is going up on that battlesmoked,
Crowded third act which is to decide this war
And yet not end it for years.
                    Turn your eyes away
From these chiefs and captains, put them back in their books.
Let the armies sleep like bears in a hollow cave.
War is an iron screen in front of a time,
With pictures smoked upon it in red and black,
Some gallant enough, some deadly, but all intense.
We look at the pictures, thinking we know the time,
We only know the screen.
                    Look behind it now
At the great parti-colored quilt of these patchwork States.
This part and that is vexed by a battle-worm,
But the ploughs go ahead, the factory chimneys smoke,
A new age curdles and boils in a hot steel caldron
And pours into rails and wheels and fingers of steel,
Steel is being born like a white-hot rose
In the dark smoke-cradle of Pittsburg—
                              a man with a crude
Eye of metal and crystal looks at a smear
On a thin glass plate and wonders—
                              a shawled old woman
Sits on a curbstone calling the evening news.
War, to her, is a good day when papers sell
Or a bad day when papers don't. War is fat black type.
Anything's realer than war.
                    By Omaha
The valleys and gorges are white with the covered wagons
Moving out toward the West and the new, free land.
All through the war they go on.
                              Five thousand teams
Pass Laramie in a month in the last war-year,
Draft-evaders, homesteaders, pioneers,
Old soldiers, Southern emigrants, sunburnt children. . . .

Men are founding colleges, finding gold,
Selling bad beef to the army and making fortunes,
Ploughing the stone-cropped field that their fathers ploughed.
(Anything's realer than war.)
                                        A moth of a woman,
Shut in a garden, lives on scraps of Eternity
With a dog, a procession of sunsets and certain poems
She scribbles on bits of paper. Such poems may be
Ice-crystals, rubies cracked with refracted light,
Or all vast death like a wide field in ten short lines.
She writes to the tough, swart-minded Higginson
Minding his negro troops in a lost bayou,
"War feels to me like an oblique place."
                                        A man
Dreams of a sky machine that will match the birds
And another, dusting the shelves of a country store,
Saves his pennies until they turn into dimes.
(Anything's realer than war.)
                                        A dozen men
Charter a railroad to go all across the Plains
And link two seas with a whistling iron horse.
A whiskered doctor stubbornly tries to find
The causes of childbed-fever—and, doing so,
Will save more lives than all these war-months have spent,
And never inhabit a railway-station tomb.
All this through the war, all this behind the flat screen. . . .

            I heard the song of breath
            Go up from city and country,
            The even breath of the sleeper,
            The tired breath of the sick,
            The dry cough in the throat
            Of the man with the death-sweat on him,
            And the quiet monotone
            We breathe but do not hear.

            The harsh gasp of the runner,
            The long sigh of power
            Heaving the weight aloft,
            The grey breath of the old.

Men at the end of strength
With their lungs turned lead and fire,
Panting like thirsty dogs;
A child's breath, blowing a flame.

The breath that is the voice,
The silver, the woodwinds speaking,
The dear voice of your lover,
The hard voice of your foe,
And the vast breath of wind,
Mysterious over mountains,
Caught in pines like a bird
Or filling all hammered heaven.

I heard the song of breath,
Like a great strand of music,
Blown between void and void,
Uncorporal as the light.
The breath of nations asleep,
And the piled hills they sleep in,
The word that never was flesh
And yet is nothing but life.

What are you, bodiless sibyl,
Unseen except as the frost-cloud
Puffed from a silver mouth
When the hard winter's cold?

We cannot live without breath,
And yet we breathe without knowledge,
And the vast strand of sound
Goes on, eternally sighing,
Without dimension or space,
Without beginning or end.

I heard the song of breath
And lost it in all sharp voices,
Even my own voice lost
Like a thread in that huge strand,
Lost like a skein of air,

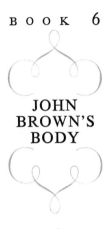

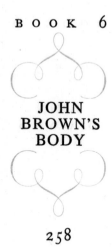
And with it, continents lost
In the great throat of Death.
I trembled, asking in vain,
Whence come you, whither art gone?
The continents flow and melt
Like wax in the naked candle,
Burnt by the wick of time——
Where is the breath of the Chaldees,
The dark, Minoan breath?
I said to myself in hate,
Hearing that mighty rushing,
Though you raise a new Adam up
And blow fresh fire in his visage,
He has only a loan of air,
And gets but a breathing-space.
But then I was quieted.

I heard the song of breath,
The gulf hollow with voices,
Fused into one slow voice
That never paused or was faint.
Man, breathing his life,
And with him all life breathing,
The young horse and the snake,
Beetle, lion and dove,
Solemn harps of the fir,
Trumpets of sea and whirlwind
And the vast, tiny grass
Blown by a breath and speaking.
I heard these things. I heard
The multitudinous river.
When I came back to my life,
My voice was numb in my ears,
I wondered that I still breathed.

———

Sophy, scared chambermaid in Pollet's Hotel,
Turned the cornhusk mattress and plumped the pillow
With slipshod hands.

Then she picked the pillow up
And sniffed it greedily.

Something in it smelt sweet.
The bright, gold lady had slept there the night before—
Oh, her lovely, lovely clothes! and the little green bottle
That breathed out flowers when you crept into the room
And pulled out the silver stopper just far enough
To get the sweetness, not far enough to be caught
If anyone came.

It made her thin elbows ache
To think how fine and golden the lady was
And how sweet she smelled, how sweet she looked at the men,
How they looked at her.

"I'd like to smell sweet," she thought,
"Smell like a lady."

She put the hard pillow back.
The lady and the green bottle had gone away.
—If only you had clever hands—after the next sleeper—
—You could steal green bottles—the room would smell stale
  again—
Hide it somewhere under your dress—as it always did—
Stale cigars and tired bodies—or even say
When they reached to give you the tip, "Don't give me a tip,
Just give me"—unwashed men with their six-weeks' beards,
Trying to hold you back when—"that little green bottle,
I want it so."—but the lady would never do it.
Ladies named Lucy. Lucy was a good name,
Flower-smelling. Sophy was just a name.

She took up her broom and swept ineffectively,
Thinking dim thoughts.

The ladies named Lucy came,
Sometimes in the winter, and then all the men got shaved
And you could look through the door at the people dancing.
But when battles drew near, the ladies went home to stay.
It was right they should. War wasn't a thing for ladies.

War was an endless procession of dirty boots.
Filling pitchers and emptying out the slops,
And making the cornhusk beds for the unshaved men

Who came in tired—but never too tired to wonder—
Look in the eyes—and hands—and suppose you didn't,
They didn't like it—and if you did, it was nothing—
But they always—and rough sometimes—and drunk now and
    then—
And a couple of nice ones—well, it didn't mean nothing.
It was merely hard to carry the heavy pails
When you didn't get fed enough and got up so soon.
But, now the army was moving, there wouldn't be
So many men or beds or slops for a while
And that meant something.
                   She sighed and dabbed with her broom

Shippy, the little man with the sharp rat-eyes,
Came behind her and put his hands on her waist.
She let him turn her around. He held her awhile
While his eyes tried to look at her and over his shoulder
At once and couldn't.
             She felt his poor body shake
But she didn't think much about it.
                  He murmured something.
She shook her head with the air of a frightened doll
And he let her go.
       "Well, I got to go anyway,"
He said, in a gloomy voice. "I'm late as it is,
But I thought that maybe—" He let the sentence trail off.

"What do you want, next time I come back?" he said.
Her face was sharper. "You bring me a bottle, Charley,
The kind that lady had, with the Richmond scent.
Hers has got a big silver stopper."
                He pursed his mouth.
"I don't know," he said. "I'll try. I'd like to all right.
You be a good girl now, Soph. Do you love me, Sophy?"
"Uh-huh," she said, in a tired voice, thinking of pitchers.

"Well, I—you're a good girl, Soph." He held her again.
"I'm late," he muttered. She looked at him and felt mean.
He was skimpy like her. They ought to be nice to each other.
She didn't like him much but she sort of loved him.

"You be a good girl till Charley comes back," he mumbled
Kissing her nervously. "I'll bring you the scent."

"It's got a name called French Lilies," she said. "Oh,
    Charley!"
They clung together a moment like mournful shadows.
He was crying a little, the wet tears fell on her chin,
She cried herself when he'd gone, she didn't know why,
But when she thought of the scent with the silver stopper
She felt more happy. She went to make the next bed.

————

Luke Breckinridge, washing his shirt in a muddy pool,
Chewed on a sour thought.
                Only yesterday
He had seen the team creak by toward Pollet's Hotel
With that damn little rat-eyed peddler driving his mules
As if he was God Almighty.
              He conjured up
A shadow-Shippy before him to hate and bruise
As he beat his shirt with a stone.
                    "If we-uns was home,
I could just lay for him and shoot him out of the bresh,
Goin' to see my girl with his lousy mules.
Tryin' to steal my girl with his peddler's talk!"

But here, in the war, you could only shoot at the Yanks,
If you shot other folks, they found out about it and shot you,
Just like you was a spyer or something mean
Instead of a soldier. There wasn't no sense to it.
"Teach him to steal my girl—if I had him home,
Back in the mountains—I told her straight the last time,
You be a good girl, Soph, and I'll buy you a dress—
We can fix the cabin up fine—and if we have kids
We'll get ourselves married. Couldn't talk fairer than that,
And she's a good girl—but women's easy to change—
God-damn peddler, givin' her Richmond trash,
And we-uns movin' away to scrimmage the Yanks
Before I git a chance to see her agin
And find out if she's been good—He'll come back this way,

Drivin' his mules—plumb easy to lay for him,
But they'd catch me, shore."

                    His mouth had a bitter twist,
His slow mind grubbed for a plan to settle his doubts.
At last he dropped his stone with a joyous whoop.
"Hey, Billy," he called to his neighbor. "Got your shirt dry?
Well, lend it here for a piece until mine's wrung out,
I got to go see the Captain."

                    Billy demurred.
"I got friends enough in this shirt," he said with a drawl.
"I ain't hankerin' after no visitors out of yours.
I'm a modest man and my crawlies is sort of shy,
They don't mix well with strangers. They's Piedmont crawlies.
Besides, this shirt, she's still got more shirt than hole,
Yours ain't a shirt—it's a doughnut."

                    They swore for a while
But finally Luke went off with the precious shirt,
Whistling the tuneless snatch of a mountain jig,
"Gawd help you, peddler," he thought, as he looked for the
    Captain.

Shippy drove his rattletrap cart along
Through the dusty evening, worried and ill at ease.
He ought to have taken the other road by the creek
But he'd wasted too much time at Pollet's Hotel
Looking for Sophy—and hardly seen her at that—
And now she wanted a bottle of scent.

                    His soul
Shivered with fear like a thin dog in the cold,
Raging in vain at the terrible thing called Life.
—There must be a corner somewhere where you could creep,
Curl up soft and be warm—but he'd never found it.
The big boys always stole his lunch at the school
And rubbed his nose in the dirt—and when he grew up
It was just the same.

                    There was something under his face,
Something that said, "Come, bully me—I won't bite."
He couldn't see it himself, but it must be there.
He was always going places and thinking, "This time,
They won't find out." But they always did find out

After a while.
                    It had been that way at the store,
That way in the army, that way now as a spy.
Behind his eyes he built up a super-Shippy
Who ordered people around, loved glittering girls,
Threw out his chest and died for a bloody flag
And then revived to be thanked by gilt generals,
A schoolboy Shippy, eating the big boys' lunch.
It was his totem. He visioned that Shippy now,
Reckless Shippy with papers sewed in his boots,
Slyly carrying fate through the Rebel lines
To some bright place where—

                    The off mule stumbled and brayed.
He cursed it whimperingly and jerked at the reins,
While his heart jerked, too. The super-Shippy was gone.
He was alone and scared and late on the road.
My God, but he was scared of being a spy
And the mute-faced woman in Richmond and war and life!
He had some papers sewn in his boots all right
And they'd look at the papers while he stood sweating before
    them,
Crumple them up and bully him with cross speech,
"Couldn't you even find out where Heth's men are?
Can't you draw a map? You don't know about Stonewall Jack-
    son?
Why don't you know it? What's this ford by the church?
My God, man, what do you think you are out there for?
You'll have to do better next time, I can tell you that.
We'll send you over Route 7. We had a man there,
But he's been reported killed—"
                    He shuddered in vain,
Seeing a rope and a tree and a dangling weight
And the mute-faced woman sending a paper off
In somebody's else's boots, and somebody saying
In an ice-cream voice to another scared little man.
"Next time, you'll try Route 7. We had a man there,
But he's been reported killed—"
                    Oh, there is a hole
Somewhere deep in the ground where the rabbits hide,

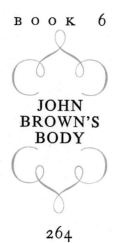
But I've never found it—
                              They stuck up signs and a flag
And it was war and you went and got scared to death
By the roar and the yells and the people trying to kill you
Till anything else seemed better—and there you were,
Driving mules with papers sewn in your boots,
But people still wanting to kill you—and no way out.
If you deserted, the mute-faced woman would know
And that would be the worst—and if you went back,
It would be Bull Run and yelling and all that blood
When it made you sick to your stomach. Even at school
You always had to fight. There was no way out.

Sophy was sweet and Sophy was a good girl
And Sophy was the warm earth where the rabbits hide
Away from danger, letting their hearts go slow,
But you couldn't stay with Sophy, you couldn't stay,
And she'd say she'd be a good girl—
                              but, in spite of himself,
He saw a big boy tearing a cardboard box
Apart, with greedy hands, in a bare school-yard,
Where a Shippy whimpered—
                              "Oh, Soph, I'll get you the scent,
Honest I will! Oh God, just let me get through,
Just this one time—and I'll pray—I'll be good—oh God,
Make these papers something they want!"

                              He clucked to his mules.
Another mile and he'd be out on the pike
And pretty safe for a while.
                              His spirit returned
To building the super-Shippy from dust again.
His head began to nod with the sway of the cart. . . .
Half a dozen men rode out from a little clearing
And casually blocked the road. He pulled up his mules,
Staring around. He saw a face that he knew,
Now queer with triumph—Sophy filling a pail
And that gangling fellow lounging against the pump,
Hungry-eyed—
                              It happened too fast to be scary.

You got stopped such a lot. It was only some new patrol.
"All the boys know me," he said. "Yes, I got my pass."
They took the pass but they did not give it back.
There was a waver shaking the dusty air,
The feel of a cord grown tauter. How dry his throat was!
He'd be driving on in a minute. "Well boys?" he said,
"Well, fellers?"
                    They didn't answer or look at him.
"I tell you that's the man," said the mountaineer.

The sergeant-feller looked dubiously at the rest,
Gentlemanly he looked like, a nice young feller
With his little black moustache and his thin, brown face,
He wouldn't do anything mean. It would be all right.
Another man was paring his nails with a knife,
His face was merry and reckless—nice feller, too,
Feller to stand you a drink and talk gay with the girls,
Not anybody to hurt you or twist your wrist.
They were all nice fellers except for the mountaineer.

They were searching him now, but they didn't do it mean.
He babbled to them all through it.
                              "Now boys, now boys,
You're making a big mistake, boys. They all know me,
They all know Charley the peddler."
                              The sergeant looked
Disgusted now—wonder why. Go ahead and look,
You'll never find it—Sophy—bottle of scent—

A horrible voice was saying, "Pull off his boots,"
He fought like a frightened rat then, weeping and biting,
But they got him down and found the papers all right.
Luke Breckinridge observed them with startled eyes,
"Christ," he thought, "so the skunk's a spy after all.
Well, I told 'em so—but I didn't reckon he was.
Little feist of a peddler, chasin' my girl,
Wanted to scare him off so he wouldn't come back—
Hell, they ought to make me a corporal now."
He was pleased.
                    Clay Wingate looked at the writhing man,

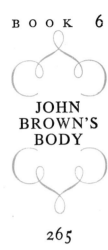

"Get up!" he said, in a hard voice, feeling sick.
But they had to drag it up before it would stand
And even then it still babbled.

His throat was dry
But that was all right—it was going to be all right—
He was alive—he was Shippy—he knew a girl—
He was going to buy her a bottle of first-class scent.
It couldn't all stop. He wasn't ready to die.
He was willing enough to be friends and call it a joke.
Let them take the mules and the cart and hurt him a lot
Only not that—it was other spies who were hung,
Not himself, not Shippy, not the body he knew
With the live blood running through it, making it warm.
He was real. He wore clothes. He could make all this go away
If he shut his eyes. They'd turn him loose in a minute.
They were all nice fellers. They wouldn't treat a man mean.
They couldn't be going to hang him.

But they were.

————

Lucy Weatherby spread out gowns on a bed
And wondered which she could wear to the next levee.
The blue was faded, the rose brocade had a tear,
She'd worn the flowered satin a dozen times,
The apricot had never gone with her hair,
And somebody had to look nice at the evening parties.
But it was hard. The blockade runners of course—
But so few of them had space for gowns any more
And, really, they charged such prices!

Of course it is
The war, and, of course, when one thinks of our dear, brave
  boys—
But, nevertheless, they like a girl to look fresh
When they come back from their fighting.

When one goes up
To the winter-camps, it doesn't matter so much,
Any old rag will do for that sort of thing.
But here, in Richmond . . .

She pondered, mentally stitching,
Cutting and shaping, lost in a pleasant dream.

Fighting at Chancellorsville and Hooker beaten
And nobody killed that you knew so terribly well
Except Jo Frear's second brother—though it was sad
Our splendid general Jackson's lost his arm,
Such an odd man but so religious.

                                        She hummed a moment
"That's Stonewall Jackson's way," in her clear cool voice.
"I really should have trained for nursing," she thought.
She heard a voice say. "Yes, the General's very ill,
But that lovely new nurse will save him if anyone can.
She came out from Richmond on purpose."
                                The voice stopped speaking.
She thought of last month and the boys and the Black Horse
    Troop,
And the haggard little room in Pollet's Hotel
Whose slipshod chambermaid had such scared, round eyes.
She was just as glad they were fighting now, after all,
Huger had been so jealous and Clay so wild,
It was quite a strain to be engaged to them both
Especially when Jim Merrihew kept on writing
And that nice Alabama major—
                            She heard the bells
Ring for a wedding—but who was the man beside her?
He had a face made up of too many faces.
And yet, a young girl must marry—
                            You may dance,
Play in the sun and wear bright gowns to levees,
But soon or late, the hands unlike to your hands
But rough and seeking, will catch your lightness at last
And with strange passion force you. What is this passion,
This injury that women must bear for gowns?
It does not move me or stir me. I will not bear it.
There are women enough to bear it. If I have sweetness,
It is for another service. It is my own.
I will not share it. I'll play in the heat of the sun.
And yet, young girls must marry—what am I thinking?

She stepped from her hoops to try on the rose brocade,
But let it lie for a moment, while she stood up
To look at the bright ghost-girl in the long dark mirror,

Adoringly.

        "Oh, you honey," she thought. "You honey!
You look so pretty—and nobody knows but me.
Nobody knows."

        She kissed her little white shoulders,
With fierce and pitying love for their shining whiteness,
So soft, so smooth, so untarnished, so honey-sweet.
Her eyes were veiled. She swayed in front of the mirror.
"Honey, I love you," she whispered, "I love you, honey.
Nobody loves you like I do, do they, sugar?
Nobody knows but Lucy how sweet you are.
You mustn't get married, honey. You mustn't leave me.
We'll be pretty and sweet to all of them, won't we, honey?
We'll always have beaus to dance with and tunes to dance to,
But you mustn't leave me, honey. I couldn't bear it.
You mustn't ever leave me for any man."

————

In the dense heart of the thicketed Wilderness,
Stonewall Jackson lies dying for four long days.
They have cut off his arm, they have tried such arts as they know,
But no arts now can save him.

        When he was hit
By the blind chance bullet-spatter from his own lines,
In the night, in the darkness, they stole him off from the field
To keep the men from knowing, but the men knew.
The dogs in the house will know when there's something wrong.
You do not have to tell them.

        He marched his men
That grim first day across the whole Union front
To strike a sleepy right wing with a sudden stone
And roll it up—it was his old trick of war
That Lee and he could play like finger and thumb!
It was the last time they played so.

        When the blue-coated
Unprepared ranks of Howard saw that storm,
Heralded by wild rabbits and frightened deer,
Burst on them yelling, out of the whispering woods,
They could not face it. Some men died where they stood,
The storm passed over the rest. It was Jackson's storm,

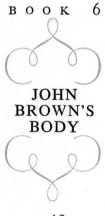

It was his old trick of war, for the last time played.
He must have known it. He loosed it and drove it on,
Hearing the long yell shake like an Indian cry
Through the dense black oaks, the clumps of second-growth pine,
And the red flags reel ahead through the underbrush.
It was the hour he did not stop to taste,
Being himself. He saw it and found it good,
But night was falling, the Union centre still held,
Another attack would end it. He pressed ahead
Through the dusk, pushing Little Sorrel, as if the horse
Were iron, and he were iron, and all his men
Not men but iron, the stalks of an iron broom
Sweeping a dire floor clean—and yet, as he rode,
A canny captain, planning a ruthless chess
Skilfully as night fell. The night fell too soon.
It is hard to tell your friend from your enemy
In such a night. So he rode too far in advance
And, turning back toward his lines, unrecognized,
Was fired upon in the night, in the stumbling darkness,
By his own men. He had ridden such rides before
Often enough and taken the chance of them,
But this chance was his bane.

      He lay on the bed
After the arm had been lopped from him, grim and silent,
Refusing importunate Death with terrible eyes.
Death was a servant and Death was a sulky dog
And Death crouched down by the Lord in the Lord's own time.
But he still had work to finish that Death would spoil.
He would live in spite of that servant.
        Now and then
He spoke, with the old curt justice that never once
Denied himself or his foe or any other
The rigid due they deserved, as he saw that due.
He spoke of himself and his storm. "A successful movement.
I think the most successful I ever made."
—He had heard that long yell shake like an Indian cry
Through the ragged woods and seen his flags go ahead.
Later on, they brought him a stately letter from Lee
That said in Lee's gracious way, "You have only lost
Your left arm, I my right."

The dour mouth opened.
"Better ten Jacksons should fall than one Lee," it said
And closed again, while the heart went on with its task
Of beating off foolish, unnecessary Death.

The slow time wore. They had to tell him at last
That he must die. The doctors were brave enough,
No doubt, but they looked awhile at the man on the bed
And summoned his wife to do it. So she told him.
He would not believe at first. Then he lay awhile
Silent, while some slow, vast reversal of skies
Went on in the dying brain. At last he spoke.
"All right," he said.
                              She opened the Bible and read.
It was Spring outside the window, the air was warm,
The rough, plank house was full enough of the Spring.
They had had a good life together, those two middle-aged
Calm people, one reading aloud now, the other silent.
They had passed hard schools. They were in love with each other
And had been for many years. Now that tale was told.
They had been poor and odd, found each other trusty,
Begotten children, prayed, disliked to be parted,
Had family-jokes, known weather and other matters,
Planned for an age: they were famous now, he was dying.

The clock moved on, the delirium began.
The watchers listened, trying to catch the words;
Some awed, one broken-hearted, a few, no doubt,
Not glad to be there precisely, but in a way
Glad that, if it must happen, they could be there.
It is a human emotion.
                              The dying man
Went back at first to his battles, as soldiers do.
He was pushing a new advance
With the old impatience and skill, over tangled ground,
A cloudy drive that did not move as he willed
Though he had it clear in his mind. They were slow today.
"Tell A. P. Hill to push them—push the attack—
Get up the guns!"
                              The cloudy assault dispersed.

There were no more cannon. The ground was plain enough now.

He lay silent, seeing it so, while the watchers listened.
He had been dying once, but that was a dream.
The ground was plain enough now.
He roused himself and spoke in a different voice.
"Let us cross the river," he said, "and rest under the shade of
the trees."

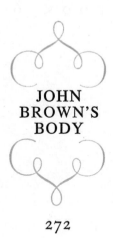

BOOK SEVEN

They came on to fish-hook Gettysburg in this way, after this
fashion.
Over hot pikes heavy with pollen, past fields where the wheat
was high.
Peaches grew in the orchards; it was a fertile country,
Full of red barns and fresh springs and dun, deep-uddered kine.

A farmer lived with a clear stream that ran through his very
house-room,
They cooled the butter in it and the milk, in their wide, stone
jars;
A dusty Georgian came there, to eat and go on to battle;
They dipped the milk from the jars, it was cold and sweet in
his mouth.

He heard the clear stream's music as the German housewife
    served him,
Remembering the Shenandoah and a stream poured from a rock;
He ate and drank and went on to the gunwheels crushing the
    harvest.
It was a thing he remembered as long as any guns.

Country of broad-backed horses, stone houses and long, green
    meadows,
Where Getty came with his ox-team to found a steady town
And the little trains of my boyhood puffed solemnly up the
    Valley
Past the market-squares and the lindens and the Quaker meeting-
    house.

Penn stood under his oak with a painted sachem beside him,
The market-women sold scrapple when the first red maples
    turned;
When the buckeyes slipped from their sheaths, you could gather
    a pile of buckeyes,
Red-brown as old polished boots, good to touch and hold in the
    hand.

The ice-cream parlor was papered with scenes from *Paul and
    Virginia,*
The pigs were fat all year, you could stand a spoon in the cream.
—Penn stood under his oak with a feathered pipe in his fingers,
His eyes were quiet with God, but his wits and his bargain sharp.

So I remember it all, and the light sound of buckeyes falling
On the worn rose-bricks of the pavement, herring-boned, trodden
    for years;
The great yellow shocks of wheat and the dust-white road
    through Summer,
And, in Fall, the green walnut shells, and the stain they left
    for a while.

So I remember you, ripe country of broad-backed horses,
Valley of cold, sweet springs and dairies with limestone-floors;

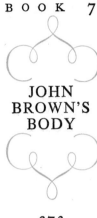

And so they found you that year, when they scared your cows
    with their cannon,
And the strange South moved against you, lean marchers lost
    in the corn.

———————

Two months have passed since Jackson died in the woods
And they brought his body back to the Richmond State House
To lie there, heaped with flowers, while the bells tolled,
Two months of feints and waiting.
                  And now, at length,
The South goes north again in the second raid,
In the last cast for fortune.
             A two-edged chance
And yet a chance that may burnish a failing star;
For now, on the wide expanse of the Western board,
Strong pieces that fought for the South have been swept away
Or penned up in hollow Vicksburg.
                One cool Spring night
Porter's ironclads run the shore-batteries
Through a velvet stabbed with hot flashes.
                 Grant lands his men.
Drives the relieving force of Johnston away
And sits at last in front of the hollow town
Like a huge brown bear on its haunches, terribly waiting.
His guns begin to peck at the pillared porches,
The sleepy, sun-spattered streets. His siege has begun.
Forty-eight days that siege and those guns go on
Like a slow hand closing around a hungry throat,
Ever more hungry.
           The hunger of hollow towns,
The hunger of sieges, the hunger of lost hope.
As day goes by after day and the shells still whine
Till the town is a great mole-burrow of pits and caves
Where the thin women hide their children, where the tired men
Burrow away from the death that falls from the air
And the common sky turned hostile—and still no hope,
Still no sight in the sky when the morning breaks
But the brown bear there on his haunches, steadfastly waiting,
Waiting like Time for the honey-tree to fall.

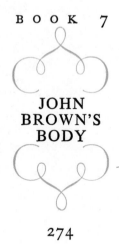

The news creeps back to the watches oversea.
They ponder on it, aloof and irresolute.
The balance they watch is dipping against the South.
It will take great strokes to redress that balance again.
There will be one more moment of shaken scales
When the Laird rams almost alter the scheme of things,
But it is distant.
　　　　　　The watchers stare at the board
Waiting a surer omen than Chancellorsville
Or any battle won on a Southern ground.

Lee sees that dip of the balance and so prepares
His cast for the surer omen and his last stroke
At the steel-bossed Northern shield. Once before he tried
That spear-rush North and was halted. It was a chance.
This is a chance. He weighs the chance in his hand
Like a stone, reflecting.
　　　　　　　　Four years from Harper's Ferry—
Two years since the First Manassas—and this last year
Stroke after stroke successful—but still no end.

He is a man with a knotty club in his hand
Beating off bulls from the breaks in a pasture fence
And he has beaten them back at each fresh assault,
McClellan—Burnside—Hooker at Chancellorsville—
Pope at the Second Manassas—Banks in the Valley—
But the pasture is trampled; his army needs new pasture.
An army moves like a locust, eating the grain,
And this grain is well-night eaten. He cannot mend
The breaks in his fence with famine or starving hands,
And if he waits the wheel of another year
The bulls will come back full-fed, shaking sharper horns
While he faces them empty, armed with a hunger-cracked
Unmagic stick.
　　　　　　There is only this thing to do,
To strike at the shield with the strength that he still can use
Hoping to burst it asunder with one stiff blow
And carry the war up North, to the untouched fields
Where his tattered men can feed on the bulls' own grain,
Get shoes and clothes, take Washington if they can,

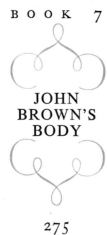

Hold the fighting-gauge in any event.

                         He weighs
The chance in his hand. I think that he weighed it well
And felt a high tide risen up in his heart
And in his men a high tide.

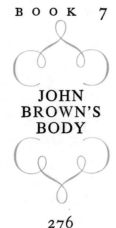
                     They were veterans,
They had never been beaten wholly and blocked but once,
He had driven four Union armies within a year
And broken three blue commanders from their command.
Even now they were fresh from triumph.

                             He cast his stone
Clanging at fortune, and set his fate on the odds.

————————

Lincoln hears the rumor in Washington.
They are moving North.

                      The Pennsylvania cities
Hear it and shake, they are loose, they are moving North.
Call up your shotgun-militia, bury your silver,
Shoulder a gun or run away from the State,
They are loose, they are moving.

                      Fighting Joe Hooker has heard it.
He swings his army back across the Potomac,
Rapidly planning, while Lee still visions him South.
Stuart's horse should have brought the news of that move
But Stuart is off on a last and luckless raid
Far to the east, and the grey host moves without eyes
Through crucial days.

                   They are in the Cumberland now,
Taking minor towns, feeding fat for a little while,
Pressing horses and shoes, paying out Confederate bills
To slow Dutch storekeepers who groan at the money.
They are loose, they are in the North, they are here and there.
Halleck rubs his elbows and wonders where,
Lincoln is sleepless, the telegraph-sounders click
In the War Office day and night.

                     There are lies and rumors,
They are only a mile from Philadelphia now,
They are burning York——they are marching on Baltimore——

Meanwhile, Lee rides through the heart of the Cumberland.
A great hot sunset colors the marching men,
Colors the horse and the sword and the bearded face
But cannot change that face from its strong repose.
And—miles away—Joe Hooker, by telegraph
Calls for the garrison left at Harper's Ferry
To join him. Elbow-rubbing Halleck refuses.
Hooker resigns command—and fades from the East
To travel West, fight keenly at Lookout Mountain,
Follow Sherman's march as far as Atlanta,
Be ranked by Howard, and tartly resign once more
Before the end and the fame and the Grand Review,
To die a slow death, in bed, with his fire gone out,
A campfire quenched and forgotten.

                          He deserved
A better and brusquer end that marched with his nickname,
This disappointed, hot-tempered, most human man
Who had such faith in himself except for once,
And the once, being Chancellorsville, wiped out the rest.
He was often touchy and life was touchy with him,
But the last revenge was a trifle out of proportion.
Such things will happen—Jackson went in his strength
Stuart was riding his horse when the bullet took him,
And Custer died to the trumpet—Dutch Longstreet lived
To quarrel and fight dead battles. Lee passed in silence.
McClellan talked on forever in word and print.
Grant lived to be President. Thomas died sick at heart.

So Hooker goes from our picture—and a spent aide
Reaches Meade's hut at three o'clock in the morning
To wake him with unexpected news of command.
The thin Pennsylvanian puts on his spectacles
To read the order. Tall, sad-faced and austere,
He has the sharp, long nose of a fighting-bird,
A prudent mouth and a cool, considering mind.
An iron-grey man with none of Hooker's panache,
But resolute and able, well skilled in war;
They call him "the damned old goggle-eyed snapping-turtle"
At times, and he does not call out the idol-shout
When he rides his lines, but his prudence is a hard prudence,

And can last out storms that break the men with panache,
Though it summons no counter-storm when the storm is done.

His sombre schoolmaster-eyes read the order well.
It is three days before the battle.
                              He thinks at first
Of a grand review, gives it up, and begins to act.

That morning a spy brings news to Lee in his tent
That the Union army has moved and is on the march.
Lee calls back Ewell and Early from their forays
And summons his host together by the cross-roads
Where Getty came with his ox-cart.
                              So now we see
These two crab-armies fumbling for each other,
As if through a fog of rumor and false report,
These last two days of sleepy, hay-harvest June.
Hot June lying asleep on a shock of wheat
Where the pollen-wind blows over the burnt-gold stubble
And the thirsty men march past, stirring thick grey dust
From the trodden pikes—till at last, the crab-claws touch
At Getty's town, and clutch, and the peaches fall
Cut by the bullets, splashing under the trees.

That meeting was not willed by a human mind,
When we come to sift it.
                              You say a fate rode a horse
Ahead of those lumbering hosts, and in either hand
He carried a skein of omen. And when, at last,
He came to a certain umbrella-copse of trees
That never had heard a cannon or seen dead men,
He knotted the skeins together and flung them down
With a sound like metal.
                              Perhaps. It may have been so.
All that we know is—Meade intended to fight
Some fifteen miles away on the Pipe Creek Line
And where Lee meant to fight him, if forced to fight,
We do not know, but it was not there where they fought.
Yet the riding fate,

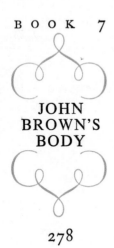

Blind and deaf and a doom on a lunging horse,
Threw down his skeins and gathered the battle there.

The buttercup-meadows
Are very yellow.
A child comes there
To fill her hands.
The gold she gathers
Is soft and precious
As sweet new butter
Fresh from the churn.

She fills her frock
With the yellow flowers,
The butter she gathers
Is smooth as gold,
Little bright cups
Of new-churned sunshine
For a well-behaved
Hoop-skirted doll.

Her frock's full
And her hands are mothy
With yellow pollen
But she keeps on.
Down by the fence
They are even thicker.
She runs, bowed down with
Buttercup-gold.

She sees a road
And she sees a rider.
His face is grey
With a different dust.
He talks loud.
He rattles like tinware.
He has a long sword
To kill little girls.

He shouts at her now,
But she does not answer.

"Where is the town?"
But she will not hear.
There are other riders
Jangling behind him.
"We won't hurt you, youngster!"
But they have swords.

The buttercups fall
Like spilt butter
She runs away.
She runs to her house.
She hides her face
In her mother's apron
And tries to tell her
How dreadful it was.

———————

Buford came to Gettysburg late that night
Riding West with his brigades of blue horse,
While Pettigrew and his North Carolinians
Were moving East toward the town with a wagon-train,
Hoping to capture shoes.
                          The two came in touch.
Pettigrew halted and waited for men and orders.
Buford threw out his pickets beyond the town.

The next morning was July first. It was hot and calm.
On the grey side, Heth's division was ready to march
And drive the blue pickets in. There was still no thought
Of a planned and decisive battle on either side
Though Buford had seen the strength of those two hill-ridges
Soon enough to be famous, and marked one down
As a place to rally if he should be driven back.

He talks with his staff in front of a tavern now.
An officer rides up from the near First Corps.
"What are you doing here, sir?"
                                The officer
Explains. He, too, has come there to look for shoes.
—Fabulous shoes of Gettysburg, dead men's shoes,

Did anyone ever wear you, when it was done,
When the men were gone, when the farms were spoiled with the
    bones,
What became of your nails and leather? The swords went home,
The swords went into museums and neat glass cases,
The swords look well there. They are clean from the war.
You wouldn't put old shoes in a neat glass case,
Still stuck with the mud of marching.
                              And yet, a man
With a taste for such straws and fables, blown by the wind,
Might hide a pair in a labelled case sometime
Just to see how the leather looked, set down by the swords.

The officer is hardly through with his tale
When Buford orders him back to his command.
"Why, what is the matter, general?"
                              As he speaks
The far-off hollow slam of a single gun
Breaks the warm stillness. The horses prick up their ears.
"That's the matter," says Buford and gallops away.

––––––––––

Jake Diefer, the barrel-chested Pennsylvanian,
Marched toward Getty's town past orderly fences,
Thinking of harvest.
                    The boy was growing up strong
And the corn-haired woman was smart at managing things
But it was a shame what you had to pay hired men now
Though they'd had good crops last year and good prices too.
The crops looked pretty this summer.
                              He stared at the long
Gold of the wheat reflectively, weighing it all,
Turning it into money and cows and taxes,
A new horse-reaper, some first-class paint for the barn,
Maybe a dress for the woman.
                        His thoughts were few,
But this one tasted rough and good in his mouth
Like a spear of rough, raw grain. He crunched at it now.
—And yet, that wasn't all, the paint and the cash,
They were the wheat but the wheat was—he didn't know—

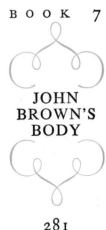

But it made you feel good to see some good wheat again
And see it grown up proper.

       He wasn't a man
To cut a slice of poetry from a farm.
He liked the kind of manure that he knew about
And seldom burst into tears when his horses died
Or found a beautiful thought in a bumble-bee,
But now, as he tramped along like a laden steer,
The tall wheat, rustling, filled his heart with its sound.

Look at that column well, as it passes by,
Remembering Bull Run and the cocksfeather hats,
The congressmen, the raw militia brigades
Who went to war with a flag and a haircloth trunk
In bright red pants and ideals and ignorance,
Ready to fight like picture-postcard boys
While fighting still had banners and a sword
And just as ready to run in blind mob-panic. . . .
These men were once those men. These men are the soldiers,
Good thieves, good fighters, excellent foragers,
The grumbling men who dislike to be killed in war
And yet will hold when the raw militia break
And live where the raw militia needlessly die,
Having been schooled to that end.

        The school is not
A pretty school. They wear no cocksfeather hats.
Some men march in their drawers and their stocking feet.
They have handkerchiefs round their heads, they are footsore
  and chafed,
Their faces are sweaty leather.

       And when they pass
The little towns where the people wish them godspeed,
A few are touched by the cheers and the crying women
But most have seen a number of crying women,
And heard a number of cheers.

       The ruder yell back
To the sincere citizens cool in their own front yards,
"Aw, get a gun and fight for your home yourself!"
They grin and fall silent. Nevertheless they go on.
Jake Diefer, the barrel-chested Pennsylvanian,

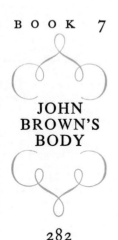

The steer-thewed, fist-plank-splitter from Cumberland,
Came through the heat and the dust and the mounting roar
That could not drown the rustle of the tall wheat
Making its growing sound, its windrustled sound,
In his heart that sound, that brief and abiding sound,
To a fork and a road he knew.
                              And then he heard
That mixed, indocile noise of combat indeed
And as if it were strange to him when it was not strange.
—He never took much account of the roads they went,
They were always going somewhere and roads were roads.
But he knew this road.
                        He knew its turns and its hills,
And what ploughlands lay beyond it, beyond the town,
On the way to Chambersburg.
                              He saw with wild eyes
Not the road before him or anything real at all
But grey men in an unreal wheatfield, tramping it down,
Filling their tattered hats with the ripe, rough grain
While a shell burst over a barn.
                              "Grasshoppers!" he said
Through stiff dry lips to himself as he tried to gauge
That mounting roar and its distance.
                              "The Johnnies is there!
The Johnnies and us is fighting in Gettysburg,
There must be Johnnies back by the farm already,
By Jesus, those damn Johnnies is on my farm!"

———————

That battle of the first day was a minor battle
As such are counted.
                    That is, it killed many men.
Killed more than died at Bull Run, left thousands stricken
With wounds that time might heal for a little while
Or never heal till the breath was out of the flesh.
The First Corps lost half its number in killed and wounded.
The pale-faced women, huddled behind drawn blinds
Back in the town, or in apple-cellars, hiding,
Thought it the end of the world, no doubt.
                              And yet,

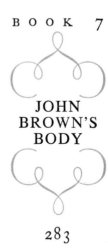

As the books remark, it was only a minor battle.
There were only two corps engaged on the Union side,
Longstreet had not yet come up, nor Ewell's whole force,
Hill's corps lacked a division till evening fell.
It was only a minor battle.

              When the first shot
Clanged out, it was fired from a clump of Union vedettes
Holding a farm in the woods beyond the town.
The farmer was there to hear it—and then to see
The troopers scramble back on their restless horses
And go off, firing, as a grey mass came on.

He must have been a peaceable man, that farmer.
It is said that he died of what he had heard and seen
In that one brief moment, although no bullet came near him
And the storm passed by and did not burst on his farm.
No doubt he was easily frightened. He should have reflected
That even minor battles are hardly the place
For peaceable men—but he died instead, it is said.
There were other deaths that day, as of Smiths and Clancys,
Otises, Boyds, Virginia and Pennsylvania,
New York, Carolina, Wisconsin, the gathered West,
The tattered Southern marchers dead on the wheat-shocks.
Among these deaths a few famous.

                    Reynolds is dead,
The model soldier, gallant and courteous,
Shot from his saddle in the first of the fight.
He was Doubleday's friend, but Doubleday has no time
To grieve him, the Union right being driven in
And Heth's Confederates pressing on toward the town.
He holds the onrush back till Howard comes up
And takes command for a while.

                  The fighting is grim.
Meade has heard the news. He sends Hancock up to the field.
Hancock takes command in mid-combat. The grey comes on.
Five color-bearers are killed at one Union color,
The last man, dying, still holds up the sagging flag.
The pale-faced women creeping out of their houses,
Plead with retreating bluecoats, "Don't leave us boys,
Stay with us—hold the town." Their faces are thin,

Their words come tumbling out of a frightened mouth.
In a field, far off, a peaceable farmer puts
His hands to his ears, still hearing that one sharp shot
That he will hear and hear till he dies of it.
It is Hill and Ewell now against Hancock and Howard
And a confused, wild clamor—and the high keen
Of the Rebel yell—and the shrill-edged bullet song
Beating down men and grain, while the sweaty fighters
Grunt as they ram their charges with blackened hands.

Till Hancock and Howard are beaten away at last,
Outnumbered and outflanked, clean out of the town,
Retreating as best they can to a fish-hook ridge,
And the clamor dies and the sun is going down
And the tired men think about food.

                       The dust-bitten staff
Of Ewell, riding along through the captured streets,
Hear the thud of a bullet striking their general.
Flesh or bone? Death-wound or rub of the game?
"The general's hurt!" They gasp and volley their questions.
Ewell turns his head like a bird, "No, I'm not hurt, sir,
But, supposing the ball had struck you, General Gordon,
We'd have the trouble of carrying you from the field.
You can see how much better fixed for a fight I am.
It don't hurt a mite to be shot in your wooden leg."

So it ends. Lee comes on the field in time to see
The village taken, the Union wave in retreat.
Meade will not reach the ground till one the next morning.

————————

So it ends, this lesser battle of the first day,
Starkly disputed and piecemeal won and lost
By corps-commanders who carried no magic plans
Stowed in their sleeves, but fought and held as they could.
It is past. The board is staked for the greater game
Which is to follow—The beaten Union brigades
Recoil from the cross-roads town that they tried to hold.
And so recoiling, rest on a destined ground.
Who chose that ground?

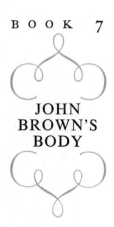

There are claimants enough in the books.
Howard thanked by Congress for choosing it
As doubtless, they would have thanked him as well had he
Chosen another, once the battle was won,
And there are a dozen ifs on the Southern side,
How, in that first day's evening, if one had known,
If Lee had been there in time, if Jackson had lived,
The heights that cost so much blood in the vain attempt
To take days later, could have been taken then.
And the ifs and the thanks and the rest are all true enough
But we can only say, when we look at the board,
"There it happened. There is the way of the land.
There was the fate, and there the blind swords were crossed."

————

You took a carriage to that battlefield.
Now, I suppose, you take a motor-bus,
But then, it was a carriage—and you ate
Fried chicken out of wrappings of waxed paper,
While the slow guide buzzed on about the war
And the enormous, curdled summer clouds
Piled up like giant cream puffs in the blue.
The carriage smelt of axle-grease and leather
And the old horse nodded a sleepy head
Adorned with a straw hat. His ears stuck through it.
It was the middle of hay-fever summer
And it was hot. And you could stand and look
All the way down from Cemetery Ridge,
Much as it was, except for monuments
And startling groups of monumental men
Bursting in bronze and marble from the ground,
And all the curious names upon the gravestones. . . .

So peaceable it was, so calm and hot,
So tidy and great-skied.
                          No men had fought
There but enormous, monumental men
Who bled neat streams of uncorrupting bronze,
Even at the Round Tops, even by Pickett's boulder,
Where the bronze, open book could still be read

By visitors and sparrows and the wind:
And the wind came, the wind moved in the grass,
Saying . . . while the long light . . . and all so calm . . .

        "Pickett came
        And the South came
        And the end came,
        And the grass comes
        And the wind blows
        On the bronze book
        On the bronze men
        On the grown grass,
        And the wind says
        'Long ago
        Long
        Ago.' "

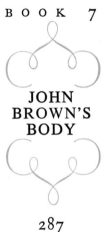
Then it was time to buy a paperweight
With flags upon it in decalcomania
And hope you wouldn't break it, driving home.

————————

Draw a clumsy fish-hook now on a piece of paper,
To the left of the shank, by the bend of the curving hook,
Draw a Maltese cross with the top block cut away.
The cross is the town. Nine roads star out from it
East, West, South, North.
                        And now, still more to the left
Of the lopped-off cross, on the other side of the town,
Draw a long, slightly-wavy line of ridges and hills
Roughly parallel to the fish-hook shank.
(The hook of the fish-hook is turned away from the cross
And the wavy line.)
                    There your ground and your ridges lie.
The fish-hook is Cemetery Ridge and the North
Waiting to be assaulted—the wavy line
Seminary Ridge whence the Southern assault will come.

The valley between is more than a mile in breadth.
It is some three miles from the lowest jut of the cross

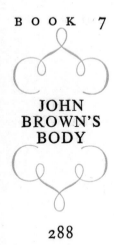
To the button at the far end of the fish-hook shank,
Big Round Top, with Little Round Top not far away.
Both ridges are strong and rocky, well made for war.
But the Northern one is the stronger shorter one.
Lee's army must spread out like an uncoiled snake
Lying along a fence-rail, while Meade's can coil
Or halfway coil, like a snake part clung to a stone.
Meade has the more men and the easier shifts to make,
Lee the old prestige of triumph and his tried skill.
His task is—to coil his snake round the other snake
Halfway clung to the stone, and shatter it so,
Or to break some point in the shank of the fish-hook line
And so cut the snake in two.

                         Meade's task is to hold.

That is the chess and the scheme of the wooden blocks
Set down on the contour map.

                         Having learned so much,
Forget it now, while the ripple-lines of the map
Arise into bouldered ridges, tree-grown, bird-visited,
Where the gnats buzz, and the wren builds a hollow nest
And the rocks are grey in the sun and black in the rain,
And the jacks-in-the-pulpit grow in the cool, damp hollows.
See no names of leaders painted upon the blocks
Such as "Hill," or "Hancock," or "Pender"—

                         but see instead
Three miles of living men—three long double miles
Of men and guns and horses and fires and wagons,
Teamsters, surgeons, generals, orderlies,
A hundred and sixty thousand living men
Asleep or eating or thinking or writing brief
Notes in the thought of death, shooting dice or swearing,
Groaning in hospital wagons, standing guard
While the slow stars walk through heaven in silver mail,
Hearing a stream or a joke or a horse cropping grass
Or hearing nothing, being too tired to hear.
All night till the round sun comes and the morning breaks,
Three double miles of live men.
Listen to them, their breath goes up through the night
In a great chord of life, in the sighing murmur

Of wind-stirred wheat.
                    A hundred and sixty thousand
Breathing men, at night, on two hostile ridges set down.

————

Jack Ellyat slept that night on the rocky ground
Of Cemetery Hill while the cold stars marched,
And if his bed was harder than Jacob's stone
Yet he could sleep on it now and be glad for sleep.

He had been through Chancellorsville and the whistling wood,
He had been through this last day. It is well to sleep
After such days.
                    He had seen, in the last four months,
Many roads, much weather and death, and two men fey
Before they died with the prescience of death to come,
John Haberdeen and the corporal from Millerstown.
Such things are often remembered even in sleep.
He thought to himself, before he lay on the ground,
"We got it hot today in that red-brick town
But we'll get it hotter tomorrow."
                              And when he woke
And saw the round sun risen in the clear sky,
He could feel that thought steam up from the rocky ground
And touch each man.
                    One man looked down from the hill,
"That must be their whole damn army," he said and whistled,
"It'll be a picnic today, boys. Yes, it'll be
A regular basket-picnic." He whistled again.

"Shut your trap about picnics, Ace," said another man,
"You make me too damn hungry!"
                              He sighed out loud.
"We had enough of a picnic at Chancellorsville,"
He said. "I ain't felt right in my stummick since.
Can you make 'em out?"
                    "Sure," said Ace, "but they're pretty far."

"Wonder who we'll get? That bunch we got yesterday
Was a mean-shootin' bunch."

"Now don't you worry," said Ace,
"We'll get plenty."
                    The other man sighed again.
"Did you see that darky woman selling hot pies,
Two days ago, on the road?" he said, licking his lips,
"Blackberry pies. The boys ahead got a lot
And Jake and me clubbed together for three. And then
Just as we were ready to make the sneak,
Who comes up with a roar but the provost-guard?
Did we get any pies? I guess you know if we did.
I couldn't spit for an hour, I felt so mad.
Next war I'm goin' to be provost-guard or bust."

A thin voice said abruptly, "They're moving—lookit—
They're moving. I tell you—lookit—"
                                        They all looked then.
A little crackling noise as of burning thornsticks
Began far away—ceased wholly—began again—
"We won't get it awhile," thought Ellyat. "They're trying the
    left.
We won't get it awhile, but we'll get it soon.
I feel funny today. I don't think I'm going to be killed
But I feel funny. That's their whole army all right.
I wonder if those other two felt like this,
John Haberdeen and the corporal from Millerstown?
What's it like to see your name on a bullet?
It must feel queer. This is going to be a big one.
The Johnnies know it. That house looks pretty down there.
Phaëton, charioteer in your drunken car,
What have you got for a man that carries my name?
We're a damn good company now, if we say it ourselves,
And the Old Man knows it—but this one's bound to be tough.
I wonder what they're feeling like over there.

Charioteer, you were driving yesterday,
No doubt, but I did not see you. I see you now.
What have you got today for a man with my name?"

————

The firing began that morning at nine o'clock,
But it was three before the attacks were launched.

MELORA VILAS
   "But now that the wind is warm, I remember my lover,
Must you blow all summer, warm wind?"

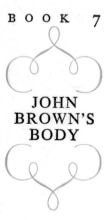
There were two attacks, one a drive on the Union left
To take the Round Tops, the other one on the right.
Lee had planned them to strike together and, striking so,
Cut the Union snake in three pieces.

It did not happen.
On the left, Dutch Longstreet, slow, pugnacious and stubborn,
Hard to beat and just as hard to convince,
Has his own ideas of the battle and does not move
For hours after the hour that Lee had planned,
Though, when he does, he moves with pugnacious strength.
Facing him, in the valley before the Round Tops,
Sickles thrust out blue troops in a weak right angle,
Some distance from the Ridge, by the Emmettsburg pike.
There is a peach orchard there, a field of ripe wheat
And other peaceable things soon not to be peaceful.

They say the bluecoats, marching through the ripe wheat,
Made a blue-and-yellow picture that men remember
Even now in their age, in their crack-voiced age.
They say the noise was incessant as the sound
Of all wolves howling, when that attack came on.
They say, when the guns all spoke, that the solid ground
Of the rocky ridges trembled like a sick child.
We have made the sick earth tremble with other shakings
In our time, in our time, in our time, but it has not taught us
To leave the grain in the field.

So the storm came on
Yelling against the angle.

The men who fought there
Were the tired fighters, the hammered, the weather-beaten,
The very hard-dying men.

They came and died
And came again and died and stood there and died,
Till at last the angle was crumpled and broken in,
Sickles shot down, Willard, Barlow and Semmes shot down,
Wheatfield and orchard bloody and trampled and taken,
And Hood's tall Texans sweeping on toward the Round Tops
As Hood fell wounded.

On Little Round Top's height
Stands a lonely figure, seeing that rush come on—

Greek-mouthed Warren, Meade's chief of engineers.
—Sometimes, and in battle even, a moment comes
When a man with eyes can see a dip in the scales
And so seeing, reverse a fortune. Warren has eyes
And such a moment comes to him now. He turns
—In a clear flash seeing the crests of the Round Tops taken,
The grey artillery there and the battle lost—
And rides off hell-for-leather to gather troops
And bring them up in the very nick of time,
While the grey rush still advances, keening its cry.
The crest is three times taken and then retaken
In fierce wolf-flurries of combat, in gasping Iliads
Too rapid to note or remember, too obscure to freeze in a song.
But at last, when the round sun drops, when the nun-footed night,
Dark-veiled walker, holding the first weak stars
Like children against her breast, spreads her pure cloths there,
The Union still holds the Round Tops and the two hard keys of
    war.

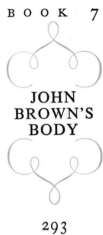

Night falls. The blood drips in the rocks of the Devil's Den.
The murmur begins to rise from the thirsty ground
Where the twenty thousand dead and wounded lie.
Such was Longstreet's war, and such the Union defence,
The deaths and the woundings, the victory and defeat
At the end of the fish-hook shank.
                     And so Longstreet failed
Ere Ewell and Early struck the fish-hook itself
At Culp's Hill and the Ridge and at Cemetery Hill,
With better fortune, though not with fortune enough
To plant hard triumph deep on the sharp-edged rocks
And break the scales of the snake.
                   When that last attack
Came, with its cry, Jack Ellyat saw it come on.

———————

They had been waiting for hours on that hard hill,
Sometimes under fire, sometimes untroubled by shells.
A man chewed a stick of grass and hummed to himself.
Another played mumbledeypeg with a worn black knife.

Two men were talking girls till they got too mad
And the sergeant stopped them.

                    Then they waited again.

B O O K   7

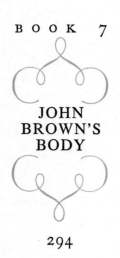

JOHN
BROWN'S
BODY

294

Jack Ellyat waited, hearing that other roar
Rise and fall, be distant and then approach.
Now and then he turned on his side and looked at the sky
As if to build a house of peace from that blue,
But could find no house of peace there.

                      Only the roar,
The slow sun sinking, the fey touch at his mind. . . .

He was lying behind a tree and a chunk of rock
On thick, coarse grass. Farther down the slope of the hill
There were houses, a rough stone wall, and blue loungy men.
Behind them lay the batteries on the crest.

He wondered if there were people still in the houses.
One house had a long, slant roof. He followed the slant
Of the roof with his finger, idly, pleased with the line.

The shelling burst out from the Southern guns again.
Their own batteries answered behind them. He looked at his
   house
While the shells came down. I'd like to live in that house.
Now the shelling lessened.

                The man with the old black knife
Shut up the knife and began to baby his rifle.
They're coming, Jack thought. This is it.

                     There was an abrupt
Slight stiffening in the bodies of other men,
A few chopped ends of words scattered back and forth,
Eyes looking, hands busy in swift, well-accustomed gestures.
This is it. He felt his own hands moving like theirs
Though he was not telling them to. This is it. He felt
The old familiar tightness around his chest.
The man with the grass chewed his stalk a little too hard
And then suddenly spat it out.

                Jack Ellyat saw
Through the falling night, that slight, grey fringe that was war

Coming against them, not as it came in pictures
With a ruler-edge, but a crinkled and smudgy line
Like a child's vague scrawl in soft crayon, but moving on
But with its little red handkerchiefs of flags
Sagging up and down, here and there.

        It was still quite far,
It was still like a toy attack—it was swallowed now
By a wood and came out larger with larger flags.
Their own guns on the crest were trying to break it up
—Smoking sand thrown into an ant-legged line—
But it still kept on—one fringe and another fringe
And another and—

    He lost them all for a moment
In a dip of ground.

     This is it, he thought with a parched
Mind. It's a big one. They must be yelling all right
Though you can't hear them. They're going to do it this time.
Do it or bust—you can tell from the way they come—
I hope to Christ that the batteries do their job
When they get out of that dip.

      Hell, they've lost 'em now,
And they're still coming.

     He heard a thin gnat-shrieking
"Hold your fire till they're close enough, men!"

         The new lieutenant.
The new lieutenant looked thin. "Aw, go home," he muttered,
"We're no militia—What do you think we are?"

Then suddenly, down by his house, the low stone wall
Flashed and was instantly huge with a wall of smoke.
He was yelling now. He saw a red battleflag
Push through smoke like a prow and be blotted out
By smoke and flash.

     His heart knocked hard in his chest.
"Do it or bust," he mumbled, holding his fire
While the rags of smoke blew off.

       He heard a thick chunk
Beside him, turned his head for a flicker of time.
The man who had chewed on the grass was injuredly trying
To rise on his knees, his face annoyed by a smile.

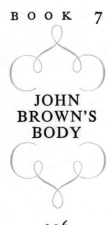

Then the blood poured over the smile and he crumpled up.
Ellyat stretched out a hand to touch him and felt the hand
Rasped by a file.
                        He jerked back the hand and sucked it.
"Bastards," he said in a minor and even voice.

All this had occurred, it seemed, in no time at all,
But when he turned back, the smoky slope of the hill
Was grey—and a staggering red advancing flag
And those same shouting strangers he knew so well,
No longer ants—but there—and stumblingly running—
And that high, shrill, hated keen piercing all the flat thunder.

His lips went back. He felt something swell in his chest
Like a huge, indocile bubble.
                        "By God," he said,
Loading and firing, "You're not going to get this hill,
You're not going to get this hill. By God, but you're not!"
He saw one grey man spin like a crazy dancer
And another fall at his heels—but the hill kept growing them.
Something made him look toward his left.
                              A yellow-fanged face
Was aiming a pistol over a chunk of rock.
He fired and the face went down like a broken pipe
While something hit him sharply and took his breath.
"Get back, you suckers," he croaked, "Get back there, you
    suckers!"
He wouldn't have time to load now—they were too near.
He was up and screaming. He swung his gun like a club
Through a twilight full of bright stabbings, and felt it crash
On a thing that broke. He had no breath any more.
He had no thoughts. Then the blunt fist hit him again.

He was down in the grass and the black sheep of night ran over
    him . . .

———————

That day, Melora Vilas sat by the spring
With her child in her arms and felt the warm wind blow
Ruffling the little pool that had shown two faces

Apart and then clung together for a brief while
As if the mouths had been silver and so fused there. . . .

The wind blew at the child's shut fists but it could not open
     them.
The child slept well. The child was a strong, young child.

"Wind, you have blown the green leaf and the brown leaf
And in and out of my restless heart you blow,
Wakening me again.
                         I had thought for a while
My heart was a child and could sleep like any child,
But now that the wind is warm, I remember my lover,
Must you blow all summer, warm wind?"

"Divide anew this once-divided flesh
Into twelve shares of mercy and on each
Bestow a fair and succourable child,
Yet, in full summer, when the ripened stalks
Bow in the wind like golden-headed men,
Under the sun, the shares will reunite
Into unmerciful and childless love."

She thought again, "No, it's not that, it's not that,
I love my child with an 'L' because he's little,
I love my child with an 'S' because he's strong.
With an 'M' because mine.
                                But I'm restless now.
We cut the heart on the tree but the bark's grown back there.
I've got my half of the dime but I want his.
The winter-sleep is over."

The shadows were longer now. The child waked and cried.
She rocked and hushed it, feeling the warm wind blow.
"I've got to find him," she said.

About that time, the men rode up to the house
From the other way. Their horses were rough and wild.
There were a dozen of them and they came fast.
Bent should have been out in the woods but he had come down

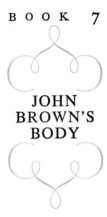

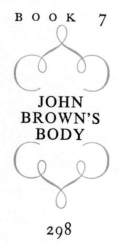
To mend a split wagon-wheel. He was caught in the barn.
They couldn't warn him in time, though John Vilas tried,
But they held John Vilas and started to search the place
While the young children scuttled around like mice
Squeaking "It's drafters, Mom—it's the drafters again!"
Even then, if Bent had hidden under the hay
They might not have found him, being much pressed for time,
But perhaps he was tired of hiding.
                                    At any rate
When Melora reached the edge of the little clearing,
She saw them there and Bent there, up on a horse,
Her mother rigid as wood and her father dumb
And the head man saying, gently enough on the whole,
"Don't you worry, ma'am—he'll make a good soldier yet
If he acts proper."
                    That was how they got Bent.
                    ————————

On the crest of the hill, the sweaty cannoneers,
The blackened Pennsylvanians, picked up their rammers
And fought the charge with handspikes and clubs and stones,
Biting and howling. It is said that they cried
Wildly, "Death on the soil of our native state
Rather than lose our guns." A general says so.
He was not there. I do not know what they cried
But that they fought, there was witness—and that the grey
Wave that came on them fought, there was witness too.
For an instant that wheel of combat—and for an instant
A brief, hard-breathing hush.
                              Then came the hard sound
Of a column tramping—blue reinforcements at last,
A doomsday sound to the grey.
                              The hard column came
Over the battered crest and went in with a yell.
The grey charge bent and gave ground, the grey charge was
    broken.
The sweaty gunners fell to their guns again
And began to scatter the shells in the ebbing wave.

Thus ended the second day of the locked bull-horns
And the wounding or slaying of the twenty thousand.

And thus night came to cover it.
                              So the field
Was alive all night with whispers and words and sighs,
So the slow blood dripped in the rocks of the Devil's Den.
Lincoln, back in his White House, asks for news.
The War Department has little. There are reports
Of heavy firing near Gettysburg—that is all.
Davis, in Richmond, knows as little as he.
In hollow Vicksburg, the shells come down and come down
And the end is but two days off.
                              On the field itself
Meade calls a council and considers retreat.
His left has held and the Round Tops still are his.
But his right has been shaken, his centre pierced for a time,
The enemy holds part of his works on Culp's Hill,
His losses have been most stark.
                              He thinks of these things
And decides at last to fight it out where he stands.

———————

Ellyat lay upon Cemetery Hill.
His wounds had begun to burn.
                              He was rising up
Through cold and vacant darknesses into faint light,
The yellow, watery light of a misty moon.
He stirred a little and groaned.
                              There was something cool
On his face and hands. It was dew. He lay on his back
And stared at a blowing cloud and a moist, dark sky.
"Old charioteer," he thought.
                              He remembered dully
The charge. The charge had come. They had beaten the charge.
Now it was moist dark sky and the dew and his pain.

He tried to get his canteen but he couldn't reach it.
That made him afraid.
                              "I want some water," he said.
He turned his head through stiff ages.
                              Two feet away
A man was lying quietly, fast asleep,

A bearded man in an enemy uniform.
He had a canteen. Ellyat wet his lips with his tongue.
"Hey Johnnie, got some water?" he whispered weakly.
Then he saw that the Johnnie had only half a head,
And frowned because such men could not lend canteens.

He was half-delirious now, and it seemed to him
As if he had two bodies, one that was pain
And one that lay beyond pain, on a couch of dew,
And stared at the other with sober wondering eyes.
"Everyone's dead around here but me," he thought,
"And as long as I don't sing out, they'll think that I'm dead
And those stretcher-bearers won't find me—there goes their lantern
No, it's the moon—Sing out and tell 'em you're here."
The hot body cried and groaned. The cool watched it idly.
The yellow moon burst open like a ripe fruit
And from it rolled on a dark, streaked shelf of sky
A car and horses, bearing the brazen ball
Of the unbearable sun, that halted above him
In full rush forward, yet frozen, a motion congealed,
Heavy with light.
                    Toy death above Gettysburg.
He saw it so and cried out in a weak, thin voice
While something jagged fitted into his heart
And the cool body watched idly.
                              And then it was
A lantern, bobbing along through the clumped dead men,
That halted now for an instant. He cried again.
A voice said, "Listen, Jerry, you're hearing things,
I've passed that feller twice and he's dead all right,
I'll bet you money."
                    Ellyat heard himself piping,
"I'm alive, God damn you! Can't you hear I'm alive?"

Something laughed, quite close now.
                                    "All right, Bub," said a cloud,
"We'll take your word for it. My, but the boy's got language!
Go ahead and cuss while we get you up on the stretcher—
It helps some—easy there, Joe."

Jack Ellyat fell

Out of his bodies into a whispering blackness
Through which, now and then, he could hear certain talking
   clouds
Cough or remark.

One said. "That's two and a half

You owe me, Joe. You're pickin' 'em wrong tonight."
"Well, poor suckers," said Joseph. "But all the same,
If this one doesn't last till the dressing station
The bet's off—take it slower, Jerry—it hurts him."

———————

Another clear dawn breaks over Gettysburg,
Promising heat and fair weather—and with the dawn
The guns are crashing again.

It is the third day.

The morning wears with a stubborn fight at Culp's Hill
That ends at last in Confederate repulse
And that barb-end of the fish-hook cleared of the grey.

Lee has tried his strokes on the right and left of the line.
The centre remains—that centre yesterday pierced
For a brief, wild moment in Wilcox's attack,
But since then trenched, reinforced and alive with guns.
It is a chance. All war is a chance like that.
Lee considers the chance and the force he has left to spend
And states his will.

Dutch Longstreet, the independent,

Demurs, as he has demurred since the fight began.
He had disapproved of this battle from the first
And that disapproval has added and is to add
Another weight in the balance against the grey.
It is not our task to try him for sense or folly,
Such men are the men they are—but an hour comes
Sometimes, to fix such men in most fateful parts,
As now with Longstreet who, if he had his orders
As they were given, neither obeyed them quite
Nor quite refused them, but acted as he thought best,
So did the half-thing, failed as he thought he would,
Felt justified and wrote all of his reasons down

Later in controversy.
                    We do not need
Such controversies to see that pugnacious man
Talking to Lee, a stubborn line in his brow
And that unseen fate between them.
                              Lee hears him out
Unmoved, unchanging.
                    "The enemy is there
And I am going to strike him," says Lee, inflexibly.

———————

Wingate cursed with an equal stress
The guns in the sky and his weariness,
The nightmare riding of yesterday
When they slept in the saddle by whole platoons
And the Pennsylvania farmer's grey
With hocks as puffy as toy balloons,
A graceless horse, without gaits or speed,
But all he had for his time of need.
"I'd as soon be riding a Jersey cow."
But the Black Horse Troop was piebald now
And the Black Horse Troop was worn to the blade
With the dull fatigue of this last, long raid.
Huger Shepley rode in a tense
Gloom of the spirit that found offence
In all things under the summer skies
And the recklessness in Bristol's eyes
Had lost its color of merriment.
Horses and men, they were well-nigh spent.
Wingate grinned as he heard the "Mount,"
"Reckon we look sort of no-account,
But we're here at last for somebody's fight."
They rode toward the curve of the Union right.

———————

At one o'clock the first signal-gun was fired
And the solid ground began to be sick anew.
For two hours then that sickness, the unhushed roar
Of two hundred and fifty cannon firing like one.

By Philadelphia, eighty-odd miles away,
An old man stooped and put his ear to the ground
And heard that roar, it is said, like the vague sea-clash
In a hollow conch-shell, there, in his flowerbeds.
He had planted trumpet-flowers for fifteen years
But now the flowers were blowing an iron noise
Through earth itself. He wiped his face on his sleeve
And tottered back to his house with fear in his eyes.

The caissons began to blow up in the Union batteries. . . .

————————

The cannonade fell still. All along the fish-hook line,
The tired men stared at the smoke and waited for it to clear;
The men in the centre waited, their rifles gripped in their hands,
By the trees of the riding fate, and the low stone wall, and the
    guns.

These were Hancock's men, the men of the Second Corps,
Eleven States were mixed there, where Minnesota stood
In battle-order with Maine, and Rhode Island beside New York.
The metals of all the North, cooled into an axe of war.

The strong sticks of the North, bound into a fasces-shape,
The hard winters of snow, the wind with the cutting edge,
And against them came that summer that does not die with the
    year,
Magnolia and honeysuckle and the blue Virginia flag.

Tall Pickett went up to Longstreet—his handsome face was
    drawn.
George Pickett, old friend of Lincoln's in days gone by with
    the blast,
When he was a courteous youth and Lincoln the strange shawled
    man
Who would talk in a Springfield street with a boy who dreamt
    of a sword.

Dreamt of a martial sword, as swords are martial in dreams,
And the courtesy to use it, in the old bright way of the tales.

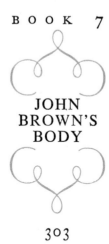

Those days are gone with the blast. He has his sword in his hand.
And he will use it today, and remember that using long.

He came to Longstreet for orders, but Longstreet would not
    speak.
He saw Old Peter's mouth and the thought in Old Peter's mind.
He knew the task that was set and the men that he had to lead
And a pride came into his face while Longstreet stood there
    dumb.

"I shall go forward, sir," he said and turned to his men.
The commands went down the line. The grey ranks started to
    move.
Slowly at first, then faster, in order, stepping like deer,
The Virginians, the fifteen thousand, the seventh wave of the
    tide.

There was a death-torn mile of broken ground to cross,
And a low stone wall at the end, and behind it the Second Corps,
And behind that force another, fresh men who had not yet
    fought.
They started to cross that ground. The guns began to tear them.

From the hill they say that it seemed more like a sea than a wave,
A sea continually torn by stones flung out of the sky,
And yet, as it came, still closing, closing and rolling on,
As the moving sea closes over the flaws and rips of the tide.

You could mark the path that they took by the dead that they
    left behind,
Spilled from that deadly march as a cart spills meal on a road,
And yet they came on unceasing, the fifteen thousand no more,
And the blue Virginia flag did not fall, did not fall, did not fall.

They halted but once to fire as they came. Then the smoke closed
    down
And you could not see them, and then, as it cleared again for a
    breath,
They were coming still but divided, gnawed at by blue attacks,
One flank half-severed and halted, but the centre still like a tide.

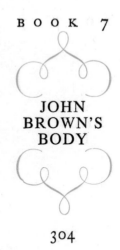

Cushing ran down the last of his guns to the battle-line.
The rest had been smashed to scrap by Lee's artillery fire.
He held his guts in his hand as the charge came up the wall
And his gun spoke out for him once before he fell to the ground.

Armistead leapt the wall and laid his hand on the gun,
The last of the three brigadiers who ordered Pickett's brigades,
He waved his hat on his sword and "Give 'em the steel!" he cried,
A few men followed him over. The rest were beaten or dead.

A few men followed him over. There had been fifteen thousand
When that sea began its march toward the fish-hook ridge and
    the wall.
So they came on in strength, light-footed, stepping like deer,
So they died or were taken. So the iron entered their flesh.

Lee, a mile away, in the shade of a little wood,
Stared, with his mouth shut down, and saw them go and be slain,
And then saw for a single moment, the blue Virginia flag
Planted beyond the wall, by that other flag that he knew.

The two flags planted together, one instant, like hostile flowers.
Then the smoke wrapped both in a mantle—and when it had
    blown away,
Armistead lay in his blood, and the rest were dead or down,
And the valley grey with the fallen and the wreck of the broken
    wave.

Pickett gazed around him, the boy who had dreamt of a sword
And talked with a man named Lincoln. The sword was still in
    his hand.
He had gone out with fifteen thousand. He came back to his lines
    with five.
He fought well till the war was over, but a thing was cracked in
    his heart.

––––––––––

    Wingate, waiting the sultry sound
    That would pour the troop over hostile ground,
    Petted his grey like a loving son

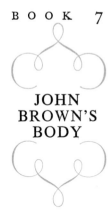

And wondered whether the brute would run
When it came to fighting, or merely shy
There was a look in the rolling eye
That he knew too well to criticize
Having seen it sometimes in other eyes.
"Poor old Fatty," he said, "Don't fret,
It's tough, but it hasn't happened yet
And we may get through it if you behave,
Though it looks just now like a right close shave.
There's something funny about this fight—"

He thought of Lucy in candlelight,
White and gold as the evening star,
Giving bright ribbons to men at war.
But the face grew dimmer and ever dimmer,
The gold was there but the gold was fainter,
And a slow brush streaked it with something grimmer
Than the proper tint of a lady's painter
Till the shadow she cast was a ruddy shadow.
He rubbed his eyes and stared at the meadow. . . .

"There was a girl I used to go with,
    Long ago, when the skies were cooler,
There was a tree we used to grow with
    Marking our heights with a stolen ruler.

There was a cave where we hid and fought once.
    There was a pool where the wind kept writing.
There was a possum-child we caught once.
    Caged it awhile, for all its biting.

There was a gap in a fence to see there,
    Down where the sparrows were always wrangling.
There was a girl who used to be there,
    Dark and thin, with her long braids dangling.

Dark and thin in her scuffed brown slippers
    With a boy's sling stuck in her apron-pocket,
With a sting in her tongue like a gallinipper's
    And the eyes of a ghost in a silver locket.

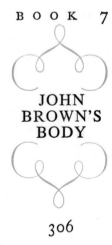

White and gold, white and gold,
You cannot be cold as she was cold,
Cold of the air and the running stream
And cold of the ice-tempered dream.

Gold and white, gold and white,
You burn with the heat of candlelight.
But what if I set you down alone
Beside the burning meteor-stone?

Blow North, blow South, blow hot, blow cold,
My body is pledged to white and gold,
My honor given to kith and kin,
And my doom-clothes ready to wrap me in
For the shut heart and the open hand
As long as Wingate Hall shall stand
And the fire burn and the water cool
And a fool beget another fool—

But now, in the hour before this fight,
I have forgotten gold and white.
I will remember lost delight.
She has the Appleton mouth, it seems,
And the Appleton way of riding,
But if she quarrels or when she gleams,
Something comes out from hiding.

She can sew all day on an Appleton hem
And look like a saint in plaster,
But when the fiddles begin to play,
And her feet beat fast but her heart beats faster,
An alien grace is alive in them
And she looks like her father, the dancing-master,
The scapegrace elegant, 'French Dupré.' "

Then the word came and the bugle sang
And he was part of the running clang,
The rush and the shock and the sabres licking
And the fallen horses screaming and kicking.
His grey was tired and his arm unsteady

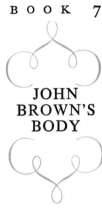

BOOK 7

JOHN
BROWN'S
BODY

307

And he whirled like a leaf in a shrieking eddy
Where every man was fighting his neighbor
And there was no room for the tricks of sabre
But only a wild and nightmare sickling.
His head felt burnt—there was something trickling
Into his eyes—then the new charge broke
The eddy apart like scattered smoke;
The cut on his head half made him blind.
If he had a mind, he had lost that mind.

He came to himself in a battered place,
Staring at Wainscott Bristol's face,
The dried blood made it a ferret's mask.

"What happened?" he croaked.

                                   "Well, you can ask,"
Said Bristol, drawling, "But don't ask me,
For any facts of the jamboree.
I reckon we've been to an Irish wake
Or maybe cuttin' a johnny-cake
With most of the Union cavalry-corps.
I don't know yet, but it was a war.
Are you crazy still? You were for a piece.
You yelled you were Destiny's long-lost niece
And wanted to charge the whole Yank line
Because they'd stolen your valentine.
You fought like a fool but you talked right wild.
You got a bad bump, too."

                              Wingate smiled
"I reckon I did, but I don't know when.
Did we win or what?"

                         "And I say again,"
Said Bristol, heavily, "don't ask me.
Inquire of General Robert Lee.
I know we're in for a long night ride
And they say we got whipped on the other side.
What's left of the Troop are down by the road.
We lost John Leicester and Harry Spode
And the Lawley boys and Ballantyne.
The Major's all right—but there's Jim Divine

And Francis Carroll and Judson White—
I wish I had some liquor tonight."

Wingate touched the cut on his head.
It burned, but it no longer bled.
"I wish I could sleep ten years," he said.

———————

The night of the third day falls. The battle is done.
Lee entrenches that night upon Seminary Ridge.
All next day the battered armies still face each other
Like enchanted beasts.
                    Lee thinks he may be attacked,
Hopes for it, perhaps, is not, and prepares his retreat.

Vicksburg has fallen, hollow Vicksburg has fallen,
The cavedwellers creep from their caves and blink at the sun.
The pan of the Southern balance goes down and down.
The cotton is withering.

Army of Northern Virginia, haggard and tattered,
Tramping back on the pikes, through the dust-white summer,
With your wounds still fresh, your burden of prisoners,
Your burden of sick and wounded,
"One long groan of human anguish six miles long."
You reach the swollen Potomac at long last,
A foe behind, a risen river in front,
And fording that swollen river, in the dim starlight,
In the yellow and early dawn,
Still have heart enough for the tall, long-striding soldiers
To mock the short, half swept away by the stream.
"Better change our name to Lee's Waders, boys!"
"Come on you shorty—get a ride on my back."
"Aw, it's just we ain't had a bath in seven years
And General Lee, he knows we need a good bath."

So you splash and slip through the water and come at last
Safe, to the Southern side, while Meade does not strike;
Safe to take other roads, safe to march upon roads you know
For two long years. And yet—each road that you take,
Each dusty road leads to Appomattox now.

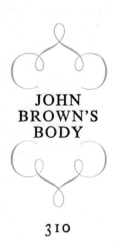

BOOK EIGHT

It is over now, but they will not let it be over.

It was over with John Brown when the sun rose up
To show him the town in arms and he did not flee,
Yet men were killed after that, before it was over,
And he did not die until November was cool
—Yellow leaves falling through a blue-grey dusk,
The first winds of November whirl and scatter them—
So now, the Confederacy,
Sick with its mortal sickness, yet lives on
For twenty-one falling months of pride and despair,
Half-hopes blown out in the lighting, heroic strokes
That come to nothing, and death piled hard upon death.

Follow that agony if you must and can
By the brushwood names, by the bloody prints in the woods,
Cold Harbor and Spottsylvania and Yellow Tavern
And all the lost court-houses and country stores
In the Wilderness, where the bitter fighting passed,
(No fighting bitterer)—follow the rabbit-runs
Through the tangled wilds where the hair of the wounded men
Caught fire from the burning trees, where they lay in the swamps
Like half-charred logs—find the place they called "Hell's Half
    Acre."
Follow the Indian names in the Indian West,
Chickamauga and Chattanooga and all the words
That are sewn on flags or cut in an armory wall.
My cyclorama is not the shape of the world
Nor even the shape of this war from first to last,
But like a totem carved, like a totem stained
With certain beasts and skies and faces of men
That would not let me be too quiet at night
Till they were figured.
                    Therefore now, through the storm,
The war, the rumor, the grinding of the machine,
Let certain sounds, let certain voices be heard.

A Richmond lady sits in a Richmond square
Beside a working-girl. They talk of the war,
They talk of the food and the prices in low-pitched voices
With hunger fretting them both. Then they go their ways.
But, before she departs, the lady has asked a question—
The working-girl pulls up the sleeve of her dress
And shows the lady the sorry bone of her arm.

Grant has come East to take up his last command
And the grand command of the armies.
                            It is five years
Since he sat, with a glass, by the stove in a country store,
A stumpy, mute man in a faded Army overcoat,
The eldest-born of the Grants but the family-failure,
Now, for a week, he shines in the full array
Of gold cord and black-feathered hat and superb blue coat,
As he talks with the trim, well-tailored Eastern men.

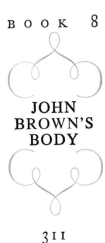

It is his only moment of such parade.
When the fighting starts, he is chewing a dead cigar
With only the battered stars to show the rank
On the shoulderstraps of the private's uniform.

It is sullen Cold Harbor. The Union attack has failed,
Repulsed with a ghastly slaughter. The twilight falls.
The word goes round the attack will be made again
Though all know now that it cannot be made and win.
An anxious officer walks through his lines that night.
There has been no mutiny yet, throughout all these years,
But he wonders now. What are the men doing now?
He sees them there. They are silently writing their names
On bits of rag and sewing the scraps of cloth
To their jackets while they can, before the attack.
When they die, next morning, somebody may read the names.

Pickett's son is born on a night of mid-July
While the two armies face each other, and Pickett's men
Light bonfires of celebration along his lines.
The fire is seen from the tents of the other camp.
The news goes back to Grant and his chief of staff.
"Haven't we any wood for the little Pickett?" says Grant,
And the Union bonfires are lighted for Pickett's son.
—All night those two lines of brush-fire, facing each other—
Next day they send the baby a silver service.
Next week or so they move upon Pickett's works.

On a muddy river, little toy boats go out.
The soldiers are swapping coffee for rank tobacco,
A Northern badge for a Southern souvenir,
A piece of white-flour bread for a hunk of corn-pone.
A Northern lieutenant swims the river at night
To go to a Southern dance at a backwoods store,
Joke with the girls, swim back, and fight the next day
With his hosts of the night before.
                                    On disputed ground,
A grey-clad private worms his way like a snake,
The Union sentries see him and start to fire.
"Aw, shut up, Yank," he calls in a weary voice,

"I just skun out to salvage the chaplain's hat,
It's the only one he's got and it just blew off."
The firing stops.
            "All right, Johnny," the sentries call,
"Get your hat, but be quick about it. We won't hurt you
But you better be back by the time our relief gets here."

A Southern sharpshooter crouched in a blue-gum tree
Drills a tiny blue-coated figure between the eyes
With a pea-ball fired from a smooth-bore squirrel-rifle.
The dead man's brother waits three days for his shot,
Then the sharpshooter crashes down through the breaking boughs
Like a lumpy bird, spread-eagled out of his nest.

The desolate siege of Petersburg begins.
The grain goes first, then the cats and the squeaking mice,
The thin cats stagger starving about the streets,
Die or are eaten. There are no more cats
In Petersburg—and in Charleston the creeping grass
Grows over the wharves where the ships of the world came in.
The grass and the moss grow over the stones of the wharves.
A Georgia belle eats sherbet near Andersonville
Where the Union prisoners rot. Another is weeping
The death of her brother, killed in a Union raid.
In the North, the factory chimneys smoke and fume;
The minstrels have raised their prices, but every night
Bones and Tambo play to a crowded house.
The hotels are full. The German Opera is here.
The ladies at Newport drive in their four-in-hands.
The old woman sells her papers about the war
The country widows stitch on a rusty black.

In the Shenandoah Valley, the millwheels rot.
(Sheridan has been there.) Where the houses stood,
Strong houses, built for weather, lasting it out,
The chimneys stand alone. The chimneys are blackened.
(Sheridan has been there.) This Valley has been
The granary of Lee's army for years and years.
Sheridan makes his report on his finished work.

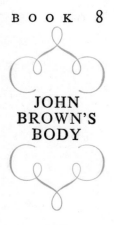
"If a crow intends to fly over the Valley now
He'll have to carry his own provisions," says Sheridan.

The lonely man with the chin like John Calhoun's
Knows it is over, will not know it is over.
Many hands are turning against him in these last years.
He makes mistakes. He is stubborn and sick at heart.
He is inflexible with fate and men.
It is over. It cannot be. He fights to the end,
Clinging to one last dream—of somehow, somewhere,
A last, miraculous battle where he can lead
One wing of the Southern army and Lee the other
And so wrench victory out of the failing odds.
Why is it a dream? He has studied grand strategy,
He was thought a competent soldier in Mexico,
He was Secretary of War once—
                                          He is the rigid
Scholar we know and have seen in another place,
Lacking that scholar's largeness, but with the same
Tight mouth, the same intentness on one concept,
The same ideal that must bend all life to its will
Or break to pieces—and that is the best of him.
The pettiness is the pettiness of a girl
More than a man's—a brilliant and shrewish girl,
Never too well in body yet living long.
He has that unforgiveness of women in him
And women will always know him better than men
Except for a few, in spite of Mexican wars,
In spite of this last, most desolate, warlike dream.
Give him the tasks that other scholar assumed,
He would not have borne them as greatly or with such skill
And yet—one can find a likeness.
                                          So now he dreams
Hopelessly of a fight he will never fight
And if worst comes to worst, perhaps, of a last
Plutarch-death on a shield.
                                          It is not to be.
He will snatch up a cloak of his wife's by accident
In the moment before his capture, and so be seen,
The proud man turned into farce, into sorry farce

Before the ignorant gapers.
                    He shades his eyes
To rest them a moment, turns to his work again.

The gaunt man, Abraham Lincoln, lives his days.
For a while the sky above him is very dark.
There are fifty thousand dead in these last, bleak months
And Richmond is still untaken.
                    The papers rail,
Grant is a butcher, the war will never be done.
The gaunt man's term of office draws to an end,
His best friends muse and are doubtful. He thinks himself
For a while that when the time of election comes
He will not be re-elected. He does not flinch.
He draws up a paper and seals it with his own hand.
His cabinet signs it, unread.
                    Such writing might be
A long historic excuse for defeated strength.
This is very short and strict with its commonsense.
"It seems we may not rule this nation again.
If so, we must do our best, while we still have time,
To plan with the new rulers who are to come
How best to save the Union before they come,
For they will have been elected upon such grounds
That they cannot possibly save it, once in our place."

The cloud lifts, after all. They bring him the news.
He is sure of being President four years more.
He thinks about it. He says, "Well, I guess they thought
They'd better not swap horses, crossing a stream."
The deserters begin to leave the Confederate armies. . . .

———

Luke Breckinridge woke up one sunshiny morning
Alone, in a roadside ditch, to be hungry again,
Though he was used to being hungry by now.
He looked at his rifle and thought, "Well, I ought to clean it."
He looked at his feet and he thought, "Well, I ought to get
Another bunch of rags if we-uns is goin'
To march much more—these rags is down to my hide."

He looked at his ribs through the tears in his dirty shirt
And he thought, "Well, I sure am thin as a razorback.
Well, that's the way it is. Well, I ought to do somethin'.
I ought to catch up with the boys. I wish I remembered
When I had to quit marchin' last night. Well, if I start now,
I reckon I'm bound to catch 'em."

But when he rose
He looked at the road and saw where the march had passed
—Feet going on through the dust and the sallow mud,
Feet going on forever—

He saw that track.
He was suddenly very tired.
He had been tired after fighting often enough
But this was another weariness.

He rubbed his head in his hands for a minute or so,
As if to rub some slow thought out of his mind
But it would not be rubbed away.

"I'm near it," he thought,
"The hotel ain't a mile from here if Sophy's still there.
Well, they wouldn't give me a furlough when I ast.
Well, it's been a long time."

On the way to the plank hotel
He still kept mumbling, "I can catch up to the boys."
But another thought too vague to be called a thought
Washed over the mumble, drowning it, forcing it down.

The grey front door was open. No one was there.
He stood for a moment silent, watching the sun
Fall through the open door and pool in the dust.
"Sophy!" he called. He waited. Then he went in.
The flies were buzzing over the dirty plates
In the dining room and nobody there at all.
It made him feel tired. He started to climb the stairs.
"Hey, Sophy!" he called and listened. There was a creak
From somewhere, a little noise like a dusty rat
Running across a dusty, sun-splattered board.
His hands felt stronger.

He was on the second floor
Slamming the doors of empty room after room

And calling "Sophy!" At last he found the locked door.
He broke it down with his shoulder in a loud noise.
She was lying in bed with the covers up to her chin
And her thin hands clutching the covers.

                               "Well, Soph," he said.
"Well, it's you," she said.

                   They stared at each other awhile.

"The rest of 'em's gone," she said. "They went off last night.
We haven't had no business. The nigger said
The Yanks were coming. They didn't have room in the cart.
They said I could stay for a while and take care of things
Or walk if I wanted. I guess Mr. Pollet's crazy.
He was talking things to himself all the time they went.
I never slept in a bed like this before.
I didn't know you could sleep so soft in a bed."

"Did they leave any shoes?" said Luke.

                         She shook her head.
"I reckon you could maybe tear up a quilt.
I reckon they wouldn't mind."

                  Luke grinned like a wolf.
"I reckon they hadn't better," he said. "Not much.
Got anything to eat? I'm hungry as hell."

They ate what food she could find and she washed his feet
And bound them up in fresh rags.

                   He looked at the rags.
"Do for a while," he said. "Well, come along, Soph.
We got a long way to go."

               Her eyes were big at him.
"The Yanks were comin'," she said. "You mean the war's over?"
He said, "I ain't had shoes for God knows how long."
He said, "If it was all Kelceys, you wouldn't mind.
Now I'm goin' to get me some shoes and raise me a crop,
And when we get back home, we'll butcher a hog.
There's allus hogs in the mountains."

                    "Well," she said.
"Well, you get your duds," he said.

               She didn't have much.

They went along two days without being stopped.
She walked pretty well for a thin sort of girl like that.
He told her she'd get fatter when they were home.

The third day, they were tramping along toward dusk,
On a lonely stretch of road, when she heard the horse-hoofs.
Luke had heard them before and shifted his rifle then.

The officer came in sight. He was young and drawn.
His eyes were old in their sockets. He reined his horse.
"You're goin' the wrong way, soldier. What's your regiment?"

Luke's eyes grew little. "—th Virginia," he drawled,
"But I'm on furlough."
                        "H'm," said the officer,
"Where are your furlough-papers?"
                                    Luke's hand slid down
By his trigger guard. "This here's my furlough," he said,
Resting the piece in the palm of the other hand.
The officer seemed to debate a thing in his mind
For a long instant. Then he rode on, in silence.
Luke watched him out of sight. When he was quite gone,
The hand slid back, the rifle was shouldered again.

The night had fallen on the narrow tent.
—Deep night of Virginia summer when the stars
Are burning wax in the near, languid sky
And the soft flowers hardly close all night
But bathe in darkness, as a woman bathes
In a warm, fragrant water and distill
Their perfume still, without the fire of the sun.
The army was asleep as armies sleep.
War lying on a casual sheaf of peace
For a brief moment, and yet with armor on,
And yet in the child's deep sleep, and yet so still.
Even the sentries seemed to walk their posts
With a ghost-footfall that could match that night.

The aide-de-camp knew certain lines of Greek
And other such unnecessary things

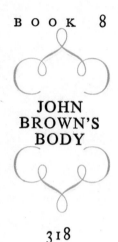

BOOK 8

JOHN
BROWN'S
BODY

318

As birds and music, that are good for peace
But are not deemed so serviceable for war.
He was a youth with an inquisitive mind
And doubtless had a failing for romance,
But then he was not twenty, and such faults
May sometimes be excused in younger men
Even when such creatures die, as they have done
At one time or another, for some cause
Which we are careful to point out to them
Much later, was no cause worth dying for,
But cannot reach them with our arguments
Because they are uneconomic dust.

So, when the aide-de-camp came toward the tent,
He knew that he was sleepy as a dog,
And yet the starlight and the gathered scents
Moved in his heart—like the unnecessary
Themes of a music fallen from a cloud
In light, upon a dark water.
                          And though he had
Some bitterness of mind to chew upon,
As well as messages that he must give
Before he slept, he halted in his tracks.

He saw, imprinted on the yellow light
That made the tent a hollow jack-o'-lantern,
The sharp, black shadow of a seated man,
The profile like the profile on a bust.
Lee in his tent, alone.
He had some shadow-papers in his hand,
But you could see he was not reading them,
And, if he thought, you could not read his thoughts,
Even as shadows, by any light that shines.
"You'd know that face among a million faces,"
Thought the still watcher, "and yet, his hair and beard
Have quite turned white, white as the dogwood-bloom
That blossomed on the way to Chancellorsville
When Jackson was alive and we were young
And we were winning and the end was near.
And now, I guess, the end is near enough

In spite of everything that we can do,
And he's alone tonight and Jackson's dead.

I saw him in the Wilderness that day
When he began to lead the charge himself
And the men wouldn't let him.
                                        Gordon spoke
And then the men themselves began to yell
"Lee to the rear—General Lee to the rear!"
I'll hear that all my life. I'll see those paws
Grabbing at Traveller and the bridle-rein
And forcing the calm image back from death.

Reckon that's what we think of you, Marse Robert,
Reckon that's what we think, what's left of us,
The poor old devils that are left of us.
I wonder what he thinks about it all.
He isn't staring, he's just sitting there.
I never knew a man could look so still
And yet look so alive in his repose.

It doesn't seem as if a cause could lose
When it's believed in by a man like that.
And yet we're losing.
                                And he knows it all.
No, he won't ever say it. But he knows.

I'd feel more comfortable if he'd move.

We had a chance at Spottsylvania,
We had some chances in the Wilderness.
We always hurt them more than we were hurt
And yet we're here—and they keep coming on.

What keeps us going on? I wish I knew.
Perhaps you see a man like that go on
And then you have to follow.
                                        There can't be
So many men that men have followed so.

And yet, what is it for? What is it for?
What does he think?

                    His hands are lying there
Quiet as stones or shadows in his lap.
His beard is whiter than the dogwood bloom,
But there is nothing ruined in his face,
And nothing beaten in those steady eyes.
If he's grown old, it isn't like a man,
It's more the way a river might grow old.

My mother knew him at old dances once.
She said he liked to joke and he was dark then,
Dark and as straight as he can stand today.
If he would only move, I could go forward.

You see the faces of spear-handling kings
In the old books they taught us from at school;
Big Agamemnon with his curly beard,
Achilles in the cruelty of his youth,
And Œdipus before he tore his eyes.

I'd like to see him in that chariot-rank,
With Traveller pulling at the leader-pole.
I don't think when the winged claws come down
They'll get a groan from him.
                              So we go on.
Under the claws. And he goes on ahead.

The sharp-cut profile moved a fraction now,
The aide-de-camp went forward on his errand.

———————

The years ride out from the world like couriers gone to a throne
That is too far for treaty, or, as it may be, too proud;
The years marked with a star, the years that are skin and bone.
The years ride into the night like envoys sent to a cloud.

Perhaps they dismount at last, by some iron ring in the skies,
Dismount and tie their stallions and walk with an armored tread
Where an outlaw queen of the air receives strange embassies
Under a tree of wisdom, between the quick and the dead.

Perhaps they are merely gone, as the white foam flies from the bit,
But the sparkling noise of their riding is ever in our ears.—

The men who came to the maze without foreknowledge of it,
The losers and the finders, under the riding years.

They pass, and the finders lose, the losers find for a space.
There are love and hate and delusion and all the tricks of the
　　maze.
There are always losers and finders. There is no abiding-place
And the years are unreturning. But, here and there, there were
　　days.

Days when the sun so shone that the statue gave its cry
And a bird shook wings or a woman walked with a certain mirth,
When the staff struck out a spring from the stones that had long
　　been dry,
And the plough moved on from the hilltop, but its share had
　　opened the earth.

So the bird is caught for an instant, and so the bird escapes.
The years are not halted by it. The losers and finders wait.
The years move on toward the sunset, the tall, far-trafficking
　　shapes,
Each with a bag of news to lay at a ghostly gate.

Riders shaking the heart with the hoofs that will not cease,
Will you never lie stretched in marble, the hands crossed over the
　　breast,
Some with hounds at your feet to show that you passed in peace,
And some with your feet on lions?
　　　　　　　　　　　　　　It is time that you were at rest.

―――――――――

John Vilas clucked to the scurvy rack of bones
Between the shafts. The rickety cart moved on
Like a tired insect, creaking through the dust.
There was another day behind them now
And any number of such days ahead
Unrolling like a long block-printed cloth
Pattered with field and stream and snake-rail fence,
And now and then, a flash of cavalry
Fording a backwoods creek; a big, slow star

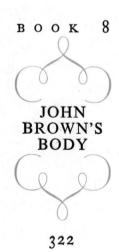

Mounting in silver over lonely woods
While the fire smelled of pine and a cougar cried;
A warm barn, full of the sweet milky breath
Of cows; a lank-haired preacher on a mule;
A red-cheeked woman who rushed after them
Armed with a hot and smoking apple-pie
And would not take a penny from the old man
Who held the mended reins as if they were
The vast, slow-sweeping scythe of Time himself
—Old Time and the last children of his age,
Drawn in a rattling cart, too poor to thieve,
By a gaunt horse, too ancient to die,
Over a rutted road, day after day,
Returning to the East from whence he came.

It was a portent in the little towns.
The time had bred odd voyagers enough;
Disbanded soldiers, tramping toward the West
In faded army blouses, singing strange songs,
Heroes and chickenthieves, true men and liars,
Some with old wounds that galled them in the rains
And some who sold the wounds they never had
Seven times over in each new saloon;
Queer, rootless families, plucked up by war
To blow along the roads like tumbleweed,
Who fed their wild-haired children God knows how
But always kept a fierce and cringing cur,
Famished for scraps, to run below the cart;
Horsedealers, draft-evaders, gipsymen;
Crooked creatures of a thousand dubious trades
That breed like gnats from the débris of war;
Half-cracked herb-doctor, patent-medicine man
With his accordion and his inked silk hat;
Sellers of snake-oil balm and lucky rings
And the old, crazy hatless wanderer
Who painted "God is Love" upon the barns
And on the rocks, "Prepare to Meet Thy God"
Lost tribes and maverick nations of the road—
The shiftless people, who are never still
But blow before the wind unquietly

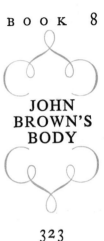

BOOK 8

JOHN
BROWN'S
BODY

323

And will so blow, until the last starved cur
Yaps at the last fat farmer, and lies down
With buckshot tearing at his ravening heart,
For the slow years to pick his carcass clean
And turn the little chapel of his bones
Into a dust so sifted by the wind
No winds that blow can sift it any more.

There were unquiet people on the road,
There were outlandish strays and travellers,
Drifting the little towns from day to day,
Stopping to mend a wheel or patch a shoe,
Beg, steal or sleep or write God's judgments out
And then pass on.
                            And yet, when these three came,
John Vilas and his daughter and her child,
Like snail-drawn Time, along the dusty track,
The story had gone on ahead of them.
And there was something in the rickety cart
Or the gaunt horse or in his driver's eyes
That made a fable of their journeying,
Until you heard John Vilas was that same
Lost Jew that wanders after every war
But cannot die in any, being curst.
He was the skipper, who first brought the slaves.
He was John Brown, arisen from his stone.
He was the drummer who had lost his way
At Valley Forge and frozen in the snow,
To rove forevermore, a dread old man
Beating a phantom drum across the wind.
He was a dozen such uncanny fetches,
And, while one must not talk with him too long,
There was no luck at all in crossing him,
Because, and in the end, the man was Time;
White-headed Time, stoop-shouldered on his scythe,
Driving a daughter and a daughter's son
Beyond the war, to some wrought-iron gate
Where they would drop their heavy load at last
—Load of all war and all misfortune's load—

On the green grass of a New England grave
Set on the sea-cliffs, looking toward the sea.

While, for the other tale, the woman's tale,
The heart-faced girl with the enormous eyes,
Roving from little town to little town
Still looking for her soldier—it became
Mixed with each story of such fortune told
Behind drawn blinds, by women, in the dusk,
Until she too grew fabulous as a song
Sung to a beechwood fiddle, and all the old
Barely-recorded chants that are the land
And no one poet's or musician's
—"Old Dan Tucker," "The Belle of Albany,"
The girl who died for love in the high woods
And cruel Barbara Allen in her pride.

So she became a concertina tune
Played in plank taverns by a blind, old man,
A jew's-harp strain, a comb-and-banjo song,
The music of a soapbox violin
Shrilled out against the tree-toads and the crickets
Through the hot nights of June. So, though she passed
Unknowing, yet she left the legend-touch
Bright as a splash of sumach still behind
Wherever the gaunt horse pulled on his load.
Till, later, those who knew no more of her
Living, than they might know of such removed
And singable creations as "Lord Randall,"
"Colombo," "Little Musgrave," or "Jay Gould's Daughter"
Yet knew enough of her to sing about
And fit her name, Melora, to the same
Slow-dropping minor of the water and earth—
The minor of the country barber-shops
That keens above the grave of Jesse James
And the lone prairie where the cowboy died,
The desolate minor of the jail-bird's song,
Luscious with sorrow, and the minor notes
That tell about the tragic end of such

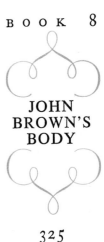

As loved too well to have such cruel fathers
But were so loving, even in the dust,
A red-rose brier grew out of their dead hearts
And twined together in a lover's knot
For all the county people to admire,
And every lost, waif ballad we have made
And, making, scorned because it smelt of the earth,
And now would seek, but cannot make again—
So she became a legend and a name.

John Vilas, moving always toward the East,
Upon his last adventure, felt the sun
Strike at his bones and warm them like the last
Heat of the wood so long within the fire
That long ago the brightness ate its heart
And yet it lies and burns upon the iron
Unready still to crumble and be cool
The white, transmuted log of purest ash
Still glowing with a late and borrowed flame.

"This is the sun of age," he thought, "and so
We enter our last journeys with that sun
Which we have watched sink down ten thousand times
Knowing he would arise like Dedalus
On the first wings of morning, and exult
Like our own youth, fresh-risen from its bed
And inexhaustible of space and light.
But now the vessel which could not be filled
By violence or desire or the great storm,
Runs over with its weight of little days
And when this sun sinks now, we'll sink with him
And not get up again.
                              I find it fit
That I, who spent the years of my desire
In the lost forest, seeking the lost stone,
With little care for Harriet or the rest,
With little trust in safety or the world,
Should now retrace at last, and in my age,
The exact highway of my youth's escape
From everything that galled it and take on,

Like an old snake resuming his cast skins,
The East I fled, the little towns I mocked,
The dust I thought was shaken from my shoes,
The sleepiness from which I ran away.
Harriet's right and Harriet is just
And Harriet's back in that chintz-curtained room
From which I took her, twenty years ago,
With all the children who were always hers
Because I gave them nothing but my seed
And hardly heard their laughter or their tears
And hardly knew their faces or their names,
Because I listened for the wind in the bough,
Because my daughters were the shooting-stars,
Because my sons were the forgotten streams
And the wild silvers of the wilderness.

Men who go looking for the wilderness-stone
And find it, should not marry or beget,
For, if they do so, they may work a wrong
Deeper than any mere intent of pain.
And yet, what I have sought that I have sought
And cannot disavouch, although it is
The double knife that cuts the giver's hand
And the unwilling taker's.
                    So I took
My wife, long since, from that chintz-curtained room
And so she has gone back to it again
After these years, with children of those years,
And, being kind, she will not teach them there
To curse me, as I think, though if she did
She could find reason in her neighbor's eyes,
And, being Harriet, she will bring them up
As all such children should and must be reared
In all such houses, till the end of time,
As if she had not been away at all.
And so, at last, she'll get the peace she should.
And yet, some time, a child may run away.

We have had sons and daughters, she and I,
And, of them all, one daughter and one son

In whom our strange bloods married with the true
Marriage that is not merely sheath and sword.
The rest are hers. Those two were partly mine.

I taught my son to wander in the woods
Till he could step the hidden paths with me
Light as a whisper, indolent as Spring.
I would not tame his sister when I might,
I let her follow patterans of leaves,
Looking for stones rejected by the wise.
I kept them by me jealously and long.

And yet, the day they took him, when he sat
There on his horse, before they all rode off,
It was his mother who looked out of him
And it was to his mother that he looked.

That is my punishment and my offence
And that is how it was. And he is dead.
Dead of a fever, buried in the South,
Dead in this war I thought a whirligig
For iron fools to play with and to kill
Other men's sons, not mine. He's buried deep.
I kept him by me jealously and long.
Well, he walked well, alive. He was my son.
I'll not make tags of him.
                              We got the news.
She could not stay beside me after that.
I see so clearly why she could not stay.

So I retrace the hard steps of my youth
Now with this daughter, in a rattling cart
Drawn by a horse as lean as famine's self,
And am an omen in the little towns—
Because this daughter has too much of me
To be content with bread made out of wheat.
To be in love and give it up for rest,
To live serene without a knife at heart.

Such is the manner and the bound escape
Of those a disproportion drives unfed

From the world's table, without meat or grace,
Though both are wholesome, but who seek instead
Their solitary victual like the fox.
And who at last return as I return
In the ironic wagon of the years,
Back to the pasture that they found too green,
Broken of every knowledge but the last
Knowledge of how escape is not a door
But a slow-winding road whose hundred coils
Return upon each other, soon or late
—And how and when and under what cold stars
The old wound bleeds beneath the armored mind.

And yet, this journey is not desolate
Nor am I desolate in it, as we crawl
Slowly from little town to little town
Always against the sun, and the horse nods,
And there's my daughter talking, and her child
Sleeping or waking, and we stop awhile
And then go on awhile, and I can feel
The slow sun creeping through me summerlong.
Until, at times, I fall into a doze
Awake, a daydream without apparitions
And, falling so, inhabit for a space
A second childhood, calmer than the first,
But wise in the same fashion, and so touch
For a long, drowsy hour of afternoon,
The ripened thing, the autumn at the heart,
The one full star of evening that is age.

Yes, I must be a second child sometimes,
For as we pass and as they watch us pass,
It seems to me their eyes make stories of us
And I can hear those stories murmuring
Like pigeons in a loft when I'm asleep,
Till sometimes I must wonder for a while
If I've not changed myself for someone else
Or grown a story without knowing it,
And, with no intermediary death,
Stepped out of flesh and taken on a ghost.

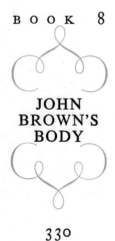
For at such times, it almost seems to me
As if I were no longer what I am
But the deluded shade of Peter Rugg
Still looking for his Boston through the storm,
Or the strange spook of Johnny Appleseed,
Crept out of heaven on a windless night
To see if his wild orchards prosper still
And leave a heap of Baldwins and sweet russets
—Moonglittered, scrubbed with rags of silver cloud
And Indian magic—by the lucky doors
Of such good people as take care of them—
While for my daughter, though I know she's real,
She and her story, yet, in the waking dream
She mixes with that song I used to know
About the Spanish lady of old days
Who loved the Englishman and sought for him
All through green England in her scarlet shoes,
Knowing no word of English but his name.

I hear her voice, where the guitar is mixed
With the sweet, jangling mule-bells of Castile,
I see her face under its high shell-comb
—And then it is my daughter's—and I wake—
And yet know, even in waking, that we are
Somewhere between a story and a dream.
And so, you see, I find a kind of peace
In this last foray, will not rail at the sun,
Eat, drink and sleep, in spite of what is past,
Talk with my daughter, watch the turning skies.
The Spanish lady found her Englishman.
Well, we may find this boy I've half-forgot,
Although our story is another story.

So life works in us for a little while
And then the ferment's quiet.
                              So we do
Wrongs much beyond intent, and suffer them.
So we go looking for the wilderness-stone.

I shall smell lilac in Connecticut
No doubt, before I die, and see the clean

White, reticent, small churches of my youth,
The gardens full of phlox and mignonette,
The pasture-bars I broke to run away.

It was my thought to lie in an uncropped
And savage field no plough had ever scored,
Between a bee-tree and a cast deer-horn.
It was my thought to lie beside a stream
Too secret for the very deer to find,
Too solitary for remembrance.
It was a dream. It does not matter now.

Bury me where the soldiers of retreat
Are buried, underneath the faded star,
Bury me where the courtiers of escape
Fall down, confronted with their earth again.
Bury me where the fences hold the land
And the sun sinks beyond the pasture-bars
Never to fall upon the wilderness-stone.

And yet I have escaped, in spite of all."

———————

Lucy Weatherby smoothed out clothes in a trunk
With a stab at her heart.
                    The trunk was packed to the lid.
There wasn't an empty corner anywhere,
Pack as she would—but the blue dress wouldn't go in.

Of course she'd be getting a lot of new dresses soon
And the blue was old—but she couldn't leave it behind.
If only Henry wasn't so selfish, at times!
But Henry was like all brothers and like all men,
Expecting a lady to travel to Canada
With just one trunk and the boxes!
                    It was too bad.
He had a trunk of his own for razors and shirts,
And yet she couldn't take two—and there were the hoops;
He kept on fussing because she wouldn't leave them
When she knew he was hoping to take all those silly books,
As if you couldn't buy books wherever you went!

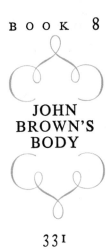

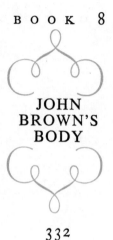
She pinched her cheek and stared at the trunk again.
The green could come out, of course, and the blue go in,
But she couldn't bear the idea of leaving the green.

The war, of course, and one thinks so much of the war,
And those terrible Yankees actually at our gates,
In spite of our fine, brave boys and poor Mr. Davis,
In spite of wearing old dresses for two whole years
And sending the servants out to work at the forts,
In spite of the cheers and the songs and the cause and the right.
Only, one must not be selfish. One must be brave.
One must think about Henry's health and be sensible,
And Henry actually thinks we can get away. . . .

The blue or the green? She couldn't decide it yet,
And there were all those letters to write tonight.
She'd simply have to write to Clay and Huger
About Henry's health—and how it just breaks my heart,
But one cannot leave one's sick brother—and afterwards,
One can always send one's address—and I'm sure if they do
We'll give them a real, old-fashioned Richmond welcome,
Though they say that the British leftenants are simply sweet
And every Southern girl is an absolute belle.
They play the "Bonnie Blue Flag" at the dances there,
And Sara Kenefick is engaged to an earl.
She saw herself, for an instant, walking the safe
Street of a calm and British-looking town.
She had on a new dress. Her shoes and her hat were new.
A white-haired, dim-faced man in a British coat
Walked beside her and looked and was listening,
While she told him all about it, and hearing the guns,
And how they'd actually lived without butcher's meat
For weeks and weeks—and the wounded—and General Lee—
And only Henry's health had forced them at last
To leave the dear South. She choked. He patted her hand.
He hoped they would stay in Canada for a while.

The blue or the green? It was dreadfully hard to choose,
And with all the letters to write—and Jim Merrihew
And that nice Alabama Major—

She heard the bells
Ring for a wedding, but this was a different groom,
This was a white-haired man with stars on his coat,
This was an Order wrapped in an English voice.

Honey, sugar-lump honey I love so dearly,
You have eluded the long pursuit that sought you,
You have eluded the hands that would so enclose you
And with strange passion force you.
                              What was this passion?
We do not know, you and I, but we would not bear it
And are gone free.
                So at last, if fair girls must marry,
As young girls should, it is after another fashion
And not with youth but wisely.
                          So we are ransomed,
And I am yours forever and you are mine,
Honey, sugar-lump honey.
                      So we attain,
The white-haired bridegrooms with the stars on their coats
And yet have the beaus to dance with, for we like dancing,
So all the world finds our wifely devotion charming,
So we play all day in the heat of the sun.

She held the blue dress under her chin once more
And smoothed it with one white hand. Then she put it down
Smiling a little. No, it couldn't go in,
But she would see if she couldn't help Henry pack,
And if she did, the blue could go with his shirts.
It hardly mattered, leaving some shirts behind.

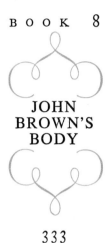
———————

Sherman's buzzin' along to de sea,
Jubili, Jubilo!
Sherman's buzzin' along to de sea,
Like Moses ridin' on a bumblebee,
Settin' de prisoned and de humble free!
Hit's de year of Jubilo!

Massa was de whale wid de big inside,
Jubili, Jubilo!

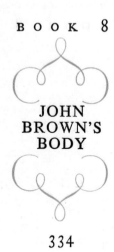
Massa was de lion and de lion's hide.
But de Lord God smacked him in his hardheart pride,
And de whale unswallered, and de lion died!
Hit's de year of Jubilo!

Oh, hit don't matter if you's black or tan,
Jubili, Jubilo!
Hit don't matter if you's black or tan,
When you hear de noise of de freedom-ban'
You's snatched baldheaded to de Promise Lan',
Hit's de year of Jubilo!

Oh, hit don't matter if you pine or ail,
Jubili, Jubilo!
Hit don't matter if you pine or ail,
Hit don't matter if you's been in jail,
De Lord's got mercy for your mumblin' tale!
Hit's de year of Jubilo!

Every nigger's gwine to own a mule,
Jubili, Jubilo!
Every nigger's gwine to own a mule,
An' live like Adam in de Golden Rule,
An' send his chillun to de white-folks' school!
In de year of Jubilo!

Fall down on your knees and bless de Lord,
Jubili, Jubilo!
Fall down on your knees and bless de Lord,
Dat chased old Pharaoh wid a lightnin'-sword,
And rose up Izzul fum de withered gourd,
Hit's de year of Jubilo!

Shout thanksgivin' and shout it loud!
Jubili, Jubilo!
Shout thanksgivin' and shout it loud,
We was dead and buried in de Lazrus-shroud,
But de Lord came down in a glory-cloud,
An' He gave us Jubilo!

———————

So Sherman goes from Atlanta to the sea
Through the red-earth heart of the land, through the pine-smoke
  haze
Of the warm, last months of the year.
                              In the evenings
The skies are green as the thin, clear ice on the pools
That melts to water again in the heat of noon.
A few black trees are solemn against those skies.
The soldiers feel the winter touching the air
With a little ice.
                        But when the sun has come up,
When they halt at noonday, mopping their sweaty brows,
The skies are blue and soft and without a cloud.
Strange march, half-war, half trooping picnic-parade,
Cutting a ruinous swathe through the red-earth land;
March of the hardy bummers and coffee-coolers
Who, having been told to forage, loot as they can
And leave a wound that rankles for sixty years.
March of the honest, who did not loot when they could
And so are not remembered in Southern legend.
Rough-bearded Sherman riding the red-earth roads,
Writing home that his rascals are fat and happy,
Saying or else not saying that war is hell,
Saying he almost trembles himself to think
Of what will happen when Charleston falls in the hands
Of those same rascals—and yet, when we read that march
Hardly the smoking dragon he has been called,
But the mere rough-handed man who rode with a hard
Bit through the land, unanxious to spare his foe
Nor grimly anxious to torture for torture's sake,
Smashing this and that,—and yet, in the end,
Giving such terms to the foe struck down at last
That the men in Washington disavow them and him
For over-kindness.
                        So now, through the pine-smoke Fall,
The long worm of his army creeps toward Savannah
Leaving its swathe behind.
                              In the ruined gardens
The buried silver lies well hid in the ground.
A looter pocks bullet-marks in an old oil-portrait.

A woman wails and rages against the thieves
Who carry her dead child's clothes on their drunken bayonets.
A looter swings from a pine tree for thefts too crude.
A fresh-faced boy gets scars he will carry long
Hauling a crippled girl from a burning house,
But gets no thanks but hate from the thing he saved,
And everywhere,
A black earth stirs, a wind blows over black earth,
A wind blows into black faces, into old hands
Knotted with long rheumatics, cramped on the hoe,
Into old backs bent double over the cotton,
The wind of freedom, the wind of the jubilo.

They stray from the lost plantations like children strayed,
Grinning and singing, following the blue soldiers,
They steal from the lonesome cabins like runaways
Laden with sticks and bundles and conjur-charms;
A huge black mother carries her sucking child
Wrapped in a quilt, a slim brown girl and her lover
Wander November woods like Adam and Eve,
Living on roots and rabbits and liberty,
An old grey field hand dimly plods through the mud,
Looking for some vague place he has heard about
Where Linkum sits at a desk in his gold silk hat
With a bag of silver dollars in either hand
For every old grey field hand that comes to him,
All God's chillun got shoes there and fine new clothes,
All God's chillun got peace there and roastin'-ears,
Hills of barbecue, rivers of pot-licker,
Nobody's got to work there, never no more.

His feet are sore with the road but he stumbles on,
A hundred, a thousand others stumble as he,
Chanting, dizzied, drunken with a strange fever,
A child's delight, a brightness too huge to grasp,
The hidden nation, untaught, unrecognized,
Free at last, but not yet free with the free,
Ignorant, joyful, wronged, child-minded and searching,
Searching the army's road for this new wild thing
That means so much but can't be held in the hand,

That must be there, that yet is so hard to find,
This dream, this pentecost changing, this liberty.

Some wander away to strange death or stranger life,
Some wander awhile and starve and come back at last,
Some stay by the old plantation but will not work
To the great disgust of masters and mistresses,
Sing idly, gamble, sleep through the lazy hours,
Waiting for friendly heaven to rain them down
The mule and the forty acres of their desire.
Some, faithful beyond the bond that they never signed,
Hold to that bond in ruin as in the sun,
Steal food for a hungry mistress, keep her alive,
Keep the house alive, try to pick the weeds from the path,
Gather the wood and chop it and make the fire,
With pitying scorn for the runaway sheep of freedom,
Freedom's a ghost and freedom's a foolish talk,
What counts is making the fire as it should be made. . . .
Oh, blackskinned epic, epic with the black spear,
I cannot sing you, having too white a heart,
And yet, some day, a poet will rise to sing you
And sing you with such truth and mellowness,
—Deep mellow of the husky, golden voice
Crying dark heaven through the spirituals,
Soft mellow of the levee roustabouts,
Singing at night against the banjo-moon—
That you will be a match for any song
Sung by old, populous nations in the past,
And stand like hills against the American sky,
And lay your black spear down by Roland's horn.

Meanwhile, in Georgia, the scythe of the march mows on,
The Southern papers discount it as best they can.
Lincoln is anxious, Davis more anxious still.
The war is in its last winter of strife and pain.

—————

Cudjo buried the silverware
On a graveyard night of sultry air
While the turned sods smelled of the winter damp
And Mary Lou Wingate held the lamp.

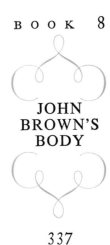

They worked with a will. They did not speak.
The light was yellow. The light was weak.
A tomb-like casting a last, brief flame
Over the grave of Wingate fame.
The silver bowl of the Wingate toasts,
The spoons worn hollow by Wingate ghosts,
Sconce and ladle and bead-rimmed plate
With the English mark and the English weight,
The round old porringer, dented so
By the first milk-teeth of the long ago,
And the candlesticks of Elspeth Mackay
That she brought with her youth on her wedding-day
To light the living of Wingate Hall
While the mornings break and the twilights fall
And the night and the river have memories. . . .

There was a spook in Cudjo's eyes
As he lowered the chests where they must lie
And patted the earth back cunningly.
He knew each chest and its diverse freight
As a blind man knows his own front gate
And, decade by decade and piece by piece,
With paste and shammy and elbow-grease,
He had made them his, by the pursed-up lips
And the tireless, polishing fingertips,
Till now as he buried them, each and all,
What he buried was Wingate Hall,
Himself and the moon and the toddy-sippers,
The river mist and the dancing-slippers,
Old Marse Billy and Mary Lou
And every bit of the world he knew,
Master and lady and house and slave,
All smoothed down in a single grave.
He was finished at length. He shook his head.
"Mistis, reckon we's done," he said.
They looked at each other, black and white,
For a slow-paced moment across the light.

Then he took the lamp and she smoothed her shawl
And he lit her back to the plundered Hall,

ULYSSES S. GRANT

It is five years
Since he sat, with a glass, by the stove in a country store,
A stumpy, mute man in a faded army overcoat

To pray, with her old serene observance
For the mercy of God upon faithful servants
And a justice striking all Yankees dead
On her cold, worn knees by the great carved bed,
Where she had lain by a gentleman's side,
Wife and mother and new-come bride,
Sick with the carrying, torn with the borning,
Waked by the laughter on Christmas morning,
Through love and temper and joy and grief,
And the years gone by like the blowing leaf.

She finished her prayer with Louisa's child,
And, when she had risen, she almost smiled.
She struck her hand on the bedstead head,
"They won't drive me from my house," she said,
As the wood rang under her wedding-ring.
Then she stood for a moment, listening,
As if for a step, or a gentleman's name,
But only the gnats and the echoes came.
Cudjo, being less fortified,
Covered his ears with his hands and tried
To shut the noise of the risen wind
Out of the trouble of his mind.
He thought, "Ain't right for dat wind to blow.
She wasn't blowing awhile ago.
Jus' riz up fum de earth somewhere
When we buried dat orphan silver dere.
Got to hide it, and so we tried,
But silver like dat don't like to hide,
Silver's ust to be passed aroun'
Don't like lyin' in lonesome groun',
Wants to come back to de Hall, all right.
Silver, I always shone you bright,
You could see yo'self in de shine—
Silver, it wasn't no fix of mine!
Don't you come projeckin' after me!"

His eyes were shut but he still could see
The slow chests rising out of the ground
With an ominous clatter of silver sound,

The locks undoing, the bags unfastening,
And every knife and platter and spoon
Clinking out of the grave and hastening
Back to the Hall, in the witches' moon;
And the wind in the chimney played such tricks
That it was no wind, be it soft or loud,
But Elspeth seeking her candlesticks
All night long in her ruffled shroud,
The deep voice haunting the ocean-shell
To give her judgment and weave her spell,
"Thrift and love for the house and the chief
And a scone on the hob for the son of grief,
But a knife in the ribs for the pleasant thief."

Cudjo heard it, and Cudjo shook,
And Cudjo felt for the Holy Book,
And the wind blew on without peace or rest,
Blowing the straws from the dried-up nest.

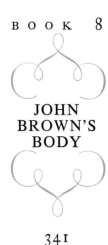

Bailey, tramping along with Sherman's bummers,
Grumbled and found life pleasant and hummed his tune.
He was well, the blood ran in him, he ate for ten,
He and the gang had salvaged a wall-eyed nig
To fix their victuals—and if the captain was on,
The captain had a blind eye.

                      Last night it was turkey,
The night before it was duck—well, you couldn't expect
Such things to keep on forever, but while they did
It was pretty soft—it was war like it ought to be.
The Old Man marched 'em hard, but that was all right,
The Old Man knew his job and the nig was a buster
And the gang was as good a gang as you'd hope to find,
None of your coffee-coolers and straggle-tails
But a regular gang that ran like an eight-day clock.
Oh it was gravy, it was the real duck soup,
Marchin' into Atlanta after the fight
And then this marchin'—well, they were due for it,
And he was a sergeant now.

And up in his pack
Were souvenirs for the red-haired widow in Cairo,
Some of 'em bought and some just sort of picked up
But not a damn one stolen, to call it stealin'.
He wasn't a coffee-cooler or a slick Susio.
Poor little kid—she'd had a pretty tough time—
Cry like a fool when she gets a squint at that brooch—
They said you couldn't tell about widows much,
But what the hell—he wasn't a barnyard virgin—
He liked a woman who'd been over the bumps
And kept her get-up-and-git and her sassiness.
Spitfire-sweetie, you're my valentine now,
Bet the kids have red hair—well you can't help that—
But they'll all look like Poppa or he'll know why.

He mused a moment, thinking of Ellyat now.
There was another kid and a crazy kid,
Sort of missed him, hope he's gettin' it soft,
Must have got a banger at Gettysburg,
Wrote me a letter a couple of months ago,
Maybe six, I dunno, I sort of forget.
Ought to give him his old spread-eagle now,
Darn good kid, but done enough for his pay.
Hope he finds that girl he was talkin' about,
Sounds like a pretty good piece for a storm-and-strife,
Skinny, though—we like 'em more of a weight,
Don't we, Carrots?
Well, it's all in a life.
Ought to write him sometime if we get a chance,
Wish we was West—we'd have him out to the weddin',
Me and Bessie, show him the Cairo girls,
Hand him the fireman's grip and give him a time.

His heart was overflowing with charity,
But his throat was dry as the bottom of his canteen.
There was a big, white house, some way from the road. . . .

He found his captain, saluted and put his question.
The captain's eyes were satiric but not displeased.
"All right, Sergeant, take your detail and forage,

We're running low on bacon, it seems to me,
And if you happen to find a pigeon or two
Remember the Colonel's penchant for pigeon-pie.
But don't waste time and don't put your hopes too high,
The Nth Corps must have gone by there hours ago
And they're the biggest thieves in this whole, wide army.
You'll be back, in ranks, all sober, in just two hours
Or you won't have stripes. And if I find one more man
Trying to take a pet with him on this march,
I don't care if it's only a treetoad, I'll skin him alive."

So Bailey came to the door of Wingate Hall,
With the high wind blowing against him and gave his orders
"Make it quick now, boys—don't cut any monkeyshines,
But be sure and get the pigeons if they're around.
Clark, you and Ellis stay with me by the door,
I'm going to talk to the house if there's anyone left."

He knocked and called. There was a long, heavy silence.
"Hey you, the house!" The silence made him feel queer.
He cursed impatiently and pushed at the door.
It swung wide open. He turned to Ellis and Clark.
"I'm goin' in," he said. "If you hear me yell
Come in bilin'."
                    They watched him with mocking eyes.
"Wish to hell they'd make me a sergeant, Clark,"
"A three-stripe souvenir sergeant."
                                        "Aw, hell," said Clark,
"Bailey's all right. He'll let us in on the juice
If there's any lawful juice that a man could get."
"Sure, he's all right. Who says that he ain't all right!"
"But all the same, he's a sergeant."
                                        Bailey, meanwhile
Was roving like a lost soul through great, empty rooms
And staring at various objects that caught his eye.
Funny old boy with a wig, hung up on the wall,
Queer sort of chairs, made your hands feel dirty to touch 'em
Though they were faded.
                        Everything faded and old
And quiet—and the wind blowin'—he moved as on tiptoe

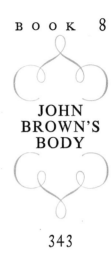

Though he couldn't say why he did.

                                      Old workbasket there.

He opened it idly—most of the things were gone
But there was a pair of little, gold-mounted scissors
Made like a bird, with the blades the beak of the bird.
He picked it up and opened and shut the blades.
Hadn't rusted—sort of handsome and queer—
Bessie would certainly like it—

                                He held it a minute.

Wouldn't take up any room. Then he frowned at the thing.
"Aw hell," he said, "I got enough souvenirs.
I ain't no damn coffee-cooler."

He started to put the scissors back in the case
And turned to face a slight grey-headed old woman
Dressed in black, with eyes that burned through his skin
And a voice that cut at his mind like a rawhide whip,
Calling him fifty different kinds of a thief
And Yankee devil and liar and God knows what,
Tearing the throat of her dress with her thin old hands
And telling him he could shoot her down like a dog
But he'd steal her children's things over her dead body.
My God, as if you went around shootin' old women
For fun, my God!

                            He couldn't even explain.
She was like all of 'em, made him sick in his lunch.
"Oh hell," he yelled. "Shut up about your damn scissors,
This is a war, old lady!"

                          "That's right," she said,
"Curse a helpless female, you big, brave soldier."
Well, what was a man to do?

                             He got out of the house,
Sore and angry, mean as a man could feel,
But her voice still followed, reviling, making him burn.
Now, where in hell was that detail?

                             He saw them now,
All except Clark and Ellis, gathered around
A white-polled nigger wringing his hands and weeping.
One man had a neck-wrung pigeon stuffed in his blouse.

Well, that was something.

               He laid his hand on the nigger.
"Hey, Uncle, where's the well? You folks got a well?"
But the nigger just kept on crying like an old fool.
"He thinks we're goin' to scalp him," said one of the men,
"I told him twict that he's free but the shine won't listen.
I give him some money, too, but he let it drop.
The rest of 'em run away when the army came."

"Well, tell him he's safe and make him rustle some water,
I'm dry as a preacher's tongue. Where's Ellis and Clark?"

He found Clark solemnly prodding the hard dirt floor
Of a negro cabin, while Ellis lighted the task
With a splinter of burning pine.

                  His rage exploded
In boiling lava. They listened respectfully.
"And next time, I give you an order," he ended up,
"Why you—— —— ——"

               Clark wiped his face with his sleeve.
"Sorry, Sergeant," he said in an awed, low voice.
"Well you better be! What the hell do you think you're at,
Playin' tit-tat-toe or buryin' somebody's dog?"
"Well, Sergeant," said Ellis, humbly, "I allus heard
They buried stuff, sometimes, under these here cabins.
Well, I thought we could take a look—well—"

                 "Huh?" said Bailey.
He seized the torch and looked at the trodden floor
For an instant. Then his pride and his rage returned.
"Hell's fire!" he said, and threw the splinter aside,
"That's just about what you would think, you and Clark!
Come out of there on the double! Yes, I said you!"
They were halfway down the driveway when Ellis spoke.
"Sergeant," he said. "There's somethin' on fire back there."
Bailey stopped—looked back—a smoke-puff climbed in the
Sky and the wind was high.

             He hesitated a moment.
The cabin must have caught from the burning splinter.
Then he set his jaw. Well, suppose the cabin had caught?
—Damned old woman in black who called him a thief.

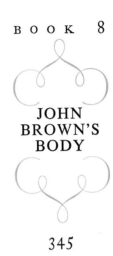

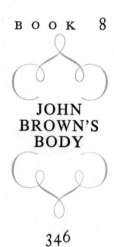
Serve her right if all her cabins burnt up.
The house wouldn't catch—and here they were, losing
   time—

"Oh well," he said. "That nigger'll put it out.
It ain't our detail—mosey along with it there—
The Cap won't mind if we run it on him a little,
Now we got the Colonel's squab, but we better step."

They hurried along. The smoke rose higher behind them.
The wind blew the burning flakes on Wingate Hall.

————

Sally Dupré stared out of her bedroom window
As she had stared many times at that clump of trees.
And saw the smoke rise out of it, thick and dark.

They hadn't had much trouble at Appleton.
It was too far off the main road—and, as for the slaves,
Those who straggled after the troops were better away.
The aunts complained, of course—well, the aunts complained.
They were old, and, at least, they had a man in the house,
Even if the man were but crippled old Uncle Paul.
It was the end of the world for him and the aunts.
It wasn't for her.
          The years had worn on her youth,
Much had worn, but not the crook from her smile
Nor the hidden lightness out of her narrow feet.

She looked at the smoke again, and her eyes were grey
And then they were black as that smoke. She felt the fire
Run on her flesh. "It's Wingate Hall and it's burning?
House that married my lover before he saw me,
You are burning, burning away in a little smoke,
Burning the wall between us with your fierce burning,
Burning the strife between us in your black flame,
Burning down."
          She trod for an instant there
A light glass floor of omen, brighter than sleet
Over a hurtless fire.

Then she caught her breath.
The flesh was cool, the blackness died from her eyes.
"We'll have to get the slaves if the slaves will go.
I know Ned will. I'm not sure about Bob or Jim.
Uncle Paul must give me his pistol. I'll have to start them.
They won't go without me. The aunts won't be any use.
Why wouldn't she come over here when we all first heard?
I know why she wouldn't. I never liked her so much.
Hurry, Sally!"
                    She ran downstairs like the wind.

They worked at the Hall that night till the dawn came up,
Two smoke-stained women, Cudjo and Bob and Ned,
But when the dawn had risen, the Hall was gone
And Elspeth's candles would not light it again.

———————

Wingate wearily tried to goad
A bag of bones on a muddy road
Under the grey and April sky
While Bristol hummed in his irony
"If you want a good time, jine the cavalry!
Well, we jined it, and here we go,
The last event in the circus-show,
The bareback boys in the burnin' hoop
Mounted on cases of chicken-croup,
The rovin' remains of the Black Horse Troop!
Though the only horse you could call real black
Is the horsefly sittin' on Shepley's back,
But, women and children, do not fear,
They'll feed the lions and us, next year.
And, women and children, dry your eyes,
The Southern gentleman never dies.
He just lives on by his strength of will
Like a damn ole rooster too tough to kill
Or a brand-new government dollar-bill
That you can use for a trousers-patch
Or lightin' a fire, if you've got a match,
Or makin' a bunny a paper collar,
Or anythin' else—except a dollar.

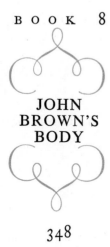
Old folks, young folks, never you care,
The Yanks are here and the Yanks are there,
But no Southern gentleman knows despair.
He just goes on in his usual way,
Eatin' a meal every fifteenth day
And showin' such skill in his change of base
That he never gets time to wash his face
While he fights with a fury you'd seldom find
Except in a Home for the Crippled Blind,
And can whip five Yanks with a palmleaf hat,
Only the Yanks won't fight like that.

Ladies and gentlemen, here we go!
The last event in the minstrel show!
Georgia's genuine gamboliers,
(Ladies and gentlemen, dry those tears!)
See the sergeant, eatin' the hay
Of his faithful horse, in a lifelike way!
See the general, out for blood,
And try to tell the man from the mud!
See the platoon in its savage lair,
A half-grown boy on a wheezy mare.
Ladies and gentlemen, pass the hat!
We've got one trick that you won't forget,
'The Vanishin' Commissariat'
And nobody's found the answer yet!
Here we go, here we go,
The last parade of the circus-show,
Longstreet's orphans, Lee's everlastin's
Half cast-iron and half corn-pone,
And if gettin' to heaven means prayer and fastin's
We ought to get there on the fasts alone.

Here we go with our weddin' bells,
Mr. Davis's immortelles,
Mr. Lincoln's Thanksgivin' turkey,
Run right ragged but actin' perky,
Chased right handsome, but still not carved,
—We had fleas, but the fleas all starved.
We had rations and new recruits,

Uniforms and cavalry-boots,
Must have mislaid, for we can't find 'em.
They all went home with their tails behind 'em.
Here we are, like the old man's mutton,
Pretty well sheared, but not past buttin',
Lee's last invalids, heart and hand,
All wropped up in a woolen band,
Oh, Dixie land. . . . oh, Dixie land! . . ."
He tossed his hat and caught it again
And Wingate recalled, without grief or pain
Or any quietus but memory
Lucy, under another sky,
White and gold as a lily bed,
Giving toy ribbons to all her dead.
She had been pretty and she was gone,
But the dead were here—and the dead rode on,
Over a road of mud and stones,
Each one horsed on a bag of bones.

Lucy, you carried a golden head,
But I am free of you, being dead.
Father's back in that cluttered hall
Where the beds are solid from wall to wall
And the scrubbed old floor has a rusty stain.
He'll never ride with the dogs again,
Call Bathsheba or Planter's Child
In the old, high quaver that drives them wild
—Rocketing hounds on a red-hot scent—
After such wounds, men do not ride.
I think that his heart was innocent.
I know he rode by the riverside,
Calling Blue Ruin or Georgia Lad
With the huntsman's crotchet that sets them mad.
His face was ruddy—his face is white—
I wonder if Father died last night?
That cloud in the sky is a thunderhead.
The world I knew is a long time dead.

Shepley looks like a knife on guard,
Reckon he's taking it mighty hard,

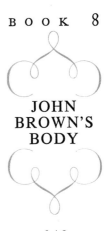

Reckon he loved her and no mistake,
Glad it isn't my wedding cake,
Wainscott oughtn't to plague him so,
Means all right but he doesn't know.
"Here we go, here we go,
The last events of the minstrel-show!"

Shepley suddenly turned his head.
"Mr. Bristol's funny," he said.
The voice was flat with an injury.
Bristol stared at him, puzzledly.
"What's the matter with you, Huger?
Lost your dog or your rosy cheeks?
Haven't been human for weeks and weeks.
I'll sing you a hymn, if you're so inclined,
But the rest of the boys don't seem to mind.
Are you feelin' poorly or just unkind?"

Shepley looked at him with the blind
Eyes of a man too long at war
And too long nursing a secret sore.
"Mr. Bristol's funny," said he,
In a level voice of enmity.
Bristol laughed, but his face grew red.
"Well, if you take it like that—" he said.

"Here we go, here we go,
The old Confederate minstrel-show!"
His mouth was merry, he tossed his hat,
"Belles skedaddled and left us flat—"

Shepley leaned from his swaying hips
And flicked him over the singing lips.
"Will you take it?" he said, "or let it go?
You never could sing for shucks, you know."
The color drained out of Bristol's face.
He bowed with an odd, old-fashioned grace.
"Name your people and choose your land,
I don't take a slap from God's own hand.
Mr. Shepley, your servant, sir."

They stared at each other across a blur.
The troop stared with them, halted and still.
A rider lunged from the top of the hill,
Dusty man with a bandaged hand
Spilling his orders.

    "Who's in command?
Well, it doesn't signify, more or less.
You can hold the Yanks for a while, I guess.
Make 'em think you're the whole rear guard
If you can do it—they're pressin' hard
And somebody's got to lose some hair.
Keep 'em away from that bend down there
As long as a horse or a man can stand.
You might give 'em a charge, if you think you can,
And we'll meet sometime in the Promised Land,
For I can't spare you another man."

Bristol whistled, a shrill, sweet slur.
"Beg to acknowledge the orders, sir.
Boys, we're booked for the shivaree.
Give our regards to the infantry
And tell Marse Robert, with fortitude,
We stacked up pretty as hickory-wood.
While might I ask, while bein' polite,
How many Yank armies we aim to fight?"

"Well," said the other, "about a corps.
Roughly speakin'—there may be more."

"Thank you," said Bristol, "that's mighty sweet,
You will not remain at the mourner's seat?
No sir? Well, I imagined not,
For from this time hence it will be right hot."
He turned to Shepley with his punctilious
Air of the devil turned supercilious
When the damned display a vulgar nettlement.
"Sir, I regret that our little settlement
Must be postponed for a fitter season,
But war and necessity know no reason,
And should we survive in this comin' fracas
I'll do you the honors—you damned old jackass!"

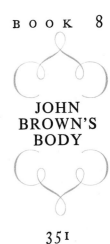

Shepley grinned at his sometime friend.
They took the cover they must defend.
Wingate, fighting from tree to tree,
Felt a red-hot skewer surgeon his knee
And felt his shoulder hitting the ground.
He rolled on his side and made a sound,
Dimly seeing through failing sight
The last brief passion of his last fight.
One Cotter dying, the other dead
With the brains run out of his shattered head.
Stuart Cazenove trying to squirm
His way to the road like a scythe-cut worm,
Weakly humming "Cadet Rousselle,"
Shot through the belly and half in hell,
While Shepley croaked through a bloody spray,
"Come on, you bastards, and get your pay.
We've fought you mounted and fought you standin'
And I got a hole I could put my hand in—
And they're comin', Wayne—and it hurts my head—"
Bristol looked at him, lying dead.
"Got the start of me, Shep," he said.
"Dirty welchers, killin' Huger
Before we could settle up properly."
He stooped to the body and took its pistol
And Wingate saw, through a rising mist,
The last, cold madness of Wainscott Bristol,
Walking out like a duellist
With his torn coat buttoned up at the throat
As if it were still the broadcloth coat
Duellists button to show no fleck
Of telltale white at the wrists or neck.
He stepped from his cover and dropped his hat.
"Yanks, come get it!" he said and spat
While his pistols cracked with a single crack,
"Here we go on the red dog's back!"
High, low, jack and the goddam game."
And then the answering volley came.

Wingate waked from a bloodshot dream.
They were touching his leg and he heard his scream.

A blue-chinned man said a word or two.
"Well now, Johnny, you ought to do
Till the sawbones comes with his movin'-van,
And you're lucky you're livin', little man.
But why the hell did you act so strict,
Fightin' like that when you know you're licked,
And where's the rest of your damn brigade?"
The voice died out as the ripples fade
Into the flow of the running stream,
And Wingate sank to the bloodshot dream.

———

Richmond is fallen—Lincoln walks in its streets,
Alone, unguarded, stops at George Pickett's house,
Knocks at George Pickett's door. George Pickett has gone
But the strange, gaunt figure talks to George Pickett's wife
A moment—she thinks she is dreaming, seeing him there—
"Just one of George Pickett's old friends, m'am."
                                        He turns away.
She watches him down the street with wondering eyes.
The red light falls upon him from the red sky.
Houses are burning, strange shadows flee through the streets.
A gang of loafers is broaching a liquor-barrel
In a red-lit square. The liquor spills on the cobbles.
They try to scoop it up in their dirty hands.

A long, blue column tramps by, shouting "John Brown's Body."
The loafers scatter like wasps from a half-sucked pear,
Come back when the column is gone.
                                        A half-crazy slave
Mounts on a stoop and starts to preach to the sky.
A white-haired woman shoos him away with a broom.
He mumbles and reels to the shadows.
                                        A general passes,
His escort armed with drawn sabres. The sabres shine
In the red, low light.
                                        Two doors away, down the street,
A woman is sobbing the same long sob all night
Beside a corpse with crossed hands.
                                        Lincoln passes on.

On the way to Appomattox, the ghost of an army
Staggers a muddy road for a week or so
Through fights and weather, dwindling away each day.
For a brief while Davis is with them and then he goes
To be tracked by his private furies into the last
Sad farce of his capture, and, later, to wear his chains.
Benjamin is with them for some few days,
Still sleek, still lively, still impeccably dressed,
Taking adversity as he took success
With the silk-ribbed fan of his slight, unchangeable smile.
Behind that fan, his mind weighs war and defeat
In an old balance.
                           One day he is there and smiling.
The next he is gone as if he had taken fernseed
And walked invisible so through the Union lines.
You will not find that smile in a Northern prison
Though you seek from now till Doomsday. It is too wise.
You will find the chief with the chin like John Calhoun's,
Gadfly-stung, tormented by hostile fate,
You will find many gallant blockheads and tragic nobles
But not the black-eyed man with life in his eyes.

So this week, this death-march, these final, desperate strokes,
These last blood-spots on the harvest—until, at length,
The battered grey advance guard, hoping to break
A last, miraculous hole through the closing net,
Sees Ord's whole corps as if risen out of the ground
Before them, blocking all hope.
                                        The letters are written,
The orders given, while stray fighting goes on
And grey men and blue men die in odd clumps of ground
Before the orders can reach them.
                                        An aide-de-camp
Seeks a suitable house for the council from a chance farmer.
The first one found is too dirty to please his mind,
He picks another.
                           The chiefs and the captains meet,
Lee erect in his best dress uniform,
His dress-sword hung at his side and his eyes unaltered.
Chunky Grant in his mudsplashed private's gear

With the battered stars on his shoulders.
                          They talk a while
Of Mexico and old days.
                    Then the terms are stated.
Lee finds them generous, says so, makes a request.
His men will need their horses for the spring-ploughing.
Grant assents at once.
                     There is no parade of bright swords
Given or taken. Grant saw that there should not be.
It is over, then. . . .
                    Lee walks from the little room.
His face is unchanged. It will not change when he dies.
But as he steps on the porch and looks toward his lines
He strikes his hands together once with a sound. . . .

In the room he has left, the blue men stare at each other
For a space of heartbeats, silent. The grey ride off.
They are gone—it is over. . . .

The room explodes like a bomb, they are laughing and shouting,
Yelling strange words, dragging chairs and tables outdoors,
Bearded generals waltzing with one another
For a brief, wild moment, punching each others' ribs,
Everyone talking at once and nobody listening,
"It's over—it's done—it's finished!"
                              Then, order again.
The grey ghost-army falls in for the last time,
Marching to stack its arms.
                        As the ranks move forward
The blue guns go to "Present." Gordon sees the gesture.
He sweeps his sabre down in the full salute.
There are no cheers or words from blue lines or grey.
Only the sound of feet. . . .
It is over, now. . . .
                     The arms are stacked from the war.
A few bronzed, tattered grey men, weeping or silent,
Tear some riddled bits of cloth from the color-staffs
And try to hide them under their uniforms.

_____

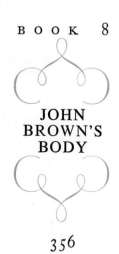
Jake Diefer, ploughing, a day of the early Spring,
Smelt April steam from the ground as he turned it up
And wondered how the new forty would do this year.

The stump of his left arm ached in the living wind.
It was not a new pain.
                         When he got back to the house
The woman would ease it some with her liniments
But there wasn't much you could do.
                                      The boy had been smart.
The boy had fixed the jigger so he could plough.
It wasn't an arm you could show to company
With a regular-looking hand, but it did the work.
The woman still hankered after the varnished one
They'd seen that day in the Philadelphia store
—Well, he'd tried it on, and it was a handsome arm,
And, if the new forty did well—
                                  Meanwhile, the huge
Muscles of his right shoulder bulged with the strain
As the plough sheared on.
                           Sometimes, the blade of the plough
Still turned up such odd harvest as bullets leave,
A spoilt canteen, the brass of a cartridge-pouch,
An eyeless skull, too white for the grin it wore.
But these were rarer now.
                           They had cleaned the well.
They could drink from the well again.
                                        The earth was in plough.

He turned his team and started the backward furrow.
He was clumsy still, in some matters, but he could manage.
This year he'd see his own wheat.
                                   He thought to himself:
"You ain't the feller you was but the ground looks good.
It smells like good plantin' weather. We cleaned the well.
Maybe some time we'll get you that varnished arm,
For Sundays, maybe. It'd look good on Sundays."
He gazed ahead.
                 By the end of the farther fence
A ragamuffin-something leaned on the rail,

Regarding him and his team.
                              "Tramp feller," he thought,
"Colored man, too—well, he can't hang around this farm,
Him or no other tramps. I wish I could get
An honest to God cheap hired man."
                              The team drew near.
The negro did not move.
                    Jake halted the team.
They stared at each other. One saw a crippled ox,
The other a scar-faced spectre with haunted eyes
Still dressed in the rags of a shoddy uniform.
"Well, feller?" said Jake.
                    The negro said " 'Scuse me, Sarjun."
He scratched his head with the wreck of a forage-cap.
His eyes remembered a darkness.
                              "Huh!" said Jake,
Sharply, "Where did you get it?"
                              The negro shrank.
"I was in de Crater, boss," he said with a dull
Stain in his voice. "You mebbe heard about us.
You mebbe heard of de Crater at Petersburg.
I doan' like thinkin' about it. You need a fiel'-han'?"

Jake thought for a moment. "Crater," he said at last.
"Yuh, I heard about that Crater."
                              The wind blew on
Hurting his arm. "I wasn't to there," he said.
"I knew some boys that was there."
                              The negro said,
"I'd work for my keep, boss, honest. I knows a team.
I knows how to work. I got hurt bad in de Crater
But I knows how to work a farm."
                              He coughed and was dumb.
Jake looked at him as he might have looked at a horse,
Measuringly.
              "I ain't runnin' a hospital,"
He said, in an aggrieved voice. "You was to the Crater.
I seen the way you colored folks farm down South.
It ain't no way to farm. You ought to be et.
We'll eat you up to the house when it's mealin'-time.

I don't know where we'll sleep you. How do I know
You can work your keep?"

                The negro said nothing at all.
His eyes had resumed their darkness.

                  "Huddup!" said Jake,
As the team swung round.

              "Dat's ploughin'!" the negro said.

Jake spat. "The woman'll fix you a snack to eat
If you holler the house."

              The negro shook his head.
"I'll wait till you's done furrowin', boss," he said.
"Mebbe I kin help you unhitch when it's time for dat."

"Well," said Jake, "I ain't payin' a hired man much."

"Dey call me Spade," said the negro.

                The plough went on.
The negro watched it, cutting the furrow clean.

––––––––

Jack Ellyat, an old cudgel in his fist,
Walked from the town, one day of melting ice,
Past fields still patched with old snow but warm in the sun,
His heart and mind being something like those fields. . . .
Behind him, in the town, the spangled flags
Still fluttered or hung limp for fallen Richmond,
And here or there, in corners, you could see
The burst firecracker-cases, rotten with rain,
The guttered stumps of torches flung away
And other odds and ends of celebration
Not yet swept up.

              The old cannon in the Square
Still had a blackened mouth from its salutes,
The little boys would not be good all week
And everything wore airs of Monday morning. . . .

Jack Ellyat, remembering it all,
Was glad enough when he got past the houses
And could see nothing but the road ahead

Going up hills and down.
                         "It's over now.
Finished for good. Well, I was part of it.
Well, it is over."
                         When he reached the crest
Of the Long Hill, he paused and felt the wind
Blow on his face, and leaned upon his stick,
Gazing at troubled Spring.
                         He carried still
Wounds of a sort, some healed into the scars
And some that hardly would be healed awhile,
Being in stuff few surgeries can reach,
But he was well enough, although the wind
Felt colder than it had in other Springs.

"Oh, yes," he thought, "I guess that I'm all right.
I guess I'm lucky. I remember once
Coming along this road with poor old Ned
Before they fired on Sumter. Well, it's over.
I was a part of it."
                         He flipped a stone
Down toward the hill and watched it strike and strike
And then lie quiet, while his mind recalled
The long, white, bloodless months of getting well
And the strange feel of first civilian clothes.
Well, that was over, too, and he was back,
And everybody knew he'd settled down,
Only he couldn't stand it any more.

He had a picture of Melora's face,
Dim with long looking-at, a carried image,
He tried to see it now, but it was faint.
He'd tried to find her but he couldn't find her.
Couldn't get any news while he was sick,
And then, at last, the news that they were gone—
That and no more—and nobody knew where.

He saw the clock upon the mantelpiece
Back in the house, ticking its fettered time
To fettered Phaëton.

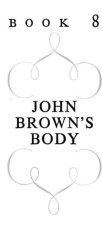

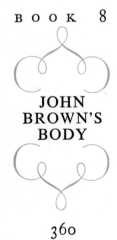
"I'll settle down.
I will forget. I'll wear my riddled coat
Fourth of Julys and have boys gape at me.
I'll drink and eat and sleep, marry a girl;
Be a good lawyer, wear the hunger out.
I hardly knew her. It was years ago.
Why should the hunger stay? A dozen men
Might find a dozen girls and lose them so
And never once think of it, but perhaps
As a dim fragrance, lost with their first youth,
A seashell in a box of cedarwood,
A silver mist that vanished with the day.
It was such years ago. She must have changed.
I know that I have changed.
                                    We find such things
And lose them, and must live in spite of it.
Only a fool goes looking for the wind
That blew across his heartstrings yesterday,
Or breaks his hands in the obscure attempt
To dig the knotted roots of Time apart,
Hoping to resurrect the golden mask
Of the lost year inviolate from the ground.
Only a fool drives horses in the sky."

And here he was, out walking on this road
For no more reason than a crazy yarn
Just heard, about some gipsy travellers
Going through towns and looking for a soldier.
And even and supposing it were she . . .

He saw Melora walking down from the wood
With the sun behind her, low in the western cloud.
He saw the long shadow that her slight body made.

The fetters fell like straws from the clock of time.
The horses moved from the gate.
                                    This life, this burning,
This fictive war that is over, this toy death,
These were the pictures of Phaëton.
                                    This is Phaëton.

He cast a final look down at the town,
Another at the fields still patched with snow.
The wind blew on his face. He moved away
Out toward the crossroads, where the wagons pass,
And when he got there, waited patiently
Under a windbreak of three twisted elms
Half-hidden from the road.
                    "Find her," he said.
"I guess we'll go back West then. Well, that's that."
The wind burned at his flesh. He let it burn,
Staring at a lost year.
                    So he perceived
A slow cart creaking up a slope of hill,
Drawn by a horse as gaunt as poverty
And driven by a woman with great eyes.

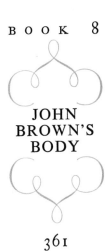

———————

Edmund Ruffin, old Secessionist,
Firer of the first gun that rang against Sumter,
Walks in his garden now, in the evening-cool,
With a red, barred flag slung stiffly over one arm
And a silver-butted pistol in his right hand.
He has just heard of Lee's surrender and Richmond's fall
And his face is marble over his high black stock.
For a moment he walks there, smelling the scents of Spring,
A gentleman taking his ease, while the sun sinks down.
Now it is well-nigh sunken. He smiles with the close,
Dry smile of age. It is time. He unfolds the flag,
Cloaks it around his shoulders with neat, swift hands,
Cocks the pistol and points it straight at his heart.
The hammer falls, the dead man slumps to the ground.
The blood spurts out in the last light of the sun
Staining the red of the flag with more transient red.

———————

The gaunt man, Abraham Lincoln, woke one morning
From a new dream that yet was an old dream
For he had known it many times before
And, usually, its coming prophesied
Important news of some sort, good or bad,
Though mostly good as he remembered it.

He had been standing on the shadowy deck
Of a black formless boat that moved away
From a dim bank, into wide, gushing waters—
River or sea, but huge—and as he stood,
The boat rushed into darkness like an arrow,
Gathering speed—and as it rushed, he woke.

He found it odd enough to tell about
That day to various people, half in jest
And half in earnest—well, it passed the time
And nearly everyone had some pet quirk,
Knocking on wood or never spilling salt,
Ladders or broken mirrors or a Friday,
And so he thought he might be left his boat,
Especially now, when he could breathe awhile
With Lee surrendered and the war stamped out
And the long work of binding up the wounds
Not yet begun—although he had his plans
For that long healing, and would work them out
In spite of all the bitter-hearted fools
Who only thought of punishing the South
Now she was beaten.
                            But this boat of his.
He thought he had it.
                            "Johnston has surrendered.
It must be that, I guess—for that's about
The only news we're waiting still to hear."
He smiled a little, spoke of other things.
That afternoon he drove beside his wife
And talked with her about the days to come
With curious simplicity and peace.
Well, they were getting on, and when the end
Came to his term, he would not be distressed.
They would go back to Springfield, find a house,
Live peaceably and simply, see old friends,
Take a few cases every now and then.
Old Billy Herndon's kept the practice up,
I guess he'll sort of like to have me back.
We won't be skimped, we'll have enough to spend,

Enough to do—we'll have a quiet time,
A sort of Indian summer of our age.

He looked beyond the carriage, seeing it so,
Peace at the last, and rest.

They drove back to the White House, dressed and ate,
Went to the theatre in their flag-draped box.
The play was a good play, he liked the play,
Laughed at the jokes, laughed at the funny man
With the long, weeping whiskers.
                              The time passed.
The shot rang out. The crazy murderer
Leaped from the box, mouthed out his Latin phrase,
Brandished his foolish pistol and was gone.
Lincoln lay stricken in the flag-draped box.
Living but speechless. Now they lifted him
And bore him off. He lay some hours so.
Then the heart failed. The breath beat in the throat.
The black, formless vessel carried him away.

———

Sally, waiting at Appleton
On an autumn day of clear, bright sun,
Felt her heart and body begin to burn
As she hummed the lesson she had to learn.
"Yellow cornmeal and a jackass colt
And a door that swings on a broken bolt.
Comfort the old and pity the wise
And see your lover with open eyes.
Mend the broken and patch the frayed
And carry the sorrow undismayed
When your lover limps in the falling rain,
Never quite to be whole again.
Clear the nettle and plant the corn
And keep your body a hunting-horn.
Succor your love at fire and frost
When your lover remembers the blood he lost,
And break your hands on the hard-moved wheel

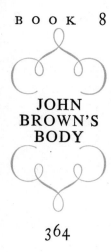
Till they are tougher than hands of steel,
Till the new grass grows on the barren plain
And the house is built from the dust again,
With thrift and love for the house and the chief,
A scone on the hob for the son of grief,
A knife in the ribs for the pleasant thief,
While the night and the river have memories . . ."
She stared at the future with equal eyes.
And yet, in her glance, there was something still
Not to be ground by Wingate will
Or under the honor of Elspeth's name,
A dancing flicker that went and came
But did not falter for joy or grief
Or the years gone by with the blowing leaf.
—French Dupré with his alien grace
Always turning the buried ace.
French Dupré in his dancer's pride,
Leading a reel with his stolen bride—
She smiled a little and turned to see
A weed-grown path and a scarlet tree
And Wingate coming there, painfully.

———

John Brown's body lies a-mouldering in the grave.
Spread over it the bloodstained flag of his song,
For the sun to bleach, the wind and the birds to tear,
The snow to cover over with a pure fleece
And the New England cloud to work upon
With the grey absolution of its slow, most lilac-smelling rain,
Until there is nothing there
That ever knew a master or a slave
Or, brooding on the symbol of a wrong,
Threw down the irons in the field of peace.
John Brown is dead, he will not come again,
A stray ghost-walker with a ghostly gun.
Let the strong metal rust
In the enclosing dust
And the consuming coal
That was the furious soul
And still like iron groans,

Anointed with the earth,
Grow colder than the stones
While the white roots of grass and little weeds
Suck the last hollow wildfire from the singing bones.

Bury the South together with this man,
Bury the bygone South.
Bury the minstrel with the honey-mouth,
Bury the broadsword virtues of the clan,
Bury the unmachined, the planters' pride,
The courtesy and the bitter arrogance,
The pistol-hearted horsemen who could ride
Like jolly centaurs under the hot stars.
Bury the whip, bury the branding-bars,
Bury the unjust thing
That some tamed into mercy, being wise,
But could not starve the tiger from its eyes
Or make it feed where beasts of mercy feed.
Bury the fiddle-music and the dance,
The sick magnolias of the false romance
And all the chivalry that went to seed
Before its ripening.

And with these things, bury the purple dream
Of the America we have not been,
The tropic empire, seeking the warm sea,
The last foray of aristocracy
Based not on dollars or initiative
Or any blood for what that blood was worth
But on a certain code, a manner of birth,
A certain manner of knowing how to live,
The pastoral rebellion of the earth
Against machines, against the Age of Steam,
The Hamiltonian extremes against the Franklin mean,
The genius of the land
Against the metal hand,
The great, slave-driven bark,
Full-oared upon the dark,
With gilded figurehead,
With fetters for the crew

And spices for the few,
The passion that is dead,
The pomp we never knew,
Bury this, too.

Bury this destiny unmanifest,
This system broken underneath the test,
Beside John Brown and though he knows his enemy is there
He is too full of sleep at last to care.

He was a stone, this man who lies so still,
A stone flung from a sling against a wall,
A sacrificial instrument of kill,
A cold prayer hardened to a musket-ball:
And yet, he knew the uses of a hill,
And he must have his justice, after all.

He was a lover of certain pastoral things,
He had the shepherd's gift.
When he walked at peace, when he drank from the watersprings,
His eyes would lift
To see God, robed in a glory, but sometimes, too,
Merely the sky,
Untroubled by wrath or angels, vacant and blue,
Vacant and high.

He knew not only doom but the shape of the land,
Reaping and sowing.
He could take a lump of any earth in his hand
And feel the growing.

He was a farmer, he didn't think much of towns,
The wheels, the vastness.
He liked the wide fields, the yellows, the lonely browns,
The black ewe's fastness.

Out of his body grows revolving steel,
Out of his body grows the spinning wheel
Made up of wheels, the new, mechanic birth,
No longer bound by toil

To the unsparing soil
Or the old furrow-line,
The great, metallic beast
Expanding West and East,
His heart a spinning coil,
His juices burning oil,
His body serpentine.
Out of John Brown's strong sinews the tall skyscrapers grow,
Out of his heart the chanting buildings rise,
River and girder, motor and dynamo,
Pillar of smoke by day and fire by night,
The steel-faced cities reaching at the skies,
The whole enormous and rotating cage
Hung with hard jewels of electric light,
Smoky with sorrow, black with splendor, dyed
Whiter than damask for a crystal bride
With metal suns, the engine-handed Age,
The genie we have raised to rule the earth,
Obsequious to our will
But servant-master still,
The tireless serf already half a god——

Touch the familiar sod
Once, then gaze at the air
And see the portent there,
With eyes for once washed clear
Of worship and of fear:
There is its hunger, there its living thirst,
There is the beating of the tremendous heart
You cannot read for omens.
                              Stand apart
From the loud crowd and look upon the flame
Alone and steadfast, without praise or blame.
This is the monster and the sleeping queen
And both have roots struck deep in your own mind,
This is reality that you have seen,
This is reality that made you blind.

So, when the crowd gives tongue
And prophets, old or young,

Bawl out their strange despair
Or fall in worship there,
Let them applaud the image or condemn
But keep your distance and your soul from them.
And, if the heart within your breast must burst
Like a cracked crucible and pour its steel
White-hot before the white heat of the wheel,
Strive to recast once more
That attar of the ore
In the strong mold of pain
Till it is whole again,
And while the prophets shudder or adore
Before the flame, hoping it will give ear,
If you at last must have a word to say,
Say neither, in their way,
"It is a deadly magic and accursed,"
Nor "It is blest," but only "It is here."